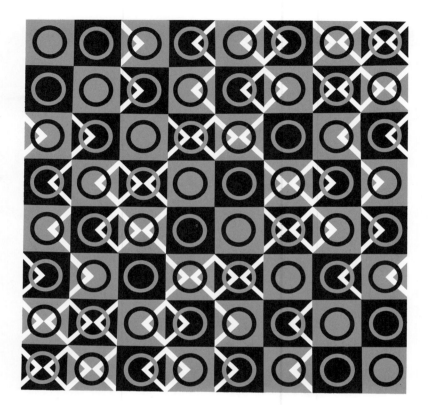

IDEAS IN MATHEMATICS

AVRON DOUGLIS *Professor of Mathematics, University of Maryland*

WITH THE SUPPORT OF THE NATIONAL SCIENCE FOUNDATION

1970   W. B. SAUNDERS COMPANY   PHILADELPHIA • LONDON • TORONTO

W. B. Saunders Company: West Washington Square
Philadelphia, Pa. 19105

12 Dyott Street
London W.C.1

1835 Yonge Street
Toronto 7, Ontario

Print No.   1   2   3   4   5   6   7   8   9

To

MY MOTHER

and

MY FATHER'S MEMORY

PREFACE

PREFACE

This book is designed for a terminal course in mathematics for college students in liberal arts. The reader should have had a year of algebra and a year of geometry in high school but is not expected to possess great technical skill. All the mathematics in this book is uncompromisingly simple and elementary. Nevertheless, we aim at a respectable intellectual level, seeking to expose subtleties in familiar concepts and in many ways to demonstrate the power of abstract reasoning. In contexts a layman can appreciate, we exemplify and try to cultivate a mathematician's habits of thought, which are as distinctive as a dancer's habits of posture and motion or a musician's habits of playing his instrument. To the extent that space permits, we try to connect mathematics with other disciplines — logic, philosophy, science, art — and hope to persuade the reader that mathematical ideas are relevant for himself, no matter what his interests.

How to convey the humane values of mathematics to non-mathematical students is a question to which I was drawn originally through reading Morris Kline's eloquent, nontechnical history, *Mathematics in Western Culture.*† Subsequently, during almost ten of the years from 1959 to 1969, I gave a course in mathematics for liberal arts students at the University of Maryland and worked out what ultimately became the content, organization, and approach of this book.

The book itself was undertaken in 1963 at the instigation of Professor Paul C. Rosenbloom, a distinguished research mathematician who had become involved in problems of mathematics and science education and curriculum reform. With support from the National Science Foundation and, to a lesser extent, the State of Minnesota, Rosenbloom had set up an organization, the Minnesota School Mathematics and Science Center (MINNEMAST), to design new curricula from kindergarten up and test them. Under MINNEMAST auspices, scores of experts were brought together at that time in summer sessions: teachers (including some who were famous for their virtuosity) from elementary and secondary public, private, and parochial schools, from schools for gifted children, and from schools in depressed communities; principals and supervisors; a psychologist; a historian; an artist; an editor; a musician to compose songs for children in kindergarten and the lower grades; and university specialists in different branches of science and mathematics. There were also undergraduate and graduate students, who assisted in many ways, and experimental classes at different levels upon whom new ideas could be tested at once. Curricula created in Minneapolis over the summer were tried out in a number of cooperating institutions during the ensuing year, overhauled that summer, then tried out again, again rewritten, and so forth. Rosenbloom prized imagination in the new curricula and provided in his own constant inventiveness a standard and a spur to all his co-workers, of whom I became one.

---

†Kline, M.: *Mathematics in Western Culture.* London, Oxford Univ. Press, 1953.

To prepare those who would teach the new curricula, Rosenbloom felt that a year's course in mathematics at the college level was needed and wished me to develop an appropriate book for it. He and I agreed that an elementary school teacher ought to have a mathematical background such as would be suitable for any educated person and thus that the book should be designed for general liberal arts programs rather than for teachers' colleges alone. The major question was that of the level at which the book should be written, since students are so variable in preparation and ability. Rosenbloom advised me to write principally for the intelligent student with a good high school mathematics background who has forgotten most of it, and I have tried to do so scrupulously. Many opportunities are provided for review. I have taken great pains in the attempt to convey the essence of ideas as well as their details, searching my mind for the psychological origins of my own ways of thinking mathematically. After seeing how my explanations worked in class, I have altered them accordingly, tested the new explanations, made new alterations, and so on, until they seemed effective. They have always seemed more effective with the more mature students, juniors and seniors in my classes tending to fare better than freshmen and sophomores despite the greater lapse of time since their high school training.

The earliest sections of each chapter and the beginning of almost every section are designed to introduce their subjects gently for the benefit especially of the diffident or ill prepared. A weak class might well be confined to these. In no class need a teacher hesitate to skip or cut short, for the entire book contains far more material than can usually be crammed into two semesters, and most chapters rest only lightly on the previous material. Omissions and changes of order thus are the ordinary expectation. Some topics can be stressed one year and others the next, with the remaining material always available for the occasional student who asks for more.

Most of my effort on this book during the period from 1963 to 1967 was supported by MINNEMAST with funds from the National Science Foundation. In addition, MINNEMAST financed several graduate students working under my direction: Halldor Gudjonsson, who provided valuable contributions to my discussions in Chapter 12 of axiomatic systems and the theory of proof; George J. Rothstein, who did first drafts for much of the material on groups (Sections 1 to 3 of Chapter 6, Section 6 of Chapter 7) and also is responsible for large numbers of fine exercises throughout the book; Camilo Schmidt, who produced the earliest draft on number theory (Chapter 11); Peter M. Tomsich, who searched out suitable problems in puzzle books and other sources; and John Wood, who wrote the first half of the present section on inequalities (Section 5 of Chapter 2). My numerous teaching assistants at the University of Maryland also were responsible for many exercises and for many ideas that have led to additions and improvements.

Colleagues and associates at MINNEMAST and elsewhere who

have read portions of the manuscript and given thoughtful criticism include Paula Giese, A. M. Glicksman, Carol Karp, George L. Kilbourn, Inda Lepson, Don Meyers, W. Moser, Lore Rasmussen, F. A. Scherk, and H. F. Weinberger. Others who made useful suggestions are Jack Barr, Herbert Fox, Peter and Anneli Lax, J. B. Marion, Ralph E. Schwartz, David Sprecher, Raymond Stites, and T. A. Willke.

T. B. Jones, Professor of History at the University of Minnesota and a colleague at MINNEMAST, gave me indispensable guidance in preparing the historical notes; the responsibility for errors, however, is entirely mine.

In matters of exposition, my wife Marjorie has often brought insight and constructive criticism.

Robert Sorley and others under his supervision provided practically perfect typescripts for five preliminary versions of this book, handsomely produced by the University of Minnesota for classroom use. The hundreds of figures and illustrations in these versions were drafted with clarity and style chiefly by Mrs. Barbara Morris Buraimo.

Mrs. Shirley Hanes typed efficiently and speedily the extensive revisions and additions to the last of the Minnesota versions.

The cover design is the original creation of Miss Lorraine Battista of Saunders. It embodies an idea concerning mathematics and art put forth by MINNEMAST Art Director Sonia Forseth.†

All who have aided me in this endeavor I thank most gratefully. To Paul C. Rosenbloom, for his initiative, suggestions, and contagious enthusiasm, I express my particular appreciation. I also owe much to James H. Werntz, Rosenbloom's successor as Director of MINNEMAST, for his continued interest and encouragement.

I am under special obligation to Mrs. Jeanne Kyle, my copy editor, who carried out the exacting task of writing the answer book that accompanies this text. I wish also to mention the pleasure I have had in all my dealings with W. B. Saunders Company and particularly with Mathematics Editor George Fleming, whose quick understanding of my aims and tactful prodding certainly contributed to the completion of the manuscript and its speedy publication.

Finally, I am grateful to the University of Maryland Mathematics Department for its consent year after year to my teaching a course in which I could work out and test material suitable for this book and for its generous assistance in relieving me of other teaching for one semester.

AVRON DOUGLIS

---

†Mrs. Forseth's idea is explained in Chapter 3 of "Criteria for Creativity," her master's thesis, accepted by the Department of Art Education, College of Education, University of Minnesota, in the spring of 1969.

SUGGESTED
COURSES OF
STUDY FROM
THIS BOOK

Suggested Courses of Study from this book

REMARKS

1. Chapter 1 on logical reasoning is worthwhile for most classes. It is intended to be an introduction in familiar contexts to fastidious, methodical thinking such as mathematics requires. It might be followed by Chapter 12, in which propositional calculus is developed, although we prefer to review algebra first.

2. Chapters 2 to 5 deal with elementary algebra and some of its straightforward or traditional applications. A light review of this subject might be confined to Chapter 2, Sections 1, 2a, 2b, 2g, and might include some of the recreational problems of Chapter 2, Section 3, or Pythagorean triples (Chapter 4, Section 1); the latter show what a little algebra and much imagination can accomplish. A more solid review of algebra might cover, in addition, selected topics from Chapters 3, 4, and 5. To prepare for groups (Chapter 6) or number theory (Chapter 11), it is perhaps advisable to do Chapter 2, Section 2c. The concept of limit and its many applications (beginning in Chapter 4, Section 4) require inequalities (Chapter 2, Section 5). All of Chapter 2, except possibly Section 4, may be needed before undertaking Chapter 15 on real numbers.

3. Euclidean plane geometry is reviewed in Chapter 7, Section 1, and in exercises of Sections 1, 2, and 4. Trigonometric functions (Chapter 7, Section 5a) are helpful in coordinate geometry (Chapters 8 and 9), more advanced formulas (Chapter 7, Section 5) being necessary for our treatment of circles (Chapter 15, Section 5). The discussion of area (Chapter 7, Section 3) is probably not essential to that of the sectional approximation of areas and volumes (Chapter 14, Sections 6 and 7). Notice the applications in Chapter 7 to arithmetic (Section 2) and design (Section 4), in Chapter 8 to economics (Sections 4 and 7), and in Chapter 9 to perspective drawing (Sections 6 and 7) and measurement from photographs (Section 8).

4. The chapter on groups (Chapter 6) has prerequisites and applications as indicated in the following diagram:

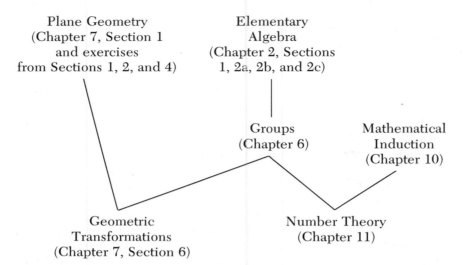

Plane Geometry
(Chapter 7, Section 1
and exercises
from Sections 1, 2, and 4)

Elementary
Algebra
(Chapter 2, Sections
1, 2a, 2b, and 2c)

Groups
(Chapter 6)

Mathematical
Induction
(Chapter 10)

Geometric
Transformations
(Chapter 7, Section 6)

Number Theory
(Chapter 11)

SUGGESTIONS FOR ONE-SEMESTER COURSES OF STUDY

1. Logical reasoning (Chapter 1)
Elementary algebra review (Chapter 2, Sections 1, 2a, 2b; Chapter 4, Section 1)
Axiomatics, circuit algebra, propositional calculus (Chapter 12)
Infinite processes (Chapter 14, Sections 1 to 6)

2. Logical reasoning (Chapter 1)
Elementary algebra (Chapter 2, Sections 1, 2a, 2b, 2g, 3; topics from Chapters 3, 4, 5)
Plane geometry and trigonometry (Chapter 7, except Sections 5d, 6)
Plane coordinate geometry (Chapter 2, Section 2g; Chapter 8)
Mathematical induction (Chapter 10), Axiomatics (Chapter 12), or Space geometry (Chapter 9)

3. Logical reasoning (Chapter 1)
Elementary algebra (Chapter 2, Sections 1, 2a, 2b, 2c; Chapter 4, Section 1)
Boolean algebra and related subjects (Chapter 12)
Probability and statistics (Chapter 13)

4. Logical reasoning (Chapter 1)
Elementary algebra (Chapter 2, Sections 1, 2a, 2b, 2c; Chapter 4, Section 1)
Groups (Chapter 6)
Mathematical induction (Chapter 10)
Number theory (Chapter 11)
Axiomatics (Chapter 12)

Suggestions for Two-Semester Courses of Study

First semester: Chapters 1, 2; topics from Chapters 3, 4, 5; Chapters 6, 7, 8.

Second semester: selected topics from Chapters 9 to 15. Note that mathematical induction (Chapter 10) should precede number theory (Chapter 11), Boolean algebra (in Chapter 12) should precede probability (Chapter 13), infinite processes (Chapter 14, Sections 1, 2, 4, and selected sections) should precede real numbers (Chapter 15).

CONTENTS

CONTENTS

CHAPTER 10

MATHEMATICAL INDUCTION 384

CHAPTER 11

THE THEORY OF NUMBERS 415

CHAPTER 12

THE AXIOMATIC METHOD AND APPLICATIONS IN ALGEBRA...... 466

CHAPTER 1

LOGICAL REASONING

Mathematics is grounded on logic, mainly very simple logic not far removed from common sense. Common sense is a practical way of reasoning used often in circumstances not wholly known or understood. Logic is a systematic discipline providing exact methods of reasoning in mathematically clear-cut situations. This rigid discipline, in its most basic aspects, is our present subject.

1.

Logic and common sense contrasted

In human situations, which are usually confused through too little reliable information or too much information of questionable validity, logic may find little scope. Common sense seems better adapted to such situations, since it draws on intuitive insights, is sensitive to intangibles, makes use of both experience and knowledge, and benefits somehow from unconscious wisdom. Thus, common sense is a serviceable guide in the ordinary affairs of life, while logic often is not. Still, familiarity with logical reasoning may enable us, even in ordinary affairs, to exercise our common sense more systematically, more critically, and, hence, more effectively than we otherwise should. We hope this will be apparent in the following illustrative situation, which is based on an old joke:

A: How did you break my camera?

B: I didn't break it. I never even had it.

A: You never even had my camera! Why, you borrowed it a week ago when my cousin was here.

B: That's true, but I returned it in perfect condition.

A: No. After I got it back, the shutter stuck.

B: Well, the shutter was already sticking when you gave me the camera, and not one of my pictures came out.

What are we to make of this dialogue? B has said, in effect, that he never had the camera, that he returned it in perfect condition, and that it was broken when he got it (and, by implication, when he returned it). Logic, noting these three mutually contradictory statements, concludes that at least two of the statements are false, but Logic does not say which two. What can Common Sense say? It may seem likely at first that B broke the shutter and lied to escape the blame, but there are other possibilities:

1. A third party damaged the camera, while B is so constituted as always to put himself in the wrong.

2. A and B together made the whole conversation up to tease A's mother, whom they believed to be listening.

3. The shutter was broken when the camera was given to B. B repaired it himself, afterwards returning the instrument in good condition and forgetting the whole incident. A then again broke the shutter and tried to blame B.

Common Sense recognizes that more information is needed.

Suppose we have now succeeded in finding out that A and B are adults of normal intelligence, that their conversation was perfectly serious, that A has a reputation for being reliable and honest, and that B is known to have broken his own camera earlier, to have lost his watch, and to have cheated at bridge. Common Sense, not to spoil a good case by being impulsive, might well resume the argument by calling attention to B's first two statements. B, originally denying he ever had the camera, admitted having had it when a possible witness was mentioned. Common Sense judges the denial was a lie. Logic cannot agree without having an explicit principle to invoke, such as: "If a person known to be careless and negligent and to cheat at games is charged by one of good reputation with a careless or negligent act, and if said person first denies said charge but, after mention of a possible witness, later admits it, then the original denial was an intentional lie." If such a principle is accepted, Logic then convicts B of lying. If such a principle is not accepted, Logic fails to convict.

If it is established somehow that B did briefly have A's camera, we can now consider the next point of disagreement. This is B's assertion that he had returned the camera in perfect condition. Common Sense knows that a man who lies once may well lie twice and is unlikely to believe B's assertion in the face of A's charge. But Logic is more fastidious than Common Sense and can draw no conclusion not imposed by exact principles explicitly adopted. Does lying follow exact rules? Consider, for instance, this one: "If a known liar denies an accusation made by a person of good repute, the denial is a lie." Is this rule acceptable? One who can accept it or anything like it ending with the same confident declaration will convict B of lying for the second time without further ado. A doubter who suspects that no such rule is always right may, however, forsake strict logic and, before reaching a decision, give some attention to imponderables: Was *B*'s manner that of a man honestly struggling to remember something; did he look *A* in the face? How did I reply when once falsely accused of breaking a dish or when lying about not spilling paint on the rug? Both the doubter wrestling with intangibles and the man of rigid principle ignoring them may err, for it is hardly possible to be certain when dealing with people. Decisions and judgments, however, there must be: to take this job, to marry that girl, to go to this school, to vote for which candidate, to acquit or to convict. Hair-splitting logic can rarely be of much use in such matters.

We have still to consider whether *B* actually broke the shutter.

EXERCISES

1. Discuss the question of whether *B* broke the shutter, contrasting the strictly logical with the common sense view, in the spirit of the preceding text.

2. Suppose that a piece of cloth from a coat is found in the hand of a murdered man and that a coat with a piece torn off and belonging to the man's gardener is found in the gardener's own room. What logical principles would support the conclusion that the gardener was the assailant? †

3. The following dilemma arose in a lawsuit in Greece in the 5th Century, B.C., between Protagoras, a teacher of legal rhetoric, and his former pupil, Eulathus. Protagoras had agreed to instruct Eulathus in the art of pleading cases before juries, and not to ask payment during the course of instruction, but to wait for his fee until Eulathus won his first case. Eulathus completed the course, but neither took a case nor paid his fee. Protagoras, impatient, brought suit against Eulathus, arguing as follows: "If Eulathus loses this case, he must pay me by the judgment of the court. If he wins this case, he must pay me by the terms of the contract. Therefore, Eulathus must pay me." Eulathus said, in reply: "If I lose this case, I do not have to pay Protagoras by the terms of the contract. If I win this case, I do not have to pay by the judgment of the court. Therefore, I do not have to pay Protagoras." How is this dilemma to be resolved? ‡

4. Try to formulate the role logic, with its capabilities and limitations, should play in ordinary life.

---

† Morris R. Cohen and Ernest Nagel, *An Introduction to Logic and Scientific Method*, New York, Harcourt, Brace and World, Inc., 1934, p. 4.

‡ Irving M. Copi, *Introduction to Logic*, second edition, New York, The Macmillan Company, 1961, pp. 231-232.

2.

When logic applies

Logic is an extreme kind of reasoning, accepting no conclusions but the inescapable. With such stringent standards, logic cannot endure the least degree of vagueness. An issue is not amenable to logical treatment until every principle involved and every qualification and exception have been declared explicitly. But in any affair of man or nature, how can one assemble such a comprehensive declaration? If the declaration were assembled, how could one draw from that complexity inescapable conclusions of any consequence? Is it reasonable to expect that reality will fit into our logical bottle?

We do not try to include all of reality in tidy statements. Indeed, words are inadequate to express the inexhaustible detail existing in any real situation. But often, by ignoring what seems trivial, taking account only of what seems essential, we can describe a given situation *exactly enough* for our purposes. If the description is simple and clear, logical reasoning may be possible. If the conclusions arrived at by this reasoning accord well with reality, then the description itself and the previous judgments as to what is essential are vindicated. If some conclusions arrived at through reasoning accord poorly with reality, then to that degree our description of the situation and the judgments on which it was based become unacceptable and have to be changed.

Such a description is a bundle of *ideas* and is therefore said to be "ideal" and to define an "ideal" situation, as distinguished from a real one. The Greeks, in geometry, were the first to apply logic systematically to a situation idealized for that purpose, compressing innumerable spatial pheonomena into half a dozen ideal principles. Having simplified these principles to an extreme degree with their "points" without spread, "lines" without width, and so forth, they built upon them, solely by the exercise of logic, a structure so large and rich and so spectacularly close to reality as to justify their method of idealization and logical process to the ages. This method of first idealizing and then reasoning underlies all mathematics and exact science.

A simple and amusing example of this method is adapted from *An Introduction to Logic and Scientific Method,* by M. R. Cohen and E. Nagel. We ask: At each instant, do two people in New York exist with the same number of hairs on their scalps?

It is quite remarkable that this question can be answered at all. How? By a scalp census, not missing a hair, of nearly 8 million people, and so rapidly performed as to permit no one, by combing, brushing, washing, pulling, or scratching, to change his scalp count during its course? If we are denied such a census, then can we answer the question by some other kind of observation? For surely the answer to the question must be based on observation.

To the last query we can answer yes. Observations of the right kind, appropriately interpreted in logical argument, do enable us to answer the question.

The critical information, which is given by Cohen and Nagel, consists in the following facts:

(1) Physiologists have noted that the maximum number of hairs per square centimeter on any human scalp is less than 5000.

(2) Anthropologists have found no human scalp with an area as great as 1000 square centimeters.

(3) The population of New York City, according to the census of 1960, totaled 7,781,984 persons.

Guided by these facts, we formulate the following idealized hypotheses:

(1′) No human scalp holds more than 5000 hairs per square centimeter.

(2′) The area of no human scalp exceeds 1000 square centimeters.

(3′) At no instant does New York City have as few as 5,000,000 inhabitants.

Under these ideal hypotheses, we can settle the question rapidly. From hypotheses (1′) and (2′), we conclude that no human scalp holds more than 5 million hairs. From hypothesis (3′), we see that, if no two New York City scalps held the same number of hairs, some would have more than 5 million hairs. The previous sentence states, however, that this cannot be. Therefore there are New Yorkers with the same number of hairs, and the question raised is answered in the idealized situation in the affirmative.†

This answer is no more certain, however, than the ideal hypotheses, (1′), (2′), and (3′), on which the argument depends. These hypotheses seem safe enough generalizations of observed data, but observations are always open to doubt. It is at least conceivable that new data could upset these hypotheses and so alter the argument and the conclusions. To the extent that we believe this to be likely, we will doubt the answer given. To the extent that we believe this to be unlikely, we will tend to accept it. Our confidence in the answer, in short, equals our confidence in the data on which our ideal hypotheses were based.

The following puzzles and problems are given to help the reader recall the many points of logic he already knows and knows how to apply. He may try or disregard them at his pleasure.

---

†Cohen and Nagel, *op. cit.*, pp. 5-7.

EXERCISES

1. Can the question discussed in this section be answered with absolute confidence?

2. A Gallup Poll investigator reported speaking to 100 persons, of whom 70 were white, 10 were women, and five were non-white men. Why was this investigator justly fired? †

3. Mr. Buick, Mr. Chrysler, and Mr. Ford owned a Buick, a Chrysler, and a Ford (not necessarily in that order). The Chrysler's owner often beat Ford at

---

† Max Black, *Critical Thinking: An Introduction to Logic and Scientific Method*, second edition, Englewood Cliffs, N.J., Prentice-Hall, Inc., 1952, p. 11.

cards. Ford was the brother-in-law of the Buick's owner. Chrysler had more children than the Chrysler's owner. Who owned the Buick?

4. There were three prisoners, one of whom was blind. Their jailor offered to free them all if any one could succeed in the following game. The jailor produced three white hats and two red hats and, in a dark room, placed a hat on each prisoner. Then the prisoners were taken into the light where, except for the blind one, they could see one another. The game was for any prisoner to state correctly what color hat he himself was wearing. The jailor asked one of those who could see if he knew, and the man answered no. Then the jailor asked the other prisoner who could see, and he answered no. The blind prisoner at this point correctly stated the color of his own hat, winning the game for all three. How did he know?†

5. There are three musicians: a violinist, a cellist, and a pianist. Their names are Brown, Town, and Gown. Each is the father of a grown son. The cellist and Town, Jr., are six feet tall. The pianist is five feet tall. Gown, Jr., is six inches shorter than Town, Jr. The violinist is five feet nine. The violinist has exactly one-third as many phonograph records as that man (among the other five) who is nearest his own height. The pianist's son has 313 orchestral records and 409 vocal records. Brown, Jr.'s father has more false teeth than the cellist. What is the name of the violinist?‡

6. A father wished to leave his fortune to the most intelligent of his three sons. He said to them: "I shall presently take each one of you away separately and paint either a white or a blue mark on each of your foreheads, and none of you will have any chance to know the color of the mark on his own head. Then I shall bring you together again, and anybody who is able to see two blue marks on the heads of his companions is to laugh. The first of you to deduce his own color is to raise his hand, and on convincing me that his solution is correct, will become my heir." After all three had agreed to the conditions, the father took them apart and painted a white mark on each forehead. When they met again, there was silence for some time, at the end of which the youngest brother raised his hand, saying: "I'm white." How was he able to deduce the color of the mark on his forehead?§

7. On a certain train, the crew consists of three men: the brakeman, the fireman, and the engineer. Their names listed alphabetically are Jones, Robinson, and Smith. On the train are also three passengers with corresponding names, Mr. Jones, Mr. Robinson, and Mr. Smith. The following facts are known:

(a) Mr. Robinson lives in Detroit.

(b) The brakeman lives halfway between Detroit and Chicago.

(c) Mr. Jones earns exactly $20,000 a year.

(d) Smith once beat the fireman at billiards.

(e) The brakeman's next-door neighbor, one of the three passengers mentioned, earns exactly three times as much as the brakeman.

(f) The passenger living in Chicago has the same name as the brakeman.

What was the engineer's name?††

---

†Copi, op. cit., pp. 16-17.
‡Black, op. cit., p. 11.
§Ibid., p. 12.
††Copi, op. cit., p. 17.

8. The members of a small loan company are Mr. Black, Mr. White, Mrs. Coffee, Miss Ambrose, Mr. Kelly, and Miss Earnshaw. The positions they occupy are manager, assistant manager, cashier, stenographer, teller, and clerk, but not necessarily in that order. The assistant manager is the manager's grandson; the cashier is the stenographer's son-in-law; Mr. Black is a bachelor. Mr. White is 22 years old; Miss Ambrose is the teller's stepsister; and Mr. Kelly is the manager's neighbor. Who holds each position? †

9. Benno Torelli, genial host at Jamtrack's most exclusive night club, was shot and killed by a racketeer gang because he fell behind in his protection payments. After considerable effort on the part of the police, five men were brought before the District Attorney, who asked them what they had to say for themselves. Each of the men made three statements, two true and one false. Their statements were:

Lefty: "I did not kill Torelli. I never owned a revolver. Spike did it."
Red: "I did not kill Torelli. I never owned a revolver. The other guys are all passing the buck."
Dopey: "I am innocent. I never saw Butch before. Spike is guilty."
Spike: "I am innocent. Butch is the guilty man. Lefty lied when he said I did it."
Butch: "I did not kill Torelli. Red is the guilty man. Dopey and I are old pals."

Whodunnit? ‡

10. Five men who were buddies in World War II are having a reunion. They are White, Brown, Peters, Harper, and Nash, who by occupation are printer, writer, barber, neurologist, and heating-contractor. By coincidence, they live in the cities of White Plains, Brownsville, Petersburg, Harpers Ferry, and Nashville, but no man lives in the city having a name similar to his, nor does the name of his occupation have the same initial as his name or the name of the city in which he lives.

The barber doesn't live in Petersburg, and Brown is neither heating-contractor nor printer—nor does he live in Petersburg or Harpers Ferry. Mr. Harper lives in Nashville and is neither barber nor writer. White is not a resident of Brownsville; nor is Nash, who is neither a barber nor a heating-contractor.

If you have only the information given, can you name the city where Nash lives? §

11. Of two tribes inhabiting a South Seas isle, members of one tribe always tell the truth, and members of the other always lie. A logician vacationing on the isle comes to a fork in the road and has to ask a native bystander which branch he should take to reach a village. He cannot tell whether the native is a truth-teller or a liar but succeeds in framing a single question so cleverly that he will nevertheless know from the reply which road to take. What question would have served?

---

†Ibid.
‡Ibid., p. 18.
§Ibid., p. 19.

The following three alternative questions have been proposed.† Justify them: (1) "If I were to ask you if this road leads to the village, would you say 'yes'?" (2) "If I asked a member of the other tribe whether this road leads to the village, would he say 'yes'?" (3) "Of the two statements, 'You are a liar' and 'This road leads to the village,' is one and only one of them true?"

12. A teacher announced an examination to be held on one of the weekdays, Monday through Friday, inclusive, of the following week. He declined to reveal the exact day, which would invite last-minute cramming, and promised to cancel the examination altogether if anyone could figure out its actual day at any time in advance. A student then argued that, under these circumstances, the examination could not possibly be held. First, Friday was excluded as a possible day: if Friday were the day designed, everyone would know it when the examination failed to come off by Thursday afternoon, and the teacher thus would be bound to cancel it. Then Thursday was excluded: for Friday was already out, and the students would be able to recognize Thursday plans as soon as Wednesday ended without the examination. Similarly, Wednesday, Tuesday, and Monday were successively excluded as days on which the examination could be held. Was the student right?‡

13. Imagine that you have three boxes, one containing two black marbles, one containing two white marbles, and the third containing one black marble and one white marble. The boxes were labeled for their contents — BB, WW, and BW — but someone has switched the labels so that every box is now incorrectly labeled. You can determine the contents of all the boxes from the color of one marble that you draw from a particular box without looking inside. How?

HINT: Recall that all the boxes are wrongly labeled. Draw the marble from the box labeled BW and reason from that point. §

14. In a certain problem of addition, all ten digits (from 0 through 9, inclusive) appear. We make a puzzle out of this problem by substituting letters for the digits, using one and the same letter for each individual digit, wherever it may occur, but using different letters for the different digits. The puzzle so obtained reads:

$$
\begin{array}{r}
\text{F O R T Y} \\
+\text{T E N} \\
+\text{T E N} \\
\hline
\text{S I X T Y}
\end{array}
$$

What was the original problem? ††

---

†Martin Gardner, *The Scientific American Book of Mathematical Puzzles and Diversions,* New York, Simon and Schuster, 1959, pp. 25, 28-29.

‡C. Stanley Ogilvy, *Tomorrow's Math,* New York, Oxford University Press, 1962, pp. 38-40.

§Gardner, *op. cit.,* p. 25.

††Martin Gardner, *The 2nd Scientific American Book of Mathematical Puzzles and Diversions,* New York, Simon and Schuster, 1961, p. 240.

3.

Premises and argument

Any logical argument, i.e., logical train of thought, begins with certain statements called *premises* that for the sake of the argument are assumed to be true. (In Section 2, the idealized hypotheses (1′), (2′), and (3′) are the premises.) From the premises, by logical reasoning, we may arrive at other statements that we will accept as true *if* the premises are true. Every principle and every fact on which the argument depends must be stated explicitly in the premises. Logic brooks no intangibles and no secret predilections or prejudices: all presumptions in a logical argument must be made explicit.

May we, for example, draw these conclusions:

Premise	*Conclusion*
He is almost sixteen years old.	He will die soon.
He was graduated from high school with a good record.	He will get into a good college.

In fact, both conclusions are unjustifiable in the absence of further information, which would have to be included in the premises. The first conclusion would be more likely if we added the premise that "he" is a dog, but the conclusion would not be logically justifiable without a third premise stating explicitly that dogs do not live much more than sixteen years. The second conclusion also requires a previously unstated premise; for instance, that anyone who is graduated from high school with a good record will get into a good college.

The existence of an unspoken premise may be the basis of unconscious humor, as in the following anecdote† about President Charles William Eliot of Harvard. Eliot, the "topmost oak" of New England, transformed Harvard against the bitter opposition of traditionalists from an 18th Century backwater into a modern university, in so doing influencing the whole American system of higher education. One year a star baseball player was left off the Harvard team because of low marks. Eliot remarked to someone that this was no loss, because the player was known to resort to deception. "Why," he explained, "they boasted of his making a feint to throw a ball in one direction and then throwing it in ANOTHER!"

---

†From Barbara Tuchman, *The Proud Tower*, New York, The Macmillan Company, 1966, p. 147.

EXERCISES

Try to give the stated and the unstated premises involved in the following assertions:

1. Since the sun rises every day, it will rise tomorrow.

2. Since men will sit in a subway train while women stand, New Yorkers have no manners.

3. With such decent parents, he must be sincere.

4. The ephemerality of fashion proves that women are more volatile and more extravagant than men.

5. Topless bathing suits are just another index of the decadence of our culture.

6. He's not so smart; he can't even fix a flat tire.

7. He would not take the crown;
Therefore 'tis certain he was not ambitious.

8. A five-year-old child should not be permitted to appear at cocktail parties, sipping make-believe ginger ale cocktails and imitating drunks.

9. Look to her, Moor, if thou hast eyes to see:
She has deceived her father, and may thee.

10. Early to bed and early to rise,
Makes a man healthy, wealthy, and wise.

11. A driver should glance over his left shoulder before making a left turn. But he need not if a car has just passed him traveling in the opposite direction.

12. I had to ask our dinner guests, who had just arrived, to entertain themselves while we finished dressing. But I was not embarrassed, for they were half an hour early.

13. If the baby is kept waiting for his bottle, he will cry. Ethel wasn't prompt, and therefore he was crying.

14. The first domino, if it falls, will knock the second domino down, the second, the third, and so on. The child pushed over the first domino, and one by one the others inevitably followed.

15. The fishing must be good there, since he caught seven trout. So we'd better go there for our vacation.

16. In a debate on the problem of high school "drop-outs" a debater gave the following argument against encouraging "drop-outs" to return to school:

(1) Either students are willing and eager to learn or they are unwilling and not eager to learn. (2) If they are willing and eager to learn, they will remain in school if at all possible. (3) If they are unwilling and not eager to learn, they will only hamper those students who are willing and eager to learn, and, hence, they do not belong in school. (4) Therefore, students either will remain in school if at all possible or do not belong in school. (5) Therefore "drop-outs" should not be encouraged to return to school.

After the debate two students had the following discussion of this argument:

Student A: "That was a very logical argument against encouraging 'drop-outs' to return to school, but I don't agree with the conclusion. I still think we should encourage 'drop-outs' to return to school, but I don't see what's wrong with his argument. I seem to agree with everything he says, but I just can't accept his conclusion."

Student B: "How can you say it was a logical argument if you don't agree with the conclusion? If the argument were logical, then wouldn't the conclusion have to follow from the argument?"

Student A: "I guess you are right, but I can't put my finger on exactly what is wrong with the argument."

Student B: "I'm not sure what is wrong with the argument either; I guess that guy was just a smooth talker; everything he said seemed so logical."

Questions:

(a) What is wrong with the argument, and how can it be disputed?

(b) Do you agree with student *B* that if we agree with the statements of the argument, then the conclusion follows logically?

(c) Which statements in the argument are premises and which are conclusions?

(d) What unstated premises are there in this argument?

(e) Can you suggest any general rules for disputing this type of argument?

(f) Is the confusion of the two students (who are unfamiliar with logic) understandable? How does knowledge of logic help to resolve the confusion?

The process of reasoning by which one judges other statements in the light of the accepted premises is called *logical deduction* or *inference*. This process is exclusively verbal. Sentences are its raw materials; sentences are its finished product. Arts of persuasion are the germ and inspiration of its methods; distillations of familiar principles of discourse are its laws. The rules of logic thus are not strange to any discriminating user of his mother tongue. This is why no special logical training was needed for the puzzles in Section 2, nor is detailed, formal study of logic a requisite for many fields of mathematics. A careful reasoner should, however, be consciously aware of the most important rules of logic and logical deduction.

Some of these rules have been illustrated. For instance, we deduced that at least two persons exist in New York City with the same scalp hair count by showing that to suppose the contrary involved us, under the given premises, in a contradiction. Our argument thus rested on the principle that two contradictory statements cannot both be true. This principle also underlay most of the other given instances and, in fact, can reasonably be regarded as the first law of logic. We reformulate it as follows.

The Law Against Contradiction.   No statement is both true and false.

Additional laws, which are actually logical consequences of this one, will be developed.

4.

Logical exactness. Symbolism.

Exact reasoning calls, first of all, for precision of utterance and thus for care in syntax and grammar. Without such care, even the simplest thought can be botched, as we shall illustrate with some excerpts from actual advertisements, news items, magazine stories, cookbook recipes, and so forth:†

Quiet, clean gentleman seeks comfortable room where he can cook himself on a spirit stove.

TURKEY CARPET for sale good condition the property of a lady too large for her rooms.

WANTED, Smart Young Man for butchers. Able to cut, skewer, and serve a customer.

In reply to your valued enquiry, we enclose illustrations of Dining Table of Oak, seating fourteen people with round legs and twelve people with square legs, with prices attached.

TEETH EXTRACTED WITH THE GREATEST PAINS

Dr. W. T. _____ read an interesting paper on "Idiots from Birth." There were over two hundred present.

A full charge of shot struck Mr. Cozad squarely in the back of the henhouse.

Man critical after Bus Backs into Him.

WOMAN HURT WHILE COOKING HER HUSBAND'S
BREAKFAST IN A HORRIBLE MANNER

The Biblical story, based on a libretto by Oscar Wilde, recounts that . . . .

Mrs. _____ wishes to thank the nurse and doctor for their kind cooperation in the loss of her husband.

There will be a procession next Sunday afternoon in the grounds of the Monastery; but if it rains in the afternoon, the procession will take place in the morning.

If it is a cold day, cut a few slices from your tongue and serve with a brown sauce.

When the baby is done drinking it must be unscrewed and laid in a cool place under a tap. If the baby does not thrive on fresh milk it should be boiled.

Pitfalls for the unwary writer abound. Perhaps none is a greater hindrance to precise expression than the ability of a word to convey a variety of related meanings. In a discussion that purports to be logical, this hindrance is overcome by agreeing to use the word in just *one* sense consciously selected for the purposes at hand. The ambiguous word thus is redefined; this is an artificial procedure but apparently necessary for the exactness logic demands.

A common example of an ambiguous word requiring such redefinition is the conjunction "or." Contrast, for example, the two italicized sentences: "We must find out! *The rebel will give his in-*

---

†These are all taken from Denys Parsons' collection, *"Nothing Brightens the Garden like Primrose Pants,"* Hanover House, Garden City, New York, 1955.

formation or be shot." "You will hear from me. *I will either phone or write.*" Both sentences are essentially promises. Is the first a lie if the rebel *both* gives his information *and* is shot? Is the second a lie if the speaker *both* phones *and* writes? If these questions deserve opposite answers, the two sentences exemplify different usages of "or." Forced to select a single meaning of the word, to which they will thereafter always adhere, logicians have picked a definition under which "I will either phone or write" means: "I will *either* phone or write, or else will *both* phone *and* write." Under this definition, similarly, "She will sing or dance" means: "She will *either* sing or dance, or else will *both* sing *and* dance." The logician's meaning of "or" thus may be rendered roughly by means of "either or both." We shall now give an exact definition.

To do so intelligibly we must use symbols. In fact, symbols are essential whenever we wish to refer to statements being talked about without having to repeat them and without mixing them up. To use them in logic is as natural as not writing out Cash on Delivery, The American Society for the Prevention of Cruelty to Animals, Dollars, or Plus but employing such abbreviations as COD, ASPCA, $, and + instead. The more compact our symbols, the better. Hence, we shall ordinarily denote statements by single letters. If the symbol adopted for a specified sentence is, say, the letter A, we say that A *denotes, designates,* or *represents* the sentence. Symbols for individual words or expressions are similarly described.

In order now to define the logician's usage of "or," let A and B denote any two statements. The compound sentence "A or B" then is understood to mean: "A, or B, or else both A and B." (If, for instance, A denotes: "I will phone," and B denotes: "I will write," "A or B" represents the compound sentence: "I will phone, or I will write." This is equivalent to the sentence used in the second example given, and according to the logician's lexicon means: "Either I will phone, or I will write, or else I will both phone and write.") Thus, the logician uses "or" in its inclusive sense solely. If he wishes to use "or" in its exclusive sense (as, for instance, in "I will phone or write, but not both"), he will say so explicitly. We shall follow these practices here.

5.

Truth and falsity. Composite statements.

Syntax and grammar govern the verbal expression of thought but are only indirectly related to "the laws of thought," the ultimate rules on which reasoning depends. These rules belong to logic. In order to formulate them simply, it has been found desirable to regard any statement considered either as true or, if not true, as false. Hence, any sentence admitted to logical discourse must first of all be perfectly clear. For instance, we cannot admit the statement "This is a triangle" without knowing the antecedent of "this." The same words with different antecedents for the pronoun count of course as different statements. Similarly, the sentence "He signed the contract" is inadmissible unless the person, the contract, and the occasion—for instance, the date and time—are precisely specified. For another person, another contract, or another occasion, the same words would constitute another sentence. (Nevertheless, we shall use such sentences in examples, pretending we have made the necessary explanations.) On the other hand, sentences like the following are meaningful as they stand:

"Some triangles have a right angle."
"In all triangles, the angles total 180°."

The first of these is essentially an assertion that something (in this case, at least one triangle with a right angle) *exists.* The second is an example of a *generalization,* which is a declaration that something is the case for *all* objects of a certain class, or under *all* circumstances, and so forth. Such a sentence as

"*No one* can run as fast as a horse"

is also a generalization, this sentence meaning:

"*Everyone* has less ability than a horse to run fast."

Paraphrasing like this is often necessary to bring out the logical aspects of an English sentence.

EXERCISE

1. Indicate which of the following passages are generalizations and which are statements of existence.†
   (a) It is a wise father who knows his own son.
   (b) A bird in the hand is worth two in the bush.
   (c) You can't teach an old dog new tricks.
   (d) No man is an island.
   (e) You can lead a horse to water, but you can't make him drink.
   (f) There'll be a hot time in the old town tonight.
   (g) All is vanity.
   (h) The true male never yet walked
       Who liked to listen when his mate talked. (Anna Wickham‡)

---

†The footnoted items refer to John Bartlett, *Familiar Quotations,* 13th edition, Boston, Little, Brown and Company, 1955.
‡*Ibid.,* p. 930a.

(i) Oh! somewhere in this favored land the sun is shining bright;
The band is playing somewhere, and somewhere hearts are light;
And somewhere men are laughing and somewhere children shout,
But there is no joy in Mudville — mighty Casey has struck out.
(Ernest Lawrence Thayer †)

(j) From birth to eighteen, a girl needs good parents. From eighteen
to thirty-five, she needs good looks. From thirty-five to fifty-five, she
needs a good personality. From fifty-five on, she needs good cash.
(Sophie Tucker at sixty-nine ‡)

(k) People who know little are usually great talkers, while men who
know much say little. (Rousseau §)

(l) Provided a man is not mad, he can be cured of every folly but
vanity. (Rousseau §)

(m) Men will sometimes jealous be,
Though but little cause they see. (Thomas Campion ††)

(n) Something is rotten in the state of Denmark. (Hamlet)

(o) When sorrows come, they come not single spies,
But in battalions. (Hamlet)

(p) To fear the worst oft cures the worse. (Troilus and Cressida)

(q) Oft expectation fails, and most oft there
Where most it promises. (All's Well That Ends Well)

(r) Good counsellors lack no clients. (Measure for Measure)

(s) Some rise by sin, and some by virtue fall. (Measure for Measure)

(t) A poet can survive everything but a misprint. (Oscar Wilde ‡‡)

(u) We are all in the gutter, but some of us are looking at the stars.
(Oscar Wilde §§)

(v) I can resist everything except temptation. (Oscar Wilde §§)

(w) To love oneself is the beginning of a lifelong romance.
(Oscar Wilde †††)

---

† Ibid., p. 808a.
‡ Ibid., p. 929b.
§ Ibid., p. 344b.
†† Ibid., p. 220b.
‡‡ Ibid., p. 767b.
§§ Ibid., p. 768b.
††† Ibid., p. 769b.

The logician's requirement that his sentences be absolutely definite and clear — and then be unquestionably true or else unquestionably false — is sometimes artificial. For instance, if you wish to admit into logical discourse the statement "Jack is of normal intelligence," you must adopt fixed, definite standards that permit you to establish "normal intelligence" quite decisively. Such standards, of course, will be somewhat arbitrary, and the "truth" they define will be arbitrary to the same extent. Rigid classification into true and false is idealization and cannot escape some artificiality.

It will be useful to agree to say that a statement, if true, is "in the *state* of being true," or more briefly, is "in the *T* state," and, if false, is "in the *state* of being false," or is "in the *F* state." We shall see that a statement's state (of truth or falsity) is pertinent to logic, while its meaning is not.

To illustrate how the convention as to truth and falsity works, consider the following three statements:

A: "He uttered a polite word."
B: "He uttered a joke."
C: "He uttered a polite word or a joke."

(A denotes the first statement, B the second, and C the third.) Whether C is true or false depends upon the truth or falsity—i.e., upon the states—of A and B. Certainly, C is true if A is true and B false, or if B is true and A false; and C is false if A and B are both false. If A and B are both true, the definition of "or" ("either or both") adopted in the previous section requires us to consider C to be true. We can clearly display these relationships in a table (Table 1-1), in which we indicate the truth or falsity of C for each possible combination of states of A and B. Such a table is called a *truth table*. The first two vertical columns, which are headed A and B, list the conceivable states (*T* and *F*) of these respective assertions. In the horizontal rows occur each of the four conceivable *combinations* of states of A and B and the corresponding states of C. The table says nothing more nor less than what had been previously declared in words, namely that C is true unless A and B are both false.

A	B	C
T	T	T
T	F	T
F	T	T
F	F	F

Table 1-1   *A truth table*

If A and B denote any two statements, the sentence "A or B" is called the *disjunction* of A and B. Usually we shall omit the quotation marks, but we may enclose the sentence in parentheses to stress that it is being considered as a whole. This sentence has a truth table (Table 1-2) exactly like Table 1-1, as is also seen from the previous discussion. Both truth tables simply express the definition of "or" we have adopted.

A	B	(A or B)
T	T	T
T	F	T
F	T	T
F	F	F

Table 1-2   *Truth table for disjunction of two sentences*

A sentence such as (A or B), in which two or more *constituent* sentences are combined, is called a *composite* sentence or statement.

Let us now draw up a truth table relating a composite statement of another kind to its constituents. Consider these statements:

D: "Jack is good at tennis."
E: "Jack is good at swimming."
G: "Jack is good at tennis and swimming."

(D denotes the first statement, E the second, and G the third.) G is true if D and E are both true but is false if either D or E is false (or both D and E are false). Arranging this information in tabular form gives us Table 1-3.

Table 1-3 *A truth table*

D	E	G
T	T	T
T	F	F
F	T	F
F	F	F

If A and B are any statements, the sentence "A and B" is called their *conjunction*. The truth table for any conjunction (Table 1-4) is exactly like Table 1-3. We can regard this table as defining "and" for the logician.

Table 1-4 *Truth table for conjunction of two sentences*

A	B	(A and B)
T	T	T
T	F	F
F	T	F
F	F	F

A composite sentence made up of three constituents has a truth table with eight rows, one row for each of the eight possible combinations of states of the constituents. We illustrate with Table 1-5

Table 1-5 *A three-variable truth table*

A	B	C	(B and C)	[A or (B and C)]
T	T	T	T	T
T	F	T	F	T
F	T	T	T	T
F	F	T	F	F
T	T	F	F	T
T	F	F	F	T
F	T	F	F	F
F	F	F	F	F

for the sentence, "A or (B and C)." (An example of such a sentence is: "Either I will call for it today, or he will get it and then bring it to me tomorrow.") The fourth column gives the state of (B and C) for each combination of states of B and of C. The state of [A or (B and C)], which is entered in the fifth column, is T if either A or (B and C) is true, but is F if A and (B and C) are both false.

EXERCISES

Analyze the following eleven composite statements into their constituents, and draw up appropriate truth tables.

2. He is thinking or studying.

3. They are eating and drinking.

4. Self-interest speaks all sorts of tongues, and plays all sorts of roles, even that of disinterestedness. †

5. We are never so happy nor so unhappy as we imagine. †

6. Everyone complains of his memory, and no one complains of his judgment. †

7. Most people judge men only by their success or their good fortune. †

8. The Constitution requires that the President be at least 35 years old, a natural-born citizen of the United States, and a resident of the country for 14 years.

9. The Judicial Power of the United States is vested in one Supreme Court and in such inferior courts as the Congress may from time to time ordain and establish.

10. "I shall never ask, never refuse, nor ever resign an office." (Benjamin Franklin)

11. "You can fool all of the people some of the time, and you can fool some of the people all of the time, but you can't fool all of the people all of the time." (Abraham Lincoln)

12. People are poor because "they made the mistake of being born to the wrong parents in the wrong section of the country, in the wrong industry, or in the wrong racial or ethnic group." ‡

13. Consider these two statements:

D: "The Society sponsored a bridge tournament."

E: "We played in the tournament."

Write a statement, denoted by G, for which Table 1-3 is a correct truth table.

14. Consider these two statements:

A: "The sky will be overcast."

B: "It will rain."

Write a statement, denoted by C, for which Table 1-1 is a correct truth table.

Draw up truth tables for the following five sentences:

15. (A or B or C)

---

† Maxim of La Rochefoucauld, quoted from John Bartlett, op. cit., p. 265.
‡ Michael Harrington, quoted in The Washington Post, Jan. 31, 1966, p. 1.

16. (A and B and C)
17. (Neither A nor B)
18. (A, but neither B nor C)
19. (A and also either B or C)
20. Draw up a truth table for composite sentences of the form: "Not only A, but also B."

6.

Logical equivalence

The rules and definitions we have been studying exhibit a fundamental characteristic of the logic of propositions. Recall, for instance, the definition of "A or B," the statement that is true unless A and B are both false, or the Law Against Contradictions, holding that no statement is true and also false. Both the definition and the law pertain to the *states* of arbitrary sentences without regard for what the sentences mean. In logic, all definitions, relations, and rules for arbitrary sentences are similarly framed in terms of states alone, regardless of what the sentences might individually mean. Consequently, two sentences that have the same state must play the same role in any purely logical relation or process and thus need not be distinguished logically. For this reason, two such sentences — sentences that have the same state, the one being true if the other is true, false if the other is false — are said to be *logically equivalent.* The following pairs of sentences (in each pair, we assume the pronouns to refer to the same antecedent) are, for instance, logically equivalent:

He wants to eat and drink. He wants to eat, and he wants to drink.
The baby is asleep. The baby is slumbering.
He is another son of my parents. He is my brother.
It will die some day. It will die.
I certainly am not. I am not.

Sentences that mean quite different things also can be equivalent:

The jury decided he was not guilty. After a jury trial, he was acquitted.
This is a rectangle. This is a parallelogram with equal diagonals.

The equivalence of the first pair of sentences is the result of an advance in justice. The equivalence of the second pair is a theorem in geometry.

We sometimes assert the equivalence of two statements by saying that one of them is true *if and only if* the other is. Each of the two equivalent statements is also said to be a *necessary and sufficient condition* for the other.

The symbol used for logical equivalence is ≡. We express

symbolically that two statements which we denote by A and B, respectively, are equivalent by writing

$$A \equiv B.$$

By the truth table for the relation of logical equivalence we mean the truth table for the sentence "$A \equiv B$." Indeed, this table (Table 1-6) declares the sentence "$A \equiv B$" to be true if A and B are both true or both false, and to be false if A is false and B true, or if A is true and B false. Thus, the table faithfully represents the definition of logical equivalence.

A	B	$(A \equiv B)$
T	T	T
T	F	F
F	T	F
F	F	T

Table 1-6   *Truth table for logical equivalence*

If two statements are each logically equivalent to a third, then the two are logically equivalent to each other. In symbols: if $A \equiv C$ and $B \equiv C$, then $A \equiv B$. Indeed, the state of A is the same as the state of C (since $A \equiv C$), and the state of B also is the same as the state of C (since $B \equiv C$). Hence, the states of A and B are the same, and (by definition) A and B are logically equivalent.

Many—perhaps most—statements that seem to assert merely the equivalence of two sentences actually involve something more. Consider, for instance, this statement: "The three angles of a triangle are equal if and only if the three sides of the triangle are equal." At first glance, this statement may seem to say

$$"A \equiv B,"$$

with A denoting the sentence "The three angles of a triangle are equal" and B the sentence "The three sides of the triangle (mentioned in A) are equal." But the statement does not refer to a particular, or individual, triangle; it really asserts:

$$\text{"For } any \text{ triangle, } A \equiv B."$$

Thus, this statement is a generalization, not a mere single equivalence. Failure to note such a distinction may lead to confusion, as the following example illustrates. Consider the fragments of intelligence expressed in the following two sentences:

   C: "It is a portrait."
   D: "It is an oil painting."

If the object in question is indeed a portrait in oils, then C and D are both true, and we read from the first row of Table 1-6 that they are logically equivalent. Does this mean that being a portrait is equivalent to being an oil painting? This question asks whether C and D are equivalent *in all instances*. Hardly, and, indeed, we asserted the equivalence only in the particular instance at hand.

EXERCISES

1. If $A \equiv B$, $B \equiv C$, and $C \equiv D$, prove that $A \equiv D$.

2. Let A and B denote any statements. Which of the following assertions are true, and which are false? If the assertion is true, prove it; if the assertion is false, illustrate with a specific example.

(a) If $A \equiv (A$ or $B)$, then $A \equiv B$.

(b) If $(A$ and $B) \equiv (A$ and $C)$, then $(B \equiv C)$.

(c) If $(A$ and $B) \equiv (A$ or $B)$, then $A \equiv B$.

7.

Negation

By the negation of a statement we mean, roughly, the statement derived from the original by inserting "not." (Special rules are often needed to tell us how to negate complex statements. Grammar, however, is sometimes a guide.) For instance, the negation of the statement "I am tall" is "I am not tall"; that of "He lives in the land of make-believe" is "He does not live in the land of make-believe"; that of "His memory will never die" is "His memory will die." Such examples suggest that we define the negation of a given statement as the statement that is false when the given statement is true and is true when the given statement is false.

How do we apply this kind of definition? How do we actually write a "statement that is false when the given statement is true and is true when the given statement is false"? Consider again several examples: the negation of "I *must* do it" is "I *do not have to* do it"; the negation of "He *sat* down quietly to eat" is "He *did not sit* down quietly to eat"; the negation of "*All* are lost" is "*Some* are *not* lost"; the negation of "*Some love* it" is: "*No one loves* it." In none of these instances could the negation be expressed just by inserting the single word "not." In fact, a good universal rule for expressing negations cannot be given. We shall, however, discuss specific rules for certain types of sentences, and we shall always take it for granted that any sentence can be negated in good English somehow.

More generally, whenever we define a composite sentence by specifying its state for each combination of states of its constituents, we shall tacitly assume that a way exists to put this sentence into English.

If A denotes a given statement, the negation of the statement is symbolized by $\sim A$ (pronounced "not A"). Table 1-7 is the truth table for the negation. Indeed, this table declares $\sim A$ to be false when A is true and to be true when $\sim A$ is false. Thus, this table faithfully represents the definition of negation.

A	$\sim$A
T	F
F	T

Table 1-7 *Truth table for negation*

It is to be stressed that definitions such as those of Tables 1-2, 1-4, and 1-7 are *general*, "A" or "A and B" denoting any statements whatsoever. We shall illustrate this fact by obtaining a truth table for the composite sentence: "$\sim A$ and $\sim B$." Table 1-4 defines "A and B." Since A and B in this table are arbitrary, we may replace A by $\sim A$ and B by $\sim B$ to arrive at Table 1-8. This is a truth table relating the sentence "$\sim A$ and $\sim B$" to the statements $\sim A$ and $\sim B$. A truth table (Table 1-9) relating this sentence directly to A and B is immediately obtainable from Table 1-8.

$\sim$A	$\sim$B	($\sim$A and $\sim$B)
T	T	T
T	F	F
F	T	F
F	F	F

Table 1-8 *Conjunction of negations*

A	B	($\sim$A and $\sim$B)
F	F	T
F	T	F
T	F	F
T	T	F

Table 1-9 *Conjunction of negations related to original constituents*

What is the negation of a negation? Symbolically, what is $\sim(\sim A)$? The answer is suggested by examples. The negation of the statement "You are late" is "You are not late"; the negation of the latter is "You are late." The last is the original statement. The negation of the assertion "We are old, and you are young," is "Either we are not old, or you are not young," and the negation of this statement, which denies both the alternatives, is "We are old, and you are young" —again the original assertion. Is the negation of the negation of A always again A?

The answer to this question is Yes, in the sense that $\sim(\sim A)$ is *logically equivalent* to A. In symbols,

$$\sim(\sim A) \equiv A.$$

To be certain of this, we must show that $\sim(\sim A)$ is true when A is true and is false when A is false. Perhaps the clearest way to do this is to compare the truth table for A and $\sim A$ (Table 1-7) with that for $\sim A$ and $\sim(\sim A)$ (Table 1-10). In Table 1-10, to stress the parallelism with Table 1-7, we have first used the symbol B to stand for $\sim A$ and, correspondingly, the symbol $\sim B$ to stand for $\sim(\sim A)$. Then, to the right, we copied the table thus obtained, but with B replaced by $\sim A$.

Table 1-10 *Truth table for the negation of a negation*

B	~B	~A	~(~A)
F	T	F	T
T	F	T	F

To relate A and $\sim A$, we combine Tables 1-10 and 1-7 (Table 1-11). From Table 1-11 it is apparent that A and $\sim(\sim A)$ are either both true or both false. Hence, they are equivalent, as contended.

Table 1-11 *Truth table for a statement, its negation, and the negation of its negation*

A	~A	~(~A)
T	F	T
F	T	F

EXERCISES

1. Find truth tables for these sentences:
   (A and $\sim B$)
   ($\sim A$ or $\sim B$)
   ((A and $\sim B$) or ($\sim A$ and B))
   ((A or $\sim B$) and ($\sim A$ or B))
   $\sim(A \equiv B)$ ("A is not equivalent to B")
   $\sim(A \equiv \sim B)$ ("A is not equivalent to the negation of B")
2. Use truth tables to prove that if $A \equiv B$, then $\sim A \equiv \sim B$.
3. Consider the statements (A and $\sim A$), (B and $\sim B$), where the constituent parts A and B represent any statements.
   (a) What is the state of (A and $\sim A$)?
   (b) Do the states of "(A and $\sim A$)" and of "(B and $\sim B$)" always agree?
   (c) To what extent must statements that are logically equivalent have essentially the same meaning?

As we have remarked, many sentences are not easy to negate without referring to appropriate rules. As an example of such a rule, let us now show how to express the negation of (A or B) in terms of the negations of A and of B. For this purpose we draw up a truth table for the negations of all three sentences concerned. First we copy our previous truth table for (A or B). Then we add three columns to indicate the states of $\sim A$, $\sim B$, and $\sim(A$ or $B)$. We thus obtain Table 1-12.

A	B	(A or B)	~A	~B	~(A or B)
T	T	T	F	F	F
T	F	T	F	T	F
F	T	T	T	F	F
F	F	F	T	T	T

Table 1-12   *Truth tables for a disjunction and its negation*

The right half (the last three columns) of this table is a truth table for $\sim(A \text{ or } B)$ displaying the states of $\sim A$ and $\sim B$. If we compare it with Table 1-8, we perceive that it is also a truth table for $(\sim A \text{ and } \sim B)$. But two sentences with the same truth table are equivalent. Hence,

$$\sim(A \text{ or } B) \equiv (\sim A \text{ and } \sim B).$$

This is the rule required. We can illustrate it, for instance, with

$$A \equiv \text{"He uttered a polite word,"}$$

and

$$B \equiv \text{"He uttered a joke."}$$

As noted previously,

$$(A \text{ or } B) \equiv \text{"He uttered a polite word or a joke,"}$$

and our rule now shows that

$$\sim(A \text{ or } B) \equiv (\sim A \text{ and } \sim B)$$
$$\equiv \text{"He did not utter a polite word, and he did not utter a joke."}$$

A rule also exists for expressing $\sim(A \text{ and } B)$ in terms of $\sim A$ and $\sim B$:

$$\sim(A \text{ and } B) \equiv (\sim A \text{ or } \sim B).$$

We can obtain this by arguing from the truth tables, but we also can deduce it directly from the previous rule. The latter states that

$$\sim(A \text{ or } B) \equiv (\sim A \text{ and } \sim B)$$

for any two statements A and B whatsoever. We may replace A and B, in particular, by $\sim A$ and $\sim B$, respectively. Doing so, we obtain:

$$\sim(\sim A \text{ or } \sim B) \equiv (\sim(\sim A) \text{ and } \sim(\sim B)).$$

But $\sim(\sim A) \equiv A$ and $\sim(\sim B) \equiv B$. Hence,

$$\sim(\sim A \text{ or } \sim B) \equiv (A \text{ and } B).$$

Now negating both members of this equivalence (see the previous exercise) gives us, finally,

$$(\sim A \text{ or } \sim B) \equiv \sim (A \text{ and } B),$$

the rule we were seeking to prove.

EXERCISES

4. Prove the rule for negating conjunctions by arguing from truth tables.

5. A woman offered a bus driver five dollars and asked for tokens. Admire his reply: "I'm sorry, lady, but there ain't no bus driver got no change or no tokens, no time, nowhere, no more." (Bill Gold's column, "The District Line," *The Washington Post*, Oct. 17, 1968.)

Two of the most important kinds of assertions that are affirmed and denied in argument are generalizations and statements of existence. Thus, it is important to know how to express their negations. Consider, for instance, this generalization:

A: "All statesmen are wise."

(We label the sentence A.) How shall we put its negation, a sentence that must be true if A is false and must be false if A is true? Is the following sentence, in particular, the desired negation:

B: "No statesmen are wise"?

No, for it is at least conceivable that some statesmen are wise and some not, under which circumstances both A and B would be false. The real negation of A is

"Some statesmen are not wise,"

or, more precisely,

"A statesman exists who is not wise."

In the same way, any generalization of the form

"For *all* members of this-or-that class, such-and-such *is* the case"

has this negation:

"A member of the indicated class *exists* for which such-and-such is *not* the case."

Thus, the negation of a generalization is a statement of existence.

Conversely, the negation of any statement of existence is a generalization. This and the previous points are brought out in the following exercises.

EXERCISES

6. Negate the following sentences, some of which are certainly intended as generalizations:
  (a) Jack and Jill went up the hill.
  (b) Every dream is painting pictures in the air.
  (c) Somewhere over the rainbow, bluebirds fly.
  (d) If it rains, he changes his socks or goes to sleep.
  (e) She was dressed in yellow and blue.
  (f) Everybody here likes milk or coffee.
  (g) Somebody up there likes me.
  (h) Faint heart ne'er won fair lady.
  (i) A miss is as good as a mile.

7. Negate these sentences:
  (a) With all my worldly goods I thee endow.
  (b) All our yesterdays have lighted fools the way to dusty death.
  (c) Nothing is certain but death and taxes.
  (d) We all have strength enough to endure the misfortunes of others.†
  (e) Nothing is given so profusely as advice.‡
  (f) Mediocre minds usually dismiss anything which reaches beyond their own understanding.‡
  (g) Mediocre minds always dismiss anything which reaches beyond their own understanding.
  (h) Nothing prevents our being natural so much as the desire to appear so.‡
  (i) Most women are not so young as they are painted.§
  (j) No woman is so young as she is painted.
  (k) Some have too much, yet still do crave....††

8. Let A be the statement: "He is a gentleman." Let B be the statement: "He is a scholar."
  (a) Write each of the following statements in symbolic form:
    (i)   He is neither a gentleman nor a scholar.
    (ii) Either he is not a gentleman or he is not a scholar.
    (iii) He is a gentleman and a scholar.
    (iv) He is a gentleman or a scholar.
  (b) Prove that exactly two of the previous four statements are necessarily true and that exactly two of the four are necessarily false.

---

† La Rochefoucald, in Bartlett, op. cit., p. 264.
‡ Ibid., pp. 265-266.
§ Sir Max Beerbohm, ibid., p. 857.
†† Edward Dyer, ibid., p. 101.

9. (a) Prove that $\sim[(A \text{ and } B) \text{ or } C] \equiv [(\sim A \text{ or } \sim B) \text{ and } \sim C]$.

(b) Suppose that the following rule defines the conditions under which a student will be admitted to the football stadium: "Either he must present a valid Student Identification card and agree to sit in the student section, or else he must purchase a general admission ticket." Under what circumstances will a student be *denied* admission to the stadium?

10. Let A and B be any statements.

(a) Under what conditions (if any) on the states of A and of B are the following four statements simultaneously true?

$$\sim(A \text{ and } B), \quad A \text{ and } \sim B, \quad \sim(\sim A \text{ or } B), \quad \sim(\sim A \text{ and } \sim B)$$

(b) Under what conditions (if any) on the states of A and of B are the four statements simultaneously false?

(c-d) Answer (a) and (b) for these four statements:

$$\sim(A \text{ and } B), \quad A \text{ or } \sim B, \quad \sim A \text{ or } B, \quad \sim A \text{ or } \sim B.$$

11. Let A and B be any statements. Which of the following assertions are true, and which are false? If an assertion is true, prove it; if false, illustrate with a specific example.

(a) If A is not logically equivalent to B, then either $(A \text{ and } \sim B)$ is a true statement or $(\sim A \text{ and } B)$ is a true statement.

(b) If $(\sim A \text{ or } B) \equiv (A \text{ and } \sim C)$, then $B \equiv C$.

12. If A and B denote any two statements, prove or disprove that

$$(A \equiv B) \equiv [(A \text{ and } B) \text{ or } (\sim A \text{ and } \sim B)].$$

8.

An application to law

Ideal scientific description of any kind of social situation perhaps requires an exhaustive list of potentially relevant circumstances from which the particular conditions that occur in an individual situation can be named. Each situation of the given kind would be describable by sentences from the list, or negations of such sentences, connected by "and" or "or." A good example is to be found in a recent study of decisions in workmen's compensation cases.† When an employee is

---

† Reed C. Lawlor is the author of the study, which was summarized and discussed by Fred Kort in the article "Simultaneous equations and Boolean algebra in the analysis of Judicial decisions," *Law and Contemporary Problems*, Vol. 28, 1963, pp. 143-163.

injured, his employer may be liable, but the law does not specify in detail the conditions under which this is so. Hence, the administrative tribunals that hear the claims for compensation and the courts in which these hearings are reviewed cannot base their decisions solely on statute but are guided by the body of previous decisions. Accumulating over the years, these previous decisions carry great force as precedents, and a lawyer who wishes to know precisely what combinations of facts will result in a finding, say, for the employee, must know them. In the study referred to, workmen's compensation cases reviewed by the Connecticut Supreme Court of Errors were found to involve exactly 19 potentially relevant kinds of circumstances, including, for instance, these:

F_1: An accident or harmful act occurred in the course of an activity which was permitted by the employer.

F_2: An accident or harmful act occurred in the course of an activity conducive to efficient work.

F_3: An accident or harmful act occurred in the course of an activity which was indispensable for the performance of the work.

F_4: An accident or harmful act occurred on the premises of employment, in an area annexed to the place of employment, or in an area where the work normally is performed.

F_5: An accident or harmful act occurred during an activity which did not involve unnecessary, self-imposed hazardous conduct, such as taking a "joy-ride" on a conveyor belt for unloading coal.

F_6: The alleged injury became immediately apparent to the employee, as a result of an accident.

F_7: The accident or the act which caused the alleged injury was observed by other persons.

F_8: The alleged injury became immediately apparent to other observers, as a result of an accident or harmful act.

The principal aim of the study was to find reliable rules to predict the decision of the court in an individual case from the circumstances surrounding that case. Some of the logical questions that arise in an attempt to arrive at such rules will be apparent in the following exercises, which, however, are simplified and unrealistic. To handle effectively the 19 kinds of circumstances with which the study referred to actually deals requires the use of an electronic calculator.

EXERCISES

1. In every workmen's compensation case reviewed by the courts in a certain state:

(a) if F_1 was true, the courts decided in favor of the workman;

(b) if F_1 was false, and either F_4 or F_7 also was false, then the courts decided against the workman;

(c) if F_3 was the only one of the facts listed that was true, then the courts decided against the workman.

    (i) Using the symbols F_1, F_2, and so forth, write a composite sentence telling the conditions, in summary of the previous information, under which the courts decided in favor of the workman.

    (ii) What conclusions can be drawn as to future decisions of the courts of this state in workmen's compensation cases?

    (iii) What additional assumptions must be made to justify predicting future decisions from the preceding information?

2. In a certain state, the courts consistently handed down the following decisions:

Facts Present in Case	Court's Decision
F_1, F_2, F_3, F_4	pro workman
F_1, F_2, F_4	pro workman
F_2, F_3	con workman
F_1, F_2	pro workman
F_2, F_4	con workman
F_1, F_3	pro workman
F_3, F_4	con workman
F_1, F_4	pro workman
F_2, F_3, F_4	con workman
F_1	con workman

(a) Is the following statement true of the decisions summarized in the table given:

If the statement "F_1 and (F_2 or F_3 or F_4)" is true, then this state's courts decide in favor of (i.e., pro) the workman.

(b) Does the information in the table justify the last statement with respect to future cases? What additional information, if any, is needed before one could say that this statement is certainly true?

9.

Implication

a. IMPLICATION AS ORDINARILY EXPRESSED

If the premises of a given logical argument are combined into one statement, denoted by P, and the conclusions, similarly combined, are symbolized by C, the outcome of the argument can be summarized in the assertion:

$$\text{"If } P \text{, then } C \text{."}$$

Other statements of this type also occur frequently. They may be of strictly logical or mathematical origin, such as: "If it is new, it is

not old" or "If a closed polygon has three sides, it has three vertices."
They may state results of experience: "If you shout too long, you will
get hoarse." They may be declarations of intent: "If you move, I
will shoot." They may be statements that others may doubt: "If you
love me, the stars will dance around the moon." Whatever their
substance or origin, these statements of the form "If A, then B,"
where A and B denote any statements, are called *implications*. The
implication "If A, then B" is also expressed by saying "A *implies* B."
In this implication, A is called the *antecedent* and B the *consequent*.

Implications can be put into words in many ways. All the following statements, for instance, can be paraphrased as assertions of the
form "If A, then B," "Under such-and-such conditions: if A, then B,"
and so forth, and thus are — or contain — implications:

Be weak, and perish. Be strong, and overcome.
To live, you must take risks.
To persevere is to succeed.
Owning property entails paying taxes.
No work, no pay.
In order to reach the office by nine, I have to be up by seven.
Money makes money.
What goes up comes down.
A heated gas expands.
Under favorable circumstances, he would run for governor.
A rose by any other name would smell as sweet.
To vote, it is necessary to be at least twenty-one.
To be able to vote, it is sufficient to be a citizen over twenty-one.

The last two examples illustrate a frequent usage. When A
implies B, A often is called a *sufficient condition* for B, and B is called
a *necessary condition* for A. A sufficient condition is one that implies; a necessary condition, one that is implied.

As another illustration, consider the following implication: "If
you work overtime, you are paid at higher rates." Equivalently, we
might say "A necessary condition for working overtime is that you be
paid at higher rates" or "A sufficient condition for being paid at higher
rates is that you work overtime."

EXERCISES

1. For any ten of the preceding sentences containing implications, indicate the antecedent and the consequent.

2. Restate five of the sentences in the form of necessary conditions.
Restate five as sufficient conditions.

3. In Exercise 1 of Section 8, what is a necessary condition for the courts
to decide in favor of the workman? What is a sufficient condition for the courts
to decide in favor of the workman?

4. In Exercise 2 of Section 8, which of the following sentences are true, and which are false?

(a) F_1 is a necessary condition for a "pro" decision.

(b) F_1 is a sufficient condition for a "pro" decision.

(c) (F_2 or F_3 or F_4) is a necessary condition for a "pro" decision.

(d) (F_2 or F_3 or F_4) is a sufficient condition for a "pro" decision.

5. Each of the following sentences is of a logical form we have studied, i.e., is a conjunction, a generalization, a statement of existence, an implication, and so forth. Paraphrasing, put each sentence into its proper logical form. (For instance, paraphrase "Hot air rises" as: "If air is hot, then it will rise.")

(a) No one knows everything.

(b) Who steals my purse steals trash.

(c) He secretly agrees, but says nothing.

(d) Neither gifts nor flattery could win her.

(e) He's either right or wrong.

(f) The sky is grey but lovely.

(g) Mary's hair curls whenever the weather is rainy.

(h) I don't go to bed without brushing my teeth.

(i) I'll leave early unless I meet someone I know.

b. ENTAILING

The assertion "A implies B" is perhaps taken ordinarily to mean something like: "If A is true, then B is true as a result." But the last three words of this explanation introduce an idea that seems inappropriate to logic. While science and philosophy may be concerned with whether something occurs "as a result" of a particular cause, logic is simply a study of relations among sentences in which notions of cause and effect are beside the point. In trying to define "A implies B," therefore, consider this more straightforward condition:

"If A is true, then B is true."

For reasons we shall bring out soon, this condition still is not an acceptable definition. Yet it is of interest. Let us for the time being consider the expression "A entails B" to be synonymous with this condition. We shall call such a condition an *entailing*.

The difficulty with entailing becomes apparent when we try to draw up a truth table for it. Let C denote the sentence: "If A is true, then B is true." Since C is a composite with two constituents, A and B, its truth table should have four lines, as in Tables 1-2 and 1-4. But the meaning of C makes it apply only if A is true. C asserts nothing at all in the opposite case and then can hardly be said to be either true or false. The truth table for C (Table 1-13) is therefore incomplete. Under the standards of logic we agreed to accept, C therefore is not

A	B	C
T	T	T
T	F	F
F	T	
F	F	

Table 1-13 *Truth table for the composite sentence "If A is true, then B is true," denoted by C.*

an admissible sentence. Hence, entailing, which we sought to define through this sentence, is not an admissible concept.

Implication will be defined admissibly. Its truth table will be complete, with the first two lines of the table the same as those for entailing. Before going on to this, however, let us give three rules for entailing that are of the utmost importance in argument. These rules are valid no matter how the truth table for entailing might be completed.

The first rule relates entailing to equivalence. Let A and B denote two statements. We have:

(1) If A entails B, and B entails A, then A and B are logically equivalent.

The conclusion, that A and B are logically equivalent, means that A and B are in the same state. To justify this rule, assume that A entails B and that B entails A. Two cases arise, the first case that in which A is true, the second case that in which A is false. (These are the only possible cases.) First case: if A is true, then B is true, because A entails B. Second case: If A is false, we shall use the Law Against Contradiction to prove that B, too, is false. In fact, if B were true, our hypothesis that B entails A shows that A would be true. This would contradict the supposition in the second case that A is false. A contradiction being untenable, we must discard the assumption that led to *this* contradiction and thus find that B is false. The second case is complete, and the rule proved.

The converse to statement (1) is also true:

(1a) If A and B are logically equivalent, then A entails B, and B entails A.

Hence, the two statements

(a) A and B are logically equivalent

and

(b) A entails B, and B entails A

mutually entail each other.

To prove statement (1a), we merely recall from the definition that if A and B are logically equivalent, then they are both true or both false. Consequently, B is true if A is true (i.e., A entails B), and A is true if B is true (i.e., B entails A).

The second rule for entailing enables us to combine two entailings in order to obtain a third. As an example, consider the following statements taken as premises:

(i)   The senator makes wild statements when he is on television.

(ii) When the senator makes wild statements, his wife gets indigestion.

(It is implicit that the sentences refer to all occasions.) From them both we can conclude:

(iii) When the senator speaks on television, his wife gets indigestion.

Similarly, from the two premises that:

(i)   When you visit, I serve crab,

and

(ii) When crab is served, I overeat,

we deduce:

(iii) When you visit, I overeat.

(Again, the sentences implicitly refer to all occasions.) The rule embodied in both these arguments is:

(2) If A entails B, and B entails C, then A entails C.

To prove the rule, we need merely record what the two assumptions mean: B is true if A is true, and C is true if B is true. It is clear then that if A is true, B is true as a consequence, and that therefore C is true, too. Hence, C is true if A is true; i.e., A entails C, as asserted.

The third rule is a statement about negations of A and B when A entails B:

(3) If A entails B, then $\sim B$ entails $\sim A$.

As an example of this rule, consider the statement (supposedly referring to all occasions): "If the button is pushed, the bell rings." Rule (3) tells us that then: "If the bell is not ringing, the button is not being pushed." Let us prove the general rule, as follows. The assumption that A entails B means that B is true if A is true. The conclusion expressed by the rule that $\sim B$ entails $\sim A$ means that $\sim A$ is true if $\sim B$ is true. Again we shall use the Law Against Contradictions. If the conclusion indicated by the rule were false, $\sim A$ would be false when $\sim B$ was true. Thus, A would be true. But B is true if A is true (since A entails B). Hence, B would be true when $\sim B$ was true, a contradiction. The contradiction resulted from our assuming that the conclusion expressed by the rule was false. This assumption thus is untenable, the conclusion must be true, and the rule is proved.

EXERCISES

Write the following implications in contrapositive form:

1. If a student is a Hippie, then he is against the war.
2. To know him is to suspect him.
3. If we arrive early, we won't stay late.
4. If you are not careful, you may fall on your face.
5. Any boy who eats Hay-Ho can kick higher.

c. THE CONCEPT OF IMPLICATION

We define implication in such terms that its truth table will necessarily be complete.

Definition.   If A and B are arbitrary sentences, the statement "A implies B" means:

$$\sim (A \text{ and } \sim B).$$

The symbol for "implies" is $\Rightarrow$, the expression "$A \Rightarrow B$" thus standing for the sentence "A implies B."

The reader can get a first impression of how close implication is to entailing by trying it out on some examples. For instance, take $A \equiv$ "You step on the dog's tail" and $B \equiv$ "The dog barks."

To discuss the definition of implication systematically, let us draw up an appropriate truth table. In Table 1-14, we first give the states of $\sim B$, $(A \text{ and } \sim B)$, and $\sim (A \text{ and } \sim B)$, the last sentence by definition being equivalent to $(A \Rightarrow B)$. The first two and the last columns of the table give the truth table for $(A \Rightarrow B)$ (Table 1-15).

A	B	$\sim$B	(A and $\sim$B)	$\sim$(A and $\sim$B)
T	T	F	F	T
T	F	T	T	F
F	T	F	F	T
F	F	T	F	T

Table 1-14   Truth table for $\sim$(A and $\sim$B)

A	B	(A $\Rightarrow$ B)
T	T	T
T	F	F
F	T	T
F	F	T

Table 1-15   Truth table for (A $\Rightarrow$ B)

This and Table 1-13 show that the sentences "A implies B" and "A entails B" mean the same thing when A is true, thus agreeing whenever the latter relation pertains to anything at all. On the other hand, as we shall see, strong objections can be raised to all ways of completing the truth table for entailing (Table 1-13) except the one in Table 1-15. Thus, it seems justifiable to regard implication, despite some eccentricities, as a sort of housebroken version of the less tamed concept of entailing. Logicians, in any case, do this, thankful to be able so simply to preserve the advantages of having two states.

Logicians employ the words "If A, then B" synonymously with "$A \Rightarrow B$," but we shall also use the first expression informally, as in the past.

A glance at Table 1-15 shows that the definition of implication can be restated as follows:

"A implies B" is the statement that is false if A is true and B false and is true in any other circumstances.

But is it not odd to consider the statement "A implies B" to be true whenever, in particular, A is false? What led us to this questionable definition? We first agreed that in the truth table (Table 1-13) for entailing we must fill in the blank spaces somehow in order to save the two-state requirement. Two blank spaces exist, and for each space there are exactly two symbols from which to choose. Thus, there are exactly four ways in which this truth table can be completed, Table 1-13 representing only one such way. Might one of the other three ways be superior? To answer this question, we exhibit in Table 1-16 all four ways of filling in the blanks in the truth table for entailing, numbering these ways from I to IV. Column I corresponds to the choices for the blank spaces we actually made when we defined $(A \Rightarrow B)$ as we did (this column coincides with the third column in Table 1-15). Columns II, III, and IV are easily seen to correspond to the sentences $(A \equiv B)$, B, and $(A$ and $B)$, respectively, all of which make most unsuitable surrogates for the relation "A entails B." Eliminating these three leaves Column I as the only reasonable choice.

A	B	I	II	III	IV
T	T	T	T	T	T
T	F	F	F	F	F
F	T	T	F	T	F
F	F	T	T	F	F

Table 1-16   Alternative ways to complete Table 1-13

EXERCISES

1. Prove that Columns II, III, IV in Table 1-16 give the states of $(A \equiv B)$, B, and $(A$ and $B)$, respectively, corresponding to the indicated states of A and of B.

2. Following is a truth table for six composite sentences that are built up out of two constituent statements, A and B. In the first two columns of the table, all possible combinations of states of A and B are represented, and each subsequent column gives the corresponding states of a composite sentence. For instance, the third column gives the states of $(A$ and $B)$. Determine sentences whose states are given by the remaining columns of the table. (In other words, find appropriate sentences to head the remaining columns.)

A	B	(A and B)					
T	T	T	F	F	T	T	F
T	F	F	T	T	T	T	F
F	T	F	T	T	F	F	T
F	F	F	T	F	T	F	F

The foregoing rules for entailing, which are all we shall ever need in practice, have these counterparts for implications:

Rule (1)   If $A \Rightarrow B$ and $B \Rightarrow A$, then $A \equiv B$.
Rule (1a) If $A \equiv B$, then $A \Rightarrow B$ and $B \Rightarrow A$.
Rule (2)   If $A \Rightarrow B$ and $B \Rightarrow C$, then $A \Rightarrow C$.
Rule (3)   If $A \Rightarrow B$, then $\sim B \Rightarrow \sim A$.

To verify Rule (2), for instance, we note in the first place that the conclusion $A \Rightarrow C$ is certainly true (rows 3 and 4, Table 1-15) if A is false. If A is true, from $A \Rightarrow B$ we conclude (rows 1 and 2, Table 1-15) that B is true and from $B \Rightarrow C$ that C is true; since A and C are thus both true, we have (row 1, Table 1-15) that $A \Rightarrow C$. Hence, $A \Rightarrow C$ in all cases, as asserted. The other rules can be similarly proved. Another mode of proof will be described later.

Rule (2) is called the *transitive law* of implication. Rule (3) gives the so-called *contrapositive form* of an implication. If in Rule (3) we replace A by $\sim B$ and B by $\sim A$ and use the facts that $\sim(\sim A) \equiv A$ and $\sim(\sim B) \equiv B$, we obtain:

Rule (3a) If $\sim B \Rightarrow \sim A$, then $A \Rightarrow B$.

Rules (1) and (1a) show that "$A \Rightarrow B$ and $B \Rightarrow A$" is logically equivalent to "$A \equiv B$." Rules (3) and (3a) show the implication "$A \Rightarrow B$" to be logically equivalent to its contrapositive form, "$\sim B \Rightarrow \sim A$."

Such rules as these for implication can be proved quite mechanically through truth tables. As an illustration, let us justify Rule (2) by this method. Rule (2) is itself an implication with the antecedent

$$[(A \Rightarrow B) \text{ and } (B \Rightarrow C)]$$

and the consequent

$$(A \Rightarrow C).$$

Denote the antecedent and the consequent, respectively, by E and G:

$$E \equiv [(A \Rightarrow B) \text{ and } (B \Rightarrow C)]$$
$$G \equiv (A \Rightarrow C).$$

In this notation, Rule (2) states: "If E, then G." The method of proof we now wish to describe is to draw up a truth table for E and G giving their states under all possible conditions. If a case can be found in which E is true and G false, then Rule (2) is contradicted, but if no such case exists, then Rule (2) is proved. The truth table in question (Table 1-17) has eight rows, one for each possible combination of states of A, B, C. Despite the formidable appearance of Table 1-17 it can be filled in very quickly. First, the eight possible combinations of states of A, B, C must be set down (Columns I, II, III). To do Column IV, we recall that $(A \Rightarrow B)$ is true with the single exception of the case in which A is true and B false. This exceptional case occurs only in rows 2 and 6. We therefore enter F in Column IV, rows 2 and 6, and then place T in all the other spaces of the column. Columns V and VII are filled in similarly, the encircled symbols being the ones in each column that are entered first. Column VI is done by referring to Columns IV and V only. Recall that if L and M are any sentences, then $(L$ and $M)$ is false with the single exception of the case in which L is true and M is true. It follows, in particular, that E is false, except in the case in which $(A \Rightarrow B)$ is true and $(B \Rightarrow C)$ is true. This exceptional case occurs just on rows 1, 3, 4, and 8. Therefore, we enter T (in Column VI) on those lines and immediately afterwards place F in every remaining space in Column VI. (The symbols entered first are again encircled.)

Table 1-17 *A truth table with E and G as defined in the text.*

	I	II	III	IV	V	VI	VII
	A	B	C	$(A \Rightarrow B)$	$(B \Rightarrow C)$	E	G
1	T	T	T	T	T	Ⓣ	T
2	T	F	T	Ⓕ	T	F	T
3	F	T	T	T	T	Ⓣ	T
4	F	F	T	T	T	Ⓣ	T
5	T	T	F	T	Ⓕ	F	Ⓕ
6	T	F	F	Ⓕ	T	F	Ⓕ
7	F	T	F	T	Ⓕ	F	T
8	F	F	F	T	T	Ⓣ	T

In the 32 entries of Columns IV to VII, care had to be exercised only with the 10 that are encircled. Thus, the whole table can be worked out very quickly.

Now we compare Columns VI and VII to see if any case exists in which E is true and G false. None such case occurring, we conclude that E implies G and thus that Rule (2) is correct, as asserted.

EXERCISES

3. By appropriate remarks about Table 1-15 prove that a true statement is implied by any statement.

4. Prove that a false statement implies any statement.

5. Prove from Table 1-15 that, if "A implies B" is true, then either A is false or B is true.

6. From Exercise 5 and the foregoing discussion, prove similarly that the statement "A implies B" is logically equivalent to the following statement: "Either A is false or B is true."

Prove the next two statements from truth tables:

7. (A and B) $\Rightarrow$ A. HINT: First record the states of (A and B) corresponding to all combinations of states of A and B. From the states of A and (A and B) then read off in each case the corresponding state of ((A and B) $\Rightarrow$ A).

8. A $\Rightarrow$ (A or B).

9. What is the error in the following argument: The statement that the moon is blue is false. This implies that I am a millionaire. Therefore, I am a millionaire.

10. Let A and B denote any statements. We define a certain composite statement, which we denote by A Δ B, in Table 1-18.

A	B	A Δ B
T	T	T
T	F	T
F	T	F
F	F	T

Table 1-18

Prove that

$$A \Delta B \equiv (\sim A \Rightarrow \sim B)$$

11. The following composite sentence contains one premise, hints at a second premise, and draws a conclusion: "If the University of Maryland football team wins its remaining games, it will become the Conference champion and, as such, receive a bid to a post-season Bowl game."

(a) What premise is stated?

(b) What second premise is hinted at, but is not fully stated?

(c) What is the conclusion drawn?

(d) Assign symbols to the constituents of the sentence. (Regard the unstated premise as one of the constituents.)

(e) Express the sentence symbolically.

(f) What law or laws of logic justify this sentence?

12. Let A represent the statement: "John goes to the movies." Let B represent the statement: "Mary goes to the movies."

(a) Write each of the next three statements using just the symbols A and B, $\Rightarrow$ ("implies"), $\sim$ ("not"), $\equiv$ ("is equivalent to"); the words "or," "and," and also parentheses as needed:

(i) If Mary does not go to the movies, then John does not go to the movies.

(ii) Either John and Mary both go to the movies or John does not go to the movies.

(iii) If Mary goes to the movies, then John goes to the movies.

(b) Prove or disprove that (i) and (ii) are logically equivalent statements.

(c) Prove or disprove that (ii) and (iii) are logically equivalent statements.

13. What conclusion does the transitive law for implications permit from these two statements:

(a) If a soldier doesn't wear his hat, he is not in correct uniform.

(b) If a soldier is not in correct uniform, the Military Police will arrest him.

14. How does the transitive law for implications apply to this maxim from Benjamin Franklin: "A little neglect may breed mischief; for want of a nail the shoe was lost; for want of a shoe the horse was lost; for want of a horse the rider was lost."

15. Analyze this composite statement into its constituents, and draw up a truth table for it: "He will, unless she objects."

16. Analyze this composite statement into its constituents and draw up a truth table for it: "Justice will be achieved only when those who are not injured feel as indignant as those who are." (Attributed to Solon [638--558 B.C.].)

17. Suppose A implies B, B implies C, and C implies D. State and prove an appropriate conclusion. If $D \Rightarrow A$, what further conclusions can be drawn?

18. Give a truth table for the statement $\sim(A \Rightarrow B)$ ("A does not imply B").

19. Prove: $(A \text{ and } B) \equiv \sim(A \Rightarrow \sim B)$.

20. Express (A or B) as an implication.

21. Let A and B represent any statements. We shall define a new kind of composite statement, which we shall denote by "$A \square B$" and which will be true if $A \Rightarrow B$ or if $B \Rightarrow A$; otherwise it will be false.

(a) Give a truth table for $A \square B$.

(b) Prove that $A \square B \equiv B \square A$.

22. Suppose that both implications

$$A \Rightarrow B$$

and

$$A \Rightarrow \sim B$$

are true. Then what can you say about A? Why?

23. Let A and B be any statements. Decide which of the following assertions are true and which are false. If an assertion is true, prove it; if false, illustrate with a specific example.

(a) If $A \equiv \sim B$, then $B \equiv \sim A$.

(b) If (A and $\sim B$) is a true statement, then $(A \Rightarrow B)$ is a false statement.

(c) It is possible that A entails B and that A does not imply B.

(d) It is possible that $A \Rightarrow B$ but that A does not entail B.

(e) If $(A \Rightarrow B)$ and $(\sim A \Rightarrow \sim B)$ are both true statements, then $(A \equiv B)$ is a true statement.

(f) If $(A \Rightarrow B)$ and $(A \Rightarrow \sim B)$ are both true statements, then A is a true statement.

(g) If $(A \text{ and } B) \Rightarrow (A \text{ and } \sim C)$, then $B \Rightarrow \sim C$.

(h) If $(A \text{ and } B) \Rightarrow (A \text{ or } B)$, then $(\sim A \text{ and } \sim B) \Rightarrow (\sim A \text{ or } \sim B)$.

(i) $[A \Rightarrow (A \text{ or } B)]$ is always a true statement.

(j) $[A \Rightarrow (A \text{ and } B)]$ is always a true statement.

(k) $[(A \text{ and } B) \Rightarrow B]$ is always a true statement.

(l) $[(A \text{ or } B) \Rightarrow B]$ is always a true statement.

(m) $(B \Rightarrow \sim B)$ is never a true statement.

(n) $(\sim B \Rightarrow B)$ is never a true statement.

(o) $(A \text{ and } \sim B) \Rightarrow (A \Rightarrow B)$ is never a true statement.

(p) If A is a false statement, then A $\Rightarrow$ B is always false.

(q) If for three sentences A, B, C, $\left[A \text{ or } (A \Rightarrow B) \right] \Rightarrow C$, then C is true.

Prove the following statements by means of truth tables:

24. $\sim A \Rightarrow (A \Rightarrow B)$. HINT: For all combinations of states of A and B, record the states of $\sim A$ and $(A \Rightarrow B)$. These indicate the corresponding states of $(\sim A \Rightarrow (A \Rightarrow B))$.

25. $B \Rightarrow (A \Rightarrow B)$.

26. $((A \Rightarrow B) \text{ or } (B \Rightarrow A))$.

27. $\left[A \Rightarrow (B \text{ and } C) \right] \equiv \left[(A \Rightarrow B) \text{ and } (A \Rightarrow C) \right]$ and $\left[A \Rightarrow (B \text{ or } C) \right] \equiv \left[(A \Rightarrow B) \text{ or } (A \Rightarrow C) \right]$.

28. If $(B \equiv C)$, $(A \Rightarrow B)$, and $(C \Rightarrow D)$, then $A \Rightarrow D$.

29. $\left[(p \Rightarrow q) \text{ and } (q \Rightarrow r) \right] \Rightarrow (p \Rightarrow r)$.

30. $\left[(p \text{ and } q) \Rightarrow r \right] \Rightarrow \left[p \Rightarrow (q \Rightarrow r) \right]$.

31. $\left[p \Rightarrow (q \Rightarrow r) \right] \Rightarrow \left[(p \text{ and } q) \Rightarrow r \right]$.

32. $\sim(p \text{ and } q) \equiv (\sim p \text{ or } \sim q)$.

33. $(p \equiv q) \equiv \left[(p \Rightarrow q) \text{ and } (q \Rightarrow p) \right]$.

34. $(p \equiv q) \equiv \left[(p \text{ and } q) \text{ or } (\sim p \text{ and } \sim q) \right]$.

35. The composite sentences $\left[(A \Rightarrow B) \Rightarrow C \right]$ and $\left[A \Rightarrow (B \Rightarrow C) \right]$ need not be equivalent.

d. IMPLICATIONS THAT OCCUR IN GENERALIZATIONS

We have already noticed that many implications — perhaps most — occur in the context of generalizations. As an additional example, one who says,

A: "If you shout at the dog, he will bark," will usually really mean something like

B: "On *all* occasions, if you shout at the dog, he will bark." When a statement is intended to be a generalization, for some purposes it is important to indicate this fact explicitly, as we have done in sentence B. This is so, in particular, for instance, if you wish to negate the sentence. Let

$$C \equiv \text{"You shout at the dog,"}$$
$$D \equiv \text{"He will bark."}$$

Sentence A states that $(C \Rightarrow D)$ or, equivalently,

$$\sim (C \text{ and } \sim D).$$

Hence, the negation of A is

$$(C \text{ and } \sim D),$$

saying: "You shout at the dog, and he will not bark." Sentence B states: "On *all* occasions, $(C \Rightarrow D)$." Its negation (see the discussion in Section 7) is: "On *some* occasion, $\sim(C \Rightarrow D)$," or, equivalently, "On some occasion, $(C$ and $\sim D)$," which means: "On some occasion, you will shout at the dog, and he will not bark." The negations of sentences A and B thus are quite different.

EXERCISES

Negate these sentences:
1. If you ignore this child, he will cry.
2. If you press the button, the bell will ring.
3. If wishes were horses, beggars would ride.
4. To persevere is to succeed.
5. What goes up comes down.
6. A rose by any other name would smell as sweet.
7. If you forgive people enough, you belong to them, and they to you . . .
(James Hilton)†

8. If you go long enough without a bath even the fleas will let you alone.
(Ernie Pyle)†

---

†From Bartlett, *op. cit.*, p. 986a.

10.

On the formal nature of inference

Inference is the process of drawing conclusions from given premises by logical means. Most inferences both in daily life and in a large part of mathematics are based on such concepts and laws as were discussed in this chapter: the classification of statements as true or false, the law against contradictions, the means by which negations, disjunctions, conjunctions, and other sentences may be negated, the rules for implication (transitivity, the contrapositive form, the relation to equivalence), and so forth. In fact, these concepts and these laws are of exceedingly wide scope, and this work will abound in applications of them. They owe their generality to their abstract and formal character.

Definitions and propositions in logic such as we have discussed concern sentences that are permitted to be arbitrary. In the law for double negation,

$$\sim(\sim A) \equiv A,$$

for instance, A denotes an arbitrary sentence. In the definition of the expression "A and B" both A and B are arbitrary. The sense of such a definition or the truth of such a proposition thus is determined not by the *meanings* of the sentences concerned, but by *how* these sentences are *juxtaposed* with parentheses, signs of negation, equivalence, and implication, the words "or" and "and," and so forth. Substance is nothing, form everything. For instance, the proposition "If *A* implies *B*, and *B* implies *C*, then *A* implies *C*" is true, no matter what individual statements *A*, *B*, and *C* may denote. This assertion (expressing the transitivity of implication) is an abstract form devoid of concrete meaning. Concrete, meaningful assertions are obtained by substituting individual statements for *A*, *B*, and *C*, as, for instance, in the following sentences:

> If it is against the law to insult a policeman, and if anyone who breaks the law will go to jail, then anyone who insults a policeman will go to jail.
>
> If food remaining in the mouth causes teeth to decay, and if sweets leave a residue of food in the mouth, then eating sweets causes teeth to decay.

Although these sentences are about law and dentistry, respectively, their truth derives neither from law nor from dentistry, but from the transitive rule for implications. Since this abstract form is valid, all concrete assertions derived from it are valid regardless of their individual meanings. Logic is a doctrine consisting wholly of such abstract forms. This is why we say that logic is formal, concerned with form and not with meaning.

Because logical relations among statements depend on statement form, not content, logic is applicable whether the premises be true or false. The aim of reasoning under false premises is to rule them out by showing that they lead to contradictions. Thus disposing one by one of all possible alternatives except the true one is a common procedure in mathematics, and we have already used it.

Logic is indifferent to the criteria by which "true" statements are distinguished from "false," except for the requirement that the criteria be clear and unequivocal in every instance. The needs of logic are met completely if the statements to be considered have been divided somehow into any two classes containing no statements in common. Then the statements in one class may be labeled "*T*" and the statements in the other class labeled "*F*." (Or the statements in the first class might be written in black ink and those in the second class in red. The method of labeling does not matter.) Equivalence, conjunction, disjunction, negation, implication, and so forth can be defined by the same truth tables as before, in which "*T*" and "*F*," however, no longer need have any of the metaphysical connotations that attach to "true" and "false." The same laws would exist for these relations as before, and exactly the same logic would result. Thus, the laws of logic have nothing to do with metaphysical truth.

We end this discussion with a caution. We have developed the formal rules of logic most informally without qualms, for instance, about using "if" and "then" before implication was defined, or about writing sentences (as in "entailing") that may be neither true nor false in violation of the first commandment of the subject. We were still able to develop all the rules we shall need, but deeper studies would require a more rigorous approach, in a mathematical spirit, in which natural language is replaced by an artificial tongue without logical impurity. We shall have a glimpse of this mathematical approach in Chapter 12.

EXERCISES

1. What is "the logic of events"? Relate it to logic.

2. A set of statements is said to be *consistent* if they produce no contradiction. How is consistency related to truth?

3. Comment on this remark: "Logic cannot force us to accept a statement except on the basis of our prior acceptance of another statement."

4. What is your opinion of this famous affirmation of Blaise Pascal (1623–62): "The heart has its reasons, which reason does not know."†

---

†For a brief account of Pascal's life and thought in its historical context, see, for instance, *The Age of Louis XIV*, by Will and Ariel Durant, Simon and Schuster, 1963, pp. 55-67.

11.

A historical remark

Logical method—scrupulously stating premises, keeping to agreed and explicit definitions, jumping to no unjustified conclusions—is a hard discipline, which, in the geometry of the Greeks as expounded by Euclid, received vindication enough for all time. Both logical method and the systematic geometry it supports were products of the extraordinary intellectual climates of Greece from about the 6th to the 4th Centuries, B.C. During this period, many aspects of thought developed simultaneously—mathematics and its accompanying logic, in particular, as well as philosophy, rhetoric, and law. Possibly, as Professor T. B. Jones has conjectured, all these disciplines reinforced one another, law at first being the dominating factor.

When justice operates under a written code and an "adversary" system with each side advancing its own contentions and refuting those of its opponents, can justice escape all logic? In Athens,† a written legal code had endured since the reforms entrusted to Solon in 594 B.C., and the adversary system had been in force at least since

---

†Details concerning Athenian trials are to be found in the following two books: Kathleen Freeman, *The Murder of Herodes and Other Trials from the Athenian Law Courts*, London, MacDonald and Co., Ltd., 1946; and Robert J. Bonner, *Lawyers and Litigants in Ancient Athens*, Chicago, University of Chicago Press, 1927.

the Periclean Age (5th Century, B.C.). The amount of litigation was extraordinary. All cases were tried before "juries," frequently consisting of more than 500 members, who declared both verdict and judgment by majority vote and admitted no appeal. A principal in a case, while he might engage another person to write a speech for delivery to the jury, had otherwise (with minor exceptions) to conduct his case himself. For all these reasons, law in Athens, by the 5th Century, B.C., was a pervasive influence, and Athenian gentlemen were well educated both in law and in rhetoric, the art of argumentation. Many examples of legal rhetoric by professional speech writers of the 5th and 4th Centuries, B.C., are still extant. These speeches displayed all the skills that move an audience: drama, sarcasm, exaggeration, distortion, appeals to pity and to prejudice, artful plain speaking, specious and honest logic. For the first time in history, as a type of climax to two centuries of judicial free contention, reasoning thus appears and with it, perhaps, an atmosphere hospitable to rational thought. In this way, the Athenian court system may have contributed to the emergence of systematic geometry and rigorous logical method.

CHAPTER 2

THE IDEAS IN
ELEMENTARY ALGEBRA

1.

Introduction

a. ON ABSTRACTION

Actually winning a battle may be more important than knowing in principle how to fight it, but having the answer to a mathematical problem ordinarily is incomparably less important than knowing how to find it. To know how to find an answer generally means to know a method that works in solving any similar problem. Often, the same method will work in problems that are seemingly unlike but prove to have the same structure. Mathematics, being concerned with method and with structure, is thus inherently abstract.

Elementary mathematics is abstract, however, in the same, familiar way in which language itself is abstract. Most nouns denote not individual things but general classes of things, as the word "chair," for instance, denotes innumerably many and diverse kinds of chairs: large and small, of metal, wood, and stone, polished, painted, and varnished, upholstered and bare, with arms and without, high-backed and low-backed, decorated and plain. Most statements are not about particular objects but about classes of objects, or about unspecified members of such classes, or about unknown or even nonexistent members. Thus, to say "I should like to buy a house" is not to say which house, from whom, or for how much, or even that I will actually purchase a house at all. To say "I had a stone in my shoe" is not to specify either the stone or the shoe. The most commonplace remarks thus often are couched in abstract terms.

Any description of a general rule or procedure is inherently abstract. The traffic code, for instance, covers all motorists, all vehicles, all streets, all intersections, all traffic signal lights, while none need be individually named. Even greater abstraction is involved in any reasoned argument—a court decision, a brief to alter land zoning, an interpretation of relations between Russia and China—for reasoning calls on logic, which forbids contradictions and permits deductions by abstract laws. A jurist or a historian intends to convey abstract ideas and is guided more or less by abstract principles. A mathematician must follow abstract principles even more consistently.

EXERCISES

1. List some nouns that are not abstract.

2. Are adjectives of abstract nature? Discuss the following: soft, bitter, patient.

3. Discuss the abstractness of the following words: thing, whiteness, justice, pattern.

4. Describe briefly what makes a joke or situation funny, and note the abstract level of your exposition.

b. Symbolism in Algebra

Elementary arithmetic teaches how to add, multiply, subtract, and divide. This is practical mathematics sufficient for workaday uses. Elementary algebra, serving subtler purposes, asks about general relations among the four arithmetic operations. Here is an example of such a general relation: *Let three numbers, which we shall refer to as the first, the second, and the third, be given. If to the sum of the first two numbers we add the third, we obtain the same result as if to the sum of the last two numbers we had added the first.* We illustrate this relation with the three numbers 6, 7, 8: the sum of the first two is 13, and adding the third gives 21; the sum of the last two is 15, and adding the first again gives 21. The two calculations are different, but their results, as the rule predicts, are the same.

The foregoing rule names no individual numbers. Like a tax law, it is abstract and clumsy. Its underlying thought is simple, but the rule, because of its generality, is expressed only awkwardly in words. Can the simple thought be simply put?

Present algebraic notation was devised for such purposes. Any number entering the discussion, but not explicitly specified, is symbolized by a letter, different numbers by different letters, the same number invariably in a given problem by one and the same letter. Accordingly, let the letters a, b, and c denote the first, second, and third numbers, respectively, of the foregoing rule. The sum of the first and the second numbers is written as $a + b$ and this sum added to the third number as $(a+b)+c$. (The parentheses enclosing $a+b$ indicate that the value of this sum is to be found before any other operation — here, adding c — is carried out.) The sum of the last two numbers is $b+c$, and the latter sum added to the first number is $a+(b+c)$. The rule in question thus states that

$$(a+b)+c = a+(b+c),$$

where a, b, and c are any numbers. Is this not a better formulation than the rhetorical one with which we began?

The rule could have been stated just as well in the words: "for any three numbers x, y, z,

$$(x+y)+z = x+(y+z)";$$

or in the words: "for any three numbers a, b, c,

$$(b+c)+a = b+(c+a)";$$

or in the words: "for any three numbers a, λ, μ,

$$(a+\lambda)+\mu = a+(\lambda+\mu)."$$

We must always tell what our symbols represent, in this case each symbol representing an arbitrary number, but the particular symbols we choose are entirely up to us.

EXERCISES

1. Argue that the three following rules are the same:
   (a) for any three numbers a, b, c, $(a+b)-c = (a-c)+b$;
   (b) for any three numbers p, q, r, $(p+q)-r = (p-r)+q$;
   (c) for any three numbers a, b, c, $(c+b)-a = (c-a)+b$.
2. Argue that the three following rules are the same:
   (a) for any two numbers a, b, $(a+b)(a-b) = a^2 - b^2$;
   (b) for any two numbers c, d, $(d+c)(d-c) = d^2 - c^2$;
   (c) for any two numbers a, c, $(c+a)(c-a) = c^2 - a^2$.
3. Express symbolically the following rule: Suppose we have three numbers, which we shall refer to as the first, the second, and the third. Let the first divide the second and the result multiply the third. The final result is the same as if the second and third had been multiplied and their product then been divided by the first number. Is the rule correct? Test it in some examples.

   Reminder: If a and b denote any two numbers, their product, a times b, is written as ab or as $a \cdot b$. The quotient, a divided by b, is written as $\frac{a}{b}$ or as a/b.

4. Express the following combinations of numbers symbolically:

(a) A number multiplied by itself and added to 1.

(b) A number divided by 4.

(c) The sum of two numbers multiplied by their difference. The sum divided by their difference. The sum added to their difference.

5. An English penny is currently worth 1.25 cents. There are 12 pence to a shilling and 20 shillings to a pound. What is the equivalent in dollars and cents of P pounds, S shillings, and C pence?

6. In a certain primitive society, ten arrows are worth one hatchet, six hatchets are worth one bear skin, and nine bear skins are worth one horse. Express the cost C in arrows of purchasing a motorcycle worth H horses and B bear skins.

7. A taxicab charges 25 cents for the first fifth of a mile and five cents for each additional fifth of a mile.

(a) Find a formula for the cost C in dollars of going M miles by taxi. Assume M is greater than 1/5.

(b) Find the total cost C of the same trip if a 15 per cent tip is added.

8. A car rental service charges eight dollars a day and five cents a mile to rent a car.

(a) Find an expression for the total cost C, in dollars, of renting a car for D days to travel M miles.

(b) Find the total cost if a sales tax of P per cent is applied.

9. Consider the following trick: Pick any number. Multiply it by 3. Add 6 to that result. Divide this result by 3 and then subtract your original number. Your answer is always 2.

(a) Perform the indicated operation using N for the number.

(b) Explain how the trick works.

10. A carton contains s spools of thread. F feet of thread are wound upon each spool. Write an algebraic formula for T, the total number of yards of thread contained in the carton. What is a formula for W, the number of *feet* of thread contained in a stockroom housing C such cartons?

11. (a) Suppose a bank pays interest at the rate of 6 per cent per year. This means that a principal of $100, held in the bank for a year, will draw $100 · .06 = $6 interest. At the end of the year, the total amount corresponding to the original principal ($100) is $106. If the original principal is a quantity denoted by P, and interest is at the rate symbolized by I per cent per year, what now is the amount of the interest at the end of the year? What is the total amount (principal plus interest) at the end of the year? Find the total amount at the end of two years.

(b) Suppose a bank pays interest at the rate of 6 per cent per year, compounded semiannually. This means, for instance, that an original principal of $100 draws $3 interest in the first *half-year*, but that interest for the second half-year is based on a principal of $103 and thus amounts to $3.09. Interest for the third half-year would be based on $106.09 as principal, and so forth. Now suppose the principal is to be denoted by P and the per cent rate of interest annually by I, and suppose the interest is to be compounded semiannually. Give expressions for the interest drawn the first half-year, the total amount after the first half-year, the interest drawn the second half-year, and the total amount at the end of the second half-year.

12. (a) A vehicle is said to travel at *constant speed* if the distance it moves in any time whatever is proportional to this time. We then define:

$$\text{Speed} = \frac{\text{Distance traveled}}{\text{Time required}}$$

For instance, if an automobile has constant speed of 88 feet per second (60 m.p.h.), it will go 176 feet in two seconds, 264 feet in 3 seconds, and so forth. Express the formula for speed in symbols.

(b) Suppose a boat moves down a river at a speed that, in still water, would cover 15 miles in an hour. If the current is 4 m.p.h. in the direction of the boat's motion, the boat will move at the actual rate, relative to objects on the river banks, of 19 m.p.h. We can easily see this by imagining a rigid platform in place of the stream and a vehicle moving along the platform in place of the boat, platform and vehicle proceeding in the same direction at the rates of 4 and 15 m.p.h., respectively. See Figure 2-1. Imagine the vehicle's starting point marked both on the platform and on the earth beneath. At the end of an hour, the point marked on the platform will have gone 4 miles from that marked on the earth, while the boat will have traveled 15 miles from its starting point on the platform. The boat thus will have covered $15 + 4 = 19$ miles from its original geographical position, as asserted. Now suppose the boat to move at such a speed as to cover a m.p.h. in still water, and suppose the current to be b m.p.h. in the same direction. What now is the average speed of the boat relative to objects on the river banks?

Figure 2-1 *Movement on a moving platform.*

(c) Answer the same question, but suppose that the current opposes the motion of the boat.

13. Suppose that you have before you two pitchers, one containing water, the other containing wine. Pour some of the water into the wine, and return an equal amount of the diluted wine to the pitcher containing the water. Each pitcher thus contains its original amount of liquid. Is there now more wine in the water than water in the wine, is there less, or are the amounts the same? (Ignore the fact that a mixture of water and alcohol, in practice, occupies a little less volume than the sum of the volumes of the two liquids before they are mixed.) HINT: Let x denote the amount of wine ultimately transferred to the

water pitcher. The space this amount of wine originally occupied in the wine pitcher must now be filled with water.†

14. A simple mathematical formula to give the approximate average distance from each planet to the sun was discovered towards the close of the 18th Century by a German astronomer, J. E. Bode. The distances in this formula are in astronomical units (A.U.), one such unit being defined as the average distance between the earth and the sun, about 93,000,000 miles. Bode first took 0 and 3, and then doubled 3 and every number thereafter, to obtain this succession of numbers:

$$0, 3, 6, 12, 24, 48, 96, \ldots$$

To each number of this succession, he added 4 to obtain:

$$4, 7, 10, 16, 28, 52, 100, \ldots$$

Then he divided these numbers by 10 ending with:

$$.4, .7, 1.0, 1.6, 2.8, 5.2, 10.0, \ldots$$

The last succession provided his estimate of the average distances from the planets to the sun. Their agreement with fact is shown in the following table.‡

Planets	Estimated Distance by Bode's Formula	True Distances (in A.U.)
Mercury	0.4	0.39
Venus	0.7	0.72
Earth	1.0	1.00
Mars	1.6	1.52
Asteroids	2.8	2.65
Jupiter	5.2	5.20
Saturn	10.0	9.54
Uranus	19.6	19.19
Neptune	38.8	30.07
Pluto	77.2	39.52

Bode himself applied his formula solely to Mercury, Venus, Earth, Mars, Jupiter, and Saturn, the planets known in his day. When Uranus was discovered in 1781, and Ceres, the first of the asteroids, in 1800, they too were observed to conform fairly closely to Bode's rule. Neptune and Pluto, which were found later, deviated quite considerably. But this is less remarkable by far than the extent of the agreement with the rule, for which no good reasons ever have been given.

For the kth planet (Mercury is the first planet, Venus the second, Earth the third, and so forth), write Bode's estimate as a formula involving k.

---

†Martin Gardner, *The Scientific American Book of Mathematical Puzzles and Diversions,* New York, Simon and Schuster, 1959, pp. 97-99.

‡*From Here, Where?* prepared by National Aeronautics and Space Administration in cooperation with the U. S. Office of Education, 1965, pp. 7, 8, 103.

15. The chemical origins of the atomic theory, first promulgated by John Dalton beginning in 1803, are summarized in the words of *The Encyclopedia Britannica*: †

"Like the Greek philosophers, Dalton assumed that all material substances are composed of small indivisible and indestructible particles, which he, too, called atoms. However, he went much further than anyone before him had done, in that he assigned physically significant properties to the atom; his resultant theory, therefore, unlike Greek Atomism, was capable of explaining and correlating the results of actual experiments, and of leading to predictions regarding the results of new experiments. These additional atomic properties postulated by Dalton can be expressed by the following statements (which are given in modern terminology and not necessarily in the words used by Dalton): All atoms of any one *element* are exactly alike in all respects; in particular, they have identical weights. On the other hand, atoms of different elements have different properties; in particular, they have different weights. A *compound*, as distinguished from an element, is composed of molecules. Each molecule of any given compound consists of a certain definite integral (i.e., whole) number of atoms of each of the various elements present. All molecules of any one compound are exactly alike in all respects, but molecules of different compounds are different. A chemical reaction consists in a redistribution of atoms so that the original molecules are broken up, and new ones, containing altogether the same numbers of the same kinds of atom, are formed. In the process, none of the original *atoms* are destroyed, and no new ones are created.

"On the basis of the foregoing rather simple assumptions, Dalton was able to account for two important chemical laws. The first of these was the *law of definite proportions*, which states that in every pure substance the relative proportions by weight of all the elements present are constant and independent of the source or past history of the substance. For example, pure water is found by analysis to consist of about 11.2% hydrogen and about 88.8% oxygen, by weight. This same ratio of 11.2 to 88.8 is found in all samples of *pure* water, whether obtained from rain, from the sea, or by direct chemical union of the elements. Such a constancy of chemical composition is a simple corollary of the atomic theory." Indeed, suppose that each molecule of a certain compound consists of m atoms of element A and n atoms of element B, and suppose that the weights of individual atoms of the elements A and B are u grams and v grams, respectively.

(a) How much weight of element A is present in a single molecule of the compound? How much of element B?

(b) How much does a single molecule of this compound weigh?

(c) What proportion of the weight of the molecule is due to A? What proportion to B? What are the relative proportions by weight of the two elements A and B in this compound? Explain how your answer relates the atomic theory to the law of definite proportions.

"The second chemical law explained by Dalton's theory is the *law of multiple proportions*, which in its simplest form states that, if more than one com-

---

†1957 edition, Vol. 2, p. 642, article on "Atom."

pound can be made from a given pair of elements A and B, then the weights of A which combine with a given weight of B in the various compounds are in the ratio of small integers. For example, in the two compounds between oxygen and iron, which are now known as ferrous oxide and ferric oxide, the weights of iron combined with 1 gram of oxygen are respectively 3.49 grams and 2.33 grams, which are in the ratio of 3 to 2. This second law of chemical combination, like the previous one, is also a simple corollary of the atomic theory." Suppose, for instance, that each molecule of the first compound contains m atoms of A and n atoms of B, while each molecule of the second compound contains p atoms of A and q atoms of B; the atoms of A and B weigh u and v, respectively.

(d) How many grams of A are combined in the first compound with 1 gram of B? How many in the second compound?

(e) What is the ratio of these two quantities? Explain how your answer relates the atomic theory to the law of multiple proportions.

16. David Ricardo wrote the following about 1821 to explain how an efficient and an inefficient economy may trade to their mutual advantage. He assumes England to export cloth to Portugal in exchange for wine and takes England to be the inefficient, Portugal the efficient, country:

"Under a system of perfectly free commerce, each country naturally devotes its capital and labour to such employments as are most beneficial to each . . . . It is this principle which determines that wine shall be made in France and Portugal, that corn shall be grown in America and Poland, and that hardware and other goods shall be manufactured in England . . . .

"England may be so circumstanced that to produce the cloth [she will export to Portugal] may require the labour of 100 men for one year; and if she attempted to make the wine [she will import from Portugal], it might require the labour of 120 men for the same time. England would therefore find it her interest to import wine, and to purchase it by the exportation of cloth.

"To produce the wine [she will export to England] in Portugal, might require only the labour of 80 men for one year, and to produce the cloth [she will import from England] in the same country, might require the labour of 90 men for the same time. It would therefore be advantageous for Portugal to export wine in exchange for cloth . . . notwithstanding that the commodity imported by Portugal could be produced there with less labour than in England. Though she [Portugal] could make the cloth with the labour of 90 men, she would import it from a country where it required the labour of 100 men to produce it, because it would be advantageous to her rather to employ her capital in the production of wine, for which she would obtain more cloth from England than she could produce by diverting a portion of her capital from the cultivation of vines to the manufacture of cloth.

"Thus England would give the produce of the labour of 100 men, for the produce of the labour of 80 . . . ."†

Make the argument more general, using symbols instead of actual numbers. HINT: In this hypothetical example, Ricardo evidently assumes England to be the sole supplier of cloth to Portugal, Portugal the sole supplier of wine to England, and trade between England and Portugal to consist simply of an exchange of one commodity for the other. We can summarize his data in the following table.

	Cloth consumed in Portugal	Wine consumed in England
Cost of production in Portugal	90	80
Cost of production in England	100	120

†David Ricardo, *On the Principles of Political Economy and Taxation*, Third Edition, 1821. Republished as Volume I in *The Works and Correspondence of David Ricardo*, edited by Piero Sraffa, Cambridge University Press, 1951. These excerpts are from Chapter 7, "On Foreign Trade," pp. 133-135 of this edition.

2.

A resumé of elementary algebra

Algebra is an outgrowth of arithmetic providing systematic methods by which difficult, subtle problems can be successfully attacked. Its distinctive methods are made possible, first, as we noted previously, by the conscious recognition and use of general laws to which all arithmetical calculations conform and, secondly, by a succession of numerical inventions. The most basic invention is the concept of whole numbers, including the ability to count as high as desired and also to add and to multiply. Since whole numbers alone are not sufficient to do arithmetic, early in history they were supplemented by the positive rational numbers — the numbers we represent as fractions, such as 9/14 or 14/9. Eventually, someone thought of including zero among the numbers, particularly as an aid in writing them, and arithmetic then had the equipment to meet any ordinary call upon it. But algebra remained in an awkward stage so long as a fully satisfactory concept of negative numbers was lacking. When finally negative numbers, zero, and rational numbers were all included in the apparatus of arithmetic, its laws could be stated with unprecedented clarity, and benefiting from this conceptual gain, algebra rose to new heights.

In this and the following section, we wish to review and explain the arithmetical laws on which algebra is based. In numerous exercises, we also illustrate algebraic methods, which are applied later in practically every chapter.

a. SEVEN RULES FOR ADDITION AND MULTIPLICATION

We begin with the purely mechanical rules for addition and multiplication, using a, b, and c to denote arbitrary non-negative numbers, letting ab symbolize the product, a times b, and employing the ordinary symbols for zero and one, which play a special role. The names by which the various rules are known are printed at the left.

	Rules for Addition	Rules for Multiplication
Commutative rules:	$a + b = b + a$	$ab = ba$
Associative rules:	$(a + b) + c = a + (b + c)$	$(ab)c = a(bc)$
Rules of 0 and 1:	$a + 0 = a$	$1a = a$
Distributive rule:	$a(b + c) = ab + ac$	

It is worthwhile to check these laws by examples, as in Section 1 we illustrated the associative law for addition. To test the distributive property, take, for instance, $a = 4$, $b = 5$, $c = 6$. Here, $a(b+c) = 4(5 + 6) = 4 \cdot 11 = 44$ (it was convenient here to indicate multiplication by a dot). On the other hand, $ab + ac = 4 \cdot 5 + 4 \cdot 6 = 20 + 24 = 44$. Thus, the rule checks in this instance.

These rules hold for all numbers, whether whole or rational and whether positive, negative, or zero. In this generality, they contain a surprising amount of information. We shall see this in detail, but pause here to consider these rules in relation to whole numbers alone. In this, their simplest setting, we shall try through suitable exercises to bring them down to earth.

First, recall a notational convention. Since $a + (b + c)$ and $(a + b) + c$ are always equal (additive associative law), parentheses are generally omitted from this sum, which is thus written without confusion as $a + b + c$. Parentheses are also unnecessary in sums of more than three terms and, similarly, may be omitted from products of three or more factors.

EXERCISES

1. After adding a sum, like $5 + 8 + 3 + 16 + 7 + 2 + 9$, from left to right, frequently one will check the result by adding from right to left. Which of the foregoing laws justify this check, i.e., which of these laws imply that the two results should be the same?

2. Which laws insure that $a + a = 2a$?

3. A firm has 12 typists on the eighth floor and 14 typists on the ninth floor, these typists all receiving $92 per week. The total payroll for the typists could be calculated by multiplying 92 by 26 (the total number of typists). It could also be calculated by adding the payrolls for the typists of the eighth and ninth floors separately. What law of arithmetic guarantees that the total, calculated either way, will be the same?

4. In a high school, a census was taken of the hair color of the students. The results were as follows:

	Brown	Black	Red	Blond	Total
Boys	211	250	39	106	606
Girls	206	141	67	203	617
Total	417	391	106	309	1223

The four entries in the bottom row have the same sum as the two in the right-hand column. What laws of arithmetic are involved in this?

5. How do you justify the process of "long" multiplication exemplified in the following calculation?

$$
\begin{array}{r}
53 \\
49 \\
\hline
477 \\
212 \\
\hline
2597
\end{array}
$$

6. What arithmetical laws justify checking the last result by multiplying in reverse order?

7. With five strings of beads containing three beads each, the total number of beads is the same as with three strings containing five beads each (Figure 2-2). What arithmetic law is here involved?

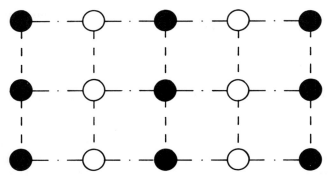

Figure 2-2 *Five strings of beads containing three beads each, or three strings of beads containing five beads each.*

8. With s strings of beads containing b beads each, what is the total number of beads? With b strings of beads containing s beads each, what is the total number of beads? What arithmetic law insures the same total in each case?

9. If we have $a + b$ strings of beads containing $c + d$ beads each, what is the total number of beads? With a diagram like that of Figure 2-2, interpret the formula $(a + b)(c + d) = ac + ad + bc + bd$.

10. Let n be a whole number. Double n, add 1, square, and subtract 1. For instance, take $n = 3$. Doubling, we have 6, and adding 1 gives 7. Squaring gives us 49, and subtracting 1 leaves us with 48. This answer is divisible by 8. Prove that the answer for any whole number n likewise is divisible by 8.

11. Suppose we carry out a procedure like that in the preceding Exercise but in the first step multiply n by 4 instead of doubling. What then can be said of the result?

12. Suppose a bank pays interest at the rate of 4 per cent annually, compounded quarterly (i.e., every three months). If P denotes the original principal, in dollars, show that the total amount (in dollars) resulting after one year is $P(1.01)^4$ and, after two years, is $P(1.01)^8$. What is the total amount after k years?

13. Take any three numbers less than 10. Letting a, b, c denote the numbers, carry out the following operations: (i) Take one of the numbers, say a, and multiply it by 2. (ii) Add 3 to the product. (iii) Multiply this by 5, and add 7 to the product. (iv) To this sum add the second number, b. (v) Multiply the result by 2. (vi) Add 3 to the product. (vii) Multiply by 5, and, to the product, add the third number, c. (viii) From the last result, subtract 235, obtaining a three-digit number as remainder. Prove that its three digits are the numbers chosen originally.†

---

†W. W. Rouse Ball, *Mathematical Recreations and Essays,* revised by H. S. M Coxeter, New York, Macmillan Company, 1960, p. 12.

14. We have seen that positive numbers, here denoted by a, b, c, possess the following multiplicative properties:

(a) $a \cdot b = b \cdot a$

(b) $a \cdot (b \cdot c) = (a \cdot b) \cdot c$

(c) $a \cdot (b + c) = (a \cdot b) + (a \cdot c)$.

Which of these properties remain in force when "$\cdot$" (the multiplication sign) is replaced by "$\div$" (the division sign), nothing else being changed?

b. THE PRINCIPLE OF SUBSTITUTION. ALGEBRAIC IDENTITIES.

Effective use of algebraic laws frequently depends on the general principle that when two expressions are equal, we may substitute either for the other in any context. In other words, we may always substitute "equals for equals." This is the Principle of Substitution. It tells what equality is. Thus it underlies the old rules that things equal to the same thing are equal to each other, that when equals are added to equals the results are equal, and so forth. The first rule asserts that if $b = a$ and $c = a$, then $b = c$. We can deduce it from the Principle of Substitution as follows. Since c and a are assumed to be equal, we may substitute c for a in the equality $b = a$, which is assumed. Doing so, we obtain $b = c$, as the rule contends. The second rule asserts that if $a = b$ and $x = y$, then $x + a = y + b$. To draw this conclusion by use of the Principle of Substitution, consider the expression $x + a$. Since x and y are equal, this expression is not changed in value if we substitute y for x in it. Hence,

$$x + a = y + a.$$

Since a and b are equal, we can substitute b for a now to obtain

$$y + a = y + b.$$

Thus, $y + b$ and $x + a$ are both equal to the same quantity, namely $y + a$, and appealing to the first rule (just proved), we conclude that they are equal to each other. In other words,

$$x + a = y + b,$$

which is what the second rule maintained.

EXERCISES

From the Principle of Substitution, prove the next four statements:

1. If $x = y$, then $y = x$.

2. If $a = b$, then $x + a = x + b$.

3. When equals are subtracted from equals, the results are equal.

4. When equals multiply equals, equal results are obtained.
5. Deduce from the preceding rules that

$$a \cdot 1 = a,$$
$$0 + a = a,$$
$$(a + b)c = ac + bc,$$

where a, b, and c denote any numbers.

6. In this exercise we shall use the symbol ∗ to indicate, like + or ·, a mode of combining two numbers. Specifically, for any two (positive, negative, or zero) numbers a and b, we define

$$a \ast b = a + b + 1.$$

Which of the following rules are true and which false?
(a) $a \ast b = b \ast a$.
(b) $a \ast (b \ast c) = (a \ast b) \ast c$.
(c) $a \ast (b \ast c) = a \ast b + a \ast c$.
(d) $a \ast 0 = a$.
(e) If $a \ast x = a \ast y$, then $x = y$.

7. For any two numbers, a and b, let us define a third number, which we shall denote by $a \ast b$, as follows:

$$a \ast b = a + b + ab.$$

(The symbol ∗ stands for an operation, thus ∗ is analogous to · and +.)
(a) Calculate: $2 \ast 1, 1 \ast 2, 3 \ast 2, 4 \ast 3$.
(b) Is ∗ commutative (i.e., is it true that $a \ast b = b \ast a$)?
(c) Is ∗ associative (i.e., is it true that $(a \ast b) \ast c = a \ast (b \ast c)$)?

We shall further illustrate the Principle of Substitution and also the arithmetical laws by expanding $(1 + x)^2$. By the definition of an exponent,†

$$(1 + x)^2 = (1 + x)(1 + x).$$

In the distributive law, substitute $1 + x$ for a, 1 for b, and x for c to obtain:

$$(1 + x)(1 + x) = (1 + x) \cdot 1 + (1 + x)x.$$

We thus have, so far:

$$(1 + x)^2 = (1 + x)(1 + x)$$
$$= (1 + x) \cdot 1 + (1 + x)x.$$

---

†We recall the usual algebraic convention of writing $x \cdot x$ as x^2, $x \cdot x \cdot x$ as x^3, and, in general, the product $x \cdot x \ldots x$ of k numbers, each of which equals x, as x^k.

Let us pause at this point and, in the interest of brevity, agree not to specify in the text substitutions that seem clear from the context. We can then rewrite the results of the calculation so far, and their justifications, more succinctly as follows:

(i) $(1+x)^2 = (1+x)(1+x)$ (definition of exponent)
       $= (1+x) \cdot 1 + (1+x)x.$ (distributive law)

We continue in this more condensed style:

(ii) $(1+x) \cdot 1 = 1 \cdot (1+x)$ (multiplicative commutative law)

        $= 1 + x$ (law for multiplication by 1)

(iii) $(1+x)x = x(1+x)$ (multiplicative commutative law)

         $= x \cdot 1 + x \cdot x$ (distributive law)
         $= x \cdot 1 + x^2$ (definition of exponent)

(iv) $(1+x) \cdot 1 + (1+x)x$
        $= (1+x) + (x \cdot 1 + x^2)$ (substitution from (ii), (iii))

        $= 1 + [x + (x \cdot 1 + x^2)]$ (additive associative law)

        $= 1 + [(x + x \cdot 1) + x^2]$ (additive associative law)

(v) $x = 1 \cdot x$ (law for multiplication by 1)

           $= x \cdot 1$ (multiplicative commutative law)

(vi) $x + x \cdot 1 = x \cdot 1 + x \cdot 1$ (substitution from (v))
        $= x(1+1)$ (distributive law)
        $= x \cdot 2$ (definition of 2)
        $= 2x$ (multiplicative commutative law)

(vii) $(1+x) \cdot 1 + (1+x)x$
        $= 1 + (2x + x^2)$ (substitution of (vi) into (iv))

(viii) $(1+x)^2 = (1+x) \cdot 1 + (1+x)x$ (result (i))
          $= 1 + (2x + x^2)$ (substitution from (vii))

Dropping the parentheses on the right, which we have seen are superfluous, we thus have finally:

$$(1+x)^2 = 1 + 2x + x^2.$$

EXERCISES

8. Prove the following by referring to the pertinent arithmetical rules:

$$(a + b)^2 = a^2 + 2ab + b^2,$$
$$(a + b)(c + d) = ac + ad + bc + bd.$$

9. Expand the following expressions (i.e., perform such operations as to dissolve parentheses): $(1 + x)^3$, $(1 + x)^4$, $(1 + x)^5$, $(x + y + z)^2$, $(w + x + y + z)^2$.

c.   POSITIVE RATIONAL NUMBERS AND FRACTIONS

By "whole numbers" we have meant

$$1, 2, 3, 4, \ldots :$$

these are known also as *natural numbers* and as *positive integers*. They have distinctive attributes of great interest both mathematically and philosophically, but a detailed discussion requires considerable care. Hence, all these properties will be tacitly assumed, being referred to explicitly only when needed.

Despite this limitation, we can describe the position of rational numbers in arithmetic rather well with the help of an eighth law.

Law of Reciprocals.   Let a denote any natural number. Then a rational number x exists such that

$$ax = 1.$$

This rational number x is called the *reciprocal* of a and is written alternatively as $1/a$ or a^{-1}. In the latter notation, for instance, the law of reciprocals states that for any natural number a

$$aa^{-1} = 1.$$

We called a^{-1} *the* reciprocal of a as though we knew that a could have no other. In fact, it cannot: every natural number has but one reciprocal. This means that if

$$ax = 1$$

and

$$ay = 1$$

for some natural number a and rational numbers x and y, then

$$x = y.$$

To demonstrate this, we multiply both sides of the equation $ay = 1$ by the number x, obtaining

$$x(ay) = x1.$$

For the right side of this equality we have

$$x1 = 1x \quad \text{(multiplicative commutative law)}$$
$$ = x \quad \text{(law for multiplication by 1).}$$

For the left side, we have
$$x(ay) = (xa)y \quad \text{(multiplicative associative law)}$$
$$ = (ax)y \quad \text{(multiplicative commutative law)}$$
$$ = 1y \quad \text{(the assumed equality } ax = 1)$$
$$ = y \quad \text{(law for multiplication by 1).}$$

Thus, the equality we are discussing reduces to

$$y = x,$$

the result claimed.

From the rule just proved that each natural number has just one reciprocal, we immediately deduce that†

(1) $$1^{-1} = 1.$$

Indeed, the Law of Reciprocals tells us that $1 \cdot 1^{-1} = 1$, while according to the law for multiplication by 1 we have $1 \cdot 1 = 1$. Therefore, $1 = 1^{-1}$ by the rule referred to.

Another immediate consequence of this rule is that

(2) $$(ab)^{-1} = a^{-1}b^{-1}$$

for all natural numbers a and b. In fact, according to the Law of Reciprocals,

$$(ab)(ab)^{-1} = 1,$$

while

$$(ab)(a^{-1}b^{-1}) = (ba)(a^{-1}b^{-1}) \quad \text{(commutative law)}$$
$$\phantom{(ab)(a^{-1}b^{-1})} = b[a(a^{-1}b^{-1})] \quad \text{(associative law)}$$
$$\phantom{(ab)(a^{-1}b^{-1})} = b[(aa^{-1})b^{-1}] \quad \text{(associative law)}$$
$$\phantom{(ab)(a^{-1}b^{-1})} = b[1b^{-1}] \quad \text{(law of reciprocals)}$$
$$\phantom{(ab)(a^{-1}b^{-1})} = bb^{-1} \quad \text{(law for multiplication by 1)}$$
$$\phantom{(ab)(a^{-1}b^{-1})} = 1 \quad \text{(law of reciprocals).}$$

Since every natural number has but one reciprocal, we conclude that $(ab)^{-1} = a^{-1}b^{-1}$, as stated.

---

†For purposes of emphasis in mathematical writing, a formula, symbolic expression, and so forth may be detached from the main body of text for display on a line to itself. Sometimes, the line is marked by a number or other identifying symbol, as the following, for instance, has been tagged to the left as "(1)." Subsequent reference to whatever is displayed on the line usually will mention the identifying symbol as a guide.

We have not really defined reciprocals but have formulated and used some of their properties. This is because our concern is how numbers work in arithmetic, not what they are metaphysically. Are we on firm ground, however, not to define our terms? We shall return to this question in Chapter 12.

If a and b are any natural numbers, we call the product

$$ab^{-1}$$

a *positive rational number*. Frequently, we represent this number as a "fraction" a/b, a being called the *numerator* and b the *denominator* of the fraction.

Any natural number a is a positive rational number, representable as the fraction $a/1$. This is because

$$
\begin{aligned}
a &= 1a &&\text{(rule for multiplication by 1)}\\
&= a1 &&\text{(commutative rule)}\\
&= a1^{-1} &&\text{(relation (2))},
\end{aligned}
$$

while $a1^{-1}$ is of the form ab^{-1} with $b = 1$.

When two positive rational numbers are multiplied, the product is again a positive rational number. This means that if a, b, c, d are any natural numbers, then $(ab^{-1})(cd^{-1})$ is a positive rational number. Indeed, we have

$$
\begin{aligned}
(ab^{-1})(cd^{-1}) &= a[b^{-1}(cd^{-1})] &&\text{(associative law)}\\
&= a[(b^{-1}c)d^{-1}] &&\text{(associative law)}\\
&= a[(cb^{-1})d^{-1}] &&\text{(commutative law)}\\
&= a[c(b^{-1}d^{-1})] &&\text{(associative law)}\\
&= (ac)(b^{-1}d^{-1}) &&\text{(associative law)}\\
&= (ac)(bd)^{-1} &&\text{(relation (2))},
\end{aligned}
$$

and the last expression by definition is a positive rational number. Thus, the product of two positive rational numbers is again a positive rational number, as stated. We describe this property by saying that the system of positive rational numbers is *closed* under the operation of multiplication.

Rational numbers owe their indispensability mainly to the following fact:

First Theorem on Division. If a and b are any natural numbers, then the equation

$$ax = b$$

is satisfied by the positive rational number $x = ba^{-1}$. No other positive rational number satisfies this equation.

(For instance, the equation $2x = 10$ is satisfied just by the value $x = 10/2 = 5$, the equation $4x = 3$ just by $x = 3/4$, the equation $3x = 7$ just by $x = 7/3$.)

To prove this theorem, imagine we knew the equation to be satisfied by *some* value of x and wished to find this value. Multiplying both sides of the supposed relation $ax = b$ by a^{-1}, we would obtain

$$a^{-1}(ax) = a^{-1}b.$$

The left side reduces to x:

$$a^{-1}(ax) = (a^{-1}a)x = (aa^{-1})x = 1x = x.$$

Hence, we would have

$$x = a^{-1}b = ba^{-1},$$

which tells us that ba^{-1} is the *only* value x can *possibly* have to satisfy the given equation $ax = b$. Does this value *actually* satisfy the equation? This means, is it true that $a(ba^{-1}) = b$? Yes, since

$$a(ba^{-1}) = a(a^{-1}b) = (aa^{-1})b = 1b = b.$$

The First Division Theorem is thus proved.

In terms of fractions, this theorem states that for any natural numbers a and b,

$$a(b/a) = b.$$

Of course we knew this fact when we began, and why then did we take the trouble to deduce it from our eight laws? The same question applies to some previous points. The answer is that we are concerned, not with the bare rules of arithmetic alone, but also with their logic. From the point of view of logic, it is of great interest that a small number of laws adopted as premises have many others as their consequences. Of the important properties implied by the eight laws stated so far, those we have just given are only the beginning.

We shall next see how all the rules for operating with fractions follow from the eight laws. These rules are, so to speak, concealed in the laws. Let us begin with the cancellation rule

$$(cb)/(ca) = b/a$$

for non-negative integers a, b, c such that $a \neq 0$, $c \neq 0$. We first multiply both sides of the equality

$$a(b/a) = b$$

by c to obtain:

$$c(a(b/a)) = cb.$$

The multiplicative associative law states that any fractional or whole numbers x, y, z, satisfy the relation

$$x(yz) = (xy)z;$$

taking $x = c$, $y = a$, $z = b/a$ gives us

$$c(a(b/a)) = (ca) \cdot (b/a).$$

Since $c(a(b/a)) = cb$, we thus have:

$$(ca) \cdot (b/a) = cb.$$

In other words, the equation

$$(ca) \cdot z = cb$$

is satisfied by the value $z = b/a$. By the First Division Theorem, only one positive rational number exists that satisfies this equation, and this number is cb/ca. Consequently,

$$(cb)/(ca) = b/a.$$

This is the well known cancellation law for fractions, appearing here as a manifestation of the multiplicative associative law, laid down among our premises.

EXERCISES

Prove the following statements, in which a, b, c, d denote arbitrary natural numbers:

1. $a/b = c/d$ if and only if $ad = bc$.
2. $(a/b) \cdot (c/d) = (ac/bd)$.

HINT: Setting $x = a/b$ and $y = c/d$, we have

$$bx = a, \quad dy = c,$$

and must prove

$$(bd)(xy) = ac.$$

The multiplicative commutative and associative laws are involved.

3. $(a/b) + (c/b) = (a + c)/b$.

HINT: Letting $x = a/b$ and $y = c/b$, we have $bx = a$ and $by = c$. We wish to prove that $b(x + y) = a + c$; the distributive law will be involved.

4. $(a/b) + (c/d) = (ad + bc)/bd$.

HINT: Write $a/b = (ad)/(bd)$ and $c/d = (bc)/(bd)$, and apply the result of the previous exercise.

5. $\dfrac{a/b}{c/d} = \dfrac{ad}{bc}$.

d. GENERAL RULES FOR POSITIVE RATIONAL NUMBERS

The concept of reciprocal readily extends to positive rational numbers.

Proposition. For any positive rational number u, a positive rational number x exists such that $ux = 1$. No positive rational number other than x satisfies this condition.

PROOF: By definition, natural numbers a and b exist such that $u = ab^{-1}$. Thus, the x we demand must satisfy the condition

$$ab^{-1}x = 1.$$

For the present imagine such an x to exist and multiply both sides of the previous condition, which we assume to be satisfied, by ba^{-1}. We obtain

$$ba^{-1}ab^{-1}x = ba^{-1}.$$

We have omitted parentheses but shall insert them where convenient, as we may. Concerning the left side of the last equation, we see in this way that

$$ba^{-1}ab^{-1}x = b(a^{-1}a)b^{-1}x = b1b^{-1}x = bb^{-1}x$$
$$= (bb^{-1})x = 1x = x.$$

Therefore, the equation reduces to:

$$x = ba^{-1}.$$

Having assumed the existence of a number x such that $ux = 1$, we thus find that for $u = ab^{-1}$ we must have $x = a^{-1}b$. No *other* value than this will satisfy the condition. But will this value satisfy it? An additional calculation verifies that it will:

$$(ba^{-1})(ab^{-1}) = b(a^{-1}a)b^{-1} = b1b^{-1} = 1.$$

Thus, the proposition is proved.

We call x in this proposition the *reciprocal* of u, and we symbolize it as u^{-1} or $1/u$. For any positive rational number u, we thus have, in particular,

$$uu^{-1} = 1.$$

The proof of the proposition shows us that if $u = a/b$, then $u^{-1} = b/a$, i.e.,

$$(a/b)^{-1} = b/a.$$

In other words, the reciprocal of a fraction is obtained by interchanging the numerator and the denominator.

It follows from the last remark that for any positive rational number u,

$$(u^{-1})^{-1} = u.$$

Indeed, if $u = a/b$, then $u^{-1} = b/a$, and therefore $(u^{-1})^{-1} = a/b = u$, the repeated interchange of numerator and denominator having no net effect upon u.

If u and v are positive rational numbers, we call the product uv^{-1} the *quotient* obtained by *dividing* u by v. We also represent this quotient as a *fraction* written as u/v.

The next theorem characterizes u/v as the number that must be multiplied by v to give u.

Second Theorem on Division. If u and v are any positive rational numbers, then the equation

$$vx = u$$

is satisfied by the quotient u/v. No other positive rational number satisfies this equation.

This theorem follows from the existence of the reciprocal v^{-1}, and its proof is word for word like that of the First Division Theorem. It says that if a, b, c, d are natural numbers, then the only value of x to satisfy the condition

$$(a/b)x = c/d$$

is

$$x = (c/d)(a/b)^{-1} = (c/d)(b/a).$$

Hence (see Exercise 2 of Section 2c),

$$x = (bc)/(ad).$$

The Second Division Theorem has consequences quite similar to those of the First Division Theorem, which are obtained by identical means.

EXERCISES

The following symbolized quantities are understood to be positive rational numbers.

1. In each instance, find a value of x to satisfy the condition indicated.
   - (a) $4x = 16$,
   - (b) $4x = 3$,
   - (c) $1/x = 1/3$,
   - (d) $1/x = 3$,
   - (e) $2/x = 5$,
   - (f) $a/x = b$,
   - (g) $a/x + 1 = b + 2$.

2. Carry out the proof of the fact stated in the Second Division Theorem that if $vx = u$ and $vy = u$, then $x = y$.

3. Prove:
   - (a) $a = a/1$,
   - (b) $\dfrac{1/a}{1/b} = b/a$,
   - (c) $(a/b)(b/c) = a/c$,
   - (d) $a/b + c/b = (a + c)/b$.

4. Prove:
   - (a) $(bc)^{-1} = b^{-1}c^{-1}$,
   - (b) $ac/bc = a/b$,
   - (c) $a/b = c/d$ if and only if $ad = bc$,
   - (d) $a/b + c/d = (ad + bc)/bd$,
   - (e) $(a/b)(c/d) = ac/bd$,
   - (f) $\dfrac{a/b}{c/d} = \dfrac{ad}{bc}$.

5. Prove:
   - (a) $a/(a + b) + b/(a + b) = 1$,
   - (b) $(a^2 + 2ab + b^2)/(a + b) = a + b$.

e. THE ROLE OF ZERO

When we stated the first seven laws of addition and multiplication (Subsection a), why did we omit the well known, important rule that

$$0a = 0$$

for any number a? The reason is that this rule is deducible from the others, as we shall now show.

To be precise, we shall prove here that

$$0u = 0$$

if u is any positive rational number or zero.

We begin by noting that

(1)
$$0 \cdot 1 = 0,$$

a consequence of the rule for multiplying by 1. From this, we have

$$0 = 0 \cdot 1 = 0(1 + 0),$$

while

$$
\begin{aligned}
0(1 + 0) &= 0 \cdot 1 + 0 \cdot 0 && \text{(distributive rule)} \\
&= 0 + 0 \cdot 0 && \text{(equality (1))} \\
&= 0 \cdot 0 && \text{(rule for adding 0).}
\end{aligned}
$$

Therefore,

$$0 \cdot 0 = 0.$$

Furthermore,

(2)
$$0 \cdot 2 = 0(1 + 1) = 0 \cdot 1 + 0 \cdot 1 = 0 + 0 = 0,$$

(3)
$$0 \cdot 3 = 0(1 + 2) = 0 \cdot 1 + 0 \cdot 2 = 0 + 0 = 0,$$

as follows from (2), and

(4)
$$0 \cdot 4 = 0(1 + 3) = 0 \cdot 1 + 0 \cdot 3 = 0 + 0 = 0,$$

as follows from (3), and so forth. Continuing in this way from one natural number to the next, we shall find after n steps that

(n)
$$0 \cdot n = 0.$$

This is the rule desired, but restricted to natural numbers.

Now we shall prove that the rule holds for reciprocals. Multiply the two sides of the last equality by n^{-1}. We obtain

$$0 \cdot n \cdot n^{-1} = 0 \cdot n^{-1},$$

while the multiplicative associative law tells us that

$$0 \cdot n \cdot n^{-1} = 0 \cdot 1 = 0;$$

hence,

$$0 \cdot n^{-1} = 0$$

for any natural number n.

At last we can show that $0 \cdot u = 0$ for any positive rational number u. Let $u = mn^{-1}$, where m and n are positive natural numbers. Since $0 \cdot m = 0$, we have

$$0 \cdot u = 0 \cdot m \cdot n^{-1} = 0 \cdot n^{-1} = 0,$$

the desired formula.

Zero and the natural numbers together, the set of numbers

$$0, 1, 2, 3, 4, \ldots,$$

are called the *non-negative integers*. Zero and the positive rational numbers together are called the *non-negative rational numbers*. We have just proved that

$$0u = 0$$

for any non-negative rational number u. This is half the following proposition.

Proposition.   The product of two non-negative rational numbers is zero if and only if one of the numbers is zero.

The as yet unproved part of this proposition is the assertion that a product of two non-negative rational numbers is zero *only if* one of the numbers is zero. This means that if u and v are non-negative rational numbers such that $uv = 0$, then either $u = 0$ or $v = 0$. To prove this, we suppose to the contrary that positive rationals u and v exist for which $uv = 0$. Since the positive rationals are closed under multiplication, the product uv is, in particular, a positive rational number, while no positive rational number is equal to zero. This contradicts the unwarranted supposition that $uv = 0$. Therefore, this supposition is untenable, and we conclude that $uv \neq 0$ for positive rationals u and v, as asserted.

We have used the fact that no positive rational number is equal to 0. Who can doubt it, but do our laws cover it, or is this fact outside our laws? If so, our laws are deficient and ought to be supplemented.

Indeed, we never formulated the properties of the integers, while such a property, the fact that

$$1 \neq 0,$$

is just what is at issue here. We wish to show that no positive rational number equals zero. Suppose to the contrary that some positive rational number w did satisfy the condition

$$w = 0.$$

Since w is a positive rational, it has a reciprocal, and multiplying both sides of this relation by the reciprocal w^{-1} gives:

$$ww^{-1} = 0w^{-1}.$$

Since $ww^{-1} = 1$ and $0w^{-1} = 0$, the last equality reduces to $1 = 0$, contradicting the fact that $1 \neq 0$. The contradiction shows the supposition $w = 0$ to be untenable, and we conclude that $w \neq 0$, as asserted.

Common sense may seem to suggest an easier proof. A positive rational number w is something, and zero is nothing. Hence, the equation $w = 0$ says that something is nothing, contradiction enough for anybody. We answer that zero in our system does not stand for "nothing," but for a number subject to certain stipulated laws. Proving any rule means deducing it from these laws, and this is what we did.

The preceding proposition shows that zero does not have a reciprocal, or rather that no non-negative rational number is a reciprocal of 0. Indeed, $0x = 0$ for every non-negative rational number x, while $0x = 1$ for a reciprocal of 0, and these two statements are in contradiction. Thus, 0 has no (non-negative rational) reciprocal. Division by zero, therefore, is impossible.

Non-negative rational numbers satisfy all the relations given in the previous subsections for positive rational numbers, except that, as we have just seen, all denominators are required to be nonzero. Proofs are trivial. Consider as an example the rule

$$\frac{u/v}{w/x} = \frac{ux}{vw}$$

with u, v, w, x permitted to be non-negative rational numbers. To comply with the condition that the denominators be nonzero, we have to assume that v, w, x are positive rationals. Then there are two cases, the first being that in which u is a positive rational; this case is known already. The second case is that in which $u = 0$. Left side and right side are both 0 in this case, and the equality is verified again. Thus, it holds in all (i.e., both) cases.

EXERCISES

The following are erroneous arguments. Find the mistakes made in them.

1. Let a denote 0. Thus, $a = 0$. Dividing the left side of this equality by a gives 1, and dividing the right side gives 0. Hence, $1 = 0$.

2. The equation $xa = 2a$ implies through division by a that $x = 2$. When $a = 0$, this equation holds with $x = 1$. Hence, $1 = 2$.

f. NEGATIVE NUMBERS AND THE RATIONAL NUMBER SYSTEM

Our summary of arithmetic ends with a consideration of negative numbers. Following the previous pattern, we first state additional general laws required and then, by deduction, obtain other rules. The laws themselves are undoubtedly elusive, their gestation period having lasted through most recorded human history. They are still a source of confusion to many. For this reason, we devote a section (Section 4) to a discussion of negative numbers from common sense standpoints to uncover the reasons behind the rules.

We shall now state the ninth law.

Law of Negatives. The number system on which elementary algebra is based includes "negative" as well as positive rational numbers, and every number in the system is positive, negative, or zero. Corresponding to any positive rational number u, a negative number denoted by $-u$ exists such that

$$u + (-u) = 0.$$

We call $-u$ *the negative of u.*

The negative of a natural number is called a *negative integer*, the negative of a positive rational number a *negative rational number*. By an *integer* is meant a positive integer, a negative integer, or zero. By a *rational number* is meant a positive rational number, a negative rational number, or zero.

The negative of 0 is defined to be zero:

$$-0 = 0.$$

The negative of a negative is defined by the relation

$$-(-u) = u,$$

u denoting an arbitrary positive (rational) number. Under these definitions supplementing the Law of Negatives, we have

$$a + (-a) = 0 \text{ and} -(-a) = a$$

for every rational number a. This is proved immediately by considering the three cases in which a is positive, negative, or zero, respectively.

The expression $a + (-b)$ is also written $a - b$, in which form it is called the *difference* obtained by subtracting b from a.

We called $-a$ *the* negative of a as though we knew that a could have no other. In fact, it cannot: each rational number has one and but one negative. This means that if

$$a + x = 0$$

and

$$a + y = 0$$

for certain (rational) numbers a, x, y, then $x = y$. To demonstrate this, we add x to both sides of the equation $a + y = 0$ to obtain

$$(a + y) + x = 0 + x.$$

The right side of this result is x by the commutative rule for addition and the rule for adding 0. For the left side, we have

$$
\begin{aligned}
(a+y)+x &= a+(y+x) && \text{(associative rule)} \\
&= a+(x+y) && \text{(commutative rule)} \\
&= (a+x)+y && \text{(associative rule)} \\
&= 0+y && \text{(the equation } a+x=0) \\
&= y+0 && \text{(commutative rule)} \\
&= y && \text{(rule for adding 0).}
\end{aligned}
$$

Thus the equality we are discussing reduces to $y=x$, the result claimed. Notice that to obtain it, we had to apply some of our rules (Subsection a) to *negative* numbers.

Reasoning very similar to the preceding shows that if a and b are any (rational) numbers, then one and just one (rational) value of x exists such that

$$a+x=b;$$

this value of x is:

$$x=b+(-a).$$

Indeed, adding $-a$ to both sides of the equation $a+x=b$ shows that *if* x satisfies the equation, then $x=b+(-a)$; direct substitution proves that this value of x does indeed satisfy the equation.

In what follows, we shall need the fact that

$$0a=0$$

for any (rational) number a. Already knowing this equality for zero or positive (rational) a, we need only consider the case in which a is negative, say $a=-u$, where u is a positive (rational) number. We must prove that

$$0(-u)=0.$$

To do so, multiply both sides of the equation

$$u+(-u)=0$$

by 0 to obtain

$$0(u+(-u))=0\cdot0=0.$$

Since the left side of this equality is

$$0(u+(-u))=0u+0(-u)=0+0(-u)=0(-u),$$

the equality reduces to

$$0(-u)=0,$$

the desired formula. Thus, $0a=0$ in all cases, as stated.

Now we shall justify the laws of signs,

$$(-a)b = a(-b) = -(ab), \ (-a)(-b) = ab,$$

which hold for all (rational) numbers a and b. We start from the equality

$$b + (-b) = 0,$$

which has been justified. Multiplying both sides by a gives

$$a(b + (-b)) = a \cdot 0,$$

and $a \cdot 0 = 0$ from the previous paragraph. Applying the distributive law to the left side thus gives us

$$ab + a(-b) = 0.$$

Now adding $-(ab)$ to both sides, we obtain

$$a(-b) = -(ab),$$

since $ab + [-(ab)] = 0$. This is one of the cited laws of signs. In a similar way, we easily prove also that

$$(-a)b = -(ab),$$

another one of the laws.

These results help us with the third law of signs. This time, multiply the equality

$$b + (-b) = 0$$

by $-a$, to obtain

$$(-a)(b + (-b)) = (-a)0.$$

The right side equals 0, while for the left we have

$$
\begin{aligned}
(-a)(b+(-b)) &= (-a)b + (-a)(-b) \quad \text{(distributive law)} \\
&= -(ab) + (-a)(-b) \quad \text{(the rule that } (-a)b = -(ab)\text{)}.
\end{aligned}
$$

Thus, we have

$$-(ab) + (-a)(-b) = 0,$$

and adding ab to both sides gives us

$$(-a)(-b) = ab,$$

the third rule.

We can now establish that negative (rational) numbers have reciprocals. For any positive (rational) number u, let $v = u^{-1}$, so that

$$uv = 1.$$

The last rule of signs shows that

$$(-u)(-v) = 1,$$

which says that $-v$ is the reciprocal of $-u$. In other words,

$$(-u)^{-1} = -(u^{-1}).$$

The fact that $-u$ has just one reciprocal follows by the same argument we gave for natural numbers.

More generally, if a stands for any nonzero (rational) number, we have

$$(-a)^{-1} = -(a^{-1}).$$

The case in which a is positive has just been treated. If a is negative, say $a = -v$, where v is a positive (rational) number, we have $-a = -(-v) = v$ and, therefore, $(-a)^{-1} = v^{-1}$; also $-(a^{-1}) = -(-v)^{-1} = -(-(v^{-1})) = v^{-1}$, v being a positive number and therefore already subject to the rule; thus, $(-a)^{-1}$ and $-(a^{-1})$ are both equal to v^{-1} and hence to each other, as required.

Since all nonzero (rational) numbers have reciprocals, we can extend the term "quotient" to all products of the form uv^{-1}, where u and v are *any* (rational) numbers with $v \neq 0$. Again, we write the quotient as the fraction u/v.

A minus sign can be applied to a fraction in any one of three locations. In fact, for any (rational) numbers u and v with $v \neq 0$,

$$-(u/v) = (-u)/v = u/(-v).$$

These rules easily follow from the previous rules, for we have

$$-(u/v) = -(uv^{-1}) = (-u)v^{-1} = (-u)/v$$

and

$$-(u/v) = -(uv^{-1}) = u(-(v^{-1})) = u(-v)^{-1} = u/(-v).$$

Since every nonzero (rational) number has a reciprocal, we can always find a number x to satisfy an equation of the form

$$ax = b,$$

where a and b are arbitrary (rational) numbers with $a \neq 0$. Indeed,

$$x = b/a;$$

no other value of x will satisfy the equation.

EXERCISES

1. Calculate as an ordinary (positive or negative) fraction:

(a) $\dfrac{1/4}{-1}$,

(b) $\dfrac{1/4}{-(1/2)}$,

(c) $\dfrac{-(1/4)}{1/2}$,

(d) $\dfrac{-(1/4)}{-(1/2)}$,

(e) $-\dfrac{-(1/4)}{-(1/2)}$,

(f) $-\dfrac{2/5}{-(4/15)}$,

(g) $-\dfrac{-(8/3)}{-(4/15)}$.

2. In each instance, find a value of x to satisfy the indicated condition:
   (a) $x + 2 = 3$,
   (b) $x - 2 = -3$,
   (c) $1 - x = 4$,
   (d) $a - x = b$ (a and b denote any numbers),
   (e) $1 - (1/x) = 3$.

3. In each instance, find a value of x to satisfy the indicated condition:
   (a) $4x = -16$,
   (b) $-2x = 3$,
   (c) $-3x = -2$,
   (d) $-1/x = 2$,
   (e) $1/(-x) = -6$,
   (f) $-a/x = 1$ ($a \neq 0$),
   (g) $-a/x = b$ ($a \neq 0$, $b \neq 0$),
   (h) $8a/(-bx) = c$ ($b \neq 0$, $a \neq 0$, $c \neq 0$).

4. Prove that a^2 is positive if a is positive or negative. HINT: If a is negative, then $-a$ is positive, while $a^2 = (-a)^2$.

5. Justify the following formulas in which the letters stand for any rational numbers, but in which the denominators are not zero:

(a) $a + (b - c) = (a + b) - c$,
(b) $a - (b - c) = (a + c) - b$,
(c) $a(b - c) = ab - ac$,
(d) $(b - c)/a = b/a - c/a$,
(e) $a/b - c/d = (ad - bc)/(bd)$.

g. THE REPRESENTATION OF NUMBERS AS POINTS ON A LINE

On any straight line, choose a point, which we shall call the *origin* and which is symbolized by the letter O. Then select either of the two possible directions of motion along the line, calling the direction selected the *positive* sense or direction. The direction opposite to the positive is called negative. Also choose a unit to measure distance on the line. We can specify any point P of the line by giving (1) its distance d, measured in the given unit, from O and (2) its direction (positive or negative) from O. Our aim is to combine this information specifying P into one number, which we will denote by the letter x. If the direction from O to P is positive, we define this number as $x = d$; if the direction is negative, we define it as $x = -d$. The number x thus corresponding to any point P might be called the address of the point; it is actually called the *coordinate* of the point. The origin has coordinate zero. A line on which the origin, the unit of distance, and the positive direction have been established, and whose points are referred to by their coordinates, is called *the number axis*. We shall sometimes refer to it more simply, however, as a *scale*. (See Figure 2-3.)

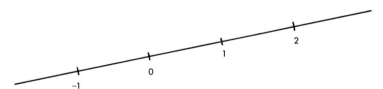

Figure 2-3   A scale with the origin and some other points marked.

The points P and P' with coordinates x and $-x$, respectively, are at the same distance from O, but on opposite sides.

If x and p are any numbers with p positive, the point with coordinate $x + p$ is that which is p units from x in the positive direction, and the point with coordinate $x - p$ (i.e., $x + (-p)$) is that which is p units from x in the negative direction. Thus, on a scale we can visualize addition and subtraction and, in particular, picture the additive commutative and associative laws.

In Chapter 7, Section 2, we use scales to represent the multiplicative commutative and associative laws.

EXERCISES

Interpret on a scale the following equalities:

1. $1 + 2 = 2 + 1$,
2. $-1 + 2 = 2 - 1$,
3. $1 - 1 = 0$,
4. $1 - 2 = -(2 - 1)$,
5. $(1 + 2) + 3 = 1 + (2 + 3)$,
6. $(1 + 2) - 3 = 1 + (2 - 3)$,
7. $(2 - 1) - 1 = 0$,
8. $-(1 + 1) = -1 - 1$.

h.   SOME HISTORICAL REMARKS †

Algebra, as we shall state more fully in Chapter 3, reached a high point of development among the Old Babylonians before 1800 B.C. The Babylonians and later ancient peoples lacked symbolism, however, not so much in stating their formulas as in exemplifying them in numerical calculations given step by step. "Tolerable" symbolic notation was developed by the Hindu mathematicians of the 7th to the 12th Centuries A.D. but was not transmitted by the Arabs to the West. In Europe, beginning in Italy in the 15th Century, our present notation developed "by almost insensible degrees as convenience suggested different marks of abbreviation to different authors; and that perfect symbolic language which addresses itself solely to the eye, and enables us to take in at a glance the most complicated relations of quantity, is the result of a large series of small improvements." ‡ Letters of the alphabet were first used to denote general or indefinite quantities by Francois Vieta, a great French mathematician, in the 16th Century. The use of x^2, x^3, and so forth was a 17th Century innovation of René Descartes.

Not long after 2000 B.C., when such identities as

$$(a - b)^2 = a^2 - 2ab + b^2$$

were first discovered, the concept of negative number became pertinent. Yet this concept seemingly occurred to no one before about the 7th Century A.D., partially emerging in India during the succeeding 500 years. The Hindu mathematicians of the 7th to 12th Centuries A.D. distinguished negative and positive numbers, apparently interpreting them on a scale, and also interpreting them as indebted-

---

† See Florian Cajori, *A History of Mathematics,* Second Edition, New York, The Macmillan Company, 1961, especially pp. 93, 125-126, 139, 141. Also David Eugene Smith, *History of Mathematics,* Vol. II, Dover Edition, New York, Dover Publications, Inc., 1958, especially pp. 257-261, 395-417.

‡ J. F. W. Herschel, "Mathematics," in *Edinburgh Encyclopedia.* Quoted from Cajori, *op. cit.,* p. 126.

ness and possession, respectively. They knew correct rules of signs. They stopped short, however, of placing negative and positive numbers on the same footing, Bhaskara, for instance, in about 1150, explicitly rejecting a negative solution, or root, of a quadratic equation because "people do not approve of negative roots."† The great algebraists of Europe in the 16th Century likewise "saw negative roots, but did not approve of them"; some, like Vieta, failed to see them. Negative numbers were not appreciated fully in the modern sense before the 17th Century, perhaps 3500 years after algebra first appeared.

3.

Linear algebraic equations and recreational problems

A *linear equation,* or an *equation of first degree,* is a condition of the form

(1) $$ax + b = c,$$

where b and c are arbitrary numbers and $a \neq 0$. *To solve* the equation is to find the value, or values, of x, if any, that satisfy this condition. Such a value of x is called a *solution,* or a *root,* of the equation.

The rules of algebra enable us to solve any linear equation quite mechanically. We begin with an example: the equation

$$2x + 4 = 7.$$

If x denoted an actual root, the equation would really hold and would then continue to hold if the number 4 were subtracted from either side. Thus,

$$2x = 3.$$

Dividing both sides by 2 again preserves the equality of the sides and tells us that

$$x = 3/2.$$

Hence, if the given equation has a root, this root is 3/2. That the equation does have a root—has 3/2 as its root—we see by testing this value, i.e., by verifying that

$$2(3/2) + 4 = 7.$$

Equation (1) with unspecified values of a, b, c is solved by a

---

† Cajori, *op. cit.,* p. 141.

precisely similar procedure. Two steps logically are involved:
(1) Assuming the equation to have a root, we find its value in terms
of a, b, and c. (2) We verify that the value so obtained is, in fact, a
root. To do the first step, assume that x denotes an actual value
(depending on a, b, c) satisfying equality (1). Adding $-b$ to either
side does not impair the equality but cancels b in the left member.
Thus, we obtain

$$ax = c - b.$$

Multiplying either side by a^{-1} cancels a in the left member to give
now:

(2) $x = (c - b)/a.$

This, then, would be the value of x if x satisfied equation (1). This
value, however, does, in fact, satisfy equation (1), as we now verify
by direct substitution:

$$a((c - b)/a) + b = (c - b) + b = c.$$

We conclude that equation (1) is satisfied by the one, and only one,
value given in (2).

EXERCISES

1. The sum of two numbers is 179, and their difference is 5. What are the
numbers?

2. A pharmacist has a certain drug in 40 per cent solution (40 parts drug
to 100 parts solution) and also in 6 per cent solution. By mixing appropriate
quantities of the two solutions, he wishes to obtain 8 ounces of a 14 per cent
solution. To calculate the quantities needed, let x denote the number of
ounces required of the 40 per cent solution.

(a) Fill in, in terms of x, the remaining entries in the following table.

	40% Solution	6% Solution	Entire Mixture
Quantity of liquid	x		8
Amount of drug contained in liquid			

(b) What relation, apparent from the terms of the problem and the
table, determines x?

(c) Find x.

3. A man gained 10 per cent on one investment and lost 8 per cent on
another, to make a net gain of $32. The sum of the two investments was $2300.
What were their amounts?

4. Two motorists left in opposite directions, at the same time, from the same place. They traveled at constant speeds, one 15 m.p.h. faster than the other. If they were 100 miles apart after 2 hours, what were their speeds?

5. A man can row five miles per hour steadily in still water. In a river with a 2 m.p.h. current, he wishes to row upstream a certain distance, rest two hours, and then row back. How far upstream can the man row if the entire trip is to take seven hours?

6. Two cars start out from the same place, both traveling north. One car proceeds at 70 m.p.h., the other at 60 m.p.h. After how long will the first car be 12 miles ahead of the second car?

7. A student working an algebra problem made the following incorrect cancellation:

$$(10 + 2x)/x = 10 + 2 = 12.$$

Yet his answer was correct for the particular value of x he was using. What was the value of x?

8. We know that the associative law, in general, does not hold for subtraction: i.e., in general, $a - (b - c) \neq (a - b) - c$. A student did not appreciate this fact, however, and when asked to evaluate $2 - (1 - x)$, wrote $2 - (1 - x) = (2 - 1) - x$. Yet his answer was correct for the particular value of x he was using. What was his final answer?

9. Of 15 farmers, one had a single apple tree in his field, another had two apple trees, another had three trees, another had four trees, another five, and so on, the last farmer having 15 trees in his orchard. Last year, each of the fifteen farmers discovered that every tree in his own orchard bore exactly the same number of apples. Furthermore, the total gathered in each orchard was almost the same. In fact, if the man with 11 trees had given one apple to the man who had seven trees, and the man with 14 trees had given three each to the men with nine and 13 trees, they would all have had exactly the same. How many apples did each farmer have? HINT: All the numbers involved are positive, whole numbers.†

10. A country baker sent off his boy with a message to the butcher in the next village, and at the same time the butcher sent his boy to the baker. Each boy went at a uniform pace, but one ran faster than the other, and they were seen to pass at a spot 720 yards from the baker's shop. Each stopped 10 minutes at his destination and then started, at the same speeds, on the return journey, when it was found that they passed each other at a spot 400 yards from the butcher's. How far apart are the two tradesmen's shops?‡ HINT: Let d denote the distance between the butcher and the baker, let t' denote the first time the two boys pass each other and t'' the second time. Let u denote the first boy's speed and v the speed of the second boy. Since distance = velocity · time, we have

$$720 = ut', \quad d - 720 = vt'$$

---

†Henry E. Dudeney, *The Canterbury Puzzles*, fourth edition, New York, Dover Publications, Incorporated, 1958, p. 143.
‡*Ibid.*, p. 147.

with a second pair of equations relating to the time t''. The first pair of equations implies that

$$d = (u + v)t';$$

the second pair of equations implies that

$$3d = (u + v)(t'' - 10).$$

The last two equations together show that $t'' - 10 = 3t'$. Substitute this into the second pair of equations (those relating to t''), and compare the results with the first pair.

11. The combined ages of Mary and Ann are 44 years, and Mary is twice as old as Ann was when Mary was half as old as Ann will be when Ann is three times as old as Mary was when Mary was three times as old as Ann. How old is Mary?† HINT: The ages of the two girls at four different times are referred to in this problem, the last mentioned time being that "when Mary was three times as old as Ann." Denoting Mary's and Ann's ages at that time by m_1 and a_1, respectively, we have

$$m_1 = 3a_1.$$

The next to the last time referred to is "when Ann is three times as old as Mary was when Mary was three times as old as Ann." If m_2 and a_2 refer to Mary's and Ann's ages, respectively, at this time, we have

$$a_2 = 3m_1.$$

(Thus, $a_2 = 9a_1$.) Two more equations are obtained similarly, the four equations so resulting enabling us to express most of the ages of the two girls at the times mentioned in terms of a_1. From the fact that the difference between Ann's and Mary's ages is the same at any time, express all the ages in terms of a_1. Then find a_1 from the final condition giving the sum of Ann's and Mary's present ages.

---

†Henry E. Dudeney, *Amusements in Mathematics*, London, Thomas Nelson and Sons, Ltd., 1949, p. 8.

4.

On negative numbers

We have described algebra as the study of general methods in arithmetic, based on conscious knowledge of the laws that govern arithmetical operations. Four such operations — addition, subtraction, multiplication, and division — exist, and the arithmetical laws must cover all four, giving answers to such questions as these: Can addition and subtraction be interchanged? Is division associative? Is subtraction commutative? Many such questions can be raised, and, seemingly, many laws should be required to answer them all. But algebra is a marvel of economy. By the use of reciprocals and negatives, division becomes multiplication, subtraction becomes addition, and the four operations of arithmetic are reduced conceptually to only two.

Reciprocals and rationals are probably a practical necessity, but negative numbers enter arithmetic almost purely because of their conceptual role in helping to simplify its laws. Perhaps this is why they were so slow to emerge, the very idea of negative numbers first appearing 2500 years later than the algebra in which they are of real use, and another millennium passing before their assimilation into mathematics was complete. (See Section 2h). In general, high school and college students today seem to be no more perceptive about negative numbers than the whole human race can claim to have been precocious. Therefore, it seems fitting to devote one section to an effort to clear the matter up.

We begin by pretending total ignorance of negatives. Thus, we are compelled to see how algebra works out when confined to positive numbers and zero. Differences will have their own laws, busy with cases that must be enumerated to avoid subtracting any number from a lesser. The idea of negative numbers will provide a means of escape from this proliferation of laws and commotion of cases. The rules for negative numbers will fall out in sequence as we develop this idea for the sole end of simplifying algebra to the utmost.

To avoid inessentials, we restrict our discussion to integers. For this reason, we use the word "number" here synonomously with "integer."

a. DEPOSITS, WITHDRAWALS, AND THE LAWS FOR SUBTRACTION

If algebra is restricted to positive numbers and zero, then, as we have indicated, the operation of subtraction must be considered by itself. Before attempting a mathematical treatment, we can gain insight into the pertinent laws by informal means, as follows.

Imagine a pile of pennies. Picture addition as the operation of putting pennies onto the pile, subtraction as the operation of taking some off. If the pile has a pennies and b are removed, the number remaining is $a-b$. Since giving back the b pennies that were removed would restore the pile to its original size, we are led to write

(1) $$(a - b) + b = a,$$

an algebraic cancellation rule. A sister rule,

(1') $$(a + b) - b = a,$$

is suggested by analogous considerations: if b pennies are added to a pile of a pennies, and, later, b pennies are removed from the pile, then a pennies will remain.

Other rules arise similarly. For instance, let us show in this way that

$$a - (b - c) = (a + c) - b$$

for any non-negative numbers a, b, c for which the several differences occurring also are non-negative. To be concrete, suppose the pile originally consists of 8 pennies. If we spend 5 of them, of course $8 - 5$ will remain. But if we can avoid spending 2 of the 5 pennies, parting with only $5 - 2$, the number of pennies remaining in the pile will be $8 - (5 - 2)$. We will be better off by 2 pennies than if we had expended the 5 we contemplated. We save the 2 pennies by curtailing expenditures. We would be in the same final position without shaving our expenditures, however, if we could earn 2 pennies to add to our original fund before spending the 5. Since the number of pennies that then remain could be calculated as $(8 + 2) - 5$, we see why

$$(8 + 2) - 5 = 8 - (5 - 2).$$

In exactly the same way, we can see how

$$(a + c) - b = a - (b - c),$$

as the rule states, where a, b, c, and the differences that occur are positive numbers or zero.

An equality that holds *for all values* of certain quantities is said to be *an identity* in these quantities. The three rules just discussed are all identities.

EXERCISES

Reason as before to justify the following six identities, assuming the differences to be non-negative.

1. $(a - b) + c = (a + c) - b$,
2. $a - (b + c) = (a - b) - c$,
3. $(a - b) + c = a + (c - b)$,
4. $(a - b) + (b - c) = a - c$,
5. $(a + b) - (b + c) = a - c$,
6. $(a - b) + (c - d) = (a + c) - (b + d)$.

7. If I have 10 dollars and owe six, my net worth is the same as if I had 12 dollars and owed eight. Which of the previous identities does this exemplify?

b. **BASIC LAWS OF ARITHMETIC FORMULATED BY MEANS OF NON-
    NEGATIVE NUMBERS ALONE. INEQUALITIES FOR NON-NEGATIVE
    NUMBERS.**

We have interpreted subtraction in terms of a concrete activity, "taking away," and in this way were able to suggest any number of relations. We have no basis, however, for proving such relations mathematically, since subtraction is really a numerical operation but has not been defined numerically. Our definition will appear in Subsection c.

Here, we specify the laws of arithmetic that will be used in our systematic discussion. These include the seven of Section 2a— commutative, associative, and distributive laws, as well as the rules for adding 0 and multiplying by 1—restricted to non-negative numbers.

Besides these, we shall apply the following law.

Ordering Law. If a and b are positive numbers or zero and $a \neq b$, then one and only one of the two conditions

$$x + b = a, \quad x + a = b$$

holds with a suitable positive number x. No positive number other than x satisfies this condition. (For instance, if $x + b = a$ and $y + b = a$, then $x = y$.) The condition $x + a = a$ holds for no value other than $x = 0$.

(If, in the eight assumptions made, the word "number" were to include rational numbers as well as integers, and if the Law of Reciprocals were adopted, our reasoning which follows would give us negative rationals as well as negative integers.)

The following cancellation rule is a trivial consequence of the Ordering Law, but will be referred to frequently.

Corollary. If x, y, a are non-negative numbers such that

$$x + a = y + a,$$

then

$$x = y.$$

PROOF: For any non-negative u, the Ordering Law permits at most one non-negative number v such that

$$v + a = u.$$

With the choice $u = x + a$, both x and y satisfy the previous relation and must therefore be equal, as stated.

The Ordering Law is the basis of this definition: a is *greater than* b if the condition $x + b = a$ is satisfied with positive x. If a is greater than b, we also say that b is *less than* a.

It is customary to write the relation "a is greater than b" symbolically as

$$a > b$$

and the relation "a is less than b" as

$$a < b.$$

The expression "a is greater than or equal to b" is written as

$$a \geq b$$

and the expression "a is less than or equal to b" as

$$a \leq b.$$

Under the new definitions, "positive" means "greater than zero," i.e., a number a is positive if and only if $a > 0$. In fact, let a denote any positive (rational) number. Since the condition

$$x + 0 = a$$

is satisfied by $x = a$, we immediately see that a is "greater than" zero in the sense of the previous definition, as asserted. Conversely, if a is greater than zero, then a is a "positive" number in the original sense. In fact, since a is greater than zero, a positive number x exists such that $x + 0 = a$. But $x + 0 = x$. Hence, a equals the positive number x; thus, a itself is positive, as asserted. The upshot of these remarks is that the two sentences "a is greater than zero" and "a is a positive number" are equivalent.

Notice that the sum of positive numbers is a positive number. This is a property of natural numbers hitherto assumed tacitly.

From the Ordering Law, we have immediately:

(a) Between any two non-negative numbers a and b subsists one, and only one, of these three relations:

$$a < b, \ a = b, \ a > b.$$

After a little argument, we shall also obtain the following propositions:

(b) If a, b, and c are non-negative numbers such that

$$a > b \text{ and } b > c,$$

then

$$a > c.$$

(This property of the relation $>$ is called transitivity. The relations $<$, $\leq$, $\geq$ are similarly transitive.)

(c) If a, b, c, d are non-negative numbers such that

$$a < b \text{ and } c < d,$$

then

$$a + c < b + d,$$

with similar results for $\leq$, $>$, or $\geq$ in place of $<$. In words: inequalities of like sense may be added.

(d) If a, b, c are non-negative numbers such that

$$a + c < b + c,$$

then

$$a < b,$$

with corresponding relations holding for $\leq$, $>$, $\geq$ in place of $<$.

PROOF OF (b): By assumption, positive numbers p and q exist such that $a = b + p$ and $b = c + q$. Therefore,

$$\begin{aligned} a &= b + p \\ &= (c + q) + p \\ &= c + (p + q), \end{aligned}$$

and

$$a > c,$$

since $p + q$ is positive.

PROOF OF (c): By assumption, positive numbers p and q exist such that, in this case,

$$b = a + p$$

and

$$d = c + q.$$

Since we can add equalities,

$$\begin{aligned} b + d &= (a + p) + (c + q) \\ &= (a + c) + (p + q), \end{aligned}$$

which tells us that

$$b + d > a + c,$$

as demanded, since $p + q$ is a positive number.

PROOF OF (d): By assumption, a positive number p exists such that

$$b + c = (a + c) + p$$
$$= (a + p) + c.$$

By the Corollary to the Ordering Theorem,

$$b = a + p.$$

Therefore, $b > a$, or $a < b$, as asserted.

EXERCISES

The quantities referred to are all assumed to be non-negative.
1. Prove that $a + u \geq a$.
2. If $a > b$, prove that $a + c > b$.

c. DIFFERENCES: DEFINITION AND LAWS

As we have noted, the chain of ideas that leads ultimately to negative numbers begins with the notion of difference. If a is equal to or greater than b, and both are positive numbers or zero, we define the *difference* $a - b$ as the number x that (according to the definition of "greater than") must be added to b to give a. Thus,

$$a - b = x,$$

where x is the single and only number that, according to our Ordering Law, satisfies the condition:

$$x + b = a.$$

(For example, the number x such that $x + 3 = 5$ is $x = 2$; hence, $5 - 3 = 2$.) *Subtracting* b from a is synonymous with forming the difference $a - b$.

Our definition of difference, formally reducing the concept of subtraction to that of addition, will enable us to apply the laws of addition to deduce other rules logically. Strictly arithmetical in nature, this definition thus will prove to be effective mathematically, while a description of subtraction in terms of a concrete activity, such as "taking away," is not.

The definition of difference says that if a, $b \geq 0$ and $a > b$, then

(1) $$(a - b) + b = a,$$

which is just the first cancellation law of Subsection a.

As an example of how to use this definition in a proof, let us demonstrate the second cancellation law

(1') $(a + b) - b = a,$

assuming $a \geq 0$ and $b \geq 0$. Set

$$x = (a + b) - b.$$

Because of (1) (definition of difference),

$$x + b = a + b,$$

and the Corollary to the Ordering Law now tell us that $x = a$, verifying (1').

As another example, let us prove

(2) $(a - b) + c = (a + c) - b,$

assuming a, b, c to be non-negative numbers such that $a \geq b$. For the right side to make sense, we must have

$$a + c \geq b,$$

which we establish as follows. Since $a \geq b$, a non-negative number p exists such that $a = b + p$. Then

$$a + c = (b + p) + c$$
$$= b + (p + c),$$

and, $p + c$ being non-negative, we have $a + c \geq b$, as required.

Now let L denote the left member of the presumed identity (2) and R the right. Thus,

$$L = (a - b) + c, \qquad R = (a + c) - b.$$

Our aim is to show that $L = R$. Since the Principle of Substitution permits us to add equal quantities to both members of any equation, from $R = (a + c) - b$ we deduce:

$$R + b = [(a + c) - b] + b.$$

By the definition of subtraction (1),

$$[(a + c) - b] + b = a + c.$$

Hence,

$$R + b = a + c.$$

We intend to show that $L + b$ is equal to the same quantity. By additive commutativity, $a - b$ being non-negative,

$$L = (a - b) + c$$
$$= c + (a - b).$$

Again by the Substitution Principle,

$$L + b = [c + (a - b)] + b,$$

while additive associativity shows that

$$[c + (a - b)] + b = c + [(a - b) + b].$$

However, $(a - b) + b = a$ by (1). Hence,

$$L + b = c + [(a - b) + b]$$
$$= c + a.$$

We thus have

$$L + b = c + a \quad \text{and} \quad R + b = a + c.$$

Additive commutativity showing that $c + a = a + c$, we conclude that

$$L + b = R + b,$$

and this implies that $L = R$ by the Corollary to the Ordering Law. Rule (2) is thus proved.

EXERCISES

1-6. Give mathematical proofs of Exercises 1-6 in Subsection a.

The previous identities give various ways to re-arrange subtractions. They are all special cases of a general re-arrangement law we now give, which will be very useful. This law pertains to differences of the form

$$(a + b) - (c + d).$$

Since we are restricted to non-negative numbers, of course, we assume

$$a + b \geq c + d.$$

This implies that either $a \geq c$ or $b \geq d$; otherwise, indeed,

$$a < c$$

and

$$b < d,$$

and by adding (Rule (c), Subsection b) we obtain

$$a + b < c + d,$$

contrary to hypothesis. We may, therefore, assume

$$a \geq c.$$

(In the contrary event, as we have just shown, $b \geq d$. If that case occurs, relabel the four numbers involved, letting a denote the larger of the two originally denominated a and b, and letting c denote the lesser of the two originally denominated c and d. After the relabeling, we will have $a \geq c$, as required.)

Now reasoning as in Subsection a leads us to surmise that:

(I) if $b \geq d$, then $(a + b) - (c + d) = (a - c) + (b - d)$,

while

(II) if $b < d$, then $a - c \geq d - b$ and $(a + b) - (c + d) = (a - c) - (d - b)$.

PROOF OF (I):   Setting $R = (a - c) + (b - d)$, we have $R \geq 0$ and

$$\begin{aligned}
R + c + d &= (a - c) + (b - d) + c + d \\
&= (a - c) + c + (b - d) + d \\
&= a + b,
\end{aligned}$$

any re-arrangements of non-negative numbers being permitted, and the first cancellation law (which is really just the definition of subtraction) being applied in the third step twice. From

$$R + (c + d) = a + b,$$

which we have just proved, the definition of difference tells us that

$$R = (a + b) - (c + d),$$

an equality equivalent to that stated in (I).

PROOF OF (II):   It is not immediately clear that

$$a - c \geq d - b,$$

as must be so for the equality we are proving to make sense. We obtain this condition from the assumed inequality

$$a + b \geq c + d$$

if we replace a by the expression $(a-c)+c$ and replace d analogously by $(d-b)+b$. The replacements are possible because of our suppositions that $a \geq c$ and $d > b$. Thus,

$$(a-c)+c+b \geq c+(d-b)+b.$$

Since the quantities in parentheses and also b and c are all non-negative, we may re-arrange them to obtain

$$(a-c)+(b+c) \geq (d-b)+(b+c).$$

Rule (d) for inequalities (Subsection c) applies, giving

$$a-c \geq d-b,$$

as required.

By the last paragraph, the expression

$$S=(a-c)-(d-b)$$

is non-negative. Hence we can carry out the following calculation, in which all quantities in parentheses or brackets, as well as a, b, c, d are non-negative and therefore may be re-arranged freely:

$$\begin{aligned} S+c+d &= [(a-c)-(d-b)]+c+d \\ &= [(a-c)-(d-b)]+(d-b)+b+c \\ &= (a-c)+c+b \\ &= a+b. \end{aligned}$$

Thus, $S+(c+d)=(a+b)$, and therefore

$$S=(a+b)-(c+d)$$

by the definition of difference. This is equivalent to the equality we were seeking.

The law just proved is illustrated in the following exercises.

EXERCISES

Use the re-arrangement law just proved to justify the following identities, assuming all differences occurring to be non-negative.

7. $(a+b)-c=(a-c)+b$. HINT: Take $d=0$ in the re-arrangement law.

8. $(a-b)-c=a-(b+c)$

9. $a-(d-b)=(a+b)-d$

10. $(a+b)-(b+d)=a-d$

11. $(a-b)+(b-c)=a-c$.

d. A BOOKKEEPING IDEA

If arithmetic is confined to positive numbers and zero, only "proper" differences, in which the number subtracted is not the greater of the two, can be allowed. Then, as we have seen, algebra is beset and afflicted by a swarm of small complexities. A bookkeeping idea provides the means of deliverance from this scourge.

Suppose the owner of a pile of pennies is permitted to incur debts. In that case, we shall call the pennies in the pile his "assets" and the pennies he may owe, his "liabilities." We measure his general financial condition by his "net worth":

$$\text{Net worth} = \text{assets minus liabilities.}$$

For instance, with assets of 50 and liabilities of 15, his net worth is 35. (All numbers are of pennies.) With assets of 50 and liabilities of 50, his net worth is 0. How shall we state the man's financial condition, however, when he has assets of 50 and liabilities of 60? We could abandon the term, "net worth," and say that he has a "net indebtedness" of 10. Alternatively, we could write 10 in red ink and say that his net worth is 10 "in the red." We shall do something like this, but with a star, or asterisk,† in place of red ink. Specifically, we shall say that the man with assets of 50 and liabilities of 60 has a net worth of 10* and shall write:

$$50 - 60 = 10*.$$

For analogous reasons, we also write

$$1 - 2 = 1*,$$
$$0 - 18 = 18*,$$
$$2 - 21 = 19*,$$

and so forth. Wherever assets a are less than liabilities b, net indebtedness being

(1a) $$b - a = d,$$

we shall say that the net worth is $d*$, and we shall write, accordingly,

(1b) $$a - b = d*.$$

The star here is merely a tag telling us that the difference on the left is improper; the number starred, d, is the value of the *proper* difference obtained by reversing the order of the terms. The symbol $d*$ in

---

† Prof. Donald E. Meyers urged me to use such a symbol.

itself is not defined arithmetically, equation (1b) stating merely that (1a) is true: (1b) thus amounts to just another way of writing (1a).

If a man with net worth 10✻ acquires new assets of 12, his new net worth will be 2, and we are led to write:

$$10✻ + 12 = 12 + 10✻ = 2.$$

Under the same interpretation, we also write

$$10✻ + 10 = 10 + 10✻ = 0,$$
$$9✻ + 22 = 22 + 9✻ = 13,$$

and so forth. More generally, if a man with net worth b✻ acquires new assets in the amount of a, and if a exceeds b, his new net worth will be $a - b$. We are thus led to write

$$b✻ + a = a + b✻ = a - b$$

and, doing so, to think of b✻ as a *kind of number* permitting arithmetic operations; the operation of *adding b✻*, in particular, is that of *subtracting b*.

It is not necessary in the previous considerations to require $a - b$ to be proper. For instance, suppose a man having net worth 10✻ aquires new assets of 7. His new net worth will be 3✻, and we write

$$7 + 10✻ = 10✻ + 7 = 3✻.$$

Similarly, if a man of net worth b✻ acquires new assets in the amount of a, and if a is less than b, then his new net worth will be $(b-a)$✻, which is $a - b$. Accordingly, we write

(2) $$a + b✻ = b✻ + a = a - b,$$

whether the difference $a - b$ is proper or not.

Conceiving of starred quantities as numbers capable of engaging in processes of arithmetic, we can ask for their laws. Before doing so, however, let us interpret addition of starred numbers upon a scale.

We can represent the system of starred and unstarred numbers on a scale quite like that described in Section 2g. On any straight line, select an origin, a positive direction, and a unit distance. For an arbitrary point P of the line, let d denote the distance between P and O, and here define the coordinate x of P to be

$$x = d \text{ if the direction from } O \text{ to } P \text{ is positive,}$$
$$= d✻ \text{ if the direction from } O \text{ to } P \text{ is negative.}$$

For convenience, we take the positive direction of the scale to the right and the negative direction to the left. If x and p are any

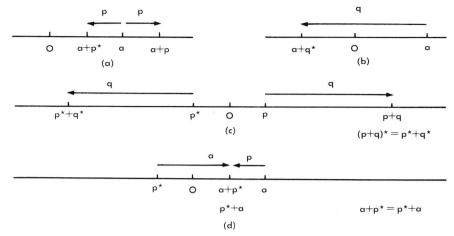

Figure 2-4 *Adding and subtracting on a scale.*

numbers with p positive, we interpret $x + p$ as the coordinate of the point that is p units to the right of x on the scale, and we interpret $x + p*$, or $x - p$, as the coordinate of the point that is p units to the left of x on the scale. Relation (2), in particular, thus immediately results (Figure 2-4). Under this interpretation (Figure 2-4C),

$$(3) \qquad\qquad p* + q* = (p + q)*.$$

Furthermore (Figure 2-4D),

$$x + q* = q* + x$$

and, in fact,

$$x + y = y + x$$

for all (starred and unstarred) numbers x and y. If P and Q are any points of the scale with positive coordinates p and q, respectively, and if Q is to the right of P, we see (Figure 2-5) that

$$(1a') \qquad\qquad q - p = d$$

is a positive number and that

$$(1b') \qquad\qquad p - q = p + q* = d*$$

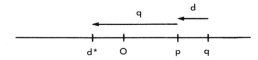

Figure 2-5 *Geometrical interpretation of an improper difference.*

This confirms equations (1a) and (1b) arising in our earlier financial interpretation of negative numbers.

Other interpretations of negative numbers than those given are possible: a negative increase is a decrease; a negative rise is a fall; a negative advance is a retreat; and so on.

EXERCISE

1. An emergency vehicle patrolling Route 1 was called during one morning's operations to six different locations. These locations, specified by their distances (in miles) north of the intersection with University Boulevard were as follows: 6*, 2, 18, 23, 17, 12. What are the distances traveled in the northward direction between consecutive stops of the emergency vehicle?

e. CONCEPTUAL REFORM OF ARITHMETIC

The preceding idea derived from accounting practice will deliver algebra from the irksome task of consistently excluding improper differences. We shall now explain how.

With each non-negative number a we associate a mathematical object we shall call the *negative* of a and denote it by $a*$. (Beyond this section, we revert to the traditional notation $-a$.) We shall not define $a*$ explicitly, but instead shall endow $a*$ with arithmetical properties suggested by the previous considerations. *These properties are the decisive factor in our program*, and a definition of $a*$ would serve only as a means of establishing them, being in itself an irrelevance.

Do you believe we are on solid ground logically in refusing to define a term? This question is taken up again in Chapter 12.

We define the negative of zero as zero:

$$0* = 0.$$

The first property we require of $a*$ is uniqueness: we shall consider two negative numbers, $a*$ and $b*$, to be equal, and shall write

$$a* = b*$$

if and only if

$$a = b.$$

If a and b are non-negative numbers and $a - b$ is a proper difference (i.e., $a > b$), then imitating (1a) and (1b) of the last subsection we define the *improper* difference $b - a$ to be

(1) $$b - a = (a - b)*.$$

Notice that
$$0 - a = a*.$$

If a and b are non-negative numbers, then following (2) of the preceding subsection we define:

(2) $a + b* = a - b.$

(The difference $a - b$ may be proper or not.) We also define:

(3) $b* + a = a + b*.$

As an illustration,

$a + (b* + c) = a + (c - b)$ if $c - b$ is a proper difference, while

$$\begin{aligned} a + (b* + c) &= a + (c - b) \\ &= a + (b - c)* \\ &= a - (b - c) \text{ if } c - b \text{ is an improper difference.} \end{aligned}$$

If $a - b$ is an improper difference, definition (1) gives us

(2′) $$\begin{aligned} a + b* &= a - b \\ &= (b - a)* \\ &= (b + a*)*. \end{aligned}$$

We have defined the sum of positive and negative and now define negative plus negative. If $a*$ and $b*$ are negative numbers, then following (3) of the previous subsection we define their sum as

(4) $a* + b* = (a + b)*.$

Definitions (2), (3), and (4) assign meaning to the sum of any two numbers, whether positive or negative, and whatever their order in the sum.

From these definitions, we see, in particular, that for any positive or zero numbers a and b,

$$a + b* = b* + a, \ a* + b* = b* + a*;$$

also (Section 2a),

$$a + b = b + a.$$

These relations can be compressed into a single statement: if x, y, and z represent any positive, negative, or zero numbers, then

$$x + y = y + x.$$

Thus, the additive commutative law holds in full generality.

This is a convenient place to consider how best to define the negative of a negative. Best for what? Our goal is simplicity in the ultimate laws of algebra. The ideal in simplicity is a set of laws that apply, without change in form, to negatives and positives alike. Rule (4) shows that the operation of applying $*$ is distributive, at least upon non-negative numbers. Thus, we should certainly further our aims by choosing a definition under which this operation was universally distributive, the relation

$$(5) \qquad\qquad (a+b)* = a* + b*$$

holding for negative as well as non-negative a and b. Under such a definition, relation $(2')$ would imply that

$$a + b* = (b + a*)*$$
$$= b* + (a*)*,$$

at least for non-negative a and b with $a - b$ improper. This condition suggests the following definition:

$$(6) \qquad\qquad (a*)* = a$$

for all non-negative a.

If we adopt this definition, condition (6) then holds for negative a as well as non-negative a. Indeed, if $a = p*$, where p is a positive number, we have $a* = p$ and, therefore, $(a*)* = p* = a$.

Under this definition, condition (5) is satisfied, as had been hoped. To prove this, we distinguish four cases, in which p and q denote arbitrary non-negative numbers.

Case 1: $a = p$, $b = q$. Rule (4) applies at once.
Case 2: $a = p*$, $b = q$. Here,

$$a + b = p* + q = q - p,$$
$$a* + b* = p + q* = p - q.$$

On the other hand, $p - q = (q - p)*$. This is true by definition if $p - q$ is improper; in the contrary case, we have $q - p = (p - q)*$, and applying $*$ to both sides gives the desired equality. In view of the two displayed equations, this equality implies (5).

Case 3: $a = p$, $b = q*$. This case is like the previous.
Case 4: $a = p*$, $b = q*$. Here,

$$a + b = p* + q* = (p + q)*,$$
$$a* + b* = p + q.$$

Thus, $a + b = (a* + b*)*$, and applying $*$ to both sides gives us (5). We conclude that (5) holds in all cases.

With the negative of a negative defined, we can generalize the notion of difference $a - b$ to include negative as well as positive (and zero) a and b: Indeed, we define

$$\text{(7)} \qquad\qquad a - b = a + b*$$

for all (positive, zero, negative) numbers a and b. Under this definition, we have

$$\text{(8)} \qquad\qquad a - b = (b - a)*$$

for all numbers a and b, positive, negative, and zero. In fact, property (8) is just a version of the distributive condition (5). Since (5) holds for any (positive, negative, zero) number, we may replace b in it by $b*$. Using (6), we obtain

$$(a + b*)* = a* + b$$

or, in view of (7),

$$(a - b)* = b - a.$$

Applying * to both sides now gives us (8).

The basic additive rules in which the operation of applying * appears are

$$a - b = a + b*,$$
$$(a + b)* = a* + b*,$$
$$(a*)* = a,$$

all as we have seen extending to negative numbers without changes in form. Our definition of the negative of a negative, therefore, has been totally successful.

Definition (6) has a striking interpretation on a scale. It means that the operation denoted by the star can be depicted as a flip,† the points on the positive side of the origin, when starred, changing to the negative, and the points on the negative side changing, when starred, to the positive, the origin alone not changing, and every point keeping the same distance from the origin as before.

f. ADDITIVE ASSOCIATIVITY

Will the additive associative law,

$$(a + b) + c = a + (b + c),$$

_____

† I am indebted to Prof. Donald E. Meyers for this vivid term.

like the commutative law, hold for all (positive, zero, negative) numbers? To find out, let a, b, c denote positive numbers or zero, and replace any one of them, any two of them, or all three of them, in the additive associative law by their negatives. According to the particular substitution (or substitutions) employed, the law takes one of the new shapes,

$$\text{(i) } (a + b) + c* = a + (b + c*),$$
$$\text{(ii) } (a + b*) + c = a + (b* + c),$$
$$\text{(iii) } (a* + b) + c = a* + (b + c),$$
$$\text{(iv) } (a + b*) + c* = a + (b* + c*),$$
$$\text{(v) } (a* + b) + c* = a* + (b + c*),$$
$$\text{(vi) } (a* + b*) + c = a* + (b* + c),$$
$$\text{(vii) } (a* + b*) + c* = a* + (b* + c*).$$

If all these are correct, then the additive associative law does hold for all (positive, negative, or zero) numbers.

All seven are in fact correct. The last is the easiest to prove.

PROOF OF (vii):   Applying twice rule (4) of the previous subsection gives us

$$(a* + b*) + c* = (a + b)* + c* = [(a + b) + c]*,$$

and, similarly,

$$a* + (b* + c*) = [a + (b + c)]*.$$

Thus, (vii) may be written as

$$[(a + b) + c]* = [a + (b + c)]*,$$

which, according to a previous assumption, is equivalent to

$$(a + b) + c = a + (b + c).$$

This is true, because a, b, c are non-negative numbers.

The remaining six laws are essentially special cases of the following re-arrangement rule, which we shall prove: for all non-negative numbers a, b, c, d,

$$(1) \qquad (a + b) + (c* + d*) = (a + c*) + (b + d*).$$

The re-arrangement rule is applied as follows.

PROOF OF (i):   Take $c = 0$ in (1) to obtain

$$(a + b) + d* = a + (b + d*).$$

If we now replace d by c, we obtain (i). (See the end of Section 1b.)

PROOF OF (iv): Take $b = 0$ in (1) to obtain

$$a + (c_* + d_*) = (a + c_*) + d_*.$$

Now replace c and d by b and c, respectively.

Equality (i) implies (ii) and (iii); equality (iv) implies (v) and (vi).

PROOF OF (iii): Reduce (iii) to (i) by interchanging a and c (i.e., by changing a to c and changing c to a).

PROOF OF (ii): In the following series of equalities, we apply just rule (i) and the general commutative rule previously established for all (positive, zero, negative) numbers:

$$\begin{aligned}
a + (b_* + c) &= a + (c + b_*) & \text{(commutative rule)} \\
&= (a + c) + b_* & \text{(rule (i))} \\
&= (c + a) + b_* & \text{(commutative rule)} \\
&= c + (a + b_*) & \text{(rule (i))} \\
&= (a + b_*) + c & \text{(commutative rule).}
\end{aligned}$$

The result is to prove (ii).

PROOF OF (vi): Reduce (vi) to (iv) by interchanging a and c.

PROOF OF (v): This proof is analogous to that of (ii). Here, we apply the general commutative rule and identity (iv) alternately.

In justifying the associative law for the positive and negative numbers equally, all that remains now is to demonstrate (1). Three cases must be considered:

(A) $a + b \geq c + d$, $a \geq c$;
(B) $a + b \geq c + d$, $b \geq d$;
(C) $a + b < c + d$.

Case (C) is the only possibility if neither (A) nor (B) occurs, for if $a < c$ and $b < d$, adding gives us $a + b < c + d$, the assumption made in Case (C).

In Case (A), a re-arrangement law proved in Subsection c gives us two alternatives:

if $b \geq d$, then $(a + b) - (c + d) = (a - c) + (b - d)$;
if $b < d$, then $(a + b) - (c + d) = (a - c) - (d - b)$.

Under our conventions, equation (1) correctly renders both alternatives.

Case (B) results from Case (A) simply by a change in notation. In Case (A), it was proved that if $a + b \geq c + d$ and $a \geq c$, then $(a + b) + (c_* + d_*) = (a + c_*) + (b + d_*)$. Let us say the same thing with a and b interchanged and also with c and d interchanged.

We obtain: if $b + a \geq d + c$ and $b \geq d$, then $(b + a) + (d* + c*) = (b + d*) + (a + c*)$. Because of the commutation rules, this is just what had to be proved in Case (B).

Case (C) results from Cases (A) and (B), which together tell us that if $a + b \geq c + d$, then $(a + b) + (c* + d*) = (a + c*) + (b + d*)$. In this statement, we interchange a and c and also interchange b and d, to have it read: if $c + d \geq a + b$, then $(c + d) + (a* + b*) = (c + a*) + (d + b*)$. Now applying * to both sides of the last equality and using the rules of the previous subsection gives (1), proving Case (C).

We conclude that (1) holds in all cases. Therefore, the general associative law is completely proved.

We can now generalize the Ordering Law of Subsection b as follows: if a and b are any (positive, negative, or zero) numbers, then a number x exists such that

$$x + b = a.$$

Only one such number exists, and it is given by

$$x = a - b.$$

PROOF: We have $(a - b) + b = (a + b*) + b = a + (b* + b) = a + 0 = a$. Hence, the condition $x + b = a$ is satisfied by $x = a - b$. On the other hand, if x denotes any number satisfying this condition, then by adding $b*$ to each side we obtain $(x + b) + b* = a + b*$, and thus $x = a + b*$, since $(x + b) + b* = x + (b + b*) = x + 0 = x$. Therefore, $a - b$ is the only number that satisfies the equation.

g.   NEGATIVE NUMBERS IN MULTIPLICATIVE PROCESSES

For non-negative numbers p, q, r such that $q - r$ is a proper difference (i.e., is non-negative), we see easily that

(1) $p(q - r) = pq - pr.$

Indeed, $q = r + (q - r)$, and both the last terms being non-negative, we have from the assumed distributive law for non-negatives,

$$pq = p[r + (q - r)]$$
$$= pr + p(q - r);$$

Adding $(pr)*$ to both sides gives us (1).

Figure 2-6 illustrates the rule just proved.

Our object now is to discover and adopt such conventions respecting multiplication by a negative number that we shall be able to arrive at this from the original distributive law,

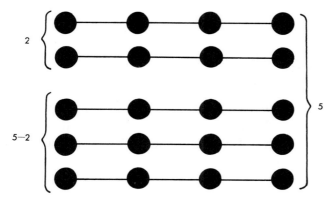

Figure 2-6 A bead figure illustrating that $4(5-2) = 4 \cdot 5 - 4 \cdot 2$.

$$a(b + c) = ab + ac,$$

by replacing a by p, b by q, and c by $r*$. Formal replacement gives us

(2) $$p(q + r*) = pq + pr*,$$

but this result will be meaningless until we have defined the product of a negative number and a positive number or zero. Our aim is to define this product in such a way that (2) will be equivalent to (1). We accomplish this aim by setting

(3) $$pr* = (pr)*;$$

at the same time, we also set

(3') $$r* \, p = pr*.$$

Under the first of these definitions, Rule (1) becomes equivalent to (2), as desired.

For any non-negative number a, we have $0a = 0$. (See Section 2d.) Hence, if we take $p = 0$ in (3), we have, in particular, that

(4') $$0 \cdot r* = 0.$$

Consequently,

(4) $$0 \cdot a = 0$$

for every number a, positive, negative, or zero.

The last result, or, rather, (4'), leads us to a final convention for negative numbers. From (4') and the fact that $p + p* = 0$ for any positive p, we have

$$0 = 0 \cdot r* = (p + p*)r*.$$

If we could apply the distributive law formally to this, we would have

$$0 = pr* + p* \, r*,$$

a result that is, however, without meaning, because the product of two negative numbers has not as yet been defined. The result acquires correct meaning if we adopt the following definition:

(5) $$p* \, r* = pr.$$

Furthermore, multiplication under the new definitions (3), (4), (5) is universally distributive: for all (positive, zero, negative) numbers $a, b, c,$

(6) $$[a(b + c)] = ab + ac.$$

To prove this, we distinguish four cases:

Case 1: $a = 0$. This case is trivial.

Case 2: a negative, $b + c$ non-negative. Equation (6) is completely equivalent to any form of the equation obtained by applying $*$ to both sides. Performing this operation transforms the left side into

$$[a(b + c)]* = a*(b + c)$$

and transforms the right side into

$$(ab + ac)* = (ab)* + (ac)* = a* \, b + a* \, c.$$

Thus equation (6) is equivalent to the following:

(6′) $$a*(b + c) = a* \, b + a* \, c.$$

If b and c are individually non-negative ($a*$ is positive), (6′) is true by the distributive law for non-negative quantities. If b or c is negative, then $b + c$ must be a proper difference (since $b + c$ is assumed to be non-negative), and rule (1) applies. In either case, (6′) is justified and, therefore, also (6).

Case 3: a positive, $b + c$ negative. From the new definitions, (6) is equivalent to

(7) $$a*(b* + c*) = a* \, b* + a* \, c*,$$

and Case 2 applies to this.

Case 4: a negative, $b + c$ negative. Again we write (6) in the equivalent form (7). This time, Case 1 applies to (7).

EXERCISE

1. Prove that for any (positive, negative, zero) numbers a, b, c, d,
$$(a - b)(c - d) = ac - ad - bc + ad.$$

h. SUMMARY

Arithmetic confined to non-negative numbers and proper differences serves household purposes well enough, but its too numerous laws are broken out with provisos concerning vexatious little cases that always have to be distinguished. Algebra, growing out of these laws, is subject to their diseases, but a miracle prescription suggested by a clerk in an accounting office effects a complete cure. By incorporating negatives into the number system, it becomes possible both to absorb the rules for differences into those for sums and also to eliminate the old provisos, which drop off like scabs once improper differences can be permitted. The general laws of arithmetic take a trim and elegant form that is of incalculable advantage in the further development of mathematics.

5.

Inequalities

With the whole system of positive and negative numbers at our disposal, we can now discuss fairly simply the arithmetical properties that pertain to comparisons of magnitude. (This treatment is independent of that of Section 4.) We shall first state and illustrate the arithmetical properties concerned. Then we shall see how they may be developed rationally from the algebraic properties of positive and negative numbers.

The statement that one quantity *a is less than* a second quantity *b* is written symbolically as $a < b$. The equivalent statement that *b is greater than a* is written $b > a$. If we mean to say that *a is less than or equal to b*, we write $a \le b$, and if that *b is greater than or equal to a*, $b \ge a$. When non-negative quantities are being compared, mathematical usage of "less than" and "greater than" agrees with ordinary usage. Thus, for instance, we write

$$1 < 2, \ 0 < 1/2, \ 9 > 6.$$

When negative numbers enter, the technical and the common meanings of these terms may, however, conflict. Thus, it is necessary to state that we shall conform strictly to the following usage of "<" ("less than") and ">" ("greater than"), which is that universally adopted by mathematicians: Of *any* two numbers a and b, we shall say that

$$a < b$$

if, on a scale, a is reached by traveling in a *negative* direction from b (or, which is the same, that b is attained by going in a positive direction from a). (See Figure 2-7.) Thus, $-2 < -1$, $-1 < 0$, $-2 < 1$. The statement "$b > a$" is regarded as equivalent to "$a < b$."

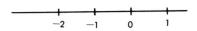

Figure 2-7   *Some numbers on a scale.*

The main rules for inequalities are these:

(a) For any two numbers a and b, one and only one of the following statements is true: $a = b$, $a < b$, $b < a$.

(b) If

$$a < b,$$

and if also

$$b < c,$$

then

$$a < c.$$

This property of the $<$ relation is called *transitivity*.

(c) If

$$a < b,$$

then

$$a + c < b + c:$$

letting $c = -d$, we also have

$$a - d < b - d.$$

(d) If

$$a < b$$

and if c is positive, i.e., $c > 0$, then

$$ac < bc.$$

(e) If

$$a < b,$$

then

$$-a > -b;$$

changing signs switches the direction of an inequality.
(f) If $a > 0$, $b > 0$, and $a < b$,

$$1/a > 1/b.$$

Other rules can be derived from these. *Example*: If $a < b$ and if $d < 0$ (d negative), then, by (e) $-d > -0$ (and therefore $-d > 0$), and, by (d), $-ad < -bd$; using (e) again gives $ad > bd$. Multiplying an inequality by any negative number changes its direction.

Rules for $\leq$ can be derived from rules for $<$ by considering the appropriate cases. As an example, we prove the statement corresponding to (c): If $a \leq b$, then $a + c \leq b + c$.

Case 1: if $a < b$, then by (b), $a + c < b + c$ and therefore
$$a + c \leq b + c.$$

Case 2: if $a = b$, then $a + c = b + c$, and therefore $a + c \leq b + c$.

When $a < b$ and $b < c$, we often write

$$a < b < c,$$

combining the two inequalities, and similarly for $\leq$, $>$, and $\geq$ in place of $<$.

It is sometimes convenient to transform a given inequality such as

(1) $$ax + b < c,$$

which (if $a \neq 0$) is called a linear inequality in x, into an equivalent inequality that has one letter, such as x, appearing alone on one side. The process is called solving the inequality for x. From (c), we have $ax + b - b < c - b$, which simplifies to

(2) $$ax < c - b.$$

If $a > 0$, then, by (d), (2) implies $(1/a)ax < (1/a)(c - b)$, which simplifies to

(3) $$x < (c - b)/a.$$

If $a < 0$, then (2) implies

(3') $$x > (c - b)/a.$$

Furthermore, (3) (or (3')) implies (2), which, by (c), implies (1). Therefore (3) (or (3')) is equivalent to (1).

EXERCISES

In these exercises, properties (a) to (e) are to be assumed as premises. (They will be justified logically later.)

1. Using (b), prove: if $a < b$ and $b \leq c$, then $a < c$.
2. Using (b) and Exercise 1, prove: if $a \leq b$ and $b \leq c$, then $a \leq c$.
3. Prove the statement for $\leq$ corresponding to (d).
4. Prove the statement for $\leq$ corresponding to (e).
5. Using (b) and (c), prove: If $a < b$ and $c < d$, then $a + c < b + d$.
6. Using (a), (d), and (e) prove: If $a \neq 0$, then $a^2 > 0$. Hence, if $a^2 = 0$ then $a = 0$.
7. Using (a), (b), (d), and (e), prove: If $a > 0$ and $a < b$, then $\sqrt{a} < \sqrt{b}$. HINT: Use the algebraic identity

$$a - b = (\sqrt{a} - \sqrt{b})(\sqrt{a} + \sqrt{b}).$$

8. Using Exercise 1 and (c) prove: If $a < b$ and $c \leq d$, then $a + c < b + d$.
9. Solve for x: $12 - x < 4x + 2$.
10. Solve for v: $2b \geq 3v$.
11. Deduce (f) from (d). HINT: Take $c = 1/(ab)$.

Let us now give arithmetical definitions of "less than" and "greater than" and indicate how they lead rigorously to the foregoing rules. Facts of elementary algebra enter, including, in particular, these properties of positive and negative numbers:

(i) If x and y are two unequal numbers, then the difference $x - y$ is either positive or negative, but not both positive and also negative.
(ii) The sum of positive numbers is positive.
(iii) The product of positive numbers is positive.
(iv) If x is negative, then $-x$ is positive; hence, in particular, if $x - y$ is negative, then $y - x$ is positive.

Referring to Property (i), we now define the symbols $<$ and $>$ ("less than" and "greater than," respectively) as follows:

Definitions.   By

$$x > y$$

or

$$y < x,$$

we mean the statement that $x - y$ is positive. (When $x - y$ is negative, in which case $y - x$ is positive [Property (iv)], we thus have $x < y$ and $y > x$.)

Property (a) follows immediately from these definitions and Property (i). Property (b) is proved as follows. The assumptions that

$a < b$ and $b < c$ mean that $b - a$ and $c - b$ are positive. Since

$$c - a = (c - b) + (b - a),$$

$c - a$ thus is the sum of positive quantities and by Property (ii) is positive.

The other rules stated for inequalities appear among the following exercises.

EXERCISES

Prove the following statements:

12. Under the definitions just given, $x > 0$ if and only if x is positive in the original sense.

13. If $a < 0$, then $0 < -a$.

14. Property (c) is correct under the new definitions.

15. Property (d) is correct under the new definitions.

16. Property (e) is correct under the new definitions.

17. If $c < 0$ and $a < b$, then $bc < ac$.

18. If $a < b$ and $c > 0$, then $a/c < b/c$, but if $c < 0$, then $a/c > b/c$.

19. If $0 < a < 1/3$, prove that

$$0 < 1/(1 - a) < 3/2.$$

20. If $|a| < 1$, then

$$1/(1 + |a|) \leq 1/(1 + a) \leq 1/(1 - |a|).$$

21. If $|a| < b < 1$, then

$$1/(1 + b) < 1/(1 - a) < 1/(1 - b).$$

HINT: In case $a > 0$, in which case

$$0 < a < b,$$

prove, in particular, that

$$1/(1 - a) < 1/(1 - b)$$

as follows. Since $a < b$, we have

$$-a > -b \quad \text{(rule (e))};$$

hence

(i) $\qquad\qquad 1 - a > 1 - b \quad \text{(rule (c))}.$

Since $1 - b > 0$ by assumption, we have

$$1 - a > 0 \quad \text{(rule (b))}.$$

Now rule (f) applies to (i), showing that

$$1/(1 - a) < 1/(1 - b),$$

as asserted.

22. If $p > 0$, then $a + p > a$.

23. If $a < b$ and $u \leq v$, then $a + u < b + v$. HINT: Writing $b + v = b + u + (v - u)$, apply the previous exercise and rule (c).

Comparisons between numbers provide a pattern for analogous comparisons between other kinds of things. We shall give several illustrations.

Example 1:   Let A, B, C, and so forth refer to alternative ways of spending an evening, for instance, at home alone, at home with company, at the theater alone, and so forth. If an individual enjoys way A not less than way B, we shall record his preference in the shorthand notation:

$$A \succ B.$$

For the relation $\succ$ thus defined, these laws seem reasonable:

(a) Either $A \succ B$ or $B \succ A$ (and both relations may hold).

(b) $A \succ A$.

(c) If $A \succ B$ and $B \succ C$, then $A \succ C$. (This is a transitive law.)

In satisfying these laws, $\succ$ shows an analogy to $\geq$.

Example 2: A sociologist studying evening practices and inclinations in a community collects detailed information on individual preferences. From these data pertaining to individuals, he hopes to be able to generalize about the preferences of the community as a whole. If, for instance, a majority of the community prefer A to B, he will say that $A \succ B$ *for the community as a whole.* He intends ultimately to obtain such a statement for every pair of ways to spend an evening, and he wishes it were then possible to arrange all these ways in a list in the order in which the community prefers them. But he knows that, in general, such a list does not exist. The following example shows why. Suppose that just three kinds of evening activities, which we denote by A, B, and C, are being compared and that the community consists of five people, who report their individual preferences as follows:

First and second persons: $A \succ B \succ C$.
(This means that $A \succ B$, $B \succ C$, and $A \succ C$.)

Third person:	$C \succ A \succ B.$	
Fourth person:	$C \succ B \succ A.$	
Fifth person:	$B \succ C \succ A.$	

To obtain majority preferences, we tabulate the results in Table 2-1.

Table 2-1   A table of group preferences

$\succ$	A	B	C
A		3	2
B	2		3
C	3	2	

The first (horizontal) row indicates that for three persons $A \succ B$ and for two $A \succ C$; the second and third rows have analogous meanings. This table shows

$$A \succ B$$

to be a majority preference, since three persons express this individual preference and only two persons the opposite. This table also shows that

$$B \succ C$$

and

$$C \succ A$$

are majority preferences. Obviously, these majority preferences fail to obey the transitive law. Hence, it is impossible to rank A, B, and C in the order of their popularity.[†]

[†] This subject is further developed in *Prelude to Analysis* by P. C. Rosenbloom and S. Schuster, Englewood Cliffs, N. J., Prentice-Hall, 1966.

EXERCISE

24. Find other patterns of individual preferences that also lead to a nullification of the transitive law in Example 2. HINT: Let a denote the number of persons expressing the first set of individual preferences ($A \succ B \succ C$), b the number expressing the second set of preferences, and so forth.

REFERENCES

School Mathematics Study Group (SMSG), *First Course in Algebra*, New Haven, Yale University Press, 1961.
School Mathematics Study Group (SMSG), *Introduction to Algebra*, New Haven, Yale University Press, 1961.

CHAPTER 3

COUNTING AND THE WRITING OF NUMBERS

The pursuit of agriculture probably early occasioned a need to count; the operations of royal court and temple, a need to record numbers. Primitive methods, by which objects such as sheep or sheaves to be counted were matched one to one with fingers and toes, with pebbles placed in a basket, with identical marks on a clay tablet, or with other standard objects, doubtless endured for ages. By the end of the fourth millenium before Christ, in Mesopotamia and Egypt, transactions of royal court and temple may have demanded better means to count and record. Writing, including the efficient writing of numbers, was first invented, in any case, in the kingly or priestly warehouses in Sumer (about 3100 B.C.) and Egypt (about 3000 B.C.), and the earliest documents in either region are lists of commodities and amounts in what appear to be records of inventories, disbursements, and deliveries. The Egyptians had hit on a scheme for writing numbers applied later in Roman numerals. The Sumerians, with greater insight, had come upon the idea for writing numbers that, transmitted with improvements by the Babylonian, Hindu, and Arabic peoples, still underlies our system today. The Sumerians thus opened, and largely resolved, what may have been the world's first significant mathematical problem.

To appreciate this problem, we first consider briefly what numbers are. First, the *natural numbers* are the members of the unending sequence 1, 2, 3, . . ., each member being obtained from the previous by the addition of 1. (Three dots, ". . .," frequently will be used to mean "and so forth, as indicated.") The *non-negative* integers consist of the natural numbers and zero; but in this chapter, where there is no danger of confusion, the non-negative integers generally will be referred to simply as numbers. By *consecutive* numbers we shall mean two numbers, such as might be denoted by n and $n + 1$, that differ by 1.

It is sometimes useful to picture the integers as a succession of equally-spaced points on a scale (Chapter 2, Section 2g), any individual (non-negative) integer, which we may denote by the letter n, corresponding to the point at n times the unit distance (in the positive direction) from the origin. In Figure 3-1, the first few such points of a scale are marked with the corresponding integers.

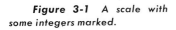

Figure 3-1   A scale with some integers marked.

Much more might be said about the nature, or definition, of numbers, but no such discussion would tell us how to *name* (twenty-four, two dozen, one score and four) or *write* (24, XXIV) them efficiently. A symbol for a number is called its *numeral*. The mathematical problem alluded to in the first paragraph is that of constructing numerals for all the numbers, using only a fixed, finite stock of original symbols. The solution discovered by the Sumerians, and perfected by the Babylonians and Hindus, lay in what we call the "place-value" principle, now universally familiar from its incorporation into the Hindu-Arabic numerals on which modern counting and calculation are based. We shall describe this idea, although in modern terms and with more consistency than was attained by ancient peoples.

1.

Three examples of place-value systems

The rules for counting and calculating by means of a place-value principle are ingrained in us from our use of the Hindu-Arabic numerals, which embody them. We tend, however, to be unconscious of the logic behind the rules. We shall later in this chapter expound this logic and then apply it to other problems, but we begin by illustrating the idea with place-value systems in bases two and three, the so-called binary and ternary systems, respectively.

In the ternary system, in particular, all numerals are built up out of three symbols representing zero, one, and two. These three original symbols may be of any kind, and we deliberately make choices here that are unfamiliar: for zero, an inverted bowl,

$$\cap,$$

for one, one stick,

$$\setminus,$$

and for two, two sticks, joined at an angle,

$$<.$$

These three symbols we shall call the *digits* of this scheme, although by the term "digit" we also may mean, ambiguously, the number the digit denotes, the context being depended upon to avoid confusion.

The process of building numerals out of the digits is accompanied by certain considerations in which the base, three, repeatedly occurs. Desiring to stress these considerations, we have chosen to denote the base, too, by a special symbol, the lower case letter t. Thus, t equals three. We emphasize that the symbol t, not being a digit, is not a numeral of the present system, but stands outside it. The same is true of expressions like $t + \setminus$ (three plus one, or four), $< \cdot t$ (two times three, or six), t^2 (three squared, or nine), t^3 (three cubed, or twenty-seven). (The reader may prefer using the new symbols as exponents, too; he is at liberty to do so.) Since these expressions represent definite numbers, we shall generally refer to them as numbers, reserving the term "numeral" exclusively for the numerals of our system.

To represent t (i.e., three) by means of digits, the idea of the place-value principle is to use *two* digits or, so to speak, a numeral with two "places" for digits instead of one. Specifically, t is written as

$$\setminus\cap,$$

with a one and a zero.

The next number $t + \setminus$ (equal to four), receives the numeral

$$\setminus\setminus,$$

and the number $t + <$ (five), the numeral

$$\setminus<.$$

The numeral for $t + t = < \cdot t$ (six) is obtained by bringing the first digit (on the *right*) back to zero and adding one to the second digit with the result

$$< \cap.$$

The numeral for $< \cdot t + \setminus$ (seven) is

$$< \setminus,$$

and that for $< \cdot t + <$ (eight),

$$< <.$$

The last-named is the highest two-place numeral.

Before going on, let us note that the digits, which properly are one-place numerals, also can be regarded as two-place numerals. As such, they would be written as

$$\cap \cap$$
$$\cap \setminus$$
$$\cap <$$

with zero in each case occupying the second place from the right. Under this convention, all the numbers from zero to eight, inclusive, are two-place numerals.

We display them concisely in Table 3-1.

Table 3-1 Two-place numerals to base three ($t =$ three)

$\cap \cap$	$\cap \setminus$	$\cap <$
$\cap \cdot t + \cap$	$\cap \cdot t + \setminus$	$\cap \cdot t + <$
(zero)	(one)	(two)
$\setminus \cap$	$\setminus \setminus$	$\setminus <$
$\setminus \cdot t + \cap$	$\setminus \cdot t + \setminus$	$\setminus \cdot t + <$
(three)	(four)	(five)
$< \cap$	$< \setminus$	$< <$
$< \cdot t + \cap$	$< \cdot t + \setminus$	$< \cdot t + <$
(six)	(seven)	(eight)

The number each numeral represents has been described in terms of t beneath the numeral, and, enclosed in parentheses, also in ordinary English. We see from the table that each number from zero to eight, inclusive, has one and only one numeral (in base three) and that the numeral is of the form

$$ba,$$

where a and b are digits (i.e., $a = \cap$, $\setminus$, or $<$ and $b = \cap$, $\setminus$ or $<$). The digits are such that, in every case,†

$$ba = b \cdot t + a.$$

---

†All multiplications throughout this chapter will be indicated with a dot, expressions like ba being interpreted as numerals in the sense explained.

After $< \cdot t + <$ (eight) comes $< \cdot t + t = (< + \backslash) \cdot t = t \cdot t = t^2$ (nine). Since the two-place numerals are exhausted, the place-value principle dictates that the three-place numeral

$$\backslash \cap \cap$$

be assigned to this number. We shall exhibit in two successive tables this and the subsequent three-place numerals, again indicating the number to which the numeral refers. This number, as before, is given underneath the numeral both as an expression in t and in ordinary English.

The lower numerals, those listed in Table 3-1, may be prefixed with zero ($\backslash <$, for instance, thus becoming $\cap \backslash <$) and then also regarded as three-place numerals. Under this convention each number from $\cap$ to $t^3 - \backslash$ (twenty-six), inclusive, has one and only one numeral (in base three) of the form

$$cba,$$

where a, b, and c are digits. These digits are such that

$$cba = c \cdot t^2 + b \cdot t + a.$$

The next number after the highest so far considered is t^3 (twenty-seven). To it, since the three-place numerals now are exhausted, we assign the first four-place numeral

$$\backslash \cap \cap \cap.$$

Then we continue as before, four-place numerals sufficing to represent the numbers less than t^4 (eighty-one). Each such number is assigned the unique numeral

$$dcba$$

Table 3-2 *Numerals in base three for the numbers from t^2 (nine) to $t^2 + < \cdot t + < = < \cdot t^2 - \backslash$ (seventeen) ($t =$ three; $\cap =$ zero, $\backslash =$ one, $< =$ two)*

$\backslash \cap \cap$	$\backslash \cap \backslash$	$\backslash \cap <$
$\backslash \cdot t^2 + \cap \cdot t + \cap$	$\backslash \cdot t^2 + \cap \cdot t + \backslash$	$\backslash \cdot t^2 + \cap \cdot t + <$
(nine)	(ten)	(eleven)
$\backslash \backslash \cap$	$\backslash \backslash \backslash$	$\backslash \backslash <$
$\backslash \cdot t^2 + \backslash \cdot t + \cap$	$\backslash \cdot t^2 + \backslash \cdot t + \backslash$	$\backslash \cdot t^2 + \backslash \cdot t + <$
(twelve)	(thirteen)	(fourteen)
$\backslash < \cap$	$\backslash < \backslash$	$\backslash < <$
$\backslash \cdot t^2 + < \cdot t + \cap$	$\backslash \cdot t^2 + < \cdot t + \backslash$	$\backslash \cdot t^2 + < \cdot t + <$
(fifteen)	(sixteen)	(seventeen)

Table 3-3 *Numerals in base three for the numbers from $< \cdot t^2$ (eighteen) to $< \cdot t^2 + < \cdot t + <\, = t^3 - \setminus$ (twenty-six) (t = three; $\cap$ = zero, $\setminus$ = one, $<$ = two)*

$< \cap \cap$	$< \cap \setminus$	$< \cap <$
$< \cdot t^2 + \cap \cdot t + \cap$	$< \cdot t^2 + \cap \cdot t + \setminus$	$< \cdot t^2 + \cap \cdot t + <$
(eighteen)	(nineteen)	(twenty)
$< \setminus \cap$	$< \setminus \setminus$	$< \setminus <$
$< \cdot t^2 + \setminus \cdot t + \cap$	$< \cdot t^2 + \setminus \cdot t + \setminus$	$< \cdot t^2 + \setminus \cdot t + <$
(twenty-one)	(twenty-two)	(twenty-three)
$< < \cap$	$< < \setminus$	$< < <$
$< \cdot t^2 + < \cdot t + \cap$	$< \cdot t^2 + < \cdot t + \setminus$	$< \cdot t^2 + < \cdot t + <$
(twenty-four)	(twenty-five)	(twenty-six)

with such digits a, b, c, and d that

$$d \cdot t^3 + c \cdot t^2 + b \cdot t + a$$

is equal to the number.

How far can this process be continued? Does it enable us to assign a ternary numeral to any number? For a number N less than eighty-one (which is t^4), for example, this question is equivalent to the two following questions:

(1) Do digits, a, b, c, d, exist such that

$$N = a + b \cdot t + c \cdot t^2 + d \cdot t^3?$$

(2) Are these digits unique? In other words, is it impossible to represent the same number N as

$$N = a' + b' \cdot t + c' \cdot t^2 + d' \cdot t^3$$

with a new set of digits, a', b', c', d', some of which differ from the corresponding digits in the original set?

If these questions have affirmative answers, and only in this case, can the listing

$$dcba$$

serve as a numeral for n.

We can give affirmative replies to these two questions by the same enumerative process used in Tables 3-1 to 3-3 for the numbers less than twenty-seven. What then, however, of eighty-one and larger? A number M less than a thousand (which is less than t^7), for instance, has a ternary numeral

$$gfedcba$$

if and only if the following two conditions are satisfied:

(1) $M = a + b \cdot t + c \cdot t^2 + d \cdot t^3 + e \cdot t^4 + f \cdot t^5 + g \cdot t^6$, a, b, c, d, e, f, g being digits.

(2) These digits are unique.

We might verify these conditions by number-by-number enumeration, as before, but larger numbers yet would present themselves, and enumeration is endless. May not the abstract logic of our numeration system enable us to prove its applicability to all numbers, universally, in one argument? We shall answer this question presently. First, we shall see how the same principles manifest themselves in other systems.

EXERCISES

1. Without consulting tables, find the base three numerals for eight, seventeen, twenty-seven, forty, fifty-nine, seventy-two, ninety-seven. HINT: Suppose we wished to find the numeral for sixty-five. One way would be to list the base three numerals in sequence, starting with 1 and continuing until reaching the numeral for sixty-five. A simpler method is suggested by the solution to the following problem: Suppose you wished to purchase sixty-five ice cream cups which were packaged singly and in packages of three, nine, twenty-seven, and so forth, each larger package consisting of three packages of the next smaller size. In this setting it is easily seen that no packages of eighty-one (t^4) are wanted, while $<$ (two) packages of twenty-seven (t^3) should be picked up, leaving eleven, which is $\setminus$ (one) package of nine (t^2), $\cap$ (zero) packages of three (t) and $<$ (two) singles. With this picture in mind, we now explain the solution in purely arithmetic terms. The base three numeral for a number represents the number as a sum of powers of t; therefore, we first determine the largest power of t that is still less than the number. Since sixty-five is more than $t^3 =$ twenty-seven and less than $t^4 =$ eighty-one, it will be represented by a numeral of the form

$$dcba = d \cdot t^3 + c \cdot t^2 + b \cdot t + a.$$

Since $< \cdot t^3 =$ fifty-four is less than sixty-five, we can let $d = <$ reducing our problem to finding $c, b,$ and a such that

$$< \cdot t^3 + c \cdot t^2 + b \cdot t + a = \text{sixty-five},$$

i.e., such that

$$c \cdot t^2 + b \cdot t + a = \text{eleven}.$$

Since $< \cdot t^2 =$ eighteen is greater than eleven, c cannot be $<$. Letting

$$c = \setminus$$

reduces the problem to $b \cdot t + a = $ two. Since $\backslash \cdot t = $ three is greater than two, we must have

$$b = \cap,$$

which makes

$$a = <.$$

Therefore sixty-five is represented in base three by the numeral

$$< \ \backslash \ \cap \ <.$$

   2. (a) Make an addition table for digits.
      (b) Carry out the following additions:

$$\begin{array}{ccc}
\backslash\ < & <\ <\ < & <\ \cap\ <\ \backslash \\
\underline{\backslash\ \backslash} & \underline{\phantom{<\ <\ }\backslash} & \underline{\backslash\ \backslash\ \cap\ <}
\end{array}$$

Check your answers.

   3. (a) Make a multiplication table for digits.
      (b) How is multiplication by t carried out? How by t^2?
      (c) Work out the following multiplications:

$$\begin{array}{ccc}
\backslash\ < & \backslash\ < & \backslash\ \cap\ <\ \backslash \\
\underline{\ <} & \underline{\backslash\ <} & \underline{<\ \cap\ \backslash}
\end{array}$$

Check your answers.

We used unfamiliar symbols for zero, one, and two to drive home the arbitrariness of symbols, and, like new clothes, to arouse fresh perceptions in the beholder. Made-up symbols are inconvenient to maintain, however; and in the future we shall use instead the Hindu-Arabic numerals, 0, 1, 2, and so forth, on which we were brought up. Thus, in the foregoing we replace $\cap$ by 0, $\backslash$ by 1, and $<$ by 2, for instance writing $< <$ (eight) as 22. In doing so we must of course be quite clear as to the base, which in this case is three. Often the base is displayed as a subscript to the numeral itself, 22_3, for instance, being written instead of 22 when the base is three.

As a second illustration of the place-value principle, we select the system with base two. Numerals in this system are all built out of two symbols,

$$0$$

and

$$1,$$

which are the "digits" here. The base is denoted by d: d equals two. The numeral for d (i.e., for two) in base two is

$$10.$$

(We might have written 10_2, but omitted the subscript because we had clearly indicated the base in the text.) The numeral for three is

$$11.$$

No more two-place numerals exist, and the next, for four, is

$$100.$$

Numerals in base two for all the numbers from zero to seven are listed in Table 3-4.

Table 3-4   *Numerals in base two for the numbers from zero to seven*

0	1
(zero)	(one)
10	11
$1 \cdot d + 0$	$1 \cdot d + 1$
(two)	(three)

100	101	110	111
$1 \cdot d^2 + 0 \cdot d + 0$	$1 \cdot d^2 + 0 \cdot d + 1$	$1 \cdot d^2 + 1 \cdot d + 0$	$1 \cdot d^2 + 1 \cdot d + 1$
(four)	(five)	(six)	(seven)

We see that each number from zero to seven, inclusive, has one and only one numeral in base two, this numeral being of the form

$$cba,$$

where a, b, and c are digits (i.e., $a = 0$ or 1, $b = 0$ or 1, $c = 0$ or 1) such that, in every case,

$$cba = c \cdot d^2 + b \cdot d + a.$$

EXERCISES

4. Write the following numbers in base two: eight, sixteen, thirty-two, thirty-three, forty, sixty-three.

5. Give the English names for the numbers represented in base two by the numerals 1010, 1110, 101010, 11000.

6. Carry out the following additions, all numerals being in base two:

1	1111	1011010011
1	1	10111011

7. Let *pqrs* denote any four-place numeral in base two. Express this numeral in terms of *d*.

8. (a) For numerals in base two, how is multiplication by *d* performed? How by d^2?

(b) Work out the following multiplications, all numerals being in base two:

101	1011	1011
11	101	1001

9. Write the numbers from one to fifteen in binary numerals.

10. Consider the following array of numbers (indicated in decimal notation):

1,	3,	5,	7,	9,	11,	13,	15
2,	3,	6,	7,	10,	11,	14,	15
4,	5,	6,	7,	12,	13,	14,	15
8,	9,	10,	11,	12,	13,	14,	15

Selecting any number from 1 to 15, inclusive, mark each (horizontal) row in which the number appears. The sum of the *first* numbers of the marked rows then is equal to the selected number. For instance, 11 appears in the first row, the first number of which is 1, in the second row with the first number 2, and in the fourth row with the first number 8, and $11 = 1 + 2 + 8$.

Can you see how to extend the rows to cover all the numbers from 0 to 31 or from 0 to 63? HINT: Connect the rows shown with the results found in Exercise 9.

11. The following problem is lengthy, but some readers may find it worthwhile: A code is set up using sixteen different symbols, different combinations of these symbols signifying different words in the code.† The symbols are binary numerals representing the integers from zero to fifteen, inclusive, and thus consist of strings

$$x_1 x_2 x_3 x_4$$

of four binary digits (which may be either 0 or 1). But errors in transmission may occur, and it is deemed important to be able to find them and correct them. For this purpose, R. W. Hamming has devised a scheme in which three new binary digits, say x_5, x_6, x_7, are joined to the original four as a check. The new digits are determined as follows: x_5 is to be 0 or 1 to insure that

$$x_1 + x_2 + x_3 + x_5$$

shall be even; x_6 is to be 0 or 1 to insure that

$$x_1 + x_3 + x_4 + x_6$$

† For further elementary discussion of this and other codes, see *Some Lessons in Mathematics*, by members of the Association of Teachers of Mathematics, edited by T. J. Fletcher, Cambridge University Press, 1965.

shall be even; x_7 is to be 0 or 1 to insure that

$$x_1 + x_2 + x_4 + x_7$$

shall be even. In all, a string of seven binary digits,

$$x_1 x_2 x_3 x_4 x_5 x_6 x_7,$$

thus is transmitted for each symbol. If one error, not more, is made in transmitting such a seven-digit symbol, the error can be found and corrected automatically.

Suppose that when the preceding seven-digit string is sent, the seven-digit string

$$X_1 X_2 X_3 X_4 X_5 X_6 X_7$$

is received and that the string received contains *at most* one error. We introduce three indicator variables, y_1, y_2, y_3, which are 0 as specified and are otherwise 1:

$$y_1 = 0 \text{ when } X_1 + X_2 + X_3 + X_5 \text{ is even,}$$
$$y_2 = 0 \text{ when } X_1 + X_3 + X_4 + X_6 \text{ is even,}$$
$$y_3 = 0 \text{ when } X_1 + X_2 + X_4 + X_7 \text{ is even.}$$

(a) In Table 3-5 fill in the values of y_1, y_2, y_3 when not more than one error is made in transmitting.

Table 3-5 *The indicator variables when not more than one error is made in transmitting a seven-digit Hamming symbol*

	y_1	y_2	y_3
No error in transmitting			
An error made in transmitting x_1			
An error made in transmitting x_2			
An error made in transmitting x_3			
An error made in transmitting x_4			
An error made in transmitting x_5			
An error made in transmitting x_6			
An error made in transmitting x_7			

(b) Now explain how single errors are caught and identified. HINT: Regard $y_1 y_2 y_3$ as a binary numeral.

(c) Consider a modified scheme in which the symbol to be transmitted is represented by the string $x_3x_5x_6x_7$,

x_4 is chosen to make $x_4 + x_5 + x_6 + x_7$ even,

x_2 is chosen to make $x_2 + x_3 + x_6 + x_7$ even, and

x_1 is chosen to make $x_1 + x_3 + x_5 + x_7$ even.

Again, for each symbol the entire seven-digit string $x_1x_2x_3x_4x_5x_6x_7$ is sent, the seven-digit string $X_1X_2X_3X_4X_5X_6X_7$ is received, and we assume the string received to contain at most one error. Let y_1, y_2, y_3 be indicator variables referring here to the first, second, and third sums, respectively (for instance, $y_3 = 0$ if $X_1 + X_3 + X_5 + X_7$ is even). After calculating the indicator variables and inspecting the binary numerals $y_1y_2y_3$, can you see the great advantage of this scheme over the previous? This is the scheme that Hamming actually proposed.

Did the foregoing processes seem strange? In their ordinary context of the Hindu-Arabic system we know them well. The Hindu-Arabic system has base ten, there being ten digits,

$$0, 1, 2, 3, 4, 5, 6, 7, 8, 9,$$

out of which the numerals of all higher numbers are constructed. To bring out the structural characteristics of the numerals in this system, we need a good symbol for ten, the base, and shall use the capital letter T (not to be confused with the lower case t previously employed as a symbol for three). Need we stress that T is not a digit and does not enter the numeral system? Because of this, we shall speak of T and of expressions in which T appears as numbers, reserving the term "numeral" for the numerals of the system.

The numeral for T is, of course,

$$10.$$

The reader is asked to note the complete analogy with this of the numeral in the system with base three for t or in that with base two for d. Any number less than T^2 (one hundred) has a two-place numeral (in base ten) written as

$$ba,$$

where a and b are digits in the system, i.e., are any of the numbers from 0 to 9, inclusive. Any number less than T^3 (one thousand) has a three-place numeral

$$cba,$$

where a, b, and c are digits, and where

$$c \cdot T^2 + b \cdot T + a$$

is equal to the number. Thus, for instance, 672 denotes the number $6T^2 + 7T + 2$. Any number less than T^4 has a four-place numeral

$$dcba,$$

where now a, b, c, and d are digits,

$$d \cdot T^3 + c \cdot T^2 + b \cdot T + a$$

being equal to the number.

A common logic underlies the three given numeral systems as well as many others. We hope to have illuminated this logic by our examples and now enter upon a more abstract discussion.

EXERCISE

12. The following statements were made in the first printed arithmetic, published in Italy in 1478: †

"Numeration is the representation of numbers by figures. This is done by means of ten letters or figures, as here shown: i, 2, 3, 4, 5, 6, 7, 8, 9, 0. Of these the first figure, i, is not called a number but the source of number. The tenth figure, 0, is called cipher or 'nulla,' i.e., the figure of nothing, since by itself it has no value, although when joined with others it increases their value. . ."

To what extent do we or do we not accept these statements today?

_____

†Taken from *A Source Book in Mathematics* by David Eugene Smith, Vol. I, New York, Dover Publications, 1959, pp. 2-3.

2.

General place-value systems: one- and two-place numerals

Any place-value system begins with a numeral for zero and numerals for all the natural numbers up to some definite limit; this limit is arbitrary and may be 1 or any higher number. These beginning, or original, numerals, including that for zero, we call the *digits* of the number system. (The term "digit" also will be used ambiguously, as in the preceding examples, to mean the number denoted by the digit, the context being depended upon to avoid confusion.) The number of digits is called the *base* of the system. The place-value idea is to build up the numerals of higher numbers as strings of digits, with the interpretation of each digit in a given numeral determined by its place in the string. The most familiar example of a place-value system is that of the Hindu-Arabic numerals, which has base ten (and, hence, is called *decimal*), the ten digits being 0, 1, 2, 3, 4, 5, 6, 7, 8, 9. The Sumerian-Babylonian scheme had sixty digits, which, by the way, were themselves written in a kind of decimal notation; having base 60, this scheme is called *sexagesimal*. The binary and ternary systems with bases two and three, respectively, have been used for illustration.

We wish now to describe the place-value principle abstractly, i.e., to give a *general* treatment in which, enjoying the advantages of algebraic symbolism, we do not specify a particular base but handle all possible bases, so to speak, at the same time. For this purpose, we denote the base by a letter, B, requiring only that it be a natural number greater than 1. All our eventual statements then will apply to the decimal scheme when we take the value of B to be ten, to the sexagesimal when we take B as sixty, to the binary when we take B as two, and so forth. This is why we have called our treatment a *general* one, all possible place-value schemes arising from it by appropriate specialization of B.

Since B, the base, is the number of digits, these digits consist of zero and the first $B-1$ natural numbers. Let us thus establish numerals, written symbols, for zero and the first $B-1$ natural numbers. As we have previously emphasized, symbols of any kind would do, but for reasons of convenience the Hindu-Arabic are those we actually use, the two digits of the binary system, for instance, being represented as 0 and 1, and the sixty digits of the sexagesimal as 0, 1, 2, . . ., 59.† (The numbers from 10 to 59 are not digits in the decimal system but are so regarded in the sexagesimal.) For later reference, we now list the digits in order as

(1) $0, 1, \ldots, B-1.$

Because B is unspecified, this listing necessarily is schematic, but each entry, made or implied, is to be understood as the (Hindu-Arabic) numeral for the number concerned.

The digits, listed in (1), constitute the original stock of symbols for our system out of which all other numerals are to be constructed. Thus, B, in particular, is not a numeral in our system, but a symbol, outside the system, for the number that is one more than the greatest digit. (We therefore generally shall refer to B, $B+1$, $2 \cdot B$, and so on as numbers, reserving the term "numeral" for the numerals of our system.) To represent B without adding to the stock of original symbols of the system, the idea of the place-value principle is to use *two* digits, or, so to speak, a numeral with two "places" for digits instead of one. In fact, the lower numbers (the digits), too, can be regarded as two-digit numbers and, as such, would be written as

---

†Three dots, ". . .", as mentioned before, are used to mean, "and so forth, as indicated."

$$0,0$$
$$0,1$$
$$0,B-1,$$

their second places from the right being occupied by zero. (In this discussion, it is convenient to mark off the "places" of a numeral by commas. We shall do so consistently.) If the letter a denotes any digit, the two-place numeral for a thus would be

$$0,a.$$

In the numeral for B, the first digit (on the right) is changed to 0, while the second digit becomes 1. B thus is written as

$$1,0.$$

Such a transition is familiar to any auto passenger who has watched the odometer change, say from 00009 to 00010. The number $B + a$ obtained by adding to B any number a belonging to the set (1) is represented as

(2) $1,a.$

The latter numerals include, for instance, $1,0(a=0)$, already mentioned, for the number B, and

$$1,1 \ (a = 1)$$

for $B + 1$. If 2 and 3 happen to be digits (i.e., if B exceeds three), as in examples we shall frequently tacitly assume, the numerals as represented in (2) also include

$$1,2 \ (a = 2)$$

for $B + 2$ and

$$1,3 \ (a = 3)$$

for $B + 3$.

The last of the two-place numerals is

$$1,B - 1 \ (a = B - 1);$$

it corresponds to the number $B + (B - 1) = 2B - 1$. The numeral for the next number, $2 \cdot B$, is obtained by bringing the first digit back to zero and increasing the second by one: Thus, this numeral is

$$2,0.$$

Moreover, if a again denotes any of the numbers (1), then

$$2,a$$

will be the numeral for $2 \cdot B + a$. The numeral for $2 \cdot B + 1$, for instance, is

$$2,1$$

and that for $2 \cdot B + 2$,

$$2,2.$$

The last such numeral, of course, is

$$2,B - 1,$$

standing for $2B + (B - 1) = 3B - 1$. The next number, $3 \cdot B$, is assigned the numeral

$$3,0,$$

and any number of the type $3 \cdot B + a$, where a is a digit, is assigned the numeral

$$3,a.$$

The foregoing discussion suggests that the two-digit numerals are naturally grouped into separate arrays, as follows. The first of the arrays,

$(3)_0$ $\qquad\qquad\qquad$ $0,0; \ 0,1; \ . . .; \ 0,B - 1,$†

consists of the numerals symbolized by $0,a$, a denoting any digit; the second,

$(3)_1$ $\qquad\qquad\qquad$ $1,0; \ 1,1; \ . . .; \ 1,B - 1,$

consists of the numerals symbolized by $1,a$. If by the letter b we denote an arbitrary digit, the array consisting of the numerals

$(3)_b$ $\qquad\qquad\qquad$ $b,0; \ b,1; \ . . .; \ b,B - 1,$

is the $(b + 1)$-st;‡ an arbitrary one of these, symbolized as

$$b,a,$$

---

†The symbols $(3)_0$, $(3)_1$, and so forth at the left of the arrays are merely identification marks just like (3) or (4), for instance, without subscripts.
‡By b-th we would mean a word analogous to "forth," "fifth," or "tenth," but pertaining to the unspecified number b. In place of "$(b + 1)$-th," we here write "$(b + 1)$-st," which we read as "b plus first." Similarly, we later write "$(b + 2)$-nd," read as "b plus second," in place of "$(b + 2)$-th."

represents the number $b \cdot B + a$. There being B digits, there are B such arrays of which $(3)_0$ and $(3)_1$ of course are the first and the second. The last such array is

$(3)_{B-1}$ $\qquad\qquad B - 1,0; \; B - 1,1; \; \ldots; \; B - 1, B - 1.$

The B arrays taken together include all the numbers from zero, corresponding to the first number of the first array $(3)_0$, to

$$(B - 1) \cdot B + B - 1 = B^2 - B + B - 1 = B^2 - 1,$$

the number whose numeral is the last entry in the last array $(3)_{B-1}$. This is because the numerals within the individual arrays are consecutive and, in addition, the last numeral in any one array is always just one less than the first numeral in the next. To check this latter statement, consider any value of b less than $B - 1$, both b and $b + 1$ then being digits. The $(b + 1)$-st array being that already indicated in $(3)_b$, the next—the $(b + 2)$-nd—is

$(3)_{b+1}$ $\qquad\qquad b + 1,0; \; b + 1,1; \; \ldots; \; b + 1, B - 1.$

The last numeral in $(3)_b$ corresponds to the number

(4) $\qquad\qquad b \cdot B + B - 1 = (b + 1) \cdot B - 1.$

The first numeral in $(3)_{b+1}$ corresponds to $(b + 1) \cdot B$. These numbers are consecutive: no gap exists between the array $(3)_b$ and its successor, $(3)_{b+1}$. Since b is a perfectly arbitrary digit (less than $B - 1$), no gap exists between *any* two consecutive arrays. It follows that the B arrays indicated do indeed contain all the numbers from 0 to $B^2 - 1$, inclusive, as asserted. Moreover, each number appears in these arrays only once.

Since b,a, by definition, is the numeral for $b \cdot B + a$, the fact that the two-place numerals include all the numbers from 0 to $B^2 - 1$ means that, if N denotes any such number, digits a and b exist such that

(5) $\qquad\qquad N = b \cdot B + a.$

That different numerals distinguish different numbers means that, for each N, a and b are uniquely determined: in other words, no equality

$$N = b' \cdot B + a'$$

with digits a', b' is possible, unless $a' = a$, $b' = b$.

EXERCISES

1. Write numerals for thirty in the systems with bases seven, thirty, and sixty.

2. How many numbers are representable by two-digit numerals in the binary, decimal, and sexagesimal systems?

3.

Three-place numerals

Two-place numerals suffice to designate the first B^2 numbers, i.e., the numbers

$(1)_0$ $$0, 1, \ldots, B^2 - 1.$$

With three-place numerals, the first B^3 numbers can be named. In the first place, we regard any two-place numeral, say b,a, as equivalent to a three-place numeral

$(2)_0$ $$0,b,a$$

whose third place from the right is occupied by zero. This numeral, as we recall, stands for the number

$(3)_0$ $$b \cdot B + a$$

which, as a and b vary over all the digits, takes each value in the set $(1)_0$ once and only once.

The greatest such number, obtained for $a = B - 1$, $b = B - 1$, is $(B - 1) \cdot B + B - 1 = B^2 - 1$; its numeral is

$$0,B - 1,B - 1.$$

To the next higher number, B^2, under the place-value principle we assign the numeral

$$1,0,0;$$

to $B^2 + 1$ we assign

$$1,0,1;$$

to $B^2 + a$, where a is any digit, we assign

$$1,0,a;$$

to $B^2 + B$,

$$1,1,0;$$

to $B^2 + b \cdot B$, b being any digit,

$$1,b,0.$$

More generally, may we assign to the number

(3)$_1$ $$B^2 + b \cdot B + a,$$

where a and b are any digits, the numeral

(2)$_1$ $$1,b,a?$$

The least of the numbers (3)$_1$ is B^2 (obtained for $a = 0$, $b = 0$); the greatest (obtained for $a = b = B - 1$) is $B^2 + (B - 1) \cdot B + (B - 1) = 2 \cdot B^2 - 1$. The numeral assignments (2)$_1$ are legitimate if (1) every number N between B^2 and $2 \cdot B^2 - 1$, inclusive, determines digits a and b such that

$$N = B^2 + b \cdot B + a,$$

and (2) no similar equality holds with other digits. These requirements are met. First, if N is a number between B^2 and $2 \cdot B^2 - 1$, then $N - B^2$ is between 0 and $B^2 - 1$ and, thus, is one of the numbers in the set (1)$_0$ with two-place numerals. Hence, digits a and b exist such that

$$N - B^2 = b \cdot B + a$$

and, consequently, such that

$$N = B^2 + b \cdot B + a.$$

The first requirement is thus satisfied. The second requirement is that no equality

$$N = B^2 + b' \cdot B + a'$$

hold with digits a' and b', unless $a' = a$ and $b' = b$. If such an equality did obtain, by subtracting from our original equation we would have

$$\begin{aligned} 0 &= (B^2 + b \cdot B + a) - (B^2 + b' \cdot B + a') \\ &= (b \cdot B + a) - (b' \cdot B + a') \end{aligned}$$

and, hence,

$$b' \cdot B + a' = b \cdot B + a.$$

This states that $b',a' = b,a$. We know from Section 2, however, that the digits in the two-place numerals are unique and conclude that

$$a' = a, \; b' = b,$$

the result required. Our contention that the numbers between B^2 and $2 \cdot B^2 - 1$ are representable uniquely in the form $(3)_1$ is thus proved and the numerals $(2)_1$ justified.

The next higher number, $2 \cdot B^2$, is now given the numeral

$$2,0,0.$$

In fact, all the numbers from $2 \cdot B^2$ to $3 \cdot B^2 - 1$, inclusive, are given numerals of the form

$(2)_2$ $\hspace{4cm}$ $2,b,a$

with the justification that each such number can be expressed as

$(3)_2$ $\hspace{4cm}$ $2 \cdot B^2 + b \cdot B + a$

in terms of digits a and b, which the number uniquely determines. This is proved in the same way that $(2)_1$ was justified.

The three-place numerals so far considered are instances of numerals of the form

(2) $\hspace{4cm}$ $c,b,a,$

obtained for particular choices of c ($c = 0$, 1, or 2). These instances suggest that we assign the numeral (2) to the number

(3) $\hspace{4cm}$ $c \cdot B^2 + b \cdot B + a,$

where a, b, and c more generally are any *three* digits. We must be sure, however, that the assignment is legitimate. It will be so if every number from 0 (obtained for $a = 0$, $b = 0$, $c = 0$) to $B^3 - 1$ (obtained for $a = B-1$, $b = B-1$, $c = B-1$) receives one and only one numeral under the assignment. To verify that this is the case, we shall divide the numbers from 0 to $B^3 - 1$ into the following B classes:

$(1)_0$ $\hspace{3cm}$ $0, 1, \ldots, B^2 - 1;$
$(1)_1$ $\hspace{3cm}$ $B^2, B^2 + 1, \ldots, 2 \cdot B^2 - 1;$
$(1)_2$ $\hspace{3cm}$ $2 \cdot B^2, 2 \cdot B^2 + 1, \ldots, 3 \cdot B^2 - 1;$

$\hspace{3cm}$ $\cdots\cdots\cdots\cdots\cdots\cdots\cdots\cdots\cdots$

$(1)_{B-1}$ $\hspace{2cm}$ $(B-1) \cdot B^2, (B-1) \cdot B^2 + 1, \ldots, B^3 - 1;$

each class consists of B^2 consecutive numbers. If c denotes an arbitrary digit, the $(c+1)$-st of these classes is

$(1)_c$ $c \cdot B^2, \ c \cdot B^2 + 1, \ \ldots, \ (c+1) \cdot B^2 - 1$

(the greatest member of $(1)_c$, that for which $a = b = B - 1$, is $c \cdot B^2 + (B-1) \cdot B + (B-1) = (c+1) \cdot B^2 - 1)$. Just as in the case $c = 1$, we can verify for any c that each number in class $(1)_c$ determines uniquely two digits, a and b, in terms of which the number is given by the expression

$(3)_c$ $c \cdot B^2 + b \cdot B + a.$

Therefore, under the scheme described, one and just one numeral of the form (2) is assigned to each member of class $(1)_c$ for $c = 0, 1, \ldots,$ $B - 1$, and different sets of numerals are used with different classes. If these classes,

$$(1)_0, (1)_1, \ldots, (1)_{B-1},$$

together contain all the numbers from 0 (for $a = b = c = 0$) to $B^3 - 1$ (for $a = b = c = B - 1$), inclusive, no number occurring twice, the scheme will be justified in full. The first class $(1)_0$ begins with 0, the last class $(1)_{B-1}$ ends with $B^3 - 1$, and the numbers in each class are consecutive. We must simply show, therefore, that gaps between successive classes do not exist, or, in other words, that the greatest number in any one class is just one less than the least number in the next. This can be done in the same way that gaps were ruled out in the previous section in the two-digit case. The result can be summarized as follows: (1) if N is any number less than B^3, then digits a, b, and c exist such that

$$N = c \cdot B^2 + b \cdot B + a;$$

(2) for each N, the digits a, b, and c are uniquely determined. Hence, each number less than B^3 is identifiable from its corresponding digits a, b, and c, and a listing of these digits, as is given in the symbol

$$c,b,a$$

legitimately serves as its numeral.

4.

Numerals with arbitrarily many places

The procedure in the previous section by which we passed from two-place to three-place numerals can be repeated with very little change to pass next from three-place to four-place, then from four-place to five-place, numerals, and so forth. This procedure, in fact, suggests how, generally, from the numerals of any given number of places, we can make the transition to the numerals of one place more.

Suppose, for instance, we already have the k-place numerals, k being some natural number. This is to suppose that the following statement is true: If N denotes a number less than B^k, one and only one set of k digits $a_0, a_1, \ldots, a_{k-1}$ (read "a sub zero," "a sub one," "a sub k minus one") exists such that

(1) $$N = a_{k-1} \cdot B^{k-1} + a_{k-2} \cdot B^{k-2} + \ldots a_1 \cdot B + a_0;$$

the numeral for N then is the listing

$$a_{k-1}, \ldots, a_1, a_0.$$

Let us denote the foregoing statement by the symbol S_k. We already know that S_2 is true, and, as was seen in the preceding section, implies S_3. Once any S_k has been established, the transition to S_{k+1} can be made, moreover, in practically the same manner as that from S_2 to S_3. We thus arrive at the following scheme: S_2 is true and implies S_3, which thus also is true. S_3, however, implies S_4, and S_4, now known to be true, implies S_5, and so on. Step by step, in this way, eventually every S_k will be proved true and k-place numerals for the numbers less than B^k therewith established. A step-by-step argument of this type is called inductive. The principle of mathematical induction will be developed more fully, and with other applications, in a later chapter.

In the following, the base for a numeral will be indicated by a subscript, and commas will be omitted unless (as, for instance, with sexagesimal numbers) the digits require more than one figure. Thus, for example,

$$10_2 = 2,$$
$$10_3 = 3,$$
$$18,2_{20} = 362.$$

EXERCISES

1. Convert the numeral 11001010_2 to base 8.

2. When a number is multiplied by B, how is its numeral in base B changed? (Considering the examples of bases two, three, and ten may help to discover both the answer and its justification.)

3. In the decimal system,

$$123456789 \cdot 9 = 1,111,111,101.$$

Can you see a simple reason for this and then state and prove an analogous

thing respecting numerals to base 5? To base B? HINT: Use the fact that
$9 = 10 - 1$.

4. The following are representations in different bases of the same number: 10, 11, 12, 13, 14, 15, 16, 17, 20, 22, 24, 31, 100, 121, 10000. What is the number?

5.

A numeral system not employing digits

Other numeral schemes than those directly based on the Sumerian may be worthwhile. One such, called to my attention by Mrs. Lore Rasmussen, constructs all numerals out of three symbols,

$$0, +, -,$$

these not playing quite the same role as digits. The following are the numerals in this scheme for the numbers from zero to ten:

zero	0
one	+
two	+−
three	+ 0
four	++
five	+−−
six	+−0
seven	+−+
eight	+0−
nine	+00
ten	+ 0+

The first three or four of these numbers may already be a sufficient clue to the scheme. If not, examine a few negative numbers:

minus one	−
minus two	−+
minus three	− 0
minus four	−−
minus five	−++

To explain the scheme, let t again denote the number three. Each place in a numeral corresponds, as in the more conventional ternary system, to a power of t, the first place on the right to $t^0 = 1$, the second place from the right to t, the third place from the right to t^2 (nine), and so forth. To evaluate a numeral, the power of t corresponding to

each particular place is added if the place is occupied by +, subtracted if the place is occupied by −, and ignored if the entry occupying that place is 0. The result of all the additions and subtractions is
the number the numeral represents. Thus, +− represents $t - 1$, +0
represents t, ++ represents $t + 1$, and +−+, for instance, represents
$t^2 - t + 1$.

EXERCISES

1. Write eleven, twenty-one, minus twenty-seven in this system.
2. Write the negatives of +0−, −−+, ++−−.
3. Write the following sums:

$$\begin{array}{ccc} + & + & - \\ + & - & - \end{array}$$

4. Using the rules apparent from the previous exercise, work out the following additions:

$$\begin{array}{ccc} +0+ & +++ & +0--- \\ +- & -++ & ++-- \end{array}$$

5. With a balance and a suitable set of standard, known weights, any
object can be weighed, say, to the nearest whole number of ounces. Show that,
for objects not heavier than 40 ounces, four standard weights suffice.

6.

Some historical remarks †

a.   FRACTIONS AND PLACE HOLDERS

The decimal point and decimal fractions were invented in the
early 15th Century by the Islamic scholar, the astronomer royal in
Samarqand, al-Kashi, and apparently reinvented in 1586 by the Dutch
mathematician, Simon Stevin. The same ideas apply to any place-
values schemes, as we illustrate in the case of the sexagesimal system
by the examples 0.1 and 0.0, 1, meaning 1/60 and 1/3600, respectively.
The Babylonians from the earliest times were aware of this, except
that they lacked what would correspond to the decimal point, but
relied on the context to tell whether 1, for instance, stood for one,
sixty, or one sixtieth. They also, in earlier times (at least until 1600
B.C.), lacked a special symbol for zero, leaving a place blank if it was
zero. In later times (certainly after 300 B.C.), a punctuation mark

---

† See, in particular, O. Neugebauer, *The Exact Sciences in Antiquity*, second edition, Brown University Press, 1957. Reprinted by Harper Torchbooks, 1962.

equivalent to our period was inserted into such a place, but no symbol for zero ever was used at the end of a numeral. These deficiencies did not noticeably hamper the Babylonians in their apparent passion for numerical calculation, the results of which are preserved in striking tables, of mathematical content in the "Old Babylonian" era of about 1800 to 1600 B.C., and of astronomical content in their latest era, the "Seleucid," from 300 to 1 B.C. (Surviving documents do not cover the 1300 years intervening between the two eras.)

At one stage in the Mesopotamian development, a large 1 was used to denote sixty and a normally sized 1, one. This usage is amusingly suggestive of our word "million," which means literally, "big thousand."

b. WEIGHTS AND MEASURES

From early times, the Sumerians' and Babylonians' main units of weight, measuring silver, seem to have been in the ratio of 60 to 1, and the same ratio later was applied to other units. The ultimate selection of 60 to be the number base, despite the earlier use of a kind of decimal system, may have been because of this. In any case, the eventual concordance reached between the units of measurement and the number base we can only deem remarkable. In our times, at least, sentiment against effecting any such consistency has reached great depths. This is to be seen, for instance, in the following verse, part of a song published by the Ohio auxiliary of the International Institute for Preserving and Perfecting Weights and Measures, organized in Boston in 1879 with the object, in part, of combating the "atheistic metrical system" of France.†

> Then down with every "metric" scheme
>   Taught by the foreign school,
> We'll worship still our Father's God!
>   And keep our Father's "rule."
> A perfect inch, a perfect pint,
>   The Anglo's honest pound,
> Shall hold their place upon the earth
>   Till time's last trump shall sound!

---

†This information, including the song fragment, is from Martin Gardner's *Fads and Fallacies in the Name of Science*, Dover Publications, Inc., New York, Second Edition, 1957.

EXERCISE

1. Write as fractions the numbers represented by the following numerals:

$$0.1_2 \qquad 0.01_2$$
$$0.1_3 \qquad 0.11_2$$

7.

Divisibility criteria

Let m and n denote two integers, m not being zero. We say that m divides n if a third integer, which we shall call p, exists such that

$$n = m \cdot p;$$

m is then called a divisor of n. The (positive) divisors of 28, for instance, are 1, 2, 4, 7, 14, 28.

Our study of numerals gives us access to a body of well-known rules on divisibility by certain numbers. We list here, as assertions or questions, some of these rules with hints as to their proofs. All numbers are written in the decimal system.

(a) The last digit determines divisibility by 2, the last two digits divisibility by 4, and the last three digits divisibility by eight: e.g., 54269832 is divisible by 8 because 832 is so divisible.

(b) The last digit determines divisibility by 5, and the last two digits divisibility by 25.

(c) A well-known condition for the divisibility by 3 of an arbitrary number N is deducible as follows.

The idea of the criterion is to find a related, but lesser, number T such that $N - T$ certainly is divisible by 3 or, in other words, is three times a whole number m: $N - T = 3 \cdot m$. The divisibility by 3 of N and T then will be the same. Suppose, for instance, that T is divisible by 3 or, in other words, that T is three times a whole number t: $T = 3 \cdot t$. From $N - T = 3 \cdot m$ we have that $N = T + 3 \cdot m = 3 \cdot t + 3 \cdot m = 3 \cdot (t + m)$ and, hence, that N, being three times a whole number $t + m$, is divisible by 3. Suppose, on the other hand, that N is divisible by 3. Since $T = N - 3 \cdot m$, an argument like that just given proves that, in this case, T is divisible by 3. Hence, N is divisible by 3 if and only if T is divisible by 3, as contended.

In explaining how to find T, for simplicity we restrict our discussion to such N as have three-place numerals in the decimal system. Such N are representable in terms of three digits a, b, c as

(1) $$N = c \cdot 100 + b \cdot 10 + a.$$

For each summand on the right side of (1) we now determine a number such that, when subtracted from the summand, a result divisible by 3 is obtained. For the first summand, this number is c, for the second summand it is b, and for the third summand, a. T is defined as the sum of these numbers:

$$T = c + b + a.$$

It is, indeed, just to combine the previous calculations to note that

$$N - T = (c \cdot 100 + b \cdot 10 + a) - (c + b + a)$$
$$= 99 \cdot c + 9 \cdot b = 9 \cdot (11 \cdot c + b),$$

so that in particular, $N - T$ is divisible by 3, as asserted.

EXERCISES

1. Give the details of the argument that if $N - T = 3 \cdot m$ and N is divisible by 3, then T is divisible by 3.

2. Extend this result to four- and five-place numerals, then to k-place numerals, where k is an arbitrary natural number (since this last part involves mathematical induction, it may be done after Chapter 10).

3. Discuss divisibility by 9.

4. For numerals in base B, deduce a criterion for divisibility by $B - 1$ analogous to that of Exercise 3.

5. State a criterion for divisibility by 6. HINT: $6 = 2 \cdot 3$.

6. Deduce a criterion for divisibility by 7. HINT: Apply the idea used in (c) to construct T. The result in this case is not neat.

7. Discuss why a number represented in the decimal system, say by a five-place numeral

$$edcba,$$

is divisible by 11 if and only if

$$a - b + c - d + e$$

is divisible by 11. Find analogous rules for other bases.

8. Let N denote a six-digit number in base 10; $N = fedcba$. Correspondingly let $N_0 = cba$ and $N_1 = fed$. Show that N is divisible by 7, 11, or 13 if $N_0 - N_1$ is divisible by 7, 11, or 13, respectively. HINT: $7 \cdot 11 \cdot 13 = 1001.$†

9. Let abc be a numeral in base 10. Prove that the number this numeral, abc, denotes is divisible by 13 if $(10 \cdot b) + c - (4 \cdot a)$ is divisible by 13.

---

†I am indebted to Prof. Charles Pinzka for this example.

8.

Perfect numbers†

The Greeks called a number perfect if it was equal to the sum of all its positive divisors other than itself. An example of a perfect num-

---

†See, for instance, D. Shanks' *Solved and Unsolved Problems in Number Theory*, Vol. I, Spartan Books, Washington, D. C., 1962.

ber is the number 6, since the positive divisors of 6 other than itself are 1, 2, 3, and $1 + 2 + 3 = 6$. The next three perfect numbers are 28, 496, and 8128. Perfect numbers have been the direct or indirect occasion of seminal work in an ancient and rich branch of mathematics known as the theory of numbers. Some insight into the nature of perfect numbers is obtained by noting how they are written in the binary system. Write the first four perfect numbers in this way. The fifth perfect number, by the way, is 33,550,336.

CHAPTER 4

BABYLONIAN MATHEMATICS[†]

About 1000 years after having invented writing, the Sumerians succumbed, yielding to three centuries of barbarian infiltration and assault. Another 150 years passed before the conquerors, assimilating the civilization they had inherited, were to advance it actively themselves. Now known from their capital as Babylonians, they pursued the Sumerian numerical tradition with remarkable avidity, to which numerous tables and problem texts, among the clay tablets that survive from the period 1800 to 1600 B.C., attest. Some of the tables, for instance the multiplication tables and compilations of reciprocals,[‡] doubtless were employed in practical affairs by this mercantile people. Other tables, lists of squares, square roots, cubes, cube roots,[§] and so forth, must have been of more purely mathematical interest. Many of the problem texts that have come down to us are concerned with matters of practical arithmetic like the following: How many bricks of given dimensions are required to cover a given surface, and what is their total volume? How large a field can be covered to a specified depth by water from a cistern of given dimensions? From appropriate data, what is the total cost of construction of a canal of given length and (rectangular or trapezoidal) cross section, how long will the construction take, how many workers will be needed, at what rate will

---

[†] See Neugebauer, *op. cit.*
[‡] The Babylonians seem to have performed division by multiplying by a reciprocal.
[§] The cube root of a given number a, is the number x for which $x^3 = a$. The fourth root is a number y such that $y^4 = a$. (If y is a fourth root, so is $-y$.) The fifth root is the number z such that $z^5 = a$, and so on. Frequently we write these numbers as $x = \sqrt[3]{a}$, $y = \sqrt[4]{a}$, $z = \sqrt[5]{a}$, and so forth. Any such sign as $\sqrt{}$, $\sqrt[3]{}$, $\sqrt[4]{}$ is known as a radical.

138

the canal deliver water, and so forth? Some of the problems go beyond ordinary arithmetic into what we call algebra. The Babylonians lacked a conscious algebraic symbolism, but, explaining all their procedures in general terms while using concrete numbers for illustration, nevertheless they may be said to have had general formulas. Two such are discussed in this chapter, both beautiful examples of mathematical inventiveness and skill.

1.

Pythagorean triples

From a recently unearthed cuneiform problem text, dated at about 1750 B.C., it is clear that the Old Babylonians knew what we call the Pythagorean theorem.† This was over a thousand years before Pythagoras. The theorem states (Figure 4-1) that, if a and b are the lengths of the two legs of a right triangle, and c is the length of the hypotenuse, then

(1) $$a^2 + b^2 = c^2.$$

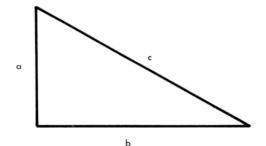

Figure 4-1   A right triangle.

Probably the Babylonians believed all numbers to be rational, in which case

$$a = a_1/a_2,\ b = b_1/b_2,\ c = c_1/c_2,$$

where a_1, a_2, b_1, b_2, c_1, c_2 are positive integers. In terms of these integers, the Pythagorean relation would read

$$(a_1)^2/(a_2)^2 + (b_1)^2/(b_2)^2 = (c_1)^2/(c_2)^2.$$

---

†See Taha Baqir in *Sumer*, Vol. XVIII (1962), pp. 12-14.

Multiplied by $(a_2)^2(b_2)^2(c_2)^2$, the relation would appear as

$$(a_1)^2(b_2)^2(c_2)^2 + (b_1)^2(a_2)^2(c_2)^2 = (c_1)^2(a_2)^2(b_2)^2,$$

or

$$(a_1 b_2 c_2)^2 + (b_1 a_2 c_2)^2 = (c_1 a_2 b_2)^2.$$

If all numbers were rational, the Pythagorean relation (1) for an arbitrary right triangle thus would lead to a relation like

(2) $$A^2 + B^2 = C^2,$$

of similar form, but for integers. (Here, $A = a_1 b_2 c_2$, $B = b_1 a_2 c_2$, $C = c_1 a_2 b_2$.) Perhaps this is why the Babylonians were interested in the problem of finding sets of three integers A, B, C standing in the relation (2). The Old Babylonians at any rate solved this problem, a table containing fifteen such "Pythagorean triples" still surviving from their era. Small numbers, such as those occurring in the following table, would not be too astonishing from a people who relish

A	B	C
3	4	5
5	12	13
7	24	25
8	15	17
9	40	41
20	21	29

Table 4-1   *Some Pythagorean triples:* $A^2 + B^2 = C^2$

calculation. The numbers in the Babylonian table are much larger, however, one triple, for instance, being (in decimal notation)

$$A = 12{,}709 \qquad B = 13{,}500 \qquad C = 18{,}541.$$

Knowledge of such large triples calls for explanation.

The Babylonians themselves left no explanation that has come down to us, but Professor Otto Neugebauer reconstructs their probable line of reasoning as follows. Since C is larger than, say, A, regard C as the sum, and A as the difference, of two other numbers. In modern notation, set

(3) $$C = p + q, \quad A = p - q,$$

where p and q are positive integers not, as yet, specified. The only requirement p and q must satisfy is that, when the expressions (3) are substituted for C and A in $C^2 - A^2$, the result is a square. This is because $C^2 - A^2 = B^2$. From (3),

$$C^2 = (p + q)^2 = p^2 + 2pq + q^2$$
$$A^2 = (p - q)^2 = p^2 - 2pq + q^2,$$

and, therefore,

$$C^2 - A^2 = p^2 + 2pq + q^2 - (p^2 - 2pq + q^2)$$
$$= 4pq.$$

The expression $4pq$ will be a square if p and q individually are squares, i.e., if $p = P^2$ and $q = Q^2$, where P and Q are any other integers. (In fact, $4pq = 4P^2Q^2 = (2PQ)^2$.) We will then have $B^2 = C^2 - A^2 = 4pq = (2PQ)^2$, and, therefore, $B = 2PQ$. At the same time, $C = p + q = P^2 + Q^2$ and $A = p - q = P^2 - Q^2$. In sum, therefore, if P and Q are any integers, the numbers determined by the formulas

(4)
$$A = P^2 - Q^2$$
$$B = 2PQ$$
$$C = P^2 + Q^2$$

satisfy the relation $A^2 + B^2 = C^2$, and thus constitute a Pythagorean triple.

EXERCISES

1. Check the last relation independently of how it was derived.
2. Determine from formulas (4) several Pythagorean triples not in Table 4-1.
3. Find values of P and Q that correspond to the triples in Table 4-1.
4. Find P and Q for the triple taken from the Old Babylonian table.
5. Prove that the following formulas determine a Pythagorean triple corresponding to each odd integer m:

$$A = m, \ B = \frac{1}{2}(m^2 - 1), \ C = \frac{1}{2}(m^2 + 1).$$

These formulas reduce to those derived in the text with $P = (m + 1)/2$ and $Q = (m - 1)/2$.

2.

Quadratic equations

The Old Babylonians were the first to find formulas for what we would describe as the solutions of quadratic equations. We shall discuss their method, reconstructed conjecturally, in Section 3, but we shall first present the subject more in the spirit of our own day. A quadratic equation, or an equation of second degree, is a condition of the form

$$(1) \qquad\qquad ax^2 + bx - c = 0$$

with $a \neq 0$; a, b, and c are called the *coefficients* of the equation. To *solve* the equation is to find the value, or values, of x, if any, that satisfy this condition. Such a value of x is called a *solution*, or a *root*, of the equation.

Quadratic equations arise from many simple geometrical problems. We shall now describe one. If a rectangle is 2 feet long and 3 feet wide, its area is 6 square feet, and its perimeter, the total distance around (the sum of the lengths of the four sides), is 10 feet. If the rectangle is x feet long and y feet wide, its area is xy square feet, and its perimeter is $2x + 2y = 2(x + y)$ feet. A farmer might well wish to know the length and breadth of a rectangular farm with stipulated area and perimeter. Let A denote the stipulated area, and let $2P$ denote the stipulated perimeter. (We write $2P$, rather than P, as a notational convenience.) The farmer then wishes to determine length x and breadth y such that

$$(2) \qquad\qquad xy = A$$

and

$$2(x + y) = 2P,$$

i.e.,

$$(3) \qquad\qquad x + y = P.$$

Here are two relations ((2) and (3)) for the two unknown sides of the desired rectangle. Either relation would give one side if the other were known. Neither relation suffices by itself to establish either of the unknown sides. This is because the area alone, or the perimeter alone, does not determine a rectangle's shape. Both relations together will, however, be sufficient to determine the exact shape of the desired rectangular farm.

With the farmer's problem now formulated mathematically in relations (2) and (3), the next step might be to solve one of these relations for y, i.e., to express y, by means of one of these relations, in terms of x. Let us, for instance, solve relation (2) for y. We obtain

$$y = A/x.$$

This result we substitute for y in relation (3) to obtain

$$x + A/x = P.$$

Multiplying both sides by x gives us

$$x^2 + A = Px,$$

from which we have, finally, that

(4) $$x^2 - Px + A = 0.$$

The latter condition is a quadratic equation, an equation of the form (1) with $a = 1$, $b = -P$, $c = A$. Unlike relations (2) and (3), it involves just one of the unknown quantities.

Reconnoitering, before frontally attacking a difficult problem, often uncovers useful information. Advance insight in this problem can be gained from considering that x might denote equally well either the larger or the smaller of the unknown sides of the rectangle. Each, therefore, should satisfy equation (4). Hence, we should expect equation (4), in general, to have two solutions. In the case in which the desired rectangle is a square (the two sides then are of the same length), equation (4), however, should have just one solution. If the farmer, by mistake, specifies too short a perimeter for the area desired (no rectangle existing with those measurements), equation (4) should have no solution. From these considerations, in summary, it is thus plausible that a quadratic equation will have two solutions, one solution, or no solution, according to the values taken by its coefficients.

We are not yet ready for a frontal assault on equation (1), but we shall first attack a special case, that of an equation of the form

(5) $$x^2 - p = 0,$$

i.e.,

(5′) $$x^2 = p.$$

Equation (4) reduces formally to this case for $A = -p$ and $P = 0$, but since no farm has negative area or zero perimeter, the agricultural interpretation is not applicable. Nevertheless, equation (5) behaves in the manner foreshadowed, having, as we shall see, two solutions, one solution, or no solution, according to the nature of the coefficient p. To solve this equation is to find a number, x, whose square has a given value p. The squares of positive and negative numbers alike, however, are positive. Hence, equation (5′) makes no immediate sense unless p is either positive or zero. If $p = 0$, equation (5′) has the one and only solution

(6) $$x = 0.$$

If p is positive, equation (5′) has two solutions, i.e., will be satisfied by either of two different values of x. These values are

(7) $$x = \sqrt{p} \text{ and } x = -\sqrt{p}.$$

(By definition, "$\sqrt{p}$" means the non-negative number whose square is p.) These, moreover, are the only solutions of (5') or (5). We see this from the algebraic identity

$$(x + a)(x - a) = x^2 - a^2,$$

according to which

$$x^2 - p = (x + \sqrt{p})(x - \sqrt{p}).$$

If x equals neither $\sqrt{p}$ nor $-\sqrt{p}$, neither factor on the right is zero and, consequently, $x_2 - p \neq 0$, i.e., x is not a solution of (5). (If $x = \sqrt{p}$, the second factor is zero, and if $x = -\sqrt{p}$, the first factor is zero, confirming that $\sqrt{p}$ and $-\sqrt{p}$ are roots of (5).) Thus, no solutions of (5) exist but those named in (6), as contended. Surprisingly, perhaps, the negative root proves to be as significant as the positive.

Our discussion of equations (5) and (5') enables us also to solve such an equation as

$$(x + 2)^2 - 9 = 0,$$

in which the squared quantity is not purely x, as in (5), but is in some way adulterated. Writing this equation as

$$(x + 2)^2 = 9,$$

and arguing as we did to obtain (7) from (5') we see that to satisfy the equation either

$$x + 2 = 3$$

or

$$x + 2 = -3;$$

hence, either $x = 1$ or $x = -5$.

The procedure just given can be extended to all equations of the form

(8) $$(x + m)^2 - p = 0,$$

where m and p are constants. As for equation (5), three separate cases occur:

(I) If $p < 0$, equation (8) does not have a solution.

(II) If $p = 0$, equation (8) reduces to

$$(x + m)^2 = 0$$

and thus to

$$x + m = 0$$

or, equivalently, to

$$x = -m.$$

(III) If $p > 0$, equation (8) is satisfied if and only if one of the two relations

$$x + m = \sqrt{p} \quad \text{or} \quad x + m = -\sqrt{p}$$

obtains. The first relation is satisfied if and only if

$$x = -m + \sqrt{p};$$

the second relation is satisfied if and only if

$$x = -m - \sqrt{p}.$$

Hence,

(9) $$\qquad\qquad -m + \sqrt{p} \quad \text{and} \quad -m - \sqrt{p}$$

are the two solutions of equation (8) in the present case.

We have stressed quadratic equations of the special form (8), because any quadratic equation is reducible to this special form, its solution or solutions then becoming apparent. The reduction of equation (1) to the form (8) can be very quickly accomplished by a simple trick based on the fact that

$$x^2 + qx \quad (q = \text{constant})$$

becomes a square when $q^2/4$ is added: more precisely,

$$x^2 + qx + q^2/4 = (x + q/2)^2.$$

The process of thus adding $q^2/4$ to $x^2 + qx$ is called "completing the square." To explain the trick, let us first consider, as an example, the equation

$$x^2 + 3x + 1 = 0.$$

The expression $x^2 + 3x$, in which $q = 3$, becomes a complete square when we add $q^2/4 = 9/4$:

$$x^2 + 3x + 9/4 = (x + 3/2)^2.$$

We therefore write the equation as

$$(x^2 + 3x + 9/4) - 9/4 + 1 = 0,$$

inserting 9/4 to complete the square and making the necessary correction in another place to preserve the equality of the two members. The result is equivalent to the equation

$$(x + 3/2)^2 - 5/4 = 0,$$

which is of form (8) with $m = 3/2$, $p = 5/4$. As we have seen, an equation of this type is easily solved. Writing it as

$$(x + 3/2)^2 = 5/4,$$

we conclude, in fact, that either

$$x + 3/2 = \sqrt{5/4} = \sqrt{5}/2$$

or

$$x + 3/2 = -\sqrt{5/4} = -\sqrt{5}/2.$$

Thus, the two solutions of this equation are

$$x = -3/2 + \sqrt{5}/2 \quad \text{and} \quad x = -3/2 - \sqrt{5}/2.$$

(They might, of course, have been read off after substitution in (9) directly.)

We take as a second example the equation

$$2x^2 - 3x + 1 = 0.$$

An attempt to complete the square in this equation may seem to be hindered by the presence of $2x^2$ in place of x^2. This apparent obstacle is removed by simply dividing all terms of the equation by 2, the result being

$$x^2 - 3x/2 + 1/2 = 0,$$

obviously equivalent to the original equation. Now we proceed as before. Since $x^2 - (3/2)x$ becomes a square on the addition of 9/16, we write

$$(x^2 - 3x/2 + 9/16) - 9/16 + 1/2 = 0.$$

This is equivalent to

$$(x - 3/4)^2 - 1/16 = 0,$$

an equation of form (8). Again following the reasoning that had led us to (9), we conclude that x to satisfy this equation must be such that either

$$x - 3/4 = 1/4$$

or

$$x - 3/4 = -1/4.$$

Hence, the equation has two solutions, $x = 1$ and $x = 1/2$.

The method just explained in special cases can be easily adapted to the general quadratic equation (1). First, we divide by the coefficient of x^2, this coefficient a being assumed not to be zero. The equation then takes the form

$$x^2 + (b/a)x + c/a = 0.$$

Converting $x^2 + (b/a)x$ $(q = b/a)$ into a square requires the addition of $(b/(2a))^2$. Hence, we now write the equation as

$$(x^2 + (b/a)x + b^2/(4a^2)) + c/a - b^2/(4a^2) = 0,$$

or

$$(x + b/(2a))^2 + c/a - b^2/(4a^2) = 0.$$

The last equation is of the form (8) with $m = b/(2a)$ and $p = -c/a + b^2/(4a^2) = (b^2 - 4ac)/(4a^2)$.

Three cases therefore must be distinguished:

(I) If $p = (b^2 - 4ac)/(4a^2) < 0$, i.e., if $b^2 - 4ac < 0$, the equation does not have a solution.

(II) If $p = (b^2 - 4ac)/(4a^2) = 0$, i.e., if $b^2 - 4ac = 0$, the equation has the single solution $x = -m$, or $x = -b/(2a)$.

(III) If $p = (b^2 - 4ac)/(4a^2) > 0$, i.e., if $b^2 - 4ac > 0$, the equation has the two solutions

$$x = -m + \sqrt{p} = -b/(2a) + \sqrt{(b^2 - 4ac)/(4a^2)}$$

and

$$x = -m - \sqrt{p} = -b/(2a) - \sqrt{(b^2 - 4ac)/(4a^2)}$$

These solutions also can be written as

$$x = \frac{-b + \sqrt{b^2 - 4ac}}{2a}$$

and

$$x = \frac{-b - \sqrt{b^2 - 4ac}}{2a}.$$

Specific problems can of course be solved by substituting in these formulas, but it is often more convenient to use the method of completing the square directly, as in the two examples.

Comments

1. While the negative square root, at first, may seem artificial, it is of obvious use in finding both solutions of a second degree equation. This is so even when both solutions are positive.

2. Equation (5), as we have noted, makes no immediate sense when p is negative. Similarly, equation (1) makes no immediate sense when $b^2 - 4ac$ is negative. This is because negative numbers do not have square roots in the ordinary sense. The square roots of negative numbers can be regarded, however, as being in themselves a new *kind* of number, and from this point of view the formulas for the solutions of (5) or (1) are meaningful and valid regardless of the sign of p or $b^2 - 4ac$, respectively. The new kind of number, by contrast with the ordinary, "real" kind, is termed "imaginary." Its invention proved to be of the most far-reaching significance, but in ways requiring advanced knowledge to understand.

EXERCISES

1. Determine rectangles, if possible, with the following areas and perimeters:

Area (square inches)	9	9	9
Perimeter (inches)	11	12	13

2. Find the solutions, if any, of the following equations:
   (a) $x^2 - 2x + 2 = 0$
   (b) $x^2 + 2x + 1 = 0$
   (c) $2x^2 + 9x - 5 = 0$
   (d) $3x^2 + x - 2 = 0$.

3. The interpretations of A and P in equation (8) suggest that A is the product, and P the sum, of the roots of the equation. Prove this from the formulas for the roots.

4. Let x_1 and x_2 be the roots of the equation $x^2 + bx + c = 0$. Show that

$$x^2 + bx + c = (x - x_1)(x - x_2).$$

HINT: Expand $(x - x_1)(x - x_2)$ (i.e., carry out the multiplications), and use Exercise 3.

5. We have seen that

$$(-a)^2 = a^2.$$

If we extract the square root of both sides, we obtain:

$$-a = a.$$

What is wrong with the argument?

6. Since

$$1 \text{ yard} = 36 \text{ inches,}$$

we have

$$1/4 \text{ yard} = 9 \text{ inches.}$$

Taking the square root of either side, we thus have

$$1/2 \text{ yard} = 3 \text{ inches.}$$

What went wrong?

The shape of an equation can be altered most variously by a process known as "changing the variable." To illustrate the process, consider the equation

$$(10) \qquad\qquad x^2 + 3x + 2 = 0.$$

Let us introduce a new variable y defined in terms of the original variable x (for $x \neq 0$) as

$$(11) \qquad\qquad y = 1/x.$$

Equation (10) for the old variable x entails a corresponding equation for y to be obtained from (10) by making the substitution

$$x = 1/y$$

equivalent (for $x \neq 0$, $y \neq 0$) to (11). We obtain

$$1/y^2 + 3/y + 2 = 0,$$

which, upon multiplication by y^2, becomes

$$1 + 3y + 2y^2 = 0.$$

Re-ordering its terms, we rewrite this (to ease its comparison with (10)) as

$$(12) \qquad\qquad 2y^2 + 3y + 1 = 0.$$

It is again a quadratic equation, but of different form from (10): i.e., the coefficients of the various powers of the variable are not the same in (12) as in (10). The roots of (12) are rigidly related, however, to the roots of (10), for if x denotes a root of (10), then $1/x$ is a root of (12); conversely, if y satisfies (12), then $1/y$ satisfies (10). Hence, to solve equation (12) is as good as to solve equation (10), and conversely. We regard equation (12) for this reason as merely a new *form* of the old equation (10).

Changing variables in different ways results in different forms of the equation. Suppose, for instance, we change from x to

(13) $$z = x + 3/2.$$

We accomplish the change by the substitution

$$x = z - 3/2$$

equivalent to (13) obtaining

$$(z - 3/2)^2 + 3(z - 3/2) + 2 = 0,$$

i.e.,

$$(z^2 - 3z + 9/4) + (3z - 9/2) + 2 = 0$$

or

(14) $$z^2 - 1/4 = 0.$$

This form is notably simpler than (10), being identical to (8) with $p = 1/4$. Equation (14) has the two roots

$$z = 1/2$$

and

$$z = -1/2,$$

and since $x = z - 3/2$, equation (10) has the roots

$$x = -1$$

and

$$x = -2,$$

correspondingly.

The change of variables (13) enabled us to solve equation (10) by reducing its form to that of (8).

As the last example illustrates, any quadratic equation can be reduced to the form (8), and thus solved, by a change of variables of the particular form

(15) $$y = x + m,$$

where m is a constant to be determined suitably. For simplicity, let us take the equation in the form

(16) $x^2 + Ax + B = 0,$

such as would result from (1) upon division by a. The indicated change of variables is accomplished by the substitution

$$x = y - m$$

equivalent to (15).

EXERCISES

7. (a) Find the quadratic equation in y resulting from this substitution.
   (b) Determine m to make the coefficient of y in this equation vanish. This value of m will depend upon A. Using this value, write the equation for y in the form (5) in which p stands for a certain expression, which you are to obtain, involving both the original coefficients A and B.
   (c) For the equation in y just obtained, discuss the three possible cases for the number of roots.
   (d) Passing from y to x by the relation (15), transfer your conclusion to (16).
8. Find a change of variable of the form $y = x + m$ that will reduce equation (10) to one of the form

$$y^2 + qy = 0.$$

Solve the latter, thereby giving another mode of obtaining the roots of (10).
9. See how the method of Exercise 8 applies to equation (16).
10. Find a change of variable of the form $y = x + m$ that will reduce the cubic equation $x^3 + 2x^2 - x + 1$ to a form in which the coefficient of y^2 is zero.

3.

The Babylonian approach to quadratic equations

The formulas in the preceding section originated with the Old Babylonians, but their approach was completely different from ours. We illustrate with the following example, which is described as a typical one, although late, being taken from a Seleucid tablet.† An

---

† See Neugebauer, pp. 40-41.

unknown number is desired such that a given number is obtained when the unknown is added to its reciprocal. In modern terms, let b denote the given number and x the desired, unknown number. Also, let the reciprocal, $1/x$, be denoted by the symbol y. The problem demands that

$$xy = 1 \quad \text{and} \quad x + y = b.$$

From these relations a mathematician of today would identify x and y as the two roots (see Exercise 3 of the preceding section) of the quadratic equation

$$t^2 - bt + 1 = 0$$

and thus as the two numbers

$$\frac{b + \sqrt{b^2 - 4}}{2}, \; \frac{b - \sqrt{b^2 - 4}}{2}.$$

We readily check that the two numbers obtained have the desired sum and, furthermore, are reciprocal. To verify the latter fact, we must prove their product to be 1. For convenience, let c abbreviate $\sqrt{b^2 - 4}$. Then we have

$$\begin{aligned}
\frac{b + \sqrt{b^2 - 4}}{2} \cdot \frac{b - \sqrt{b^2 - 4}}{2} &= (1/4)(b + c)(b - c) = (1/4)(b^2 - c^2) \\
&= (1/4)[b^2 - (b^2 - 4)] = (1/4)(4) \\
&= 1.
\end{aligned}$$

A Babylonian mathematician would not have referred explicitly to the equation but, according to Solomon Gandz,[†] would have argued as follows: If x and y were equal, their sum being b, each would be equal to $b/2$. Letting z denote the amount by which x in fact exceeds this value, we have

$$x = b/2 + z.$$

The sum of x and y being b, y falls short of $b/2$ to the same extent that x exceeds it, i.e.,

$$y = b/2 - z.$$

From $xy = 1$, however,

$$1 = xy = (b/2 + z)(b/2 - z) = (b/2)^2 - z^2.$$

Hence, $z^2 = (b/2)^2 - 1$, and $z = \sqrt{(b/2)^2 - 1}$. Finally, therefore,

---

†S. Gandz, "Origin and development of the quadratic equation," *Osiris*, Vol. III (1937), pp. 405-557.

$$x = b/2 + z = b/2 + \sqrt{(b/2)^2 - 1}$$

and

$$y = b/2 - z = b/2 - \sqrt{(b/2)^2 - 1}.$$

These are the correct formulas. They were deduced without the use of a negative square root, of which the Babylonians had no conception, and perhaps without the realization that x and y occur in an essentially symmetrical way, each being a root of the quadratic equation involved.

EXERCISES

In the following problems, numbers x and y are desired satisfying conditions actually considered by the Babylonians:

1. $xy = 1$, $x - y = b$.
2. $x + y = b$, $x^2 + y^2 = c$. HINT: Again set $x = b/2 + z$, $y = b/2 - z$.
3. $x + y = b$, $x^2 - y^2 = c$.

While linear and quadratic equations were the center of interest for Babylonian mathematicians, other algebraic problems also occupied them. Certain equations of higher degree (with higher than the second power of x) were solved by reduction to quadratic equations, and when such a reduction was impossible, roots sometimes were obtained numerically apparently by referring to tables constructed for the purpose. Some computations have been found that suggest a groping towards the idea of a limit. Certain tables seem to point in the direction of logarithms. Such advanced tendencies, however, do not appear to have flowered. "In spite of the numerical and algebraic skill and in spite of the abstract interest which is conspicuous in so many examples, the contents of Babylonian mathematics remained profoundly elementary. . . . Babylonian mathematics never transgressed the threshold of prescientific thought."†

4.

Algebraic equations of higher degree

Algebraic equations with third, fourth, or higher powers of x readily arise, for instance, in geometry. The following are two ancient problems from China‡ leading to such equations through the Pythagorean theorem. The first problem, dating from the 7th Century,

---

† Neugebauer, p. 48.
‡ The problems are taken from Cajori, p. 74.

states: "There is a right triangle, the product of whose two sides is 706 1/50, and whose hypotenuse is greater than the first side by 30 9/60. It is required to know the lengths of the three sides." To formulate the problem in modern terms, let x and y denote the sides, the hypotenuse then being $\sqrt{x^2 + y^2}$. According to the problem,

$$xy = a,$$

$$\sqrt{x^2 + y^2} - x = b,$$

where a and b denote specified numbers. We can solve the first equation for y in terms of x:

$$y = a/x.$$

Then we can obtain a condition for the single unknown x by substituting a/x for y in the second equation. We shall do so, but first make over the second equation with the object, in part, of doing away with the square root. The first step in this cosmetic process is to add x to both sides of the second equation to obtain

$$\sqrt{x^2 + y^2} = x + b.$$

Next, square the two sides, obtaining

$$x^2 + y^2 = (x + b)^2 = x^2 + 2bx + b^2,$$

then add $-x^2$ to the members of the last equality, to obtain

$$y^2 = 2bx + b^2.$$

In this form of the second equation, we can conveniently substitute a/x for y, obtaining

$$a^2/x^2 = 2bx + b^2.$$

Finally, multiplying both sides of the last result by x^2 gives us

$$a^2 = 2bx^3 + b^2x^2,$$

since $x \cdot x^2 = x^3$. The problem stated can be solved by solving the last equation. Containing the third, but no higher, powers of x, such an equation is called a *cubic equation*, or an *equation of the third degree*. The 7th Century author apparently solved this equation with the values he specified of a and b, but how he did it is not clear.

The second problem, taken from a work written by Ch'in Chiu-Shao in 1247, is as follows: A circular castle of unknown diameter has north and south gates with a great tree standing three miles north of the north gate. A man walking east from the south gate would first see this tree, the castle no longer obstructing his view, after nine miles. To find the unknown diameter, we need, besides the Pythagorean theorem, the equality of the two tangents to a circle from an exterior point, and the perpendicularity of a tangent and the radius passing through its point of contact. The reader is invited to formulate this problem in modern notation and to reduce it to an equation of the fourth degree (with the fourth, but not higher, powers of the unknown radius) (Figure 4-2). Ch'in Chiu-Shao solved this and similar problems numerically by methods that were not rediscovered in the West for more than five hundred years.

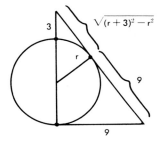

Figure 4-2 The castle problem of Ch'in Chiu-Shao.

Exact formulas for third and fourth degree equations analogous to those for quadratics may have been sought since Babylonian times. Such formulas were found in the 16th Century, more than 3000 years later. They express the solutions of algebraic equations of the third and fourth degree, like the solutions of quadratic equations, in terms of the coefficients of the equations by means of radicals.† (Square roots and cube roots enter the formulas for the roots of a third degree equation; square roots, cube roots, and fourth roots enter the formulas for an equation of the fourth degree.) Similar formulas of course were sought for equations of the fifth degree. This quest was ended in the 19th Century, not with success, but with the remarkable discovery that such general formulas do not exist: the solution of a fifth or higher degree equation cannot, in general, be expressed in terms of the coefficients of the equation by means of radicals. A question even the Old Babylonians would have understood and in some sense perhaps even raised thus was finally answered, but through processes of thought that to them would have been totally strange.

---

†See footnote p. 138.

CHAPTER 5

POLYNOMIALS

1.

The definition of polynomial

Let x be any number. Expressions like

$$x, \; x + 1, \; -3/4 + (1/4)x, \; -(10/9)x + 42,$$

involving x to the first power only, are called polynomials in x of the first degree. Expressions like

$$x^2, \; -2x^2, \; (1/2)x^2 - 4x + 7, \; -4x^2 + (1/4)x - 3,$$

involving x to the second and possibly also to the first power, are called polynomials in x of the second degree. Expressions like

$$x^3, \; 2x^3 - x, \; x^3 + 5x^2, \; 4x^3 - (1/4)x^2 + x - 8,$$

in which the third power of x, and possibly lower powers than the third, appear, are called polynomials in x of the third degree. Analogous expressions in which the nth power of x, and no power of x higher than the nth, appears are called polynomials in x of the nth degree. While the adjective "analogous" in the last sentence is not precise, these explanations and examples, necessarily formulated in symbolic terms, may help to make the following exact definitions intelligible.

156

(1) A polynomial in x of first degree is an expression of the form

$$ax + b$$

in which a and b are any numbers such that $a \neq 0$.

(2) A polynomial in x of second degree is an expression of the form

$$ax^2 + bx + c$$

in which a, b, and c are any numbers such that $a \neq 0$.

(3) A polynomial in x of third degree is an expression of the form

$$ax^3 + bx^2 + cx + d$$

in which a, b, c, d are any numbers such that $a \neq 0$.

A fixed number

$$a$$

appearing by itself (without x) is called a polynomial in x of zeroth degree; this is because $x^0 = 1$ and, therefore, $a = a \cdot 1 = ax^0$ for $x \neq 0$.

(The condition $a \neq 0$ pertains to the degree of the polynomial, for if $a = 0$ the expressions $ax + b$, $ax^2 + bx + c$, $ax^3 + bx^2 + cx + d$ are of lower degree than they look. For instance, $ax + b$ reduces to b, a polynomial of zeroth degree; $ax^2 + bx + c$ reduces to $bx + c$, a polynomial of first degree if $b \neq 0$, and of zeroth degree if $b = 0$.)

To define polynomials of nth degree, it is worthwhile to use a more elaborate notation than heretofore for the numbers, such as were denoted by a, b, c, or d, standing beside the various powers of x in the polynomial. Instead of simple letters for these numbers, we shall now use indexed letters. For instance, instead of writing

$$ax + b,$$

we shall now write

$$a_1 x + a_0;$$

instead of

$$ax^2 + bx + c,$$

we shall write

$$a_2 x^2 + a_1 x + a_0;$$

instead of

$$ax^3 + bx^2 + cx + d,$$

we shall write

$$a_3 x^3 + a_2 x^2 + a_1 x + a_0.$$

In general, the number multiplying x^k, where k is any power occurring in the polynomial, is denoted in this symbolism by a_k, the subscript k agreeing with the power of x involved in that term.

Using the foregoing notational convention, it is now easy to define a general polynomial: A polynomial in x of nth degree is an expression of the form

(1) $$a_n x^n + a_{n-1} x^{n-1} + \ldots + a_1 x + a_0$$

in which $a_0, a_1, \ldots, a_n$ are any numbers such that $a_n \neq 0$. The a's are called the *coefficients* in the polynomial, a_0 being the coefficient of x^0, a_1 the coefficient of x, a_2 the coefficient of x^2, and so forth. The reader is cautioned that, while an expression like

(2) $$a_0 + a_1 x + 1 + x^2 - x$$

is a polynomial, a_0 and a_1, for instance, are not among its coefficients. To find the coefficients in the polynomial, we must consolidate like terms — terms with the same power of x — writing (2), in particular, as

$$a_0 + 1 + (a_1 - 1)x + x^2;$$

from this form, we recognize the coefficient of x^0 to be $a_0 + 1$, the coefficient of x to be $a_1 - 1$, and the coefficient of x^2 to be 1. A similar remark applies to any polynomial: like terms must be consolidated before what we have called the coefficients of the polynomial can be identified.

The coefficients in a given polynomial in x are fixed numbers: to change the coefficients would change the polynomial. The quantity denoted by x, however, is not to be regarded as fixed, but as capable of being any value. Hence the coefficients are called *constants*, and x is called a *variable*.

EXERCISES

1. Write the following numbers as polynomials in 10 with coefficients from 0 to 9: forty-three, nine hundred two, six hundred ninety-seven. HINT: The numbers thirty-two and one hundred seven, for instance, can be written as $3 \cdot 10 + 2$ and $1 \cdot (10)^2 + 7$, respectively. (See Chapter 3, Section 2.)

2. Write the same numbers as polynomials in 5, but with coefficients that may be 0, 1, 2, 3, or 4. HINT: The numbers thirty-two and one hundred seven can be written as $1 \cdot (5)^2 + 1 \cdot 5 + 2$ and $4 \cdot (5)^2 + 1 \cdot 5 + 2$, respectively.

3. Write the same numbers as numerals to the base 5. Review Chapter 3, Section 2, if necessary.

4. Write the same numbers as polynomials in 5, but with coefficients that may be 1, 2, 3, 4, 5 (but not 0), so that every power is represented. This exercise suggests how a numeral system with any base could be constructed without a symbol for zero, but with the base included as a digit.

2.

The algebra of polynomials

For each value of the variable x, a given polynomial (in x) has a corresponding value. (For instance, the polynomial $1 + x^2$ has the value 1 for $x = 0$, 2 for $x = 1$, 5 for $x = -2$.) It is convenient to denote this value by a symbol such as $P(x)$ (read "P of x") in which the value of x is displayed. If in this way we set $P(x) = 1 + x^2$, for instance, we understand that $P(0) = 1 + 0^2 = 1$, $P(2) = 1 + 2^2 = 5$, $P(-1) = 1 + (-1)^2 = 2$. If we set $P(x) = 1 + x + x^2$, then $P(0) = 1$, $P(2) = 1 + 2 + 4 = 7$, $P(1/2) = 1 + 1/2 + 1/4 = 7/4$, $P(-1) = 1 - 1 + 1 = 1$, $P(c) = 1 + c + c^2$. P by itself is to be understood as a symbol for the *operation*, consisting of the complete set of multiplications and additions, performed on an arbitrary number x to obtain $P(x)$. (It is nonsense to think of $P(x)$ as meaning $P \cdot x$, for "P" does not represent a number.)

When different polynomials are considered at the same time, they are distinguished by different symbols. For instance, with P referring to the polynomial $1 + x + x^2$ we might use Q for $1 - x^2$: here, $Q(x) = 1 - x^2$.

Two polynomials are said to be *equal* if, for every value of x, their two values are the same. (Sometimes, for emphasis, they are called *identically* equal.) Later, we shall see that two polynomials are equal if and only if they have the same coefficients. First, however, we turn to some rather formal matters.

a. ADDING POLYNOMIALS

Two polynomials that are just rearrangements of one another, by the preceding definition, are equal. Hence, given

$$A(x) = a_0 + a_1 x + \ldots + a_k x^k,$$

and

$$B(x) = b_0 + b_1 x + \ldots + b_k x^k,$$

we can write

$$A(x) + B(x) = a_0 + a_1 x + \ldots + a_k x^k + b_0 + b_1 x + \ldots + b_k x^k$$
$$= a_0 + b_0 + (a_1 + b_1)x + \ldots + (a_k + b_k)x^k.$$

$(A(x)$ or $B(x)$ may, of course, be of different degrees, either or both, for instance, being of degree less than k. When the degree is less than k, the coefficient of x^k and, possibly, of other powers is zero.) Thus, *the sum of two given polynomials in x is a polynomial in x whose* coefficients are the sums, respectively, of the corresponding coefficients of the given polynomials.

b. MULTIPLYING POLYNOMIALS

Polynomials can be multiplied, as well as added, with another polynomial as the result. Let us illustrate this statement by calculating the product of

$$P(x) = 1 + x + x^3$$

and

$$Q(x) = 1 - x + x^2.$$

We have, first,

$$P(x)Q(x) = (1 + x + x^3)Q(x)$$
$$= Q(x) + xQ(x) + x^3Q(x).$$

Secondly,

$$Q(x) = 1 - x + x^2$$
$$xQ(x) = x - x^2 + x^3$$
$$x^3Q(x) = x^3 - x^4 + x^5.$$

Hence, by substitution,

$$P(x)Q(x) = 1 - x + x^2$$
$$+ x - x^2 + x^3$$
$$+ x^3 - x^4 + x^5.$$

Note that the terms on the right, obtained systematically in several steps, are those that would result simply from multiplying each term in $P(x)$ by each term in $Q(x)$. Now consolidating like terms we have, as the final result,

$$P(x)Q(x) = 1 + 2x^3 - x^4 + x^5.$$

A similar scheme applies in calculating the product of any two polynomials. It is thus apparent that *the products of polynomials, as well as their sums*, are again polynomials.

EXERCISE

1. Find the polynomials equal to the following products: $(1 + x)(1 + x)$, $(1 - x)(1 - x)$, $(1 - x)(1 + x)$, $(1 - x)(1 + x + x^2)$, $(1 - x)(1 + x + x^2 + x^3)$, $(1 - x)$ $(1 + x + x^2 + x^3 + x^4)$, $(1 + x)(1 - x + x^2 - x^3 + x^4)$, $(x - a)^2$, $(x - a)(x - b)$.

3.

Further remarks on the product of polynomials

Consider two polynomials of general form,

$$A(x) = a_0 + a_1 x + a_2 x^2 + a_3 x^3 + \ldots + a_j x^j$$

and

$$B(x) = b_0 + b_1 x + b_2 x^2 + b_3 x^3 + \ldots + b_k x^k,$$

in which the a's and b's are constants, and j and k are integers at least equal to 3. (The degree of $A(x)$ is *at most j*, and may be anything less. Similarly, the degree of $B(x)$ is at most k. This is because any coefficient is permitted to be zero.) The product

$$C(x) = A(x) B(x)$$

of the polynomials is equal, as we have noted, to a polynomial:

$$C(x) = c_0 + c_1 x + c_2 x^2 + c_3 x^3 + \ldots + c_h x^h,$$

where (since $x^j x^k = x^{j+k}$) $h = j + k$. The c's are obtainable by the method described in the last section, this method consisting essentially in multiplying (with regard for signs) each term in the one polynomial, $A(x)$, by each term in the other polynomial, $B(x)$, adding, and consolidating. The values of the c's obtained depend, of course, on the values of the a's and b's and, when the latter are specified (as specific numbers), can be numerically calculated. We decline, however, thus to specialize the a's and b's, since to do so is to particularize the polynomials $A(x)$ and $B(x)$. Instead, we aim for a general treatment, which would, in effect, cover all possible pairs of polynomials at once. The outcome of such a treatment, in which, of course, the a's and b's are left unspecified, is a set of formulas giving each c as an expression in pertinent a's and b's.

The formulas for some of the c's are a little tedious. Hence, we shall confine ourselves here to a common situation in which only a few of the simpler formulas arise. This is the situation in which x is held to relatively small values such that, say, x^4 is negligible for the purpose in view,† the polynomials considered then differing in-appreciably from polynomials of the third degree. We illustrate this situation with

$$P(x) = 1 + x - 20x^4 + 10x^5.$$

If x is held to numbers in absolute value ‡ less than $1/10$, $20x^4$ will be less than .002 and $10x^5$ less than .0001, and $P(x)$ is approximated by its first two terms, $1 + x$, with an error (either way) of at most .0021. If x is restricted to numbers less, in absolute value, than $1/100$, the error of this approximation would be less than .000000201.

EXERCISE

1. Suppose the polynomial $P(x) = 1 + 2x - x^2 + 3x^3$ to be approximated by its first two terms $1 + 2x$. State restrictions upon x under which the error $|P(x) - (1 + 2x)|$ will not exceed (a) .01, (b) .001, (c) .0001.

If the fourth and higher powers of x are deemed negligible, we can be content to calculate just the first four terms of the product. At the same time, only the first four terms of $A(x)$ or $B(x)$ are of interest, later terms contributing in $C(x)$ only to the higher powers of x, which are to be neglected. Generally, we shall not write explicitly quantities we intend to neglect, putting in place of them the three dots, "...," already familiar in a slightly different usage. Thus, we have

(1) $$\begin{aligned} C(x) = A(x)B(x) &= (a_0 + a_1x + a_2x^2 + a_3x^3 + \ldots)B(x) \\ &= a_0B(x) + a_1xB(x) + a_2x^2B(x) + a_3x^3B(x) + \ldots. \end{aligned}$$

Now

$$\begin{aligned} a_0B(x) &= a_0(b_0 + b_1x + b_2x^2 + b_3x^3 + \ldots) \\ &= a_0b_0 + a_0b_1x + a_0b_2x^2 + a_0b_3x^3 + \ldots \end{aligned}$$

and

$$\begin{aligned} a_1xB(x) &= a_1x(b_0 + b_1x + b_2x^2 + \ldots) \\ &= a_1b_0x + a_1b_1x^2 + a_1b_2x^3 + \ldots. \end{aligned}$$

---

† So long as x, if positive, is less than one, its powers x, x^2, x^3, x^4, ... diminish in value. Similarly, with x between 0 and -1, the powers of x decrease in absolute value as the exponents increase.

‡ We recall that the absolute value of a positive number or zero is that number itself. The absolute value of a negative number, $-c$, is the positive number c. The absolute value of an arbitrary number x is written $|x|$. Thus,

$$\begin{aligned} |x| &= x \text{ if } x \text{ is positive or zero} \\ &= -x \text{ if } x \text{ is negative.} \end{aligned}$$

(Note that the expression for $B(x)$ could be broken off sooner when multiplied by a_1x than when multiplied by a_0.) In the same way, we find

$$a_2x^2B(x) = a_2x^2(b_0 + b_1x + \ldots)$$
$$= a_2b_0x^2 + a_2b_1x^3 + \ldots$$

and

$$a_3x^3B(x) = a_3x^3(b_0 + \ldots)$$
$$= a_3b_0x^3 + \ldots .$$

Substituting these results into (1) gives us

$$C(x) = a_0b_0 + a_0b_1x + a_0b_2x^2 + a_0b_3x^3$$
$$+ a_1b_0x + a_1b_1x^2 + a_1b_2x^3$$
$$+ a_2b_0x^2 + a_2b_1x^3 + a_3b_0x^3 + \ldots$$

so that, after consolidating like terms, we have, finally,

$$C(x) = a_0b_0 + (a_0b_1 + a_1b_0)x + (a_0b_2 + a_1b_1 + a_2b_0)x^2$$
$$+ (a_0b_3 + a_1b_2 + a_2b_1 + a_3b_0)x^3 + \ldots .$$

The formulas we desired for the first four coefficients in $C(x)$ thus are:

$$c_0 = a_0b_0$$
$$c_1 = a_0b_1 + a_1b_0$$
$$c_2 = a_0b_2 + a_1b_1 + a_2b_0$$
$$c_3 = a_0b_3 + a_1b_2 + a_2b_1 + a_3b_0.$$

Similar formulas for the later coefficients, if also desired, could be found in the same way.

EXERCISES

2. Find the coefficient of x^4 in the product $C(x)$.

3. Find the first four terms in the polynomials obtained by expanding the following expressions (i.e., carrying out the implied multiplications): $(1 + x - x^2)(1 + x + x^2 - x^3)$, $(a + x)^3$, $(a + x)^4$, $(a + x)^5$, $(a + x)^6$.

4. The area of a square is far from proportional to the length of its sides. Yet if the side length s is altered by an amount h, the altered sides having length $s + h$ (Figure 5-1), the resulting alteration in area is approximately proportional to the alteration in the sides. Suppose the sides of the original square, for instance, to be 25 feet long ($s = 25$ feet). We shall compare the areas of this square and the square with sides $h + 25$ feet. Show that if $|h|$ is less than 2 feet, the difference between the areas is approximately equal to $50h$ with an error of less than one per cent. Then state and prove an analogous result relating to the volumes of cubes.

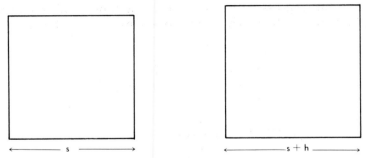

Figure 5-1　*Squares with slightly differing sides.*

5. Work out expansions up to terms of second degree of the first twelve powers of $1 + x$. As guides, we give:

$$(1 + x)^2 = 1 + 2x + x^2,$$
$$(1 + x)^3 = 1 + 3x + 3x^2 + \ldots,$$
$$(1 + x)^{12} = 1 + 12x + 66x^2 + \ldots.$$

6.† When we say that a bank pays interest at the rate of x per cent per year, compounded semiannually, we mean that the rate is $x/2$ per cent per half-year, compounded (see Exercise 11, Chapter 2, Section 1b). When we say that the rate is x per cent per year, compounded quarterly, we mean that it is $x/4$ per cent per quarter-year, compounded. (Thus, 6 per cent per year, compounded semiannually, is 3 per cent per half-year, compounded. Similarly, 6 per cent per year, compounded quarterly, is 3/2 per cent per quarter-year, compounded.) Suppose one intends to deposit a certain sum at interest for a fixed period of 3 years and has the following alternatives: 6 per cent per year, compounded quarterly, or 6 1/16 per cent per year, compounded semiannually.

    (a) Which rate is the more advantageous to the depositor?

    (b) What rate, compounded semiannually, would give approximately the same total amount at the end of 3 years as 6 per cent, compounded quarterly?

---

†I am indebted for this example to Professor M. S. Klamkin.

4.

The uniqueness of the coefficients of a polynomial

When are two polynomials,

$$A(x) = a_0 + a_1 x + \ldots + a_k x^k$$

and

$$B(x) = b_0 + b_1 x + \ldots + b_k x^k,$$

identically equal? (Any coefficient being permitted to vanish, the polynomials compared may be of different degrees.)

When is a polynomial

$$C(x) = c_0 + c_1 x + \ldots + c_k x^k$$

identically zero? This question is a special case (with $A(x)$ replaced by $C(x)$ and $B(x)$ replaced by 0) of the previous. The answer to this question will be that $C(x)$ *vanishes identically when, and only when, all its coefficients are zero.* We shall prove this in a moment, but first show that the question asked originally is reducible to this special case. This is because the equation $A(x) = B(x)$, assumed to be an identity, implies that $A(x) - B(x) = 0$, i.e., that

$$(a_0 - b_0) + (a_1 - b_1)x + \ldots + (a_k - b_k)x^k = 0$$

for all x. In fact, the last result can be written as

$$c_0 + c_1 x + \ldots + c_k x^k = 0$$

with $c_0 = a_0 - b_0$, $c_1 = a_1 - b_1$, . . ., $c_k = a_k - b_k$. Hence, if we knew that such an identity implies

$$c_0 = 0, \ c_1 = 0, \ \ldots, \ c_k = 0,$$

we would have $a_0 - b_0 = 0$, $a_1 - b_1 = 0$, . . ., $a_k - b_k = 0$, and thus

$$a_0 = b_0, \ a_1 = b_1, \ \ldots, \ a_k = b_k.$$

It would then follow that *two polynomials are identically equal only if their respective coefficients are the same.*

All that remains is to prove that, when

(1) $$C(x) = c_0 + c_1 x + c_2 x^2 + \ldots + c_k x^k = 0$$

for every value of x, all the coefficients $c_0, c_1, c_2, \ldots, c_k$ are zero. We begin by examining $C(0)$, i.e., the number obtained by substituting 0 for x in $C(x)$. Since $C(x)$ vanishes by assumption for *every* value of x, $C(0) = 0$. From (1), however, $C(0) = c_0$. Hence,

$$c_0 = 0,$$

and taking account of this fact in (1) we have

$$C(x) = c_1 x + c_2 x^2 + \ldots + c_k x^k$$
$$= x(c_1 + c_2 x + \ldots + c_k x^{k-1}).$$

If $x \neq 0$, we may divide by x to obtain

(2) $$C(x)/x = c_1 + c_2 x + \ldots + c_k x^{k-1} = 0.$$

From this we shall show $c_1 = 0$. Hampered by the restriction $x \neq 0$, we are forced, however, into a slightly different argument from that employed for c_0. Let x run through the following unending succession of *nonzero* numbers: .1, .01, .001, .0001, .00001, .000001, .0000001, and so forth. As x takes these values successively, the terms $c_2 x, \ldots,$ $c_k x^{k-1}$ diminish to values that, no matter what the constants $c_2, \ldots, c_k$ may be, are as slight as you please. Yet, by (2),

$$c_1 + \text{these ever more negligible terms}$$

unvaryingly is zero. This can be so only if

$$c_1 = 0.$$

Now we strike out c_1 from the right side of (2), factor the first power of x and (still requiring $x \neq 0$) divide by it, let x run through the same succession of numbers as before, and conclude that

$$c_2 = 0.$$

Further repetitions of this argument prove all the remaining c's in succession to be zero, as contended.

CHAPTER 6

PATTERNS OF MATHEMATICAL STRUCTURE — GROUPS

1.

Definition of a group and numerical examples

We can regard the general laws of arithmetic as blueprints of the abstract structure of arithmetic. Since the beginning of the 19th Century, such blueprints have been drawn up for other mathematical systems, many of which do not deal with ordinary numbers or arithmetical operations. (Simple examples will be given later.) Yet the blueprints of these systems — their general laws — often show patterns astonishingly like those that occur in arithmetic. Arithmetic was found to be a mirror of structure for the most diverse fields, and algebra accordingly was broadened to become the general study of structural relations in mathematical systems.

One of the most frequently found patterns of mathematical structure is described in the concept of *group*. In a group, the common attributes of addition and multiplication are abstracted. Their essence is distilled, so to speak, and it proves surprisingly potent. First we shall enumerate these common attributes of the arithmetical operations. Then we shall define a group and illustrate the definition with a variety of elementary examples, two of which will lead us into a brief theoretical discussion. In the last two sections of Chapter 7, we shall present some striking applications of the idea of a group in geometry.

These are the properties of addition and multiplication in ordinary arithmetic that are generalized in the concept of group:

(1) When two numbers are added or multiplied, the result is another number.

(2) Addition and multiplication are both associative.

(3) Adding zero, or multiplying by one, leaves a number unaltered. Thus, the numbers zero and one are "neutral" in addition and multiplication, respectively.

(4) If a number is added to its negative, zero is obtained; if a nonzero number is multiplied by its reciprocal, 1 is obtained. Each number thus has a "companion" number such that adding any number and its companion gives the additively "neutral" number (zero). Each nonzero number has another "companion" such that multiplying the number by this companion gives the multiplicatively "neutral" number (one).

Now to define a group, let S designate a set, or collection, of objects, which we shall denote by lower case letters, a, b, c, and so forth. These objects are referred to as *members,* or *elements,* of the set S. When we say that two members of S are *equal* (e.g., writing $a = b$), we shall mean that they are identical. Let a rule be given that associates some object with each pair of objects in S; the association defined by such a rule is called a *binary* association or correspondence. If a and b, in particular, denote objects belonging to S (they need not be different objects), we shall represent the object associated with them by the given rule as

$$a * b.$$

(For instance, S might be the set of all numbers, and the rule might associate with any two numbers, a and b, their sum $a + b$.) The set S is said to form a group under the given binary rule if the collection and the rule together have the following four properties:

(1) Each object associated by the rule with a pair of members of S also belongs to S: i.e., a and b being members of S, $a * b$ again is a member of S. (We also express this property by saying that S is *closed* under the given rule.)

(2) For any a, b, c of S,

$$a * (b * c) = (a * b) * c.$$

(In other words, the rule is *associative.*)

(3) S contains an element, denoted by e, such that $a * e = e * a = a$ for every member a of S. This element is called *the identity element* of the group.

(4) For any member a of S, an element x of S exists such that $a * x = x * a = e$. This element is written as $x = a^{-1}$ and is called *the inverse of* a.

The group is called a *commutative group* if:

(5) For any two members, a, b of S, $a * b = b * a$. (The given rule is then said to be commutative.)

A group with just a finite number of members is called a *finite group*. A group with infinitely many members is called an *infinite group*.

We shall write $(S, *)$ to denote the mathematical system in which a given set S is considered together with a specified rule, symbolized by $*$, that associates an object with each pair of members of S. We do not necessarily assume that $(S, *)$ is a group.

EXERCISES

In each of the following exercises, a set and a rule are specified. Answer the following questions in each instance:

(a) Is the set finite or infinite, i.e., are there finitely many or infinitely many members in the set?

(b) Is the set with the rule closed?

(c) Is there an identity element? If so, find it.

(d) Does each member of the set have an inverse? If so, describe how to find it.

(e) Does the set together with the rule form a group? Is the group commutative?

1. N is the collection of all integers which are evenly divisible by 10, and the rule for combining is ordinary addition.

2. Z is the set of all positive and negative numbers and the number zero, and the rule of combining is ordinary multiplication.

3. Z' is the same set as Z in Exercise 2, except that the number zero is omitted. The rule is ordinary multiplication.

4. Again as in Exercise 3 consider the set Z', but this time under division.

5. Let N be the set of positive and negative integers under the operation of ordinary multiplication.

6. Positive integers under addition.

7. Positive integers under multiplication.

8. Positive integers under division.

9. Positive integers under subtraction.

10. Negative numbers under multiplication.

11. Negative numbers under division.

12. Negative numbers under subtraction.

13. Negative integers under multiplication.

14. The single element zero under addition.

15. The single element zero under subtraction.

16. The single element zero under division.

17. The single element zero under multiplication.

18. The elements 1 and -1 under multiplication.

19. The single element 1 under multiplication.

20. The single element -1 under multiplication.

21. Let $A = \{1, 2, 3, 4\}$. (This means that A is the set consisting of the four numbers named.) We shall denote the *larger* of two numbers a and b by a ⊕ b. (For instance, 1 ⊕ 2 = 2, 4 ⊕ 3 = 4.)

    (a) Is A closed under the operation ⊕?

    (b) Is ⊕ associative in A?

    (c) Does A contain an identity relative to the operation ⊕?

    (d) Is (A, ⊕) a group?

    (e) Is ⊕ commutative?

Justify all your statements.

2.

Further examples of groups

In the previous section we saw many examples of groups formed by different sets of numbers under the ordinary arithmetical operations. In this section we shall see some quite different examples of groups.

Example 1: Suppose that it is June and that we wish to know what the name of the month 27 months from now will be. Since there are 12 months in a year and the months repeat themselves in periods of 12, we would "cast out," or disregard, two multiples of 12 months and count three months from June to arrive at the fact that 27 months from now it will be September. Similarly, if today were Tuesday and we desired to know the day of the week just 33 days from now, we would cast out 28 (or four multiples of seven) and count five days from Tuesday to arrive at the answer, Sunday. Again, if it were 12 o'clock noon, and we wished to know the hour of the day just 60 hours from now, we would disregard 48 hours of that time—for this would bring us back again to 12 o'clock noon—and count the remaining 12 hours to arrive at our answer of 12 o'clock midnight.

In each of these cases we concerned ourselves only with remainders after division, in the first case "casting out" all multiples of 12, in the second case all multiplies of seven, and in the third case all multiples of 24.

Let us observe the second case more carefully. In the context of this example, it makes sense to identify the numbers 7, 14, 21, 28, and so forth, or to associate them with one another, for they are all of the same kind, exact multiples of seven, and thus numbers that will bring us back to Tuesday. Similarly, the numbers 9, 16, 23, 30, and so forth are identified, or associated, with one another, because they all have remainders of two upon division by seven and thus all give rise to the answer Thursday in our example.

With this example in mind, let us then consider the set S = (0, 1, 2, 3, 4, 5, 6) and the rule symbolized by ! which associates any two members of S with the remainder that is obtained when the sum of these two numbers is divided by seven. For example 4 ! 5 would mean: add four to five, divide the sum (nine) by seven, and write the remainder, two. Thus, 4 ! 5 = 2. Table 6-1 summarizes this rule. To use this table to find 5 ! 6, for example, we read the number 5 as the sixth number in the first column, we read the number six as the seventh number in the first row, and we read the result as the number 4 in the sixth row and the seventh column of the table. We leave it as an exercise for the student to verify that $(S, !)$ forms a finite commutative group.

Table 6-1

!	0	1	2	3	4	5	6
0	0	1	2	3	4	5	6
1	1	2	3	4	5	6	0
2	2	3	4	5	6	0	1
3	3	4	5	6	0	1	2
4	4	5	6	0	1	2	3
5	5	6	0	1	2	3	4
6	6	0	1	2	3	4	5

†*Example 2*: As an example of a non-numerical group structure, consider the set P of tire rotations on a car. (We use "rotation" in the sense of changing the positions of tires from their locations to prevent wear.) P consists of the four rotations I, R_1, R_2, R_3, described as follows:

I is the rotation (or more correctly lack of rotation) that leaves each tire on a car in exactly the same position it had had. Under this "rotation," the front right, front left, rear right, and rear left tires remain unchanged.

R_1 is the tire rotation that interchanges the front right and the front left tires and also interchanges the rear right and the rear left tires.

R_2 is the tire rotation that moves the tire in the front left position to the rear left position, the tire in the rear left position to the front right position, the tire in the front right position to the rear right position, and the tire in the rear right position to the front left position.

R_3 is the tire rotation that moves the tire in the front left position to the rear right position, the tire in the rear right position to the front right position, the tire in the front right position to the rear left position, and the tire in the rear left position to the front left position. These four tire rotations are represented schematically in Figure 6-1.

---

†This example was suggested by an exercise in *Abstract Algebra* by J. Fang, Shaum Publishing Co., 1963.

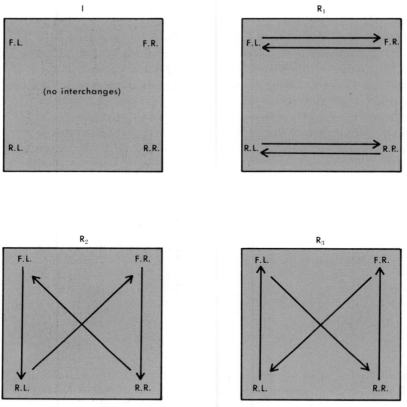

Figure 6-1   *Patterns of tire rotations.*

If R and S represented two tire rotations, by $S * R$ we shall mean the change in tire position accomplished by first carrying out R and then S. For example, let us find $R_2 * R_1$. For this purpose, we label the tires in their original positions A, B, C, D, as in Figure 6-2, and see how they permute when we apply first R_1 and then R_2. For any tire, say A, let

$$R_1(A)$$

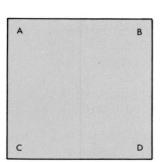

Figure 6-2   *The original position of four tires.*

denote the position taken after R_1 has been applied, and

$$(R_2 \circ R_1)(A)$$

the place occupied as a result of executing $R_2 \circ R_1$, i.e., of carrying out first R_1 and then R_2. (The operation carried out first upon A is written the nearest to A, and so forth.) To describe $R_2 \circ R_1$ is to tell its effect upon every tire, i.e., to enumerate

$$(R_2 \circ R_1)(A), \ (R_2 \circ R_1)(B), \ (R_2 \circ R_1)(C), \ (R_2 \circ R_1)(D).$$

This is easily done from Figure 6-1. For instance, again consider A. Since A originally occupies the F. L. position, $R_1(A)$ is in the F. R. position and $(R_2 \circ R_1)(A)$ thus at R. R. position. The other three tires can be traced through similarly, and all the results are depicted in Figure 6-3. But an examination of Figure 6-1 shows that these final positions are the same as those we would have obtained if we had applied R_3 to the original tire configuration. We conclude that $R_1 \circ R_2 = R_3$. We leave it as an exercise for the student to show that $(P, \circ)$ is a finite commutative group with four members.

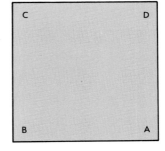

Figure 6-3 The positions of the tires after executing $R_2 \circ R_1$.

This group of tire rotations has another property of some interest. Suppose a motorist desired his tires to occupy, in the course of time, all of the positions that would result from applying R_1, R_2, R_3, or R_4 to the existing configuration of tires. Would he have to be very clever to arrange this, keep records punctiliously, give his mechanic different directions each month? No, he would not, for R_2 alone, repeated for each new rotation, would produce all of the desired configurations in the course of time. Mathematically, if we write $R_2 \circ R_2 = R_2^2$, $R_2 \circ (R_2 \circ R_2) = R_2^3$, and so forth, we have:

$$R_2^2 = R_1, \ R_2^3 = R_3, \ R_2^4 = I,$$
$$R_2^5 = R_2, \ R_2^6 = R_1, \ R_2^7 = R_3, \ R_2^8 = I, \text{ and so forth.}$$

This means that applying R_2 twice in succession leads to the configuration that would have been obtained from R_1, applying R_2 three times in succession leads to the configuration that would have been obtained from R_3, etc. (We leave it to the reader to prove these relations.) The successive powers of R_2 thus generate all the elements of this group. Once R_2 has been described, the group can be presented as consisting of

$$I, R_2, R_2^2, R_2^3,$$

the identity transformation and the first three powers of R_2, the fourth power being again the identity.

A group consisting solely of the identity and consecutive powers (starting with the first) of one of its elements is said to be *cyclic*. The tire rotation group thus is cyclic.

Example 3: This example is another group of tire rotations. The symbol ∗ will have the same significance as before: if R and S represent two tire rotations, $S ∗ R$ will mean the change in tire positions that is accomplished by first carrying out R and then S; we can describe ∗ as the operation of "compounding" R and S, or as the "composition" of R and S. The tire rotations in this group are described graphically in Figure 6-4. (We shall not trouble to put them into

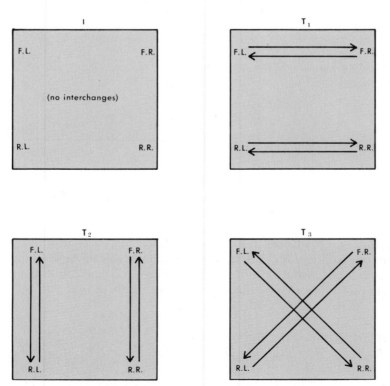

Figure 6-4   A second tire rotation group.

words.) We leave it to the student to verify that the set consisting of the four tire rotations I, T_1, T_2, T_3 is a commutative group under the composition rule which is depicted in Table 6-2. In this group, every element is its own inverse. This was not true in the first tire rotation group. Hence, this group has a different structure, although the number of members (four) is the same. Can we devise other methods of tire rotation that will make up still different four-member groups? A little study of group theory in the following section will show that we cannot.

Table 6-2   *Composition rule for second tire rotation group*

$*$	I	T_1	T_2	T_3
I	I	T_1	T_2	T_3
T_1	T_1	I	T_3	T_2
T_2	T_2	T_3	I	T_1
T_3	T_3	T_2	T_1	I

EXERCISES

1. For the group of Example 3, find the result of applying the following tire rotations to the tire in the rear left position.

    (a) $T_1 * T_2 * T_3$ (b) $T_3 * T_2 * T_1$
    (c) $T_2 * T_3 * T_1$ (d) $T_1 * T_3 * T_2$

2. For the group of Example 2, find the result of applying the following tire rotations to the tire in the front right position.

    (a) $R_1 * R_2 * R_3$ (b) $R_3 * R_2 * R_1$
    (c) $R_2 * R_3 * R_1$ (d) $R_1 * R_3 * R_2$

3. Do any other elements besides R_2 in Example 2 generate all the elements of that group?

4. Do any elements of the group of Example 3 generate all the elements of that group?

5. In Example 2 consider all the elements generated by powers of R_1. Do these elements form a subgroup of the group? †

6. Answer Exercise 5 for all the elements in the group of Example 2.

7. Answer Exercise 5 for all the elements in the group of Example 3.

8. Let $(G, *)$ be any cyclic group of just four members, which we may denote by

$$e, a, a^2, a^3,$$

---

† If $(S, *)$ is a group, and T is a subset of S (i.e., each member of T belongs to S) such that $(T, *)$ is a group, then $(T, *)$ is called a subgroup of $(S, *)$.

respectively, e being the identity. (Here, $a^2 = a * a$, $a^3 = (a * a) * a$, and

$$a^4 = [(a * a) * a] * (a = e.)$$

(a) Which of the four members is a^{-1}?

(b) Which is $(a^2)^{-1}$?

(c) Prove that this group is commutative.

Interpret these results in terms of tire rotations, as in Example 1.

In the following three exercises, a set and a rule defining a binary correspondence are specified. State which group properties the set and the rule together possess, find the identity element (if one exists), and give the inverse of each element. Also make a composition table for the rule.

9. Let S consist of the two numbers 0 and 1. For any x and y in S, define $x * y$ to be the remainder obtained after dividing $x + y$ by 2. (For instance, $0 * 1 = 1$, $1 * 1 = 0$.)

10. Let T consist of the numbers 0, 1, 2. For any x, y in T, define $x * y$ to be the remainder obtained after dividing $x + y$ by 3.

11. Let R consist of the numbers 1, 2, 3, 4. For x, y in R, define $x * y$ to be the remainder obtained after dividing xy by 5.

12. Write a composition table for Examples 1 and 2 of this section. Find the identity element and all the inverses.

13. Suppose that S consists of four objects denoted by a, b, c, d and that $*$ is a binary operation with the composition table depicted in Table 6-3. Prove that $(S, *)$ is a finite commutative group.

*	a	b	c	d
a	a	b	c	d
b	b	c	d	a
c	c	d	a	b
d	d	a	b	c

Table 6-3

14. Let X consist of the numbers 0, 1. For x, y in X, define $x * y$ to be the larger of x and y. Is $(X, *)$ a group? Why, or why not?

15. Let L consist of the numbers 1, 2, 3, 4, 5, 6. For x, y in L, define $x * y$ to be the remainder obtained after dividing xy by 7. Write the composition table for $*$. Is $(L, *)$ a group? Explain.

16. Let N be the set of positive integers. For a, b in N, define

$$a * b = a + ab + b.$$

(a) Is $(N, *)$ associative? Explain!

(b) Is $(N, *)$ commutative? Explain!

(c) Is $(N, *)$ closed? Explain!

(d) Does $(N, *)$ have an identity element? Explain!

(e) Does each element in N have an inverse in N?

(f) Is (N, ⊛) a group? Explain!

17. If (S, ⊛) is a group, show that the subset† of S consisting just of the identity element forms a subgroup of S.

18. Find all possible subgroups of all the finite groups among the examples.

19. Label the four corners of a cardboard square; color one face of the cardboard red and the other face blue. Taking the square with two sides vertical and the other two horizontal, consider the following transformations upon it:

I no movement of the square

R a rotation of the square 90° clockwise

S a rotation of the square 180° clockwise

T a rotation of the square 270° clockwise

V a flip of the square to its reverse side about its vertical axis of symmetry

H a flip of the square to its reverse side about its horizontal axis of symmetry

D a flip of the square to its reverse side about the axis going from the lower left corner of the square to the upper right corner

E a flip of the square to its reverse side about the axis going from the lower right corner of the square to the upper left corner

(a) Consider two transformations to be equal if, applied to the same initial position of the square, they result in the same final position. Prove that this set of transformations is closed under the operation of compounding.

(b) Prove that this set forms a noncommutative group under the operation of compounding.

20. Consider the equilateral triangle illustrated in Figure 6-5. Consider five transformations of this triangle: I, R, F_1, F_2, F_3, which move the triangle as follows:

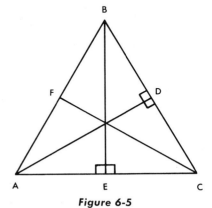

I no movement of the triangle

R rotation of the triangle 60° clockwise

F_1 rotation of the triangle about the axis AD

F_2 rotation of the triangle about the axis BE

F_3 rotation of the triangle about the axis FC

If U and V are any two transformations, by

$$U \circledast V$$

Figure 6-5

we shall mean the transformation that results when V is applied to the triangle and then U. Show that the given transformations and all those generated from them by compounding form a noncommutative group under the rule of composition ⊛.

---

†See the previous footnote.

3.

Some group theory

The last section concluded with two groups of quite different structure having four members each. We asked whether a third kind of group consisting of four members might exist. We shall prove here that there is no third kind; the two we have found are the only ones possible.

In preparation, we must prove several general facts about groups. In all our abstract reasoning, we shall continue to rely upon the Principle of Substitution first given in Chapter 2, which declares that an expression is not altered in value if any quantity in it is replaced by an equal quantity. The Principle of Substitution gives us, in particular, these rules for group elements:

(I) If $a = b$ and $b = c$, then $a = c$.

(II) If $a = b$ and $c = d$, then $a * c = b * d$.

As a special case of (II), we have:

(II′) If $a = b$, then $a * c = b * c$.

Note, however, that if $a = b$, it does not necessarily follow that $a * c = c * b$, since $b * c$ need not equal $c * b$. The equality will hold, however, whenever $*$ is a commutative operation.

Theorem 1. The identity element in any group is unique. More precisely, if a group $(S, *)$ has members a and f such that $a * f = a$, then $f = e$, where e is the identity element; and if g is a group element such that $g * a = a$, then $g = e$.

PROOF: The element a^{-1} has the property that $a^{-1} * a = e$. Since $a * f = a$, we have by (II′)

$$a^{-1} * (a * f) = a^{-1} * a = e,$$

while, by associativity,

$$a^{-1} * (a * f) = (a^{-1} * a) * f = e * f = f,$$

e being the identity element. Hence, $e = f$, and the first statement is proved. The second statement in the theorem is similarly proved.

Theorem 2. The inverse of any group element is unique. More precisely, if a group $(S, *)$ has members a and x such that $a * x = e$, where e is the identity element, then $x = a^{-1}$. Similarly, if y is an element such that $y * a = e$, then $y = a^{-1}$.

PROOF: Suppose a and x are members of the group such that

$$a * x = e.$$

We must show that $x = a^{-1}$. By (II'),

$$a^{-1} * (a * x) = a^{-1} * e$$
$$= a^{-1},$$

while the left member of this equality reduces to x, owing to associativity and to the property of an inverse. We thus have

$$x = a^{-1},$$

as contended. The second statement of the theorem is proved similarly.

Theorem 2 has the following corollary.

Theorem 2′.   The inverse of the inverse of any element is that element itself; i.e., for any group member a,

$$(a^{-1})^{-1} = a.$$

PROOF: The inverse of an arbitrary element a is the element x such that

$$a * x = x * a = e.$$

Theorem 2 states that only one such x exists. We denote it by a^{-1}: thus,

$$a * a^{-1} = a^{-1} * a = e.$$

The inverse of a^{-1}, in particular, is the group member y such that

$$a^{-1} * y = y * a^{-1} = e,$$

and just one such y exists. The foregoing shows that these relations are satisfied by the choice $y = a$. Hence, a is the desired inverse of a^{-1}, as the theorem asserts.

In arithmetic, the facts that

$$\frac{1}{1/2} = 2 \text{ and } -(-1) = 1$$

are both instances of this theorem.

The next result is a straightforward generalization of the arithmetic fact that for any pair of numbers a, b with $a \neq 0$, the condition

$$ax = b$$

is satisfied for

$$x = a^{-1} * b$$

and for no other number.

Theorem 3.   If a and b are any members of a group $(S, *)$, then the conditions

$$a * x = b \quad \text{and} \quad y * a = b$$

are satisfied by the values

$$x = a^{-1} * b \quad \text{and} \quad y = b * a^{-1}$$

and by no other values.

PROOF: If $a * x = b$, then by applying a^{-1} to each side upon the left, we have

$$a^{-1} * (a * x) = a^{-1} * b.$$

By associativity,

$$a^{-1} * (a * x) = (a^{-1} * a) * x$$
$$= e * x$$
$$= x.$$

Hence, $x = a^{-1} * b$. We have shown that *if $a * x = b$, then $x = a^{-1} * b$.* It remains to be verified that the value obtained, $x = a^{-1} * b$, actually satisfies the condition $a * x = b$, i.e., that $a * (a^{-1} * b) = b$. A simple calculation shows this to be true:

$$a * (a^{-1} * b) = (a * a^{-1}) * b$$
$$= e * b$$
$$= b.$$

The statements about x thus are verified, and those concerning y follow similarly.

EXERCISE

1. Consider any group $(S, *)$.
   (a) If a, b, c are members of the group such that $a * b = a * c$, prove that $b = c$.
   (b) By specializing this result, derive two "cancellation" rules of arithmetic.

Theorem 3 is manifested very concretely in the fact that, in a composition table, all the members of the group enter each row and also enter each column. Consider, for instance, the second row of Table 6-2 representing the second tire rotation group.

Table 6-2 *Composition rule for second tire rotation group*

*	I	T_1	T_2	T_3
I	I	T_1	T_2	T_3
T_1	T_1	I	T_3	T_2
T_2	T_2	T_3	I	T_1
T_3	T_3	T_2	T_1	I

The four entries in this row represent the multiplications

$$T_1 * x,$$

with x taking successively the values I, T_1, T_2, T_3 that head the columns. To say that all the members of the group appear in this row is to say that, for any group member z, an element y exists such that

$$T_1 * y = z.$$

This is just what Theorem 3 affirms. Thus, the second row, in particular, does indeed contain all four elements of the group and, for the same reason, all the other rows and all the columns also contain them. Since each row and each column has exactly four entries, each row and each column contains each group member once and only once. The analogous statement can be made of the table for any group.

Theorem 4. In any group with exactly four elements, an element distinct from the identity element exists with the property that it is its own inverse.

PROOF: Let $(S, *)$ represent a group. Suppose a is any element of S distinct from e, that is, $a \neq e$. If a^2 were equal to e—i.e., if $a * a = e$—we would have $a = a^{-1}$ and be finished. So let us suppose that $a^2 \neq e$. Since $(S, *)$ is a group, and a is not its own inverse, another element, call it b, is the inverse of a: $b = a^{-1}$. Since $a * b = e$, a is the inverse of b (Theorem 2). Note that b cannot equal e, since in this case $a * b$ would be equal to a. Thus, three of the four elements in $S - e$, a, b—now are accounted for. Call the fourth element c. This c has an inverse. The inverse of c cannot be e, since $c * e = c$; it cannot be a or b since each of a and b is the other's inverse. The only remaining possibility is that c be its own inverse, i.e., $c * c = e$. Thus, c is the element sought, and the theorem is proved.

Suppose we consider now an arbitrary group with four elements. We represent it by $(S, !)$. (We do not specify what the objects of S are, nor do we indicate just how the rule $!$ operates upon them.) We know by Theorem 3 that there is an element in S, let us call it a, with the property that $a^2 = e$ (i.e., $a \,!\, a = e$). Let us denote by b and c the remaining two elements of S, so that $S = (e, a, b, c)$.

If we try to set up a table for $(S, !)$, we obtain Table 6-4 at once from the property of e and the fact that $a^2 = e$.

!	e	a	b	c
e	e	a	b	c
a	a	e		
b	b			
c	c			

Table 6-4   Incomplete table for group with four members

Now recall that in the table for a group, all the members of the group enter each row and also enter each column.

Therefore, to complete the second row (the row labeled at the left by a) in Table 6-4, we must enter b in one of the blank spaces and c in the other. But we cannot have $a \,!\, b = b$, which would imply that $a = e$ (Theorem 1). Therefore, we must enter c in the third space of the second row and b in the fourth. Similar reasoning applies to the second column, and Table 6-5 shows the result.

!	e	a	b	c
e	e	a	b	c
a	a	e	c	b
b	b	c		
c	c	b		

Table 6-5   A more complete table for a group with four members

To complete the third row (the row labeled at the left by b) in Table 6-5, we must enter a in one of the blank spaces and e in the other. Table 6-5 then becomes either part (a) or part (b) of Table 6-6.

Table 6-6   Partial completions of the table for a group with four members

!	e	a	b	c		!	e	a	b	c
e	e	a	b	c		e	e	a	b	c
a	a	e	c	b		a	a	e	c	b
b	b	c	e	a		b	b	c	a	e
c	c	b				c	c	b		
		(a)						(b)		

The last two columns in parts (a) and (b) of Table 6-6 can be completed in only one way, parts (a) and (b) of Table 6-7 showing the result.

Table 6-7 *Possible completions of the table for a four-member group*

!	e	a	b	c
e	e	a	b	c
a	a	e	c	b
b	b	c	e	a
c	c	b	a	e

(a)

!	e	a	b	c
e	e	a	b	c
a	a	e	c	b
b	b	c	a	e
c	c	b	e	a

(b)

Do these tables both represent groups? In constructing them, we did not heed *all* the requirements — in particular, associativity — imposed upon groups. Hence, our methods of construction do not insure automatically that the resulting tables define groups. They do insure that no four-member group exists with any other table than one of these, and therefore, that *at most two* such groups exist. Upon testing, we find that both parts of Table 6-7 do represent groups.

EXERCISES

2. Which of the two types of groups of four elements (Table 6-7) is cyclic? Which element of the group generates the group?

3. Which of the two types of groups of four elements (Table 6-7) is like that of Example 3 of Section 2?

4. Is it true that any group with four elements is commutative?

5. Show that any group with only two elements is commutative.

6. Suppose $X = (a, b, e)$, i.e., X consists of three members, a, b, and e, and suppose $(X, *)$ is a group. Prove that $a * b = b * a = e$.

7. Prove that any group with exactly three elements is cyclic.

8. Prove that any cyclic group is commutative.

9. Is it necessary that any commutative group be cyclic? Explain.

10. Prove that any group with exactly five elements is cyclic. HINT: We can represent the members of the group as e, a, b, a^{-1}, b^{-1}. Use the fact that any product, such as $a * b$, belongs to the group and thus coincides with one of the five members listed.

4.

Group diagrams

One way to describe the structure of a group with a finite number of elements is to give its cyclic subgroups. This can be done very clearly by means of a diagram, as we now illustrate with the groups specified in Table 6-7. Taking up the second part first, we recopy its table for reference as Table 6-8. From this multiplication table, we

!	e	a	b	c
e	e	a	b	c
a	a	e	c	b
b	b	c	a	e
c	c	b	e	a

Table 6-8   *Multiplication table for a particular four-member group*

now calculate for each group element, first its second power, then its third power, and so forth, until a power is reached that is a repetition of a previous power. (For instance, $a^2 = e$, and thus $a^3 = a$ is a repetition of the first power of a.) These powers are given in Table 6-9.

Element	Second Power	Third Power	Fourth Power	Fifth Power
a	e	a		
b	a	c	e	b
c	a	b	e	c

Table 6-9   *Powers of each element other than e in the group of Table 6-8.*

(Notice that the first row terminates with the third power, which is a repetition of the first. The second and third rows terminate with the fifth power, which in both cases also repeats the first.) Now consider, for instance, the third row, which contains c, a, b, e, c. Represent the four elements there appearing by dots in an oval, and join them as in Figure 6-6. A point starting from c and moving around the circle clockwise will pass through c^2, c^3, c^4, c^5 in order (see Table 6-9). The second row in Table 6-9 shows that a point traveling from b to b^2 to b^3 to b^4 to b^5 would reach home after touching the same four bases (but in a different order); we do not give its diagram. According to the

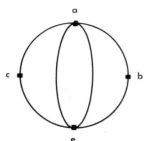

Figure 6-6   *A diagram for the group in Table 6-8.*

first row in Table 6-9, the trip from a to a^2 to a^3 is new, however, and we represent it by the inner loop in the figure. The loop of course represents the single nontrivial subgroup $\{e, a\}$ of the group in question.

Now consider the group represented by part (a) of Table 6-7, here recopied as Table 6-10. The powers of the elements of this group

!	e	a	b	c
e	e	a	b	c
a	a	e	c	b
b	b	c	e	a
c	c	b	a	e

Table 6-10 *Multiplication table for the second four-member group*

other than e are calculated from this table and those up to the first repetition entered in Table 6-11. In the diagram of this group (Figure

Element	Second Power	Third Power
a	e	a
b	e	b
c	e	c

Table 6-11 *Powers of each element other than e in the group of Table 6-10*

6-7), the first line in Table 6-11 is represented by a loop from a to e to a, the second line by a loop from b to e to b, and the third line by a loop from c to e to c. The diagram clearly displays the three nontrivial subgroups,

$$\{e, a\}, \{e, b\}, \{e, c\},$$

of this group.

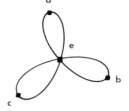

Figure 6-7 *A diagram for the group in Table 6-10.*

EXERCISES

1. From any two (integer) numbers a and b, let us obtain a third number by the following rule: multiply the two numbers together, divide their product by 15, write the remainder. This remainder is the third number we desire. We denote it by $a \,\square\, b$. Let S consist of the numbers 1, 2, 4, 7, 8, 11, 13, 14.

(a) Prove that $(S, \square)$ is a commutative group.

(b) Find all the cyclic subgroups of $(S, \square)$.

(c) Consider the diagram for this group (Figure 6-8), each dot representing an element of the group, and the circle and each of the four ovals representing cyclic subgroups. The dot at the bottom of the diagram belonging to the circle and to two of the ovals represents an element of the group that belongs to the subgroups this circle and these ovals represent. Which element is represented by each dot in the diagram?

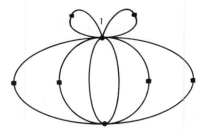

Figure 6-8   A group diagram.

2. From any two numbers a and b, obtain a third by the following rule: multiply the two numbers together, divide their product by 21, and write the remainder. This remainder is the third number alluded to and will be denoted by $a \triangle b$. Let T consist of the numbers 1, 2, 4, 5, 8, 10, 11, 13, 16, 17, 19, 20.

(a) Prove that $(T, \triangle)$ is a group.

(b) Find all the cyclic subgroups of $(T, \triangle)$.

(c) In Figure 6-9, each of the three paths—the smooth, the dotted, and the dashed—represents a subgroup that has six members. Three of the points on these paths are labeled. Find all the others.

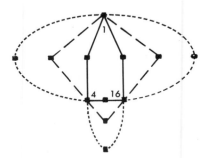

Figure 6-9   A group diagram.

3. From any two numbers a and b, obtain a third by the following rule: multiply the two numbers together, divide their product by 24, and write the remainder. This remainder is the third number alluded to and will be denoted by $a \triangledown b$. Let U consist of the numbers 1, 5, 7, 11, 13, 17, 19, 23.

(a) Prove that $(U, \triangledown)$ is a group.

(b) Find all the cyclic subgroups of $(U, \triangledown)$.

(c) Diagram them.

4. Given any member x of a group with 5 members, show that at least two powers of x coincide.

5. Given any member x of a group with n members, show that at least two powers of x coincide.

5.

Algebra in braiding†

Group structure is discernible, as we have stressed, in exceedingly diverse phenomena. Braiding is such a phenomenon.

Imagine two rods that are held parallel and a certain number of lengths of string, each tied at one end to one of the rods and at the other end to the other rod. Between their tied ends, the strings may curl, cross, intertwine, or tangle.

If we pull the securely tied strings into different positions, change their lengths (as if they were elastic), slide along the rods the knots by which the strings are attached, or move the rods a different distance apart, of course the configuration of strings alters its appearance. One aspect of the configuration, however, is unchanged. For instance, if originally the strings can be made parallel like those of a harp *without untying any knots*, they can still be made so after being additionally tangled in the indicated ways. Analogously, a certain abstract element of structure in a configuration of tied strings will always endure through such changes as we have described, changes that exclude the undoing of any of the knots. This abstract element of structure is called the *pattern of braiding* of the configuration. It will be defined— quite simply—and then discussed in algebraic terms.

We begin by idealizing the situation, replacing the rods by parallel straight lines, the strings by curves (in space) that do not intersect one another, the knots by the points of intersection of these curves with the two parallel straight lines. Thus, let L and M be two parallel straight lines. Let

$$c_1, c_2, \ldots, c_n$$

be n (in general, curved) line segments, each with one end upon L and the other end upon M, none otherwise intersecting L or M, and none intersecting the other line segments of the set. Carrying over some of our previous terminology, we shall refer to L and M as "rods," to the line segments $c_1, \ldots, c_n$ as "strings," and to the intersections of rods and strings as "attachments." The whole system, including the

---

† This section is based on E. Artin, "The Theory of Braids," *The American Scientist,* Vol. 38, No. 1, January, 1950, pp. 112-119.

exact positions relative to one another of all the rods and strings, we shall call as before the "configuration."

The straight lines L and M, being parallel, lie in a plane, and the configuration presents different aspects to observers on opposite sides of this plane. We therefore agree, once and for all, upon a particular side of the plane from which to view the configuration and then speak of strings crossing "over" or "under" other strings accordingly. When the observer is on the side agreed, we can say that he is "properly oriented" with respect to the configuration. But we can just as well say instead that the configuration is "properly oriented" (with respect to the observer) and usually shall. In this case, we shall also say that the configuration—or any part of it—"faces" the observer.

It is useful to diagram the crossing pattern for a given configuration in the following way. Imagine the plane of L and M to face the sun's rays perpendicularly and the whole configuration to cast its shadow upon a screen standing behind this plane and parallel to it, as illustrated in Figure 6-10. (The shadow is the "projection" of the configuration upon the plane of the screen. Each point P of the projec-

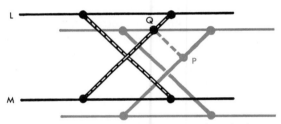

Figure 6-10   *A braiding pattern and its shadow.*

tion is related geometrically to a corresponding point Q of the configuration by the condition that the straight line PQ be perpendicular to the plane of the screen.) This shadow, or projection, is the basis of the diagram we desire, but has the unfortunate feature that when strings cross, their shadows intersect. Thus, the shadow does not indicate which string crosses over, which under. To remedy this defect, at each crossing, we interrupt the shadow of the string that crosses *below*, altering nothing else. The resulting figure is the diagram we seek. Figure 6-11 illustrates this.

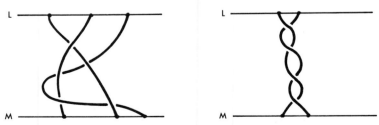

Figure 6-11   *Diagrams of braiding patterns.*

For convenience, we shall make several assumptions concerning the diagrams of our configurations. The first is this:

(A) Consider a point moving along any string in a steady direction from the attachment on L to the attachment on M. We assume that the projection of this point, in the diagram of the configuration, steadily increases its distance from L (and thus decreases its distance from M).

Two configurations will be said to represent the same *pattern of braiding* if either configuration would result from the other by changes of the following kinds:

(a) moving the rods, which, however, are required to remain parallel;

(b) moving the strings (including their points of attachment), or changing their lengths, in any way that complies with requirement (A) and does not ever require two strings to touch.

If two configurations represent the same pattern of braiding, they are said to be *equivalent*.

It is intuitively clear—and we take it for granted—that each pattern of braiding can be represented by a configuration that satisfies these further conditions:

(B) the diagram of the configuration has at most two strings crossing at any one point and has each crossing taking place at a different distance from L;

(C) the diagram of the configuration shows at most a finite number of crossings.

Thus, we consider only such configurations as satisfy conditions (A), (B), and (C).

Algebra is introduced here. Consider any two patterns of braiding, each with the same number of strings. Denote the two patterns by A and A'. Select suitable configurations to represent these patterns, calling the rods and strings corresponding to A

$$L, M, c_1, c_2, \ldots, c_n$$

and those corresponding to A'

$$L', M', c_1', c_2', \ldots, c_n',$$

respectively. We properly orient the first configuration and then make changes of types (a) and (b) in the second configuration, if necessary, to bring about a situation in which:

(i) L' coincides with M, M' and L being on opposite sides of M;
(ii) M' is in the plane of L and M;
(iii) the second configuration (as well as the first) is properly oriented;
(iv) the attachments for the second configuration upon L' coincide with the attachments for the first configuration upon M;
(v) the second configuration again satisfies conditions (A), (B), (C).

Figure 6-12   *Multiplication of patterns.*

Figure 6-12 illustrates this. If we now dissolve the line M, we have a new configuration (again satisfying (A), (B), (C)) with rods L and M'. We denote the braiding pattern represented by the new configuration by

$$A * A',$$

or, dropping the $*$, simply by

$$AA',$$

a notation that indicates how the new pattern arose. We shall refer to this new pattern AA' as the *product* of A and A' and to the operation of forming such a product as *multiplication* of braiding patterns. Multiplication of two patterns can be described briefly as a tying together.

If B_n denotes the set of all braiding patterns for configurations with n strings, we shall see that $(B_n, *)$ is a group. First, multiplying patterns results, by definition, in another pattern: hence, B_n is closed under multiplication. Secondly, we readily verify that multiplication is associative. In fact, if A, B, C are braiding patterns (with n strings), then AB is the pattern obtained by tying A and B, and $(AB)C$ that which results from tying AB to C. Thus, $(AB)C$ can be described as the pattern formed when A is tied to B and B then tied to C. Furthermore, $A(BC)$ can be described in exactly the same way. Hence,

$$(AB)C = A(BC),$$

so that multiplication is seen to be associative, as contended.

Thirdly, $(B_n, *)$ has an identity. Indeed, let I denote the pattern represented by a configuration (of n strings) without crossings (see Figure 6-13). For any braiding pattern A, we have relations

$$AI = IA = A,$$

since after tying A and I together we may shorten the strings (a change of type (b)) to return to pattern A again. Therefore, I is the identity in $(B_n, *)$.

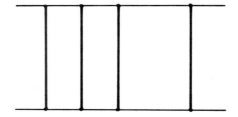

Figure 6-13 *Configuration representing the identity in the braiding
pattern group.*

The last condition needed to assure that $(B_n, *)$ is a group is that each member of B_n have an inverse with respect to $*$. This condition we postpone.

We shall now introduce certain particularly simple braiding patterns by means of which, as we shall see, all others may be algebraically expressed. To describe these elementary patterns and their combinations easily, take rod L to be above rod M in the diagrams we consider, and then label the strings $c_1, c_2, \ldots, c_n$ in the order of their attachments to L from left to right. With this convention, let s_1 denote the n-stringed braiding pattern in which c_1 crosses over c_2, with no other crossings (Figure 6-14A). Similarly, let s_2 denote the braiding pattern of an n-stringed configuration in which c_2 crosses over c_3 without other crossings (Figure 6-14B), and, in general, let s_k denote the braiding pattern of a configuration of n strings in which c_k crosses over c_{k+1}, $k = 1, 2, \ldots, n-1$† (Figure 6-14C) and no other crossings occur. Note that if t_1 denotes, for instance, the braiding pattern of an n-stringed configuration in which c_1 crosses *under* c_2 and there are no other crossings, then

(1) $$s_1 t_1 = I, \; t_1 s_1 = I.$$

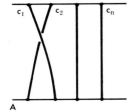

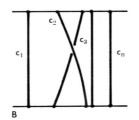

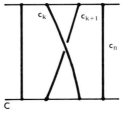

A   B   C

Figure 6-14 *Some elementary braiding patterns. A, elementary pattern s_1;
B, elementary pattern s_2; C, elementary pattern s_k.*

This is apparent from Figure 6-16, in which all crossings can be eliminated by drawing the strings so that they become taut. It follows from (1) that s_1, in particular, has an inverse and that $s_1^{-1} = t_1$.

---

†We cannot take $k = n$ here, since no c_{n+1} exists.

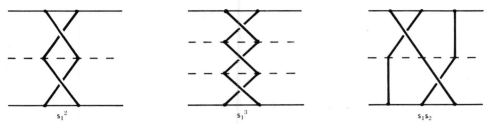

$s_1{}^2$ $s_1{}^3$ $s_1 s_2$

Figure 6-15   Some products of elementary braiding patterns.

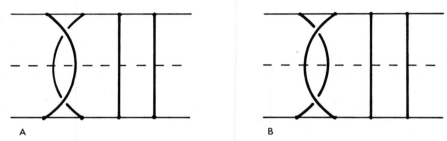

A   B

Figure 6-16   An elementary braiding pattern and its inverse.

Similarly,

$$s_k^{-1}$$

exists for each k, $k = 1, 2, \ldots, n-1$, being in fact the pattern of a configuration in which c_k crosses under c_{k+1} without other crossings occurring.

Any braid pattern A can be expressed as a product of suitable s_k's or their inverses. We shall see this easily from a diagram. By conditions (B) and (C), the crossing points in the diagram are at most finite in number, involve only two strings at a time, and are located each at a different distance from rod L. If no crossing points exist, then $A = I$; and if just one crossing point exists, some particular string crossing over or under one of its two neighbors, then $A = s_k$ or $A = s_k^{-1}$ for suitable k. If at least two crossing points occur, draw between the rods L and M a parallel line L_1 not itself passing through a crossing point and such that just one crossing point falls between L and L_1. If at least three crossing points occur, draw between L_1 and M a parallel line L_2 not itself containing a crossing point but such that just one crossing point falls between L_1 and L_2. If the diagram for A has exactly p crossing points, then continuing in this way, draw successively $p - 1$ straight lines

$$L_1, L_2, \ldots, L_{p-1}$$

parallel to L and M such that exactly one crossing point falls between L and L_1, one between L_1 and L_2, one between L_k and L_{k+1} for $k = 1, 2, \ldots, p-2$, and one between L_{p-1} and M. In this way, the diagram for A is cut up into a succession of horizontal portions, each of which contains exactly one crossing point. Each such horizontal portion by itself can be regarded as a diagram for an s_j or s_j^{-1} with suitable j, and A is their product. Figure 6-17 illustrates with a braiding pattern that is resolved into $s_1 s_3^{-1} s_1 s_2$.

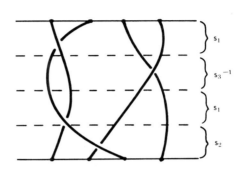

Figure 6-17 A braiding pattern regarded as a product of elementary braiding patterns or their inverses.

EXERCISES

1. Diagram these patterns:
   (a) $s_1 s_3 s_2^{-1} s_3$
   (b) $s_2 s_3^{-1} s_1 s_2 s_3^{-1}$
   (c) $s_1 s_2 s_1 s_2 s_1 s_2$
   (d) $s_1 s_2 s_3 s_3 s_2 s_1$
   (e) $s_1^{-1} s_2^{-1} s_3^{-1} s_1^{-1} s_2^{-1} s_3^{-1}$

2. Express the patterns diagrammed in Figure 6-18 as products of elementary patterns or their inverses.

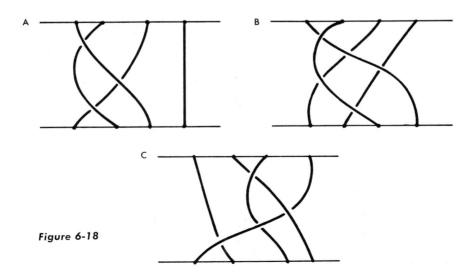

Figure 6-18

We can now easily show that any braiding pattern has a group inverse. What, for instance, is the inverse of the pattern diagrammed in Figure 6-17? Since this pattern has the expression

$$A = s_1 s_3^{-1} s_1 s_2,$$

its inverse must be

$$B = s_2^{-1} s_1^{-1} s_3 s_1^{-1}.$$

In fact,

$$
\begin{aligned}
AB &= (s_1 s_3^{-1} s_1 s_2)(s_2^{-1} s_1^{-1} s_3 s_1^{-1}) \\
&= s_1 s_3^{-1} s_1 (s_2 s_2^{-1}) s_1^{-1} s_3 s_1^{-1} \\
&= s_1 s_3^{-1} (s_1 s_1^{-1}) s_3 s_1^{-1} \quad \text{(since } s_2 s_2^{-1} = I) \\
&= s_1 (s_3^{-1} s_3) s_1^{-1} \\
&= s_1 s_1^{-1} \\
&= I,
\end{aligned}
$$

and we prove similarly that $BA = I$. Hence, $A^{-1} = B$. The same kind of argument applies to any braiding pattern, expressed as a product of the form

$$u_1 u_2 \ldots u_p,$$

where each of $u_1, u_2, \ldots, u_p$ is some s_k or s_k^{-1}. In fact, the inverse of this product is easily seen to be

$$u_p^{-1} \ldots u_2^{-1} u_1^{-1}$$

by a calculation like that just given. (Recall that $(s_k^{-1})^{-1} = s_k$.)

Since any member of B_n has an inverse, we see that $(B_n, *)$ is a group, as earlier stated. Furthermore, the group is "generated by" the $n - 1$ members $s_1, s_2, \ldots, s_{n-1}$ in the sense that every member of the group is a product of some of these or their inverses. To recognize these facts is the first step in approaching braiding patterns algebraically. The next step might be to ask for algebraic criteria to tell when two braiding patterns are equivalent. One such criterion, which is evident from Figure 6-19, is the relation $s_1 s_3 = s_3 s_1$. We have

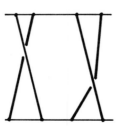 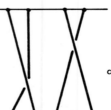

Figure 6-9 *Two equivalent braiding patterns.*

similarly $s_1 s_4 = s_4 s_1$, $s_2 s_4 = s_4 s_2$, and so forth, or, in more general notation,

(2) $\qquad\qquad\qquad s_j s_k = s_k s_j \quad$ if $\quad j - k \geq 2 \qquad$ (i.e., if j and k differ by at least 2).

Another kind of relation, which also will serve as an equivalence criterion, can be read off from Figure 6-20, whose two diagrams represent equivalent patterns. (The second string from the left — the one we called c_2 — crosses under the first and over the third, the first also over the third, in both patterns.) This relation is

(3) $\qquad\qquad\qquad s_k s_{k+1} s_k = s_{k+1} s_k s_{k+1}.$

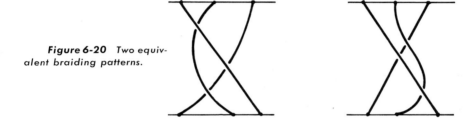

Figure 6-20 *Two equivalent braiding patterns.*

With relations (2) and (3), diagrams are no longer needed to prove the equivalence of equivalent patterns. Purely algebraic proofs can always be given.

We shall not prove the previous statement, but shall give several illustrations. First, compare s_2, diagrammed again in Figure 6-21A, with the braiding pattern represented in Figure 6-21B. In both figures, c_2 crosses over c_3. In Figure 6-21A, c_1 does not cross the other strings; in Figure 6-21B, c_1 crosses back and forth underneath the other strings, but straightening and shortening would eliminate all

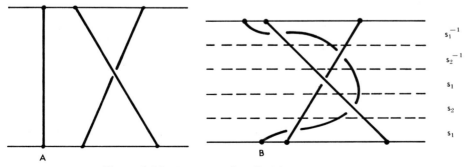

Figure 6-21   *Two equivalent braiding patterns.*

these crossings. Hence, the two figures represent the same braiding pattern. Since Figure 6-21A represents s_2 and Figure 6-21B the pattern $s_1^{-1}s_2^{-1}s_1s_2s_1$, we must have

(4) $$s_2 = s_1^{-1}s_2^{-1}s_1s_2s_1.$$

Our aim is to prove algebraically that the two braiding patterns are the same. Thus, we must prove (4) algebraically. To do so, notice that condition (3) for $k = 1$ says:

$$s_1s_2s_1 = s_2s_1s_2.$$

Hence, for the right side of (4) we have:

$$\begin{aligned} s_1^{-1}s_2^{-1}s_1s_2s_1 &= s_1^{-1}s_2^{-1}s_2s_1s_2 \\ &= s_1^{-1}s_1s_2 \quad \text{since } s_2^{-1}s_2 = I \\ &= s_2 \quad \text{since } s_1^{-1}s_1 = I \end{aligned}$$

Thus, (4) is proved.

As another example of algebraic methods, consider the braiding patterns diagrammed in Figures 6-22A and 6-22B. In each diagram, c_1 crosses over c_3, c_2 lying underneath. Furthermore, Figure 6-22B will result from Figure 6-22A from shortening c_2 to eliminate certain crossings. Hence, these two figures represent the same braiding pattern. The algebraic expression for the first pattern being $s_1s_2s_1^{-1}s_2^{-1}$ and that for the second pattern being $s_2^{-1}s_1$, the identity of the two patterns is expressed algebraically by the formula

(5) $$s_1s_2s_1^{-1}s_2^{-1} = s_2^{-1}s_1.$$

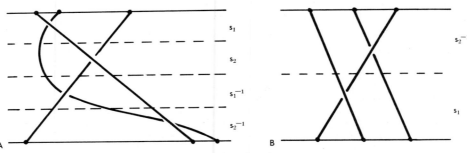

Figure 6-22   Two equivalent braiding patterns.

This too we can prove by purely algebraic means from the relation

(6) $$s_1s_2s_1 = s_2s_1s_2,$$

which we premise. Equation (5) is equivalent to the equation

(5′) $s_2 s_1 s_2 s_1^{-1} s_2^{-1} = s_2 s_2^{-1} s_1 = s_1,$

which is obtained from (5) by multiplying both sides on the left by s_2 and using the identity $s_2 s_2^{-1} = I$. We prove (5′) by substituting from (6) for the expression $s_2 s_1 s_2$ occurring on the left and then cancelling products of elements and their inverses, as before. Equation (5) results as a consequence.

Our final illustration of algebraic methods is concerned with the four-stringed group $(B_4, *)$. This group has the three generators

$$s_1, s_2, s_3.$$

Forming their product

$$a = s_1 s_2 s_3,$$

note that

$$\begin{aligned}
as_1 &= s_1 s_2 s_3 s_1 \\
&= s_1 s_2 s_1 s_3 \quad \text{since } s_1 s_3 = s_3 s_1 \text{ by (2),} \\
&= s_2 s_1 s_2 s_3 \quad \text{since } s_1 s_2 s_1 = s_2 s_1 s_2 \text{ by (3),} \\
&= s_2 a,
\end{aligned}$$

and thus that

$$s_2 = as_1 a^{-1}.$$

Similarly, we obtain

$$\begin{aligned}
as_2 &= s_1 s_2 s_3 s_2 \\
&= s_1 s_3 s_2 s_3 \\
&= s_3 s_1 s_2 s_3 \\
&= s_3 a
\end{aligned}$$

and, thus,

$$\begin{aligned}
s_3 &= as_2 a^{-1} = aas_1 a^{-1} a^{-1} \\
&= a^2 s_1 a^{-2}.
\end{aligned}$$

The formulas

$$s_2 = as_1 a^{-1}, \quad s_3 = a^2 s_1 a^{-2}$$

thus derived are interesting because they enable us to express the *three* original generators s_1, s_2, s_3 in terms of *two* elements only, namely s_1 and a, which thus also generate $(B_4, *)$.

EXERCISES

3. (a) Find algebraic expressions for each of the braid diagrams in Figure 6-23.

(b) Prove that the patterns represented by these diagrams are equal.

A   B

Figure 6-23

4. (a) Draw diagrams corresponding to the following algebraic expressions:

$$\text{(i) } s_1 s_2 s_3 s_2 s_1, \quad \text{(ii) } s_3 s_2 s_1 s_2 s_3.$$

(b) Prove algebraically that the braiding patterns represented by these two expressions are the same.

5. (a) Draw diagrams corresponding to the following algebraic expressions:

$$\text{(i) } s_1^{-1} s_3 s_1, \quad \text{(ii) } s_2^{-1} s_1^{-1} s_2 s_1 s_2, \quad \text{(iii) } s_4^{-1} s_1^{-1} s_2 s_1 s_4 s_2.$$

(b) Simplify each expression algebraically as much as possible. Then diagram the simplified expressions.

6. Consider the two configurations in Figure 6-24.

(a) Find algebraic expressions for these configurations.

(b) Prove that these two algebraic expressions are inverses of each other.

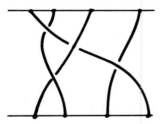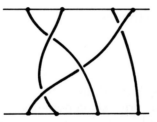

Figure 6-24

7. With respect to Figure 6-25, follow the same directions as in Exercise 3.

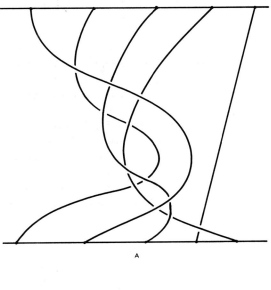

A

Figure 6-25

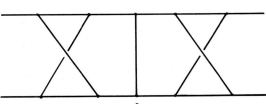

B

8. (a) Show that

$$s_1 s_2 s_3 s_1^{-1} s_2^{-1} s_1 s_2 s_1 s_3^{-1} s_2^{-1} s_3^{-1} s_4 = s_1 s_4$$

using only the following rules:

(1) $s_i s_j = s_j s_i$ for $i - j \geq 2$

(2) $s_i s_{i+1} s_i = s_{i+1} s_i s_{i+1}.$

(b) Draw braid configurations for each of the algebraic expressions in these equalities.

9. (a) Prove that

$$s_{i+1}^{-1} s_i s_{i+1} = s_i s_{i+1} s_i^{-1}.$$

(b) Prove that

$$s_{i+1} = s_i^{-1} s_{i+1} s_i s_{i+1} s_i^{-1}.$$

10. Consider $s_i, s_i^2, s_i^3, s_i^4, \ldots$, where i is some fixed index and $i \leq n$.
    (a) Are any of these powers equal?
    (b) Is $(B_n, *)$ a finite or an infinite group? Explain your answer.

11. Consider the collection

$$C = \{\ldots, s_1^{-2}, s_1^{-1}, I, s_1, s_1^2, \ldots\}$$

containing the identity and all positive and negative powers of s_1.
    (a) Prove that $(C, *)$ is a subgroup of $(B_n, *)$.
    (b) Describe geometrically the type of braid patterns which can be formed in $(C, *)$.

12. Consider Figure 6-26.
    (a) Notice that the pattern between L_1 and L_2 is repeated between L_2 and L_3. If A represents the algebraic expression for the pattern between L_1 and L_2, what is the algebraic expression for the pattern between L_1 and L_3?
    (b) Find the algebraic expression for the pattern between L_1 and L_3.

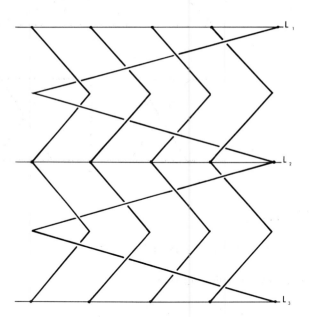

Figure 6-26

13. For the five-stringed group $(B_5, *)$, define

$$a = s_1 s_2 s_3 s_4,$$

and prove that

$$s_2 = a s_1 a^{-1}$$
$$s_3 = a^2 s_1 a^{-2}$$
$$s_4 = a^3 s_1 a^{-3}.$$

(In $(B_n, \circ)$, it is true that

$$s_k = a^{k-1} s_1 a^{-(k-1)} \quad \text{for} \quad k = 2, \ldots, n-1,$$

where

$$a = s_1 s_2 \ldots s_{n-1}.)$$

14. Show from diagrams that $s_1 s_2 \neq s_2 s_1$.

15. Prove algebraically and also check from diagrams:

$$s_1 s_4^{-1} = s_4^{-1} s_1,$$
$$s_1^{-1} s_4^{-1} = s_4^{-1} s_1^{-1},$$
$$s_1^{-1} s_2^{-1} s_1^{-1} = s_2^{-1} s_1^{-1} s_2^{-1}.$$

CHAPTER 7

LINES AND TRIANGLES IN EUCLIDEAN PLANE GEOMETRY

Greek geometry, arranged and presented in the 3rd Century, B.C., by Euclid of Alexandria, is one of the overwhelming masterpieces of thought. Delivering its rich and often astonishing results by systematic use of the closest reasoning, it is the classic demonstration of logical method and has had an incalculable influence on subsequent thought of all kinds. In a later chapter, we shall discuss its methodology, which, ironically, was strikingly misunderstood until quite recent times. In this chapter, we are concerned simply with some of its more elementary and intuitively plausible results, which are reviewed without proofs in Section 1. Sections 2 and 4 consist of exercises, essential supplements to the review in two quite different spheres: geometrical interpretation of multiplication and constructions of interest to artists. Through similar triangle proportionalities, a construction in Section 3 provides a concise interpretation of area. In Section 5 we discuss trigonometry, which is an algebraic outgrowth of geometry. Section 6 concludes the chapter with geometric transformations, in which groups play a role.

1.

Some notation, terminology, and propositions of Euclidean plane geometry

Vertical angles are equal (Figure 7-1).
A point is generally denoted by a capital letter, such as A. The

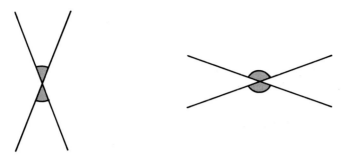

FIGURE 7-1   *Vertical angles.*

straight line segment between two specified points, say A and B, is called AB or BA; A and B are called the end points of the segment. The straight line passing through A and B will be referred to as the *line AB*. (AB thus designates either a segment or a line. When no indication is given, AB denotes the segment.) If two segments, say AB and AC, have an end point A in common, the angle included between them—or, rather, the smaller of the two angles (if there is a smaller)—is denoted by $\angle BAC$ or $\angle CAB$ (Figure 7-2). The angle is also denoted by $\angle A$ if no confusion is likely to result. The length of a segment AB is again denoted by AB; the size of an angle $\angle ABC$ is again denoted by $\angle ABC$, and so on.

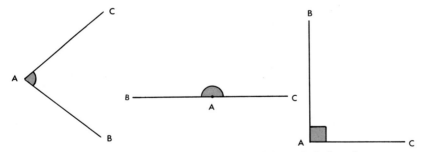

FIGURE 7-2   *Pairs of line segments and the included angle.*

If two segments, BA and AC, join smoothly at A, combining together into a straight line segment BC, the included angle at A is called a straight angle and is said to measure 180°. Half a straight angle, measuring 90°, is called a right angle. Lines that meet at a right angle are said to be perpendicular. Through a given point, one and only one perpendicular can be drawn to the line.

The triangle with vertices A, B, and C (Figure 7-3) is symbolized as ABC or, equally well, as ACB, BCA, BAC, CAB, or CBA. The angle $\angle A$ and the side BC are called opposite; similarly, $\angle B$ and AC are opposite, and $\angle C$ and AB are opposite. The triangle is called a right triangle if one of its angles measures 90°; the side opposite the right angle then is called the hypotenuse.

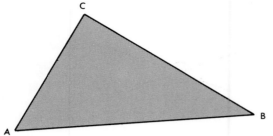

FIGURE 7-3   *The triangle ABC.*

According to the so-called Pythagorean theorem (see Section 1, Chapter 4), the square of the hypotenuse of a right triangle is equal to the sum of the squares of the two other sides. Conversely, if the square of a particular side of a given triangle is equal to the sum of the squares of the two other sides, then the triangle is a right triangle.

If two sides of a triangle are equal, the angles opposite these sides are also equal. Conversely, if two angles of a triangle are equal, the sides opposite the angles are equal. Such a triangle is called *isosceles* (Figure 7-4). A triangle for which all three sides have the same length is called *equilateral.* An equilateral triangle is equiangular, i.e., the three angles are all equal. Conversely, an equiangular triangle is equilateral.

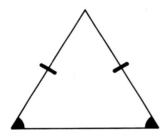

FIGURE 7-4   *An isosceles triangle.*

For any triangle, the sum of the angles is 180°. (An intuitive argument supporting this statement is given in a later chapter on mathematical induction.)

Often it is desired to compare corresponding sides and angles of two triangles. If the triangles are written, say, as ABC and $A'B'C'$ (A', read "A-prime," denotes a vertex of the second triangle, B' and C' denoting the other two vertices), then $\angle A$ is compared with $\angle A'$, $\angle B$ with $\angle B'$, and $\angle C$ with $\angle C'$. Similarly, AB is compared with $A'B'$, BC with $B'C'$, and AC with $A'C'$. Two angles or two sides thus compared are said to correspond: $\angle A$ and $\angle A'$, $\angle B$ and $\angle B'$, $\angle C$ and $\angle C'$ are pairs of corresponding angles; AB and $A'B'$, BC and $B'C'$, and AC and $A'C'$ are pairs of corresponding sides. Two triangles, ABC and $A'B'C'$, are called *similar* if corresponding angles are equal and corresponding sides proportional (Figure 7-5).

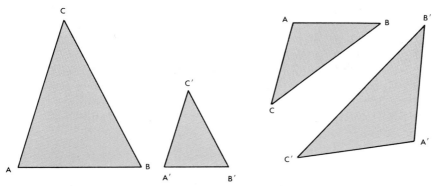

FIGURE 7-5 *Pairs of similar triangles.*

This means that

(1) $\angle A = \angle A', \angle B = \angle B', \angle C = \angle C'$

and

(2) $AB/A'B' = BC/B'C' = AC/A'C'.$

Similarity is a mathematical expression of the requirement that the triangles concerned be of the same shape. They may be of different sizes, however, either triangle being obtainable from the other by "magnifying" or "reducing" the size of the triangle without distortion. If the two triangles are similar and of the same size (i.e., the ratios in (2) are equal to 1), they will be said to be *equal*. Triangles that are equal in this sense also are called *congruent*.

Each of the following three conditions is equivalent to the similarity of triangles ABC and $A'B'C'$ (i.e., each of these conditions implies this similarity and is implied by it):

(i) Two sides of the one triangle are proportional to the corresponding sides of the other, and the included angles are equal. Symbolically, for instance,

$$AB/A'B' = AC/A'C' \text{ and } \angle A = \angle A';$$

see Figure 7-6.

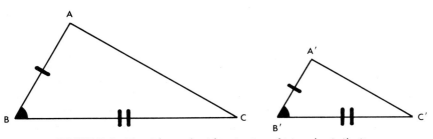

FIGURE 7-6 *The side-angle-side criterion of triangle similarity.*

(ii) Two angles of the one triangle are equal to the corresponding angles of the other; i.e., any two of the relations (1) hold.

(iii) Corresponding sides of the two triangles are proportional; i.e., the equalities (2) hold.

These criteria for similarity imply the following related conditions that two triangles, ABC and $A'B'C'$, be equal:

(i') Two sides of ABC are equal to the corresponding sides of $A'B'C'$, and the included angles are equal. Symbolically, for instance,

$$AB = A'B', AC = A'C', \angle A = \angle A'.$$

(This is called the side-angle-side criterion for congruence.)

(ii') Two angles of ABC are equal to the corresponding angles of $A'B'C'$; at the same time, the included sides are equal. Symbolically, for instance,

$$\angle A = \angle A', \angle B = \angle B', AB = A'B'.$$

(This is called the angle-side-angle criterion for congruence.)

(iii') Corresponding sides of the two triangles are equal:

$$AB = A'B', AC = A'C', BC = B'C'.$$

(This is called the side-side-side condition for congruence.)

Two lines are parallel if they have no point in common. Let a point A not lie on a given line q. Then one and but one line parallel to q passes through A. Any two parallel lines make the same angle with a third line that cuts them. (The line cutting them is called a transversal.) Conversely, if two lines, p and q, cut at the same angle any given transversal t, then p and q are parallel. (See Figure 7-7.)

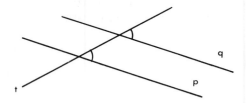

FIGURE 7-7 Parallel lines and a transversal.

EXERCISES

1. Short distances can be found without being measured directly if two people cooperate, one using a yardstick and the other a simple optical instrument we shall describe. The instrument is a straight tube of measured length with covered ends. The covers (Figure 7-8) are flat and of opaque material (cardboard, metal), one being pierced by a pinhole and the other by a straight slot of measured height. To find the distance across a room, for in-

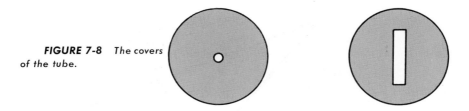

FIGURE 7-8   *The covers of the tube.*

stance, one of the two persons would hold the yardstick vertically upright against a wall. The other person, at the opposite wall, would place the tube in a horizontal position, with the slit vertical (parallel to the yardstick), so that putting his eye to the pinhole he would see part of the yardstick (Figure 7-9).

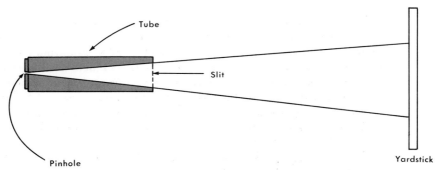

FIGURE 7-9   *Surveying by use of an optical tube.*

Holding the tube firmly thus, he would watch as the other moved his finger along the yardstick from the top to the bottom, the first announcing the highest and the lowest points at which he could see the finger through the tube. His partner, reading these points on the yardstick, would calculate the height of the section of yardstick visible through the tube. From this and the known lengths of the tube and the slit, the distance from the pinhole to the yardstick is easily found. Larger distances can be similarly measured if a telescopic lens is used in place of a pinhole.

    (a) Suppose 25 inches of yardstick are visible. If the slit is one inch long and the tube ten inches long, what is the distance from the pinhole to the yardstick?

    (b) Answer the same question if the slit is 1 cm., and the tube 10 cm., long, 25 inches of yardstick again being visible. (1 cm. is equal to .3937 inches.)

    (c) Find a general formula for the distance d from the pinhole to the yardstick, letting s denote the length of the slit, t the length of the tube, and y the length of the visible section of yardstick.

    2. Let A and B denote positions on opposite sides of a broad river (Figure 7-10) such that either can be seen from the other. A surveyor desiring to measure the distance AB can do so without crossing the river. Supposing him to

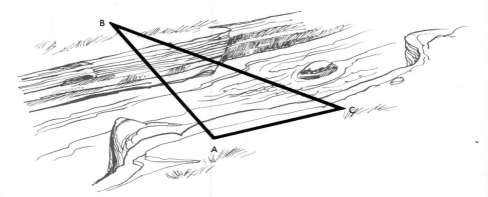

FIGURE 7-10   *The distance to an inaccessible point.*

be on the same side, say, as A, let him choose a position C on that side from which both A and B can be seen. Standing at A, he should measure the angle ∠ BAC and, standing at C, the angle ∠ BCA. By pacing off or by some other means (for instance, those of Exercise 1), he should measure the distance AC. On a piece of paper, let him now draw a straight line segment A'C' of any convenient length and then draw straight lines at the end points, A' and C', making angles with A'C' equal to ∠ BAC and ∠ BCA, respectively. After appropriate measurements made on the diagram, he can calculate AB.

     (a) How?

     (b) Does it matter how near C is selected to A?

    3. A man standing 100 feet away from a tree 50 feet high snaps a picture of the tree. The lens in the camera reduces the size of the tree to CD on the film (Figure 7-11). The point F (the center of the lens) is 6 inches from the film.

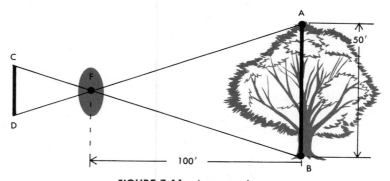

FIGURE 7-11   *A camera image.*

     (a) Prove that triangles CDF and BAF are similar.

     (b) Find the size of the image of the tree on the film.

    4. A tower of unknown height casts a shadow of 60 feet. A fence nearby which is 3 feet high casts a shadow of 4 feet. By use of similar triangles, determine the height of the tower (Figure 7-12).

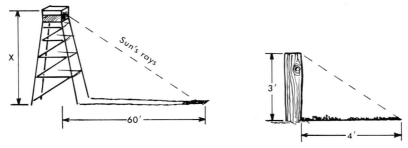

FIGURE 7-12   *Surveying a tower.*

5. Let ABC be a triangle with ∠ C = 90°. Prove: ∠ A + ∠ B = 90°.

6. Let ABC be an equilateral triangle (Figure 7-13) with CD perpendicular to AB. Prove:

FIGURE 7-13   *An equilateral triangle.*

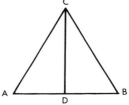

(a) AD = DB. HINT: ADC and BDC are similar and have a common side.

(b) ∠ ACD = ∠ DCB.

(c) ∠ A = 60°.

(d) ∠ ACD = 30°.

Recall that the *circle* of *radius* a about *center* O consists of all points Q such that the distance between O and Q is equal to a; a *chord* of the circle is any line segment PQ with end points P and Q on the circle; a *diameter* of the circle is a chord that passes through the center O.

7. (a) Prove that if for two right triangles an acute angle of one is equal to an acute angle of the other, then the triangles are similar.

(b) Prove that if two triangles are similar to a third triangle, then they are similar to each other.

(c) Prove that two isosceles triangles are similar if a base angle of one is equal to a base angle of the other.

8. In Figure 7-14, ∠ B and ∠ EDA are right angles. Prove that triangles ADE and ABC are similar.

FIGURE 7-14   *A right triangle dissected.*

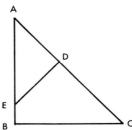

9. Let PQ be a chord of the circle with length equal to the radius. If O denotes the center of the circle, prove that $\angle\, POQ = 60°$.

10. On any circle, mark the four end points P, Q, R, S of any two perpendicular diameters. Also mark the points of the circle at a distance equal to the radius from P, Q, R, or S. Twelve points in all are thus marked. Prove that the 12 points are uniformly spaced around the circle. (If a chord joins each point with the fifth after it in the clockwise direction and the figure is shaded, we obtain Figure 7-15.†

FIGURE 7-15 *A figure obtained by equal subdivision of the circle.*

11. Given triangle ABC, let B' be a point on AB and C' be a point on AC. (See Figure 7-16.) Prove that triangles ABC and $AB'C'$ are similar if and only if BC and $B'C'$ are parallel. In other words, prove the following two statements:

(a) ABC and $AB'C'$ are similar if BC and $B'C'$ are parallel.

(b) BC and $B'C'$ are parallel if ABC and $AB'C'$ are similar.

12. Supply the justification for each step in the following proof that a line dividing two sides of a triangle proportionately is parallel to the third side (Figure 7-17).

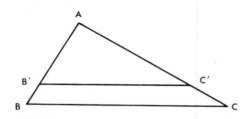

FIGURE 7-16 *A triangle with a line parallel to one of its sides.*

---

†This and other figures appear in H. V. Baravalle, "Geometric Drawing," in *Multi-Sensory Aids in the Teaching of Mathematics*, Eighteenth Yearbook of the National Council of Teachers of Mathematics, Teachers College, Columbia University, New York, 1945, pp. 64-81.

Given: *DE* intersects *AB* and *AC* so that

$$AB/AD = AC/AE.$$

Prove: *DE* and *BC* are parallel.

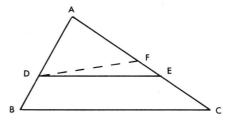

FIGURE 7-17 *A triangle, two sides of which are divided proportionately.*

PROOF: *Statements*   *Justifications*

1. Draw *DF* parallel to *BC*, meeting *AC* at *F*.
2. *AB/AD = AC/AF.*
3. *AB/AD = AC/AE.*
4. *AF = AE.*
5. *F* and *E* coincide.
6. *DF* and *DE* coincide.
7. *DE* and *BC* are parallel.

13. Prove that the bisector of an angle of a triangle divides the opposite side into two segments that are proportional to the other two sides of the triangle, taken in the same order. We state the problem more precisely as follows.

Given: *AD* bisects ∠ *A* of triangle *ABC*
and meets *BC* at *D*.

Prove: *BD/DC = AB/AC.*

HINT: From *B* draw a line parallel to *AD*. Let it meet *CA* extended at *E* (Figure 7-18). Use Exercise 11.

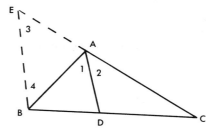

FIGURE 7-18 *Proportional bisection of triangle.*

14. Pythagoras's theorem for an isosceles right triangle is exceptionally simple. If *ABC* is an isosceles right triangle with right angle at *A*, construct the square *ABPC* and, duplicating twice, arrive at Figure 7-19. In this figure, *BCDE* is a square on the hypotenuse of the right triangle given, and Pythagoras's

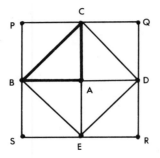

FIGURE 7-19 *Pythagoras's Theorem for an isosceles right triangle.*

theorem reduces to the statement that

$$BCDE = 2 \cdot ABPC.$$

Prove this from Figure 7-19. (According to Plato, Socrates organized a lesson to a slave boy around this proof.)

15. The simple instance of Pythagoras's theorem given in Exercise 14 suggests a general proof, which also is very ancient. It is based on Figure 7-20, in which *ABC* is an arbitrary right triangle with right angle at *A*, and *PQRS* is a square with side equal to *AB* + *AC*. (Thus, *PC* = *AB*, *CQ* = *AC*, and so forth.)

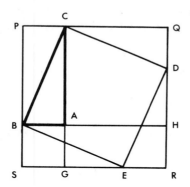

FIGURE 7-20 *A figure for Pythagoras's Theorem.*

From this figure, prove that

$$BCDE = ABSG + ACQH.$$

HINT:

$$PQRS = BCDE + 4 \cdot ABC$$

and

$$PQRS = ABSG + ACQH + \text{two rectangles,}$$

while each rectangle = 2 · *ABC*.

16. Sir George Biddell Airy (1801–1892), British Astronomer Royal, is credited with an exceedingly simple proof of the Pythagorean theorem, which is based on Figure 7-21.† Reconstruct the proof.

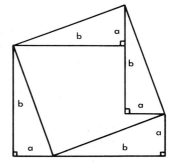

FIGURE 7-21 *Diagram for Airy's proof of Pythagorean Theorem.*

17. Let ∠ ACB be a right angle, and let CM be perpendicular to AB (Figure 7-22).

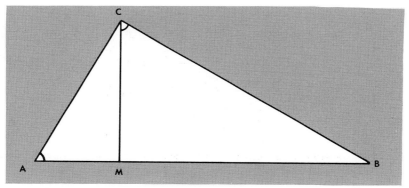

FIGURE 7-22 *Dissection of a right triangle into similar triangles.*

(a) Prove: ∠ A = ∠ BCM.

(b) Prove the triangles ABC and ACM to be similar, so that

$$AC/AM = AB/AC.$$

(c) Prove ABC and CBM to be similar, so that

$$BC/MB = AB/BC.$$

(d) Prove that

$$(AC)^2 = (AB) \cdot (AM), \; (BC)^2 = (AB) \cdot (MB).$$

†Robert Edouard Moritz, *On Mathematics and Mathematicians*, Dover Publications, Inc., New York, 1958, p. 373. Attributed to Graves' *Life of Sir W. R. Hamilton*, Vol. 3 (New York, 1889), p. 502.

From this, show:

$$(AC)^2 + (BC)^2 = (AB)^2.$$

This is another proof of the so-called Pythagorean theorem.

(e) Prove: $(CM)^2 = (AM) \cdot (MB)$. HINT: Use the similarity of AMC and CMB.

(f) Prove: $CM = (AC) \cdot (BC)/\sqrt{(AC)^2 + (BC)^2}$.

18. In Figure 7-22 find
   (a) CM and AC if AM = 4 and MB = 16
   (b) AB if AC = 4 and MB = 6

19. A surveyor wishes to find the distance between two points D and C on opposite sides of a river. (See Figure 7-23.) To do so, he places a vertical stick (BD) on one side of the river. Holding a carpenter's square with its right angle at the top of the stick and its two arms pointing towards the ground, he sights along one arm of the square towards the point C. Without changing the position of the square, he then sights along the other arm to a point on the ground A. Explain how he can determine DC.

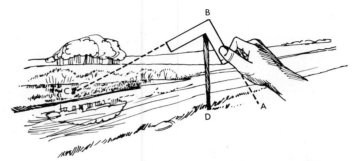

FIGURE 7-23 *Using a carpenter's square to help measure distances to an in-accessible point.*

20. A column is 200 feet high with a uniform circumference (the same at every altitude) of 16 feet 8 inches. It is wreathed in a spiral garland, which passes around it exactly five times. What is the length of the garland? HINT: If a rectangular sheet of paper is marked with a diagonal line and rolled up as a cylinder, the diagonal appears as a section of a spiral (Figure 7-24.)

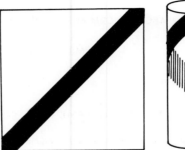

FIGURE 7-24 *A rectangle with a diagonal marked, flat and rolled up.*

2.

Geometrical constructions in arithmetic

Since numbers are represented geometrically as lengths, products can be regarded as areas or volumes (Figure 7-25), these interpretations enabling us to picture readily the associative and commutative laws of multiplication and the distributive law as well. (See the bead diagrams in Chapter 2.) But products can be interpreted as lengths also. This is shown in several constructions in Figures 7-26 and 7-27 with analogous interpretations of the commutative and associative laws for multiplication following in Figures 7-28 and 7-29. All the constructions depend simply on the geometry outlined in Section 1 and therefore are given as further exercises. Our presentation follows that of P. C. Rosenbloom.†

---

†"The MINNEMAST Mathematics Curriculum for Grades K-9," University of Minnesota, pp. 13, 16-19.

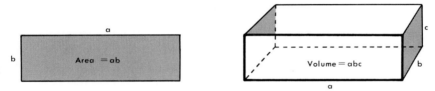

FIGURE 7-25 *Products as volumes.*

EXERCISES

In these exercises, a, b, and c will denote any nonzero numbers.

1. Establish scales (Chapter 2) on each of two intersecting lines with the two origins coinciding at the point of intersection. (The unit distances of the two scales need not be identical.) Join the 1-point (i.e., the point corresponding to the number 1) on the first scale and the a-point on the second by a straight line. Then the line parallel to this through the b-point of the first scale will intersect the second scale in its ab-point. Figure 7-26 illustrates with $a > 0$, $b > 0$.

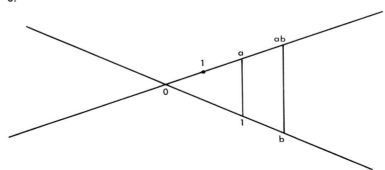

FIGURE 7-26 *Multiplication with intersecting scales.*

(a) Using Figure 7-26, prove the preceding statement in case (i) $a > 0$, $b \geq 0$.

(b) Draw figures for the three remaining cases: (ii) $a > 0$, $b < 0$, (iii) $a < 0$, $b \geq 0$, (iv) $a < 0$, $b < 0$. Then justify the statement in each case.

2. Establish scales with arbitrary origins and arbitrary units of length on each of two parallel lines. First assume the line joining the two origins intersects the line joining the 1-point of one scale to the a-point of the other, and let P denote the intersection. Then the line joining P to the b-point of the first scale intersects the second scale in its ab-point. Figure 7-27 illustrates with $a > 0$, $b > 0$. Answer questions analogous to (a), (b), and (c) of Exercise 1. Then treat the case so far omitted in which the line joining the two origins is parallel to the line joining the 1-point of the first scale to the a-point of the second.

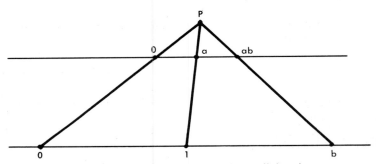

FIGURE 7-27   *Multiplication with parallel scales.*

3. Again establish scales on each of two intersecting lines with the two origins at the point of intersection. Let A denote the 1-point, and B the b-point, on scale 1. Let A' denote the 1-point, and B' the a-point, on scale 2. (See Figure 7-28.) Call C the point of intersection with scale 1 of the line through B' parallel to $A'B$; call C' the point of intersection with scale 2 of the line through B parallel to AB'. Prove that CC' is parallel to AA', and explain how this geometrical fact embodies the commutative law for multiplication.

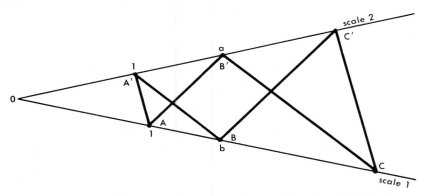

FIGURE 7-28   *A geometrical counterpart of commutativity in multiplication.*

4. Establish scales on three concurrent lines so that the origin for each is at the common point O. Let A denote the 1-point, and A' the c-point, on scale 1. Let B denote the b-point on scale 2, B' labeling the point of intersection with scale 2 of the line through A' parallel to AB. Let C denote the ab-point of scale 3, C' labeling the intersection with scale 3 of the line through B' parallel to BC. (See Figure 7-29.) Prove that A'C' is parallel to AC, and explain how this geometrical fact embodies the associative law of multiplication.

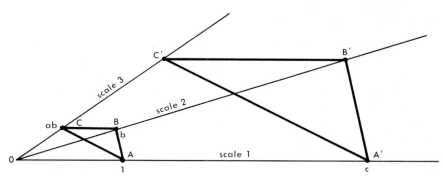

FIGURE 7-29 *A geometrical counterpart of associativity in multiplication.*

3.

Area

Similar triangle proportionalities also provide an elegant approach to the subject of areas. We continue to follow P. C. Rosenbloom.[†]

By a *rectangular region* we mean a rectangle together with the part of the plane it encloses. Similarly, by a *triangular region* we mean a triangle together with the part of the plane it encloses, and so on. The enclosing rectangle, triangle, or other figure is called the *boundary* of the region. The vertices and sides of the boundary are also called the vertices and sides of the region; the length and width of a rectangle, the length and width of the corresponding rectangular region, and so forth. If two triangles are congruent or similar, the corresponding triangular regions are also said to be congruent or similar, respectively.

It will be convenient to use the same notation for triangular or rectangular regions as for their boundaries. Then, for instance, whether *BCD* refers to a triangular region or to its boundary will be determined by the text. We shall not hesitate to abbreviate "rectangular region" by "rectangle," or "triangular region" by "triangle," when possible without confusion.

Rectangular regions of unit width (see Figure 7-30) will provide the standard with which other regions are compared.

---

†Ibid., pp. 69-71.

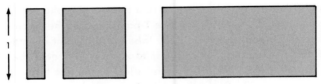

FIGURE 7-30   *Rectangles of width 1.*

Definition 1.   The area of a rectangular region of width 1 and length a is defined to be the positive number a.

To define the area of an arbitrary region S, we shall require essentially that it be possible to cut up S into pieces that can be reassembled into a rectangle R of unit width. Then we shall define the area of S to be the area of R. As a simple illustration, consider a right triangle BCD with right angle at B and $BD = 2$ (Figure 7-31). Let E be the midpoint of the segment BD, F the midpoint of CD, and G the point such that $BCGE$ is a rectangle. Since the triangles EFD and GFC are congruent, we can cut the subregion EFD out of the given triangle BCD and then move it into the position occupied by GFC. Triangles EFB and BFC are left where they are. In this way, the given triangle BCD is cut into three triangular pieces, which are reassembled as a rectangle, the region $BCGE$ of unit width. Accordingly, we say that the area of BCD is equal to the area of $BCGE$, which is BC.

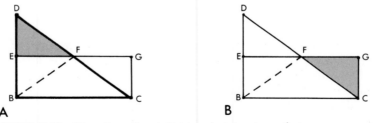

FIGURE 7-31   *Dissection of a right triangle into pieces that are re-arranged to form a rectangle.*

Let us make this process more general. We shall say that two (triangular, rectangular, and so forth) regions are *nonoverlapping*, or *do not overlap*, if they have no points in common that are not boundary points. (Under this definition, two regions may intersect—i.e., have points in common—but not overlap.) A plane region S will be said to *have a dissection*, or *be dissected*, into certain subregions if the subregions do not overlap and have union S (i.e., together make up S). (For instance, triangle BCD in Figure 7-31A was dissected into the three triangles EFD, EFB, and BFC.) The subregions will also be called *parts* or *pieces*. Now suppose U and V to be regions with dissections into the same number of triangular pieces, say U into

$$A_1, A_2, A_3, \ldots, A_n$$

and V into

$$B_1, B_2, B_3, \ldots, B_n.$$

Suppose the pieces of these dissections to be pairwise congruent: A_1 congruent to B_1, A_2 congruent to B_2, and, in general, A_k congruent to B_k for $k = 1, 2, 3, \ldots, n$. The dissections of U and V will then be said to *agree,* and U and V themselves (if different) will be said to be *different arrangements of the same parts.* (For instance, BCD and $BCGE$ in Figure 7-31B are different arrangements of the same parts.)

Definition 2. Let S be a given plane region and R a certain rectangle of unit width. If R and S are different arrangements of the same parts, then we define the area of S to be equal to the area of R.

The symbol we shall use for the area of S is $A(S)$. In this notation, our definition states that

$$A(S) = A(R)$$

under the conditions assumed.

We shall now indicate how the usual area formulas in plane geometry follow from Definitions 1 and 2.

The Area of an Arbitrary Rectangle. A rectangular region of length a and width b has area equal to the product ab.

PROOF: Consider a rectangle $BCDE$ with $BC = a$ and $BE = b$, where $b \neq 1$. Let F be a point of the line BE such that $BF = 1$ and such that

$$F \text{ is between } B \text{ and } E \text{ if } BE > 1,$$
$$E \text{ is between } B \text{ and } F \text{ if } BE < 1.$$

Figure 7-32 illustrates the case in which $BE > 1$. Draw the line through E parallel to CF, and let this line intersect CD in K and BC in G. On the line through F parallel to BC, select J so that $BGJF$ is a rectangle. It has unit width, and we shall see that it is a re-arrangement of the parts of the original rectangle in a suitable dissection. As Figure 7-32 shows, $BCDE$ is made up of the subregions enclosed by

$$KDE, \ CKEF, \ BCF,$$

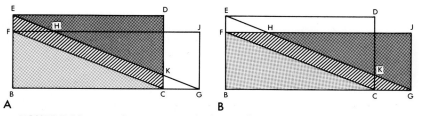

FIGURE 7-32   An arbitrary rectangle dissected into parts that can be re-assembled into a rectangle of given width.

and *BGJF* consists of the subregions enclosed by

$$GJF, CGHF, BCF.$$

Working with these subregions, it is easy to find dissections of the two rectangles into pairwise congruent triangular subregions such as Definition 2 requires. Thus, the two rectangles are different arrangements of the same parts. The area of the first rectangle is equal to that of the second, which has unit width, and thus is equal to its length *BG*. Side proportionalities of similar triangles give us

$$BG/BE = BC/BF,$$

or

$$BG/b = a/1,$$

and thus

$$BG = ab.$$

This proves that the area of the given rectangle is the product of its length by its width, as a consequence of Definitions 1 and 2.

EXERCISES

1. Fill in the details of the previous proof.
2. Work out the analogous proof in the case in which *BE* < 1.
3. If one side of a parallelogram is adopted as the *base*, then the distance along a perpendicular between this base and the opposite side is the *height*, or *altitude*, of the parallelogram. Prove that any parallelogram has area equal to the product of its base and altitude. Why is the area the same no matter which side of the parallelogram is selected as base? HINT: Figure 7-33 indicates how to re-arrange pieces of the parallelogram into a rectangle of the same base and altitude, respectively. Different choices of the base lead, however, to rectangles of different shapes. Why are their areas the same?

FIGURE 7-33 *Dissection of a parallelogram.*

4. If one side of a triangle is adopted as the *base*, then the length of the perpendicular to this side from the opposite vertex is called the *altitude*, or *height*, of the triangle. (See Figure 7-34.) Prove that any triangle has area

FIGURE 7-34   *Base and altitude of triangles.*

equal to one-half the product of its base and altitude. Why is its area the same no matter which side of the triangle is selected as the base? HINT: See Figure 7-33.

5. A trapezoid is a four-sided figure *BCDE* such that two sides are parallel and the other two sides do not intersect. (See Figure 7-35.) Prove that the area of a trapezoid is equal to the average of the two parallel sides times the perpendicular distance between. In Figure 7-35, the area thus is (1/2) (*BC* + *ED*) · *FG*, where *FG* is perpendicular to *BC*, *BC* and *ED* being parallel.

FIGURE 7-35   *A trapezoid.*

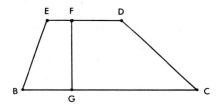

6. Let *B, C, D, E* be points of a straight line *L*. Suppose *BC* = *DE* = *FG*, the line *FG* being parallel to *L*, as in Figure 7-36. Thus, *BFGC* and *DFGE* are both parallelograms. Prove that their areas are equal. HINT: Let *O* be the intersection of *CG* and *DF*, and let *OM* be perpendicular to *EG*, *ON* perpendicular to *BF*. Then the area of *DFGE* is *OM · DF*, and the area of *BFGC* is *ON · CG*. Prove that

$$CG/DF = OG/OF$$

and that

$$OG/OF = OM/ON.$$

FIGURE 7-36   *Two parallelograms of equal area.*

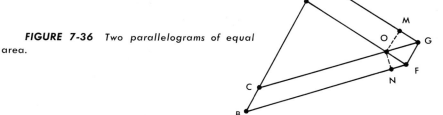

7. Find agreeing dissections of an arbitrary triangle and a corresponding rectangle of unit width.

8. Find agreeing dissections of a regular hexagon and a corresponding rectangle of unit width. (A regular hexagon is illustrated in Figure 7-37. It has six equal sides, consecutive sides meeting at the angle 120°.) HINT: Dissect the hexagon into six equal triangles, as indicated by the dotted lines.

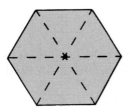

FIGURE 7-37   A regular hexagon.

It should now be clear that any region consisting of a finite number of nonoverlapping triangular, rectangular, or trapezoidal, and so forth subregions can be further cut up, if necessary, into triangular pieces that we can re-arrange into the form of a rectangle with unit width. By Definition 2, the area of the given region is that of this rectangle of unit width.

We call attention to an important fact about the areas of triangles. Suppose two triangles, say BCD and EFG, are similar, and consider the ratio of two corresponding sides. Calling the ratio k, we then have, for instance,

$$k = BC/EF;$$

the ratio k of course is the same, no matter which pair of corresponding sides is chosen. We shall prove that

$$A(BCD)/A(EFG) = k^2,$$

$A(BCD)$ standing for the area of BCD and $A(EFG)$ standing for the area of EFG. Let BC and DM be the base and the altitude of the first triangle and EF and GN the base and altitude of the second, as in Figure 7-38. Then triangles GNE and DMB are similar, and therefore

$$DM/GN = DB/GE,$$

while DB/GE, being the ratio of corresponding sides of the two original triangles, is equal to k. Hence,

$$DM/GN = k,$$

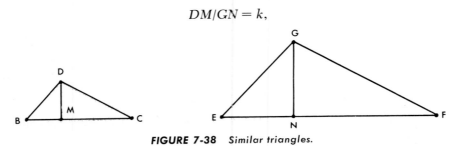

FIGURE 7-38   Similar triangles.

or

$$DM = k \cdot GN.$$

From this and the previous relation $BC = k \cdot EF$, we have

$$
\begin{aligned}
A(BCD) &= (1/2) \, DM \cdot BC \\
&= (1/2) \, k \cdot GN \cdot k \cdot EF \\
&= (1/2) \, k^2 \cdot GN \cdot EF.
\end{aligned}
$$

Therefore,

$$\frac{A(BCD)}{A(EFG)} = \frac{(1/2)k^2 \cdot GN \cdot EF}{(1/2) \, GN \cdot EF} = k^2,$$

as asserted.

This relationship is the basis of a very elegant proof of the Pythagorean theorem. Consider a right triangle BCD with right angle at D, and find the point E on BC such that DE is perpendicular to BC (see Figure 7-39). Then the triangles BCD, DCE, and BDE are all

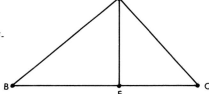

FIGURE 7-39 *Dissection of a right tri-angle into two similar triangles.*

similar (see Exercise 17, Section 1). Consider the ratios

$$r = DC/BC, \; s = BD/BC$$

of their hypotenuses. By the previous result,

$$A(DCE)/A(BCD) = r^2, \quad A(BDE)/A(BCD) = s^2,$$

while

$$A(DCE) + A(BDE) = A(BCD),$$

BCD being the union of the other two triangles. Dividing this by $A(BCD)$, we obtain

$$A(DCE)/A(BCD) + A(BDE)/A(BCD) = 1,$$

or, in view of the previous equalities,

$$r^2 + s^2 = 1.$$

Substituting the expressions that defined r and s gives us

$$(DC/BC)^2 + (BD/BC)^2 = 1$$

and, by multiplying by BC^2,

$$DC^2 + BD^2 = BC^2:$$

Pythagoras's theorem.

A remark on volumes. The foregoing definitions of area of plane figures can be generalized to volumes of solid bodies in three-dimensional space. We shall indicate how and then give some examples in the simplest cases, which are those of prisms. Other solid figures may offer considerable difficulties, some of which we shall attack later in Chapters 14 and 15.

A *prism* is a certain kind of polyhedron, or solid figure with plane faces. Two faces, which are called the *bases* of the prism, are congruent polygons† the planes of which are mutually parallel (i.e., do not meet); the other faces of the prism are all parallelograms. If these parallelograms are rectangles, the planes of which are perpendicular to the bases, then the prism is called a *right prism* (Figure 7-40). If

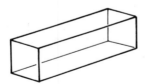 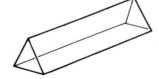

FIGURE 7-40   Some right prisms.

a right prism has rectangular bases, then each of its six faces is a rectangle, and the three edges that meet at each corner, or vertex, are mutually perpendicular line segments.‡ Such a figure is shaped, say, like a shoebox; we shall call it a *box*. By the *measurements* of a box, we mean the lengths of three mutually perpendicular edges. Any one of these measurements may be taken at pleasure as the length of the box and the other two as its width and depth. A box with the measurements a, b, c is called an "a by b by c box." A 1 by 1 by c box,

---

† A *polygon* is a plane figure with three or more straight sides joined end to end in succession. In a polygon that is the base of a prism, the first and last sides are also joined, the polygon thus enclosing a region of the plane. Such a polygon is said to be closed, triangles, squares, and trapezoids being examples of closed polygons. Two polygons are said to be *congruent* if one can be placed in exact coincidence with the other, i.e., if they have exactly the same size and shape but possibly occupy different positions.

‡ Let us here accept such familiar properties on intuitive grounds. They all easily follow from the formal development of Section 2, Chapter 9.

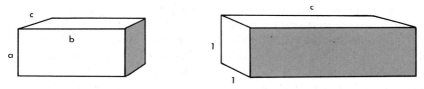

FIGURE 7-41 *Boxes.*

in particular, will be called a box of *unit cross section* and length *c*. Figure 7-41 illustrates some of these terms.

Boxes of unit cross section provide our standard of volume.

Definition 3. The volume of a rectangular box with unit cross section is defined to be the length of the box. (The volume of a 1 by 1 by *c* box is defined to be *c*.)

To define the volumes of three-dimensional figures that are not boxes of unit cross section, we use the idea of Definition 2. Generalized to space, this idea is to cut up a given region into parts that can be re-arranged to fill a box of unit cross section, then define the volume of the given figure as the volume of this box. This definition to be perfectly explicit should be accompanied by explanations analogous to those that preceded Definition 2, but such explanations are both straightforward and tedious, and we dispense with them. Let us, however, show how the definition is used to obtain the usual formula for the volume of a box.

The Volume of a Box. The volume of an *a* by *b* by *c* box is equal to the product *abc* of the three measurements.

PROOF: Two steps are involved, the first of which is to cut up the region inside the box into right prisms that can be re-arranged to fill a 1 by *ab* by *c* box. To accomplish this, consider a face *F* of the given box that has length *a* and width *b*. Dissect *F* into parts — polygons — that can be re-assembled into a rectangle of length *ab* and width 1. In general, four polygons suffice for this dissection, as illustrated in Figure 7-42 (see Figure 7-32). Each polygon determines a right prism of length *c* contained in the given box, the polygon being a base of the prism. If we re-arrange the prisms so that their bases make a rectangle of length *ab* and width 1, the prisms themselves will fill up a 1 by *ab* by *c* box. Thus, the first step is done.

FIGURE 7-42 *The dissection of F.*

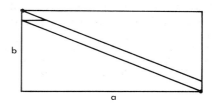

The second step is to cut up the region inside the 1 by ab by c box into new right prisms that can be re-assembled to fill up a 1 by 1 by abc box. The method is like that of the first step just described. The new right prisms consist of parts of the old. These parts, in one arrangement, fill the original a by b by c box and, in another arrangement, fill the new 1 by 1 by abc box. Hence, the first (a by b by c) box has volume abc, as asserted.

EXERCISES

By the *height* of a prism we mean the distance between its two bases.

9. Prove that the volume of a right prism with triangular base is equal to the area of the base multiplied by the height of the prism.

10. Prove that the volume of a right prism with quadrilateral base is equal to the area of the base multiplied by the height of the prism. (A quadrilateral is a closed four-sided polygon.)

11. Find a generalization of the previous two statements. Prove it.

4.

Geometrical constructions of interest to artists

Through a large part of history, geometrical or arithmetical considerations underlay the artistic representation of the human form.[†] A work of sculpture or painting in ancient Egypt was organized mechanically by means of a preparatory subdivision of the surface into a network of equal squares. The ankle then was placed on the first horizontal line, the knee on the sixth, the shoulders on the sixteenth, and so forth. Movement was represented by pictures conforming to similar canons: for instance, the length of pace in a lunging figure was fixed at 10 1/2 units compared with 4 1/2 or 5 1/2 units between the feet of a figure quietly standing. Such methods of construction resulted in static, stereotyped forms, "bodies that wait to be re-enlivened." From what we know of Egyptian religion, these were undoubtedly what the artists desired.

Greek striving for aesthetic perfection led away from the rigid stereotypes of Egypt towards sculptural methods based on an explicit knowledge of actual human proportions and a recognition of the changes resulting from muscular contraction and thickening. A detailed list of ideal proportions, afterwards accepted as canonical,

---

†The historical remarks in this section are based mainly on the second essay, "The history of the theory of human proportions as a reflection of the history of styles," pp. 55-107, in *Meaning in the Visual Arts* by Erwin Panofsky (Doubleday, Garden City, 1955).

apparently was given in the 5th Century, B.C., by Polyclitus, a sculptor who also embodied these prescripts in his statues. Polyclitus's only extant statement is his declaration that "the beautiful comes about, little by little, through many numbers."† This thought is elaborated in the following excerpt from Galen:‡ "Chrysippus ... holds that beauty does not consist in the elements but in the harmonious proportion of the parts, the proportion of one finger to the other, of all the fingers to the rest of the hand, of the rest of the hand to the wrist, of these to the forearm, of the forearm to the whole arm, in fine, of all parts to all others, as it is written in the canon of Polyclitus." Such approaches to art reached their culmination in the Renaissance, especially in the anatomical studies of Albrecht Duerer, who laboriously formulated extensive sets of proportions not, like Polyclitus, for the "ideal" form alone, but for each of 26 "characteristic" types, in addition to special subjects such as the body of the infant.

Others have tried to comprehend the design of the human body and other natural forms, such as those of shells or plants, abstractly in geometry. Following are some of the geometrical constructions (especially those of Exercises 2, 5, 6, 9, 10, 13) recommended to artists by a modern advocate of the geometrical basis of design, Jay Hambidge.§ They make fine exercises for further review of the Euclidean geometry of Section 1.

We shall start with well-known terminology and facts about rectangles. A rectangle with vertices A, B, C, D frequently is named by listing these vertices in the order in which they would occur in a circuit around the figure. For instance, the rectangles in Figure 7-43 might be called $ABCD$ and $A'B'C'D'$, respectively. The rectangle $ABCD$ is more briefly called AC or BD, care then being required to avoid confusion with the line segments AC and BD, respectively. These line segments are known as the diagonals of the rectangle. AB and CD are opposite sides of the rectangle; so also are AD and BC. Opposite sides are equal and parallel.

One of the four sides of a rectangle sometimes is distinguished as its "base." A perpendicular side then is denominated the "altitude" of the rectangle. In the first rectangle of Figure 7-43, for instance, AB might be the base and AD the altitude. The area of a rectangle is the product of the base by the altitude.

Two rectangles, $ABCD$ and $A'B'C'D'$, are said to be similar if corresponding sides are proportional, i.e., if

$$AB/BC = A'B'/B'C'.$$

———————

†E. Diels, in *Archäologischer Anzeiger*, 1889, No. 1, p. 10. Quoted from Panofsky, *ibid.*, p. 68.

‡Galen, *Placita Hippocratis et Platonia*, V, 3. Quoted in Panofsky, *ibid.*, p. 64.

§Jay Hambidge, *The Elements of Dynamic Symmetry*, Yale University Press, New Haven, 1948. Other books are listed there. I was referred to Hambidge by Dr. Raymond Stites of The National Gallery of Art, Washington, D.C.

Figure 7-43 illustrates.

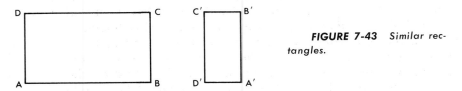

FIGURE 7-43   *Similar rectangles.*

EXERCISES

1. Prove: either diagonal divides any rectangle into two equal triangles.

2. Given a square $ABCD$ of side 1, let M be the midpoint of AB (i.e., $AM = MB = 1/2$), and let E be a point of the line AB such that $ME = MC$. Prove that if, as in Figure 7-44, A and E fall on opposite sides of M, then $AE = (1 + \sqrt{5})/2$. (HINT: Show that $MC = \sqrt{5}/2$.) The rectangle DE, for a reason that will be seen in Exercise 13, is called by Hambidge "the rectangle of the whirling squares."

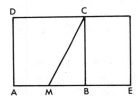

FIGURE 7-44   *Constructing the rectangle of the whirling squares.*

3. Construct by geometrical means the following three rectangles with altitude 1 and base a as specified:

(a) $a = \sqrt{2}$
(b) $a = \sqrt{3}$
(c) $a = \sqrt{5}$.

Rectangles with these proportions are called root two, root three, and root five rectangles, respectively. Marked aesthetic properties are claimed for such rectangles, as well as for the rectangle of whirling squares. The reader may judge from Figure 7-45. The root five rectangle in this figure is subdivided into a central square flanked by rectangular panels on either side; the square and one of the flanking panels alone make a whirling squares rectangle.

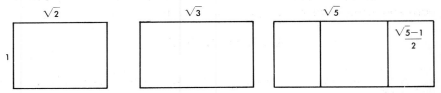

FIGURE 7-45   *Root two, root three, and root five rectangles.*

4. In painting, area comparisons are considered important. This is the reason for considering the following problem. Let a square $ABCD$ (Figure 7-46)

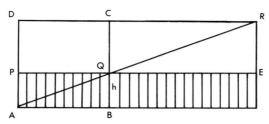

FIGURE 7-46 *Constructing a rectangle of given altitude and area.*

and an arbitrary length *h* be given. The problem is to construct a rectangle with altitude *h* and with area equal to that of *ABCD*. (This problem is equivalent to that of dividing the area of the square by an arbitrary number *h*. If the square has unit side, it is thus a geometrical construction of the reciprocal of *h*.) This problem can, of course, be solved by arithmetical calculation with the aid of several accurate measurements by a ruler. Hambidge considers the following geometrical solution preferable, however, since an artist can perform it quickly freehand without tedious measurements and calculations. First, let us assume *h* to be less than *AD*. Let *P* denote the point of *AD* at distance *h* from *A*; let *Q* denote the point of *BC* at distance *h* from *B*. Draw line *AQ*; let *R* denote its intersection with the line *CD*. Call *E* the point of intersection of the line *PQ* with the perpendicular to *DR* through *R*. Prove that *AE*, the shaded figure, is the desired rectangle. (HINT: Triangles *CQR* and *BQA* are similar.) Consider the analogous problem with *h* greater than *AD*.

From now on — except in the final exercise — *ABCD* will always denote a rectangle.

5. In Figure 7-47, *BE* is perpendicular to *AC*, *EF* is parallel to *CD*, and *EG* is parallel to *BC*. Prove the rectangles *FG* and *AC* to be similar. HINT: $\angle\,EBC = \angle\,CAB$.

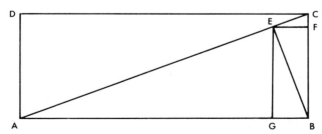

FIGURE 7-47 *A similar rectangle, abutting a side and touching a diagonal, within a given rectangle.*

6. Within a whirling squares rectangle *ABCD* (Exercise 2), construct similar rectangles, *AEHI* and *FBJG*, against the shorter ends by the process of Exercise 5. Figure 7-48 exhibits the resulting configuration. Prove that *ABJI* is a root five rectangle (i.e., $AB/BJ = \sqrt{5}$) and that *EFGH* is a square.

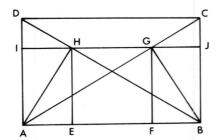

FIGURE 7-48 *A root five rectangle within a whirling squares rectangle.*

7. In Figure 7-49, let *EF* be parallel to *CD*. The problem is, avoiding arithmetical calculations, to construct on *EF* as a side a rectangle similar to *ABCD* with *EF* corresponding to *DC*. This is done as follows: First, find the point of intersection of the two lines *DE* and *CF*. Call this point *P*. Drawing the segments *PA* and *PB*, let *G* and *H* denote the points in which these segments meet the lines through *E* and *F* parallel to *AD*. Then prove that the rectangle with the vertices *E*, *F*, *G*, *H* is that desired, i.e., is similar to *ABCD* with *EF* and *DC* corresponding.

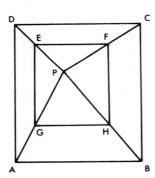

FIGURE 7-49 *A similar rectangle on a given base within a given rectangle.*

8. In Figure 7-50, let *AC* be perpendicular to *CE*. Then prove that *EFCB* and *ABCD* are similar.

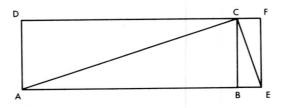

FIGURE 7-50 *An exterior, similar rectangle on an end of a given rectangle.*

9. In Figure 7-51, *AC* is perpendicular to *BE*. Prove that *ABCD* and *BCFE* are similar rectangles. (If $AD = 1$, it is easily seen that $(AB) \cdot (BF) = 1$. For this reason, Hambidge calls *BCFE* a "reciprocal" rectangle to the original. We shall follow his usage.)

The remaining exercises are all concerned with applications or special features of the last construction.

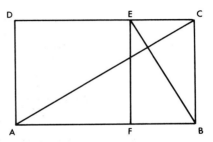

FIGURE 7-51 *Construction of a reciprocal rectangle.*

10. Prove that if *ABCD* is a whirling squares rectangle (Exercise 2), then *AFED* in Figure 7-51 is a square.

11. If *AD* = 1 in Figure 7-51, find *AB* of such length that *AF* = *FB*. The rectangles *AE* and *FC* then are equal and both similar to *ABCD*. Figure 7-52 illustrates.

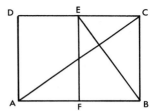

FIGURE 7-52 *A reciprocal rectangle one-half the original.*

12. Construct reciprocal rectangles (Exercise 9) against both shorter sides of *ABCD* (Figure 7-53). Thus, rectangles *FC* and *AH* are similar to the rectangle *AC*. If *AD* = 1, find *AB* of such length that *AG* = *GF* = *FB*: i.e., so that the middle rectangle is similar to the two on the sides. (In Figure 7-53, *AB* was so determined.)

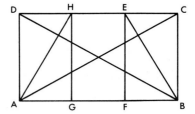

FIGURE 7-53 *Reciprocal rectangles on either end.*

13. In Figure 7-54, *ABCX* is a rectangle, and *BD* is perpendicular to *AC* at its meeting point *O*. Construct the beginning of a polygonal spiral, which coils about *O* from its inception at *A*, by drawing *DE* parallel to *BC*, *EF* parallel to *AB*, *FG* parallel to *BC*, *GH* parallel to *AB*, and so on. The spiral has the property that the distance of each vertex (*A, B, C, D, E, F, G, H*, and so on) from the "eye" *O* becomes smaller by the same proportion at each step: i.e.,

$$OA/OB = OB/OC = OC/OD = OD/OE = OE/OF = OF/OG = OG/OH,$$

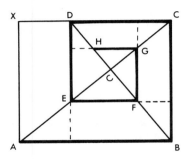

FIGURE 7-54   A spiral within a given rectangle.

and so on. Four such spirals pertain to any rectangle not a square.

    (a) Verify the preceding proportions.

    (b) Prove that the rectangles BD, CE, DF, EG, and so on are all similar to the original rectangle AC.

    (c) Prove that if ABCX is a rectangle of whirling squares, then the rectangles AD, BE, CF, DG, EH, and so on are all squares. Figure 7-55 illustrates.

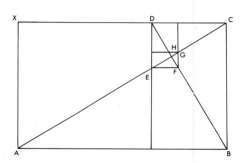

FIGURE 7-55   The whirling squares.

5.

Arithmetical methods in geometry: Trigonometry

    If two sides and the included angle of a triangle are known, the triangle is determined (Condition (i'), Section 1). This means that all three sides and all three angles are determined. Similarly, if two angles and the included side, or if all three sides, are known, the triangle again is determined. In each such case, the sides or angles that are not specified can be found by measuring directly either the triangle in question or a similar triangle, conveniently scaled. (See Exercises 1 and 2, Section 1.) Direct measurement is less accurate, however, than certain modes of calculation we shall here discuss. The theory of such calculation, elaborated by Greeks, Hindus, and Europeans over a span of perhaps 1800 years, culminated in trigonometry, an indispensable practical aid in surveying and navigation, and a background from which fundamental advances in mathematics were to be made.

a. THE TRIGONOMETRIC FUNCTIONS

The germ of trigonometry was already present in an ancient method of measuring the height of a building on level ground from the length of its shadow and the elevation of the sun. This method dates at least from the 6th Century, B.C., and has been ascribed to the Greek philosopher Thales. In Figure 7-56, *BC* represents the unknown

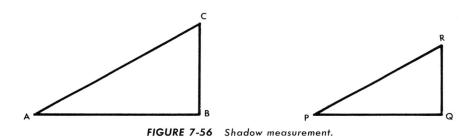

FIGURE 7-56   *Shadow measurement.*

height and *AB* the shadow, which is assumed to be known by direct measurement; *BC* is assumed to be perpendicular to *AB*. *QR* is any known height: according to one tradition, the length of Thales' staff. *PQ* is the shadow cast by *QR* and is perpendicular to it. The two shadows are supposed to be observed at the same time, so that ∠ *A* and ∠ *P* are equal, each being the angle of elevation of the sun. Since the two right angles (∠ *B* and ∠ *Q*) also are equal, triangles *ABC* and *PQR* are similar. Therefore,

$$BC/AB = QR/PQ$$

and, consequently,

$$BC = AB \cdot QR/PQ.$$

This is the formula desired, telling how to calculate *BC* from *AB*, *QR*, and *PQ*, which are all known.

A simple variation of the foregoing method might have led the Greek philosopher Thales to trigonometry over four centuries before its apparent inception. To explain this twist, first consider any two lines that intersect at an acute angle (an angle less than 90°). In Figure 7-57, this angle is at *A*. Construct a perpendicular to one of the lines at any one of its points *Q* different from *A* (*Q* ≠ *A*); then call the line *AQ*. The perpendicular meets the second line in a point we denote by *R*; accordingly, call the second line *AR*. By construction,

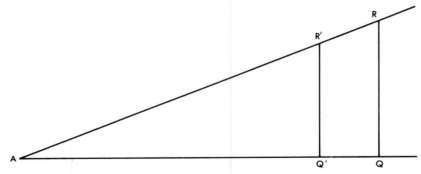

FIGURE 7-57 *Illustration for the tangent of an angle.*

AQR is a right triangle. We contend that the ratio

(1) $$QR/QA$$

is independent of the selection of Q. More precisely, let Q' denote any other point on the line AQ, and R' the point in which AR intersects the perpendicular to AQ through Q'. Our contention is that

(2) $$QR/QA = Q'R'/Q'A.$$

This follows from the fact that corresponding angles in AQR and $AQ'R'$ are equal, these triangles thus being similar.

EXERCISE

1. Justify the last relation when Q' is on AR, R' then being the point of intersection of AQ with the perpendicular to AR through Q'.

The ratio (1), as we have just proved, is independent of Q, thus depending on the angle A only. It is called the *tangent* of this angle, an appellation generally abbreviated as tan A. Thus,

(3) $$\tan A = QR/QA$$

for *any* point Q different from A on either of the two lines, R then corresponding to Q in the manner described. We could find tan A with fair accuracy from a carefully drafted figure like Figure 7-57, measuring QR and QA and calculating their ratio. In this way we could develop a serviceable table of tangents for as many angles as we pleased, although such tables are better constructed by strictly numerical processes, which we shall not here describe.†

---

† The computation of a related table, in the 2nd Century, A.D., is clearly described in Asger Aaboe, *Episodes from the Early History of Mathematics*, Random House, 1964, Chapter 4.

A table of tangents permits us to measure the height of a building even when there is no shadow. At a known distance AB (Figure 7-56) from the foot of the building, we need simply measure the angle of elevation, $\angle A$, of its summit. Since

$$BC/AB = \tan A,$$

we then find the height BC by looking up $\tan A$ in the table and multiplying by AB. The shadow method, discussed first, amounts to using this formula with $\tan A$ represented as QR/PQ.

In any right triangle ABC (Figure 7-58), the right angle occurring at B, BC is called the arm (or side) *opposite* A, AB is called the arm *adjacent* to A. Similarly, AB is the arm opposite C and BC the arm

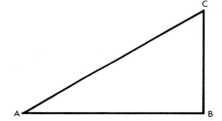

FIGURE 7-58   A right triangle.

adjacent to C. AC is the hypotenuse. In this terminology,

(4) $$\tan A = \frac{\text{opposite arm}}{\text{adjacent arm}},$$

the ratio on the right having the same value for *any* right triangle containing $\angle A$. Other ratios between sides of ABC also depend only on $\angle A$ (not otherwise on ABC) and are as important in geometry as $\tan A$. Such, in particular, are the *sine* of A and the *cosine* of A (abbreviations: $\sin A$ and $\cos A$, respectively) defined as follows:

$$\sin A = \frac{\text{opposite arm}}{\text{hypotenuse}},$$

$$\cos A = \frac{\text{adjacent arm}}{\text{hypotenuse}}.$$

These, too, can be tabulated, either by the direct method described for $\tan A$, or more advantageously by purely numerical methods.

The sine, the cosine, and the tangent have been defined for acute angles only and thus are as yet undefined for $0°$ and for $90°$. Logically, we are free to define them for these values, or not to define them, as we please. Mathematical convenience favors certain definitions, however, as the most suitable, those for $0°$ being arrived at as follows. In triangle ABC (Figure 7-59), let $\angle A$ be *near* $0°$, i.e., very small. The

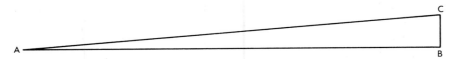

FIGURE 7-59 *A right triangle with one very small angle.*

opposite arm BC then is correspondingly small, compared with the other sides of the triangle, AC and AB. If we reduce $\angle A$ to values nearer and nearer zero, the ratios $BC/AB = \tan A$ and $BC/AC = \sin A$ also are reduced, likewise coming closer and closer to zero. At the same time, the ratio $AB/AC = \cos A$ approaches more and more closely to 1 as $\angle A$ goes to zero. For these reasons, we define:

$$\sin 0° = 0, \ \tan 0° = 0, \ \cos 0° = 1.$$

EXERCISES

2. Considering acute angles closer and closer to 90°, explain why we are led to define

$$\sin 90° = 1, \ \cos 90° = 0.$$

Why, at the same time, are we *not* led to a definite value for tan 90°?

3. In Figure 7-56, let BC, as before, denote the height of a tall building standing on level ground, and suppose AB to be known. Show how, by an appropriate measurement made at A and by use of one of the aforementioned tables, one can calculate the distance AC between the observer and the summit of the building.

4. By considering an isosceles right triangle, show that

$$\sin 45° = \cos 45° = 1/\sqrt{2}, \ \tan 45° = 1.$$

5. By considering an equilateral triangle, such as ABD in Figure 7-60, prove the following:

$\sin 30° = 1/2,$	$\sin 60° = \sqrt{3}/2,$
$\cos 30° = \sqrt{3}/2,$	$\cos 60° = 1/2,$
$\tan 30° = 1/\sqrt{3},$	$\tan 60° = \sqrt{3}.$

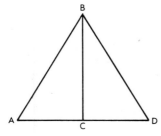

FIGURE 7-60 *An equilateral triangle bisected into right triangles.*

6. To find the distance XY between two points on opposite sides of a river (see Figure 7-61), a distance of 50 feet is paced off on one side of the river from Y to M with MY perpendicular to XY. The angle ∠ YMX is measured as 60°. Find the distance XY.

Some of the following exercises require approximate numerical values of certain trigonometric quantities. These are included in Table 7-1.

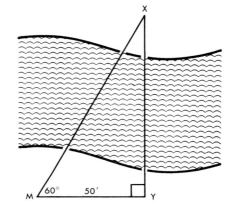

FIGURE 7-61   A method of surveying.

7. A 25-foot ladder placed against a wall makes an angle of 70° at its foot. How high on the wall does it reach? How far away from the foot of the wall?

8. From the top of a house a surveyor sights an object on the ground (see Figure 7-62). If the house is 100 feet above the ground and if the angle of depression is 21°, how far is the object from the foot of the house?

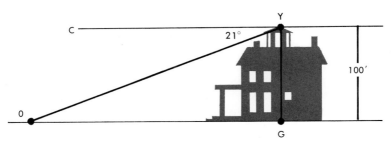

FIGURE 7-62   A surveying problem.

9. The roof of a house makes an angle of 40° with the horizontal. How much does it rise in every 10 feet of horizontal distance?

10. A man at the top of a cliff 80 feet high observes a small craft approaching the shore directly below his position. At first the angle of depression is 10°. Two hours later, the angle of depression is 50°. How fast is the craft approaching the cliff?

11. At a time when a telephone pole 31 feet tall casts a shadow 38 feet long, find the approximate angle of elevation of the sun.

Table 7-1 *Natural trigonometric functions† (Notice that the labels at the heads of the columns refer to angles from 0° to 45° and the labels at the bottoms of the columns to angles from 45° to 90°. [For instance, sin 20° = .342 = cos 70°. tan 20° = .364, tan 70° = 2.747.])*

Angle	Sin.	Tan.		Cos.	
0°	.000	.000		1.000	90°
1°	.017	.017	57.29	1.000	89°
2°	.035	.035	28.64	.999	88°
3°	.052	.052	19.081	.999	87°
4°	.070	.070	14.301	.998	86°
5°	.087	.087	11.430	.996	85°
6°	.105	.105	9.514	.995	84°
7°	.122	.123	8.144	.993	83°
8°	.139	.141	7.115	.990	82°
9°	.156	.158	6.314	.988	81°
10°	.174	.176	5.671	.985	80°
11°	.191	.194	5.145	.982	79°
12°	.208	.213	4.705	.978	78°
13°	.225	.231	4.331	.974	77°
14°	.242	.249	4.011	.970	76°
15°	.259	.268	3.732	.966	75°
16°	.276	.287	3.487	.961	74°
17°	.292	.306	3.271	.956	73°
18°	.309	.325	3.078	.951	72°
19°	.326	.344	2.904	.946	71°
20°	.342	.364	2.747	.940	70°
21°	.358	.384	2.605	.934	69°
22°	.375	.404	2.475	.927	68°
23°	.391	.424	2.356	.921	67°
24°	.407	.445	2.246	.914	66°
25°	.423	.466	2.144	.906	65°
26°	.438	.488	2.050	.899	64°
27°	.454	.510	1.963	.891	63°
28°	.469	.532	1.881	.883	62°
29°	.485	.554	1.804	.875	61°
30°	.500	.577	1.732	.866	60°
31°	.515	.601	1.664	.857	59°
32°	.530	.625	1.600	.848	58°
33°	.545	.649	1.540	.839	57°
34°	.559	.675	1.483	.829	56°
35°	.574	.700	1.428	.819	55°
36°	.588	.727	1.376	.809	54°
37°	.602	.754	1.327	.799	53°
38°	.616	.781	1.280	.788	52°
39°	.629	.810	1.235	.777	51°
40°	.643	.839	1.192	.766	50°
41°	.656	.869	1.150	.755	49°
42°	.669	.900	1.111	.743	48°
43°	.682	.933	1.072	.731	47°
44°	.695	.966	1.036	.719	46°
45°	.707	1.000	1.000	.707	45°
	Cos.	Tan.		Sin.	Angle

†Taken from *Calculus with Analytic Geometry* by Richard E. Johnson and Fred L. Kiokemeister, Boston, Allyn and Bacon, 1960, p. 655.

12. Two buildings are 98 feet apart. From the top of one, the angle of depression to the bottom of the other is 23°, and the angle of elevation to the top of the other is 14°. Find

(a) the height of the shorter building,

(b) the height of the taller building.

13. In Figure 7-58, prove: sin A = cos C and, thus, for $0° \leq \angle A \leq 90°$,

$$\sin A = \cos (90° - \angle A),$$
$$\cos A = \sin (90° - \angle A).$$

HINT: Consider separately the two cases in which (I) $\angle A$ is acute and (II) $\angle A = 0°$.

14. For $0° \leq \angle A < 90°$, prove that

$$\sin A/\cos A = \tan A.$$

15. Prove:† $\sin^2 A + \cos^2 A = 1$.

16. Prove: $1 + \tan^2 A = 1/\cos^2 A$.

17. Express cos A and tan A in terms of sin A.

18. Express sin A and cos A in terms of tan A.

---

† By $\sin^2 A$ we mean $(\sin A)^2$ with similar meanings for $\cos^2 A$, $\tan^2 A$, and so forth.

b. The Law of Sines and the Law of Cosines

The sine, the cosine, and the tangent of an angle, having been defined with reference to right triangles, may not at first seem pertinent to triangles of other shapes. Each shape seemingly might require its own tables of side ratios. This, however, is not so; right triangle ratios suffice in calculations for any shape. We shall illustrate this statement with two formulas, the first pertaining to the angle-side-angle criterion, the second to the side-angle-side criterion, for the congruence of triangles. Let ABC be any triangle (Figure 7-63),

FIGURE 7-63 An arbitrary triangle.

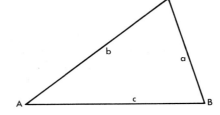

a denoting the side opposite $\angle A$, b the side opposite $\angle B$, and c the side opposite $\angle C$ (thus, $a = BC$, $b = CA$, $c = AB$). The first formula states:

(5) $$\sin A/a = \sin B/b = \sin C/c.$$

This is called the law of sines.

If the three angles of the triangle and one side, say c, are known, this formula enables us to calculate the other two sides:

$$a = c \sin A/\sin C, \; b = c \sin B/\sin C.$$

Not yet having defined the sine of an obtuse angle (an angle greater than 90°), we limit formula (5) at present to triangles whose angles are at most 90°, and then argue as follows. In Figure 7-64, let CD be perpendicular to AB, and set $h = CD$. Then

$$\sin A = h/b, \; \sin B = h/a.$$

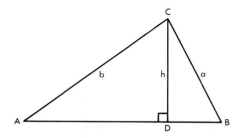

FIGURE 7-64   Dissection of a triangle into right triangles.

Hence,

$$\frac{\sin A}{\sin B} = \frac{h/b}{h/a} = a/b,$$

or

(6) $$\sin A/a = \sin B/b.$$

The same reasoning being applicable to, say, $\angle A$ and $\angle C$ in place of $\angle A$ and $\angle B$, we also have

(6′) $$\sin A/a = \sin C/c.$$

This and (6) together are equivalent to (5).

For the second formula, which pertains to the side-angle-side congruence criterion, we suppose $\angle C$ and sides a and b in Figure 7-63 to be given. This formula then states that

(7) $$c^2 = a^2 + b^2 - 2ab \cos C,$$

indicating the third side, c. It is called the law of cosines. Again, for the time being, we restrict consideration to triangles whose angles are at most 90°. Draw BD perpendicular to AC (Figure 7-65); set $p = CD$, $q = DA = b - p$, $h = BD$. In deriving formula (7), our strategy is, first, to express c by the Pythagorean law as

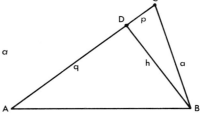

FIGURE 7-65 Another dissection of a triangle.

(8) $$c^2 = q^2 + h^2$$

and then to find q and h, neither of which is given as such, in terms of the given quantities, which are a, b, and $\angle C$. Since $p + q = b$, we have

(9) $$q = b - p.$$

On the other hand, $p/a = \cos C$, so that

(10) $$p = a \cos C.$$

From (9) and (10) we could, if we wished, express q at once in terms of a, b, and $\angle C$. But it is more expedient to hold off, now turning our attention to h. By the Pythagorean theorem again, $h^2 + p^2 = a^2$, so that

$$h^2 = a^2 - p^2.$$

In (8), we now substitute this result for h^2 and also substitute expression (9) for q. We thus have

$$
\begin{aligned}
c^2 &= q^2 + h^2 \\
&= (b - p)^2 + a^2 - p^2 \\
&= b^2 - 2pb + p^2 + a^2 - p^2 \\
&= b^2 - 2pb + a^2.
\end{aligned}
$$

Formula (7) follows from this upon the further substitution of expression (10) for p.

EXERCISES

1. When $\angle C = 90°$, how do formulas (6′) and (7) square with analogous, previous relations for a right angle?

2. In the right triangle of Figure 7-58, $BC/AB = \tan A$. Relate this to formula (5).

3. If the three sides of a triangle are given, how are the three angles to be found?

4. If two sides and the included angle of a triangle are given, how are the other two angles to be found?

5. Consider a triangle ABC with $\angle C$ obtuse (i.e., greater than 90°). Prove that

$$\sin A/a = \sin B/b = \sin (180° - \angle C)/c,$$

where a, b, c represent the sides opposite the respective angles A, B, C. (See Figures 7-66, 7-67.) This equality suggests that we *define* the sine of the obtuse angle C as

$$\sin C = \sin (180° - \angle C).$$

FIGURE 7-66 A triangle with an obtuse angle.

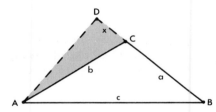

FIGURE 7-67 A construction for the law of sines.

Explain. HINT: The equality

$$\sin A/a = \sin B/b$$

is proved just as before. Let AD be perpendicular to the straight line BC at D (Figure 7-67), and let $x = CD$. Since

$$(\sin B)^2 = (AD/AB)^2 = (b^2 - x^2)/c^2,$$

we have

$$(\sin B/b)^2 = (b^2 - x^2)/(b^2 c^2) = b^2(1 - x^2/b^2)/(b^2 c^2)$$
$$= (1 - x^2/b^2)/c^2 = [1 - (\cos \angle DCA)^2]/c^2$$
$$= (\sin \angle DCA)^2/c^2$$

6. As in the previous exercise, consider a triangle ABC in which $\angle C$ is obtuse. Prove that

$$c^2 = a^2 + b^2 + 2ab \cos (180° - \angle C).$$

This equality suggests that we *define* the cosine of the obtuse angle $\angle C$ as

$$\cos C = -\cos (180° - \angle C).$$

Explain. HINT: Referring to Figure 7-67, again let $x = CD$. We have

$$c^2 = AB^2 = AD^2 + BD^2,$$

while

$$AD^2 = AC^2 - CD^2 = b^2 - x^2,$$
$$BD^2 = (a + x)^2 = a^2 + 2ax + x^2,$$

and

$$x = b \cos \angle DCA.$$

c. The area of a triangle. Heron's formula.

Elementary geometry gives the area of an arbitrary triangle as one-half the base times the altitude. How do we find the area knowing, say, two sides of the triangle and the included angle, or three sides, but not knowing the altitude directly? These are problems for trigonometry.

The first problem is the easier. Consider an arbitrary triangle ABC, denoting by a, b, c the sides opposite the vertices A, B, C, respectively (Figure 7-68). By the formula alluded to, the area T of this triangle is given by

$$T = ch/2,$$

where h is the altitude upon base c, i.e., the perpendicular to c from vertex C. By the definition of sine, $h/b = \sin A$, and equivalently, $h = b \sin A$. Substituting this expression for h in the formula for T, we have

$$T = (1/2)\,ch = (1/2)\,cb \sin A,$$

or

(1) $$T = (bc/2) \sin A.$$

In words: the area of any triangle is one-half the product of two sides and the sine of the included angle.

This formula applies even if $\angle A$ is obtuse if we understand $\sin A$ in that case to be defined as in Exercise 5 in subsection b.

The area of a triangle is given in terms of its three sides a, b, c by the formula

(2) $$T = \sqrt{s(s - a)(s - b)(s - c)},$$

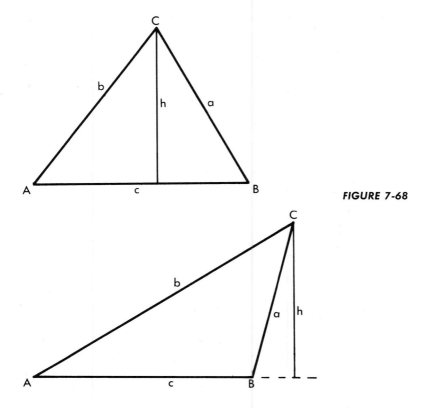

FIGURE 7-68

where s denotes half the perimeter: $s = (a + b + c)/2$. This elegant result is ascribed to Heron of Alexandria (about 100 B.C.). While its proof calls for more technicalities than the previous formula, we present it as a pretty illustration of trigonometric method.

We remark first that the quantity on the right, of which the square root is taken, is positive. In fact, $s - a$, $s - b$, and $s - c$ are all positive. For instance, $s - a = (1/2)(a + b + c) - a = (1/2)(b + c - a)$, while $b + c > a$, since the sum of two sides of a triangle exceeds the third.

Formula (1) shows that to obtain a formula for T in terms of a, b, c, it suffices to express $\sin A$ in terms of them. Since $\sin^2 A = 1 - \cos^2 A$, it is thus enough to put $\cos A$ in terms of a, b, c, and this is easily accomplished from the law of cosines,

$$a^2 = b^2 + c^2 - 2bc \cos A,$$

which implies

$$\cos A = (b^2 + c^2 - a^2)/(2bc).$$

Squaring, we have

$$\cos^2 A = (b^2 + c^2 - a^2)^2/(4b^2c^2),$$

and from this:

$$\sin^2 A = 1 - \cos^2 A = 1 - (b^2 + c^2 - a^2)^2/(4b^2c^2)$$
$$= [4b^2c^2 - (b^2 + c^2 - a^2)^2]/(4b^2c^2).$$

If a, b, c are known, we can calculate $\sin A$ from this result and then obtain T by substitution in (1). We thus already have the *kind* of formula for T we asked for, a formula giving T in terms of a, b, c alone. The formula, however, lacks elegance, which additional grooming will provide. In tidying it up, we shall make use of the following identities valid for any numbers u, v:

(a) $(u + v)^2 = u^2 + 2uv + v^2,$
(b) $(u - v)^2 = u^2 - 2uv + v^2,$
(c) $(u + v)(u - v) = u^2 - v^2.$

Identity (c) (with $u = 2bc$, $v = b^2 + c^2 - a^2$) shows, first, that

$$4b^2c^2 - (b^2 + c^2 - a^2)^2 = [2bc + (b^2 + c^2 - a^2)][2bc - (b^2 + c^2 - a^2)].$$

Applying (a) to the first factor on the right and (b) to the second, we obtain

$$4b^2c^2 - (b^2 + c^2 - a^2)^2 = [(b + c)^2 - a^2][a^2 - (b - c)^2].$$

Rewriting both right-hand factors by means of (c) gives

$$4b^2c^2 - (b^2 + c^2 - a^2)^2 = (b + c + a)(b + c - a)(a + b - c)(a - b + c)$$
$$= 16s(s - a)(s - b)(s - c),$$

since $a + b + c = 2s$, $b + c - a = (b + c + a) - 2a = 2s - 2a = 2(s - a)$, and so forth. Substituting the last result in the expression for $\sin^2 A$ give us

$$\sin^2 A = 4s(s - a)(s - b)(s - c)/(b^2c^2)$$

and, consequently,

$$\sin A = (2/(bc)) \sqrt{s(s - a)(s - b)(s - c)}.$$

(We took the positive square root because $\sin A$ is positive for any angle less than a straight angle. This is so for an acute angle by the original definition as a ratio of sides; it is so for right and obtuse angles by the extended definitions in Exercise 2 in Subsection a and Exercise 5 in Subsection b.) This formula is a counterpart to the law of cosines, to which it is equivalent. It tells how to calculate the sine of an angle from the three sides of any triangle including it.

Substituting the foregoing expression for sin A into (1) gives us:

$$T = (bc/2) \sin A = (bc/2)(2/(bc)) \sqrt{s(s-a)(s-b)(s-c)}$$
$$= \sqrt{s(s-a)(s-b)(s-c)}.$$

This is the formula we were seeking.

EXERCISE

1. Find the angles and the areas of triangles with the following sides:
   (a) 2, 3, 4.
   (b) 4, 5, 6.
   (c) 5, 6, 7.

d. DOUBLE-ANGLE FORMULAS

In Chapter 15, Section 5, we shall have to know how to express sin 2A and cos 2A in terms of sin A and cos A. This is done by the following formulas:

(1) $$\sin 2A = 2 \sin A \cos A,$$

(2) $$\cos 2A = \cos^2 A - \sin^2 A.$$

The case in which $\angle A$ is acute (i.e., $0° < A < 90°$) is the only one of interest to us, and in this case the formulas are easily obtained as follows.

We first derive formula (2). Consider an isosceles triangle PQR (Figure 7-69) in which $PQ = QR$ and $\angle Q = 2A$. We set $p = PQ = QR$ and $q = PR$. The angle bisector at Q is perpendicular to PR, which it

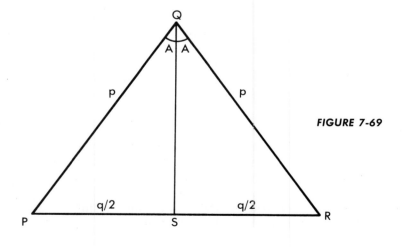

FIGURE 7-69

divides into equal segments PS and SR of length $q/2$. The law of cosines applied to $\triangle PQR$† tells us that

$$q^2 = p^2 + p^2 - 2p^2 \cos 2A$$
$$= 2p^2(1 - \cos 2A).$$

By definition, $\sin A = q/(2p)$, so that

(3) $$q = 2p \sin A,$$

and substituting this value of q in the previous formula gives

$$4p^2 \sin^2 A = 2p^2(1 - \cos 2A).$$

Multiplying both sides by $(2p^2)^{-1}$ results in

$$2 \sin^2 A = 1 - \cos 2A,$$

from which we have

(4) $$\cos 2A = 1 - 2 \sin^2 A.$$

Since $1 - \sin^2 A = \cos^2 A$, the last result also can be written as

$$\cos 2A = \cos^2 A - \sin^2 A,$$

which is formula (2).

The reader may take his choice between two methods of obtaining formula (1). The first is based on (4) and is strictly algebraic:

$$\sin^2 2A = 1 - \cos^2 2A = 1 - [1 - 2 \sin^2 A]^2$$
$$= 1 - [1 - 4 \sin^2 A + 4 \sin^4 A]$$
$$= 4 \sin^2 A - 4 \sin^4 A$$
$$= 4 \sin^2 A(1 - \sin^2 A)$$
$$= 4 \sin^2 A \cos^2 A.$$

Taking the positive square root of the left and the right sides gives us (1), $\sin 2A$ being a positive quantity because $2A$ is less than a straight angle. (See the remark in parentheses near the end of Subsection c).

The second method of proving (1) is based on Figure 7-69. By formula (1) of Subsection c, the area of $\triangle PQR$ is

(5) $$T = (p^2/2) \sin 2A.$$

On the other hand, the two triangles PQS and RQS being equal, the area of each must be $T/2$, and by formula (1) of Subsection c again,

$$T/2 = (pq/4) \sin P$$
$$= (pq/4) \sin (90° - A)$$
$$= (pq/4) \cos A$$

---

†We abbreviate "triangle PQR" by "$\triangle PQR$."

since $\triangle PSQ$ is a right triangle and $\sin(90° - A) = \cos A$ for any A. We saw in (3) that $q = 2p \sin A$, and making this substitution gives us

$$T/2 = (p^2/2) \sin A \cos A.$$

Comparing this with (5), we have

$$(p^2/4) \sin 2A = (p^2/2) \sin A \cos A,$$

and multiplying both sides of this equation by $4/p^2$ gives us

$$\sin 2A = 2 \sin A \cos A,$$

as formula (1) states.

6.

Geometric transformations

Group structure often underlies geometrical phenomena. Some examples will be given in this section.

a. THE DEFINITION OF A GEOMETRIC TRANSFORMATION

By a *geometric transformation* we shall mean a rule specifying for each point of the (Euclidean) plane an associated point. If T denotes a given geometric transformation, the point associated with an arbitrary point P under the rule T will be denoted by $T(P)$ (read "T of P"). We call $T(P)$ the *image* of P under the transformation T, and we call P the *antecedent* of its image. More generally, consider any geometrical configuration, such as a straight line, a triangle, or the points inside a circle. Let X denote the given configuration. Now apply the transformation T to each point of the configuration X. The images of these points under T constitute a configuration which we shall denote by $T(X)$. We shall refer to $T(X)$ as the *image* of X under the transformation T and also shall refer to X as the *antecedent* of its image $T(X)$.

Two rules that are expressed differently may turn out to assign the same image to each point in the plane. If so, the two rules are regarded as the same geometrical transformation. In fact, we define two geometrical transformations, S and T, to be *equal* if

$$S(P) = T(P) \textit{ for every point } P \textit{ in the plane,}$$

and in this case, we write

$$S = T.$$

Example 1. Consider a circle C with center O. With each point P of the plane, we shall associate a point P' as follows. First, if P is inside or on the circle C, we specify $P' = P$ (in this case, the point associated with P thus is P itself). But if P is outside the circle C, we draw the line segment OP (Figure 7-70) and take P' as the point of intersection of OP with the circle C. In this way, a rule is defined that specifies for each point P an associated point P'. By definition, this rule is a geometric transformation. If we let T denote this transformation, we have $T(P) = P'$ for every point P of the plane. The image under T of the inside of the circle C is again the inside of the circle; the image of C is C; the image of the outside of the circle is C; the image of a line segment OP that issues from the center of the circle is the segment OP'; the image of a square region containing C is C and the inside of C, and so on.

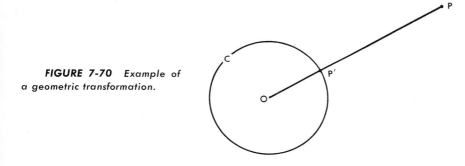

FIGURE 7-70 *Example of a geometric transformation.*

Example 2. Let L denote an arbitrary straight line in the plane. With each point P (in the plane), we shall associate a point P' as follows. First, if P is on the line L, we specify $P' = P$. Secondly, if P is not on the line L, we draw the straight line perpendicular to L through P (Figure 7-71) and call the intersection of L with this perpendicular P'. In this way, a rule is defined that specifies for each point P an associated point P'. This rule is by definition a geometric transformation, and if we let U denote the transformation, we have $U(P) = P'$ for every point P of the plane. The image under this transformation U of any straight line perpendicular to L is the single point of intersection with L. The image of any straight line not perpendicular to L is the line L. The image of any circle is a segment of L.

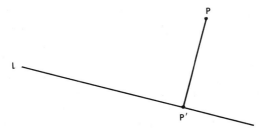

FIGURE 7-71 *Second example of a geometric transformation.*

EXERCISES

    1. In a plane, let us select an arbitrary direction as "north." Let *T* be the transformation that takes each point in the plane to a new point 2 units to the east and 3 units to the south. Let *U* be the transformation that takes each point in the plane to a new point 3 units to the south and 2 units to the east.

        (a) How are *U* and *T* related?

        (b) What geometric shape would the image of a square under the transformation *T* have?

    2. Suppose we apply the transformation *T* of Exercise 1 to a point *P* and then apply *T* to the image of *P* under *T*. In other words, suppose we apply *T* twice successively to each point in the plane.

        (a) Is the double application of *T* a geometric transformation?

        (b) Describe the double application of *T* by stating a rule.

b. TRANSLATIONS

    We shall first describe translation along a straight line *L*. Consider any two distinct points *A* and *A'* ($A \neq A'$) of this line. For an arbitrary point *P* of *L* (Figure 7-72), take *P'* to be the point of *L* such that (1) $AA' = PP'$ and (2) the direction from *P* to *P'* is the same as the direction from *A* to *A'*. (Condition (2) means that if we write the four points in the order in which they occur on *L*, with *A* preceding *A'*, then *P* precedes *P'*.) Associating *P'* with *P* defines a geometric transformation of *L* that is called a *translation along L*. This translation can be pictured as a thrusting forth or back of the whole line through the distance *AA'*.

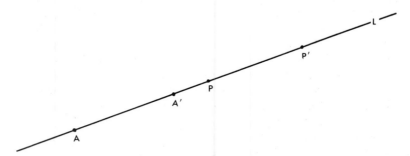

FIGURE 7-72   *Translation along a straight line.*

    Suppose *L* to be a scale (Chapter 2, Section 2g) with origin *O*. Let *O'* denote the image of *O* under a given translation along *L*; Let *c* be the coordinate of *O'* (p. 75) and *x* the coordinate of an arbitrary point *P* of *L*. In Figure 7-73, we have taken $c > 0$, so that the translation is a thrust in the positive direction of *L* to a new position *L'*, on which *O* occupies the place formerly occupied by *O'*, *P* the place formerly occupied by *P'*, and so forth. Then the translated position of each point of *L* is obtained by adding *c* to the original coordinate of the

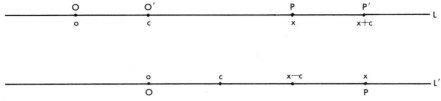

FIGURE 7-73 *The translation of a scale. (The original scale is labeled L; the translated scale, L'.)*

point. If X is the coordinate of P' (related to the original position of O), we thus have

$$X = x + c.$$

This equation expresses the translation along L algebraically.

EXERCISE

1. Let S and T be two translations along L. Representing them by their equations, then find the equation for $S * T$, the composition of S and T (see Subsection e). Prove algebraically that $S * T = T * S$.

Now we shall define translations in a plane. Let L be an arbitrary straight line in the plane, and let T_0 denote a translation along L, as previously defined. If P is on L, we define P' to be the image of P under this translation T_0, along L. In this case, P' is obtained by moving P a fixed distance along L in a fixed direction. If P is not on L, we take any point A of L and its image (under T) A', and define P' as the point such that $APP'A'$ is a parallelogram (Figure 7-74). The resulting assignment of P' to P is called a translation in the plane.

FIGURE 7-74 *Translation in the plane.*

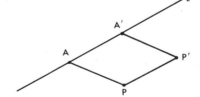

c. TRANSLATIONS AND VECTORS

Considering further the translation just defined, let $\mathscr{L}$ denote the family of straight lines consisting of L and all straight lines parallel to L. If P is an arbitrary point and M is the straight line passing through P belonging to the family $\mathscr{L}$, then P' also is located on M (the appropriate distance and direction from P). (See Figure 7-75.) Hence, a trans-

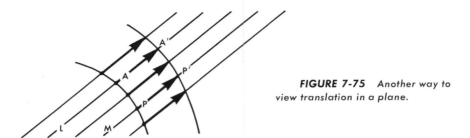

FIGURE 7-75   *Another way to view translation in a plane.*

lation in a plane can be pictured as a rigid shifting of the plane through a certain distance in a certain direction. In the notation used previously, the distance shifted was the length AA' and the direction of shift that from A to A'.

In the same figure, imagine A and A' to determine an arrow with its tail end at A and its head at A'. This arrow thus points from A to A'. Think of the arrow as moveable in the plane without change in its direction or length. If we move the arrow (not changing its direction or length) to place its tail end at an arbitrary point P, it will point from P to the image P'. The moveable arrow thus indicates for each point its image.

If from this picture of a moveable arrow we abstract two attributes—its length and its direction—we have the concept of *vector*. A vector is specified fully by stating its length and direction. For instance, the vector concerned in the preceding translation is that which has the length AA' and the direction from A to A', but it also can be described as the vector with the length PP' and the direction from P to P', where P' is the image of an arbitrary point P under the translation in question. The notation for this vector is $\overrightarrow{AA'}$ or $\overrightarrow{PP'}$. A vector is represented in a diagram by an arrow of the indicated length and direction, as in Figure 7-75, placed wherever convenience may suggest. Any translation determines a corresponding vector, as we have shown; conversely, any vector determines a translation to which it corresponds.

We shall say that two vectors, say $\overrightarrow{AB}$ and $\overrightarrow{CD}$ ($A \neq B$, $C \neq D$), are *equal* if their lengths and directions are the same. In this case, we write

$$\overrightarrow{AB} = \overrightarrow{CD},$$

this equality thus having the following meaning: (1) the straight lines AB and CD either coincide or are parallel; (2) if the lines coincide, then the direction from A to B is the same as the direction from C to D, and $AB = CD$; if the lines are parallel, then $ACDB$ is a parallelogram. (See Figure 7-76). The definition of translation shows that equal vectors determine identical translations.

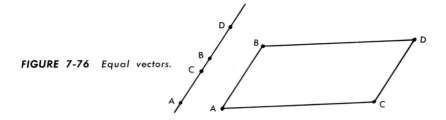

FIGURE 7-76   *Equal vectors.*

EXERCISES

1. A motorist is traveling south at 35 m.p.h., and another motorist is traveling north at 40 m.p.h. We wish to illustrate their relative speeds and directions graphically. How can the concept of vector be of help?

2. An athlete is able to run up a 45° incline for 4 minutes before becoming tired but can only run for 2 minutes on a 60° incline before becoming tired. Illustrate these facts graphically by means of vectors and explain how the vectors are being used.

d. GEOMETRIC ASPECTS OF TRANSLATION

Our picture of translation as a rigid shifting of the plane suggests the following properties, which then are easily proved.

(1) *Under translation, the image of a line segment is a parallel (or collinear†), equal line segment.* To be more precise, consider any straight line segment PQ and a translation of the plane under which P and Q have the images P' and Q', respectively (Figure 7-77). From our discussion of Subsection c, we have

$$\overrightarrow{PP'} = \overrightarrow{QQ'},$$

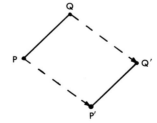

FIGURE 7-77   *A translated line segment.*

and the assertion follows from properties of parallel lines. Figure 7-77 illustrates just the case in which PQ is not parallel to the direction of translation.

---

†To be "collinear" is to be situated on the same straight line.

(2) *The distance between two points is preserved by translation.*
Let P and Q denote any two points, which we may assume to be
distinct. If P' and Q' are their respective images, our assertion is
simply that $PQ = P'Q'$. This follows from (1).

(3) *The angle between two straight lines is preserved by translation.* To be more precise, consider two straight lines AB and AC
intersecting at A. First, if the two lines coincide, then their images
coincide; hence, the angle between the antecedent lines is 0°, the
angle between the image lines is 0°, and the two angles are equal in
this case, as asserted. Secondly, consider the case in which the
straight lines AB and AC are not the same (Figure 7-78). Let A', B', C'
denote the images of A, B, C, respectively. Property (1) shows:

AB and $A'B'$ are parallel; AC and $A'C'$ are parallel.

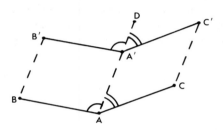

FIGURE 7-78 Preservation of
angles under translation.

Let D be a point of the line AA' such that A, A', and D occur on the
line in the order named. It follows from the statements about parallels
that

$$\angle BAD = \angle B'A'D, \ \angle DAC = \angle DA'C'$$

and, by addition, that

$$\angle BAC = \angle B'A'C',$$

the property that here is asserted.

e. ALGEBRAIC ASPECTS OF GEOMETRIC TRANSFORMATIONS

Let S and T denote any two geometric transformations of the
plane. We have already used the notation $T(P)$ to denote the point
obtained when T is applied to an arbitrary point P. Accordingly,
$S(T(P))$ is the point obtained by the action of S upon $T(P)$. (Figure
7-79 illustrates.) The assignment of the point $S(T(P))$ to P as an
associate is just the kind of rule that defines a geometric transformation (Subsection a). We name this geometric transformation the
composition of S and T and write it

$$S \circ T$$

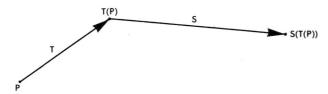

FIGURE 7-79 *Two geometric transformations acting successively.*

to indicate how it arose. The operation of making a composition is called *compounding* the two transformations involved. By definition, the effect of $S * T$ upon an arbitrary point P is

$$(S * T)(P) = S(T(P)).$$

The operation $*$, compounding, is associative. Let S, T, U, V denote any four geometric transformations. By definition,

$$(T * U)(P) = T(U(P)),$$
$$(S * V)(Q) = S(V(Q))$$

for any points P, Q in the plane. Hence,

$$[S * (T * U)](P) = S((T * U)(P))$$
$$= S(T(U(P))),$$

and

$$[(S * T) * U](P) = (S * T)(U(P))$$
$$= S(T(U(P))).$$

This shows that the two geometric transformations $S * (T * U)$ and $(S * T) * U$ have the same effect, which is to associate with an arbitrary point P the image $S(T(U(P)))$. Hence, the two geometric transformations are the same, and we see that $*$ is associative, as asserted.

Let $\mathscr{G}_0$ denote the set of all geometric transformations of the plane. We saw when we defined compounding that $\mathscr{G}_0$ is closed under this operation, and we have just verified that this operation is associative. These are two of the four condtions that $(\mathscr{G}_0, *)$ must satisfy to be a group. The condition that $(\mathscr{G}_0, *)$ have an identity also holds. In fact, define I to be the geometric transformation that associates each point of the plane with itself. We then have $I(P) = P$ for each point P in the plane, and consequently

$$I * T = T, \; T * I = T$$

for every geometric transformation T. Hence, I is the identity for $(\mathscr{G}_0, *)$. Nevertheless, $(\mathscr{G}_0, *)$ is not a group, for the condition that every member of $\mathscr{G}_0$ have an inverse is violated.

EXERCISES

1. Let a translation along a line be represented by $X = x + c$, as in Subsection b. What is the inverse of this translation, and how is it represented algebraically?

2. Suppose P, Q, and R are three noncollinear points in the plane and that P', Q' and R' are their respective images under a translation T. Prove that $\triangle PQR \cong \triangle P'Q'R'$.†

3. Suppose P and Q are any two points in the plane and P' and Q' are their respective images under a translation T. Prove that $PP'Q'Q$ is a parallelogram.

4. Prove that the geometric transformations in Examples 1 and 2 of Subsection a do not have inverses.

5. A geometric transformation T is said to be *one-to-one* if distinct points have distinct images, i.e., if

$$T(P) = T(Q) \Rightarrow P = Q.$$

We shall say that T "maps the plane onto the plane" if every point is the image of an appropriate point as antecedent, i.e., if for each point Q in the plane, at least one point P exists such that $T(P) = Q$. Letting $\mathscr{G}$ denote the set of all one-to-one geometric transformations that map the plane onto the plane, prove that $(\mathscr{G}, \ast)$ is a group.

f. ALGEBRAIC ASPECTS OF TRANSLATIONS

If $\mathscr{T}$ is the set of all translations, we shall prove that $(\mathscr{T}, \ast)$ is a group, where $\ast$ denotes the operation of compounding defined in the previous subsection. First, we must show that $\mathscr{T}$ is closed under this operation, or, in other words, that if S and T denote arbitrary translations of the plane, then the geometric transformation

$$S \ast T$$

is again a translation. Let P and Q denote any points of the plane, let P' and Q' denote their respective images under the translation T, and let P'' and Q'' denote the images of P' and Q', respectively, under S:

$$P' = T(P), \qquad Q' = T(Q),$$
$$P'' = S(P'), \qquad Q'' = S(Q').$$

Thus, in particular, we have

$$P'' = S(T(P)) = (S \ast T)(P),$$
$$Q'' = S(T(Q)) = (S \ast T)(Q).$$

---

†This means that triangles PQR and $P'Q'R'$ are congruent.

Since T and S are translations, we have

(1)
$$\overrightarrow{PP'} = \overrightarrow{QQ'}, \; \overrightarrow{P'P''} = \overrightarrow{Q'Q''}$$

and to prove that $S \circ T$ is a translation, we must show that

(2)
$$\overrightarrow{PP''} = \overrightarrow{QQ''}.$$

Figure 7-80 illustrates the three possible cases:

      Case a: S and T are motions in the same direction,
      Case b: S and T are motions in opposite directions,
      Case c: S and T are motions that are not in the same, or in oppo-
      site, directions.

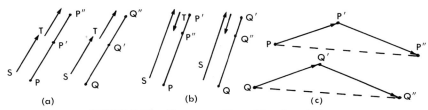

FIGURE 7-80 *The composition of two translations.*

Cases a and b are particularly trivial, and we leave them to the reader. In Case c, the equalities (1) mean that

$$PP' = QQ', \quad PP' \text{ is parallel to } QQ',$$

and

$$P'P'' = Q'Q'', \quad P'P'' \text{ is parallel to } Q'Q''.$$

The statements about parallelism imply that $\angle P' = \angle Q'$, the side-angle-side criterion then proving that

$$\triangle PP'P'' \cong \triangle QQ'Q''.$$

It follows that

$$PP'' = QQ''$$

and also that $\angle P'PP'' = \angle Q'QQ''$, which with the fact that PP' and QQ' are parallel shows PP'' to be parallel to QQ''. Consequently, $PQQ''P''$ is a parallelogram, and we have

$$\overrightarrow{PP''} = \overrightarrow{QQ''},$$

the relation (2) desired. We conclude that $S \circ T$ is a translation, and thus that $(\mathcal{T}, \circ)$ is closed, as asserted.

The associativity of ⁕ was proved in $\mathscr{G}_0$ in Subsection e. Since $\mathscr{T}$ is contained in $\mathscr{G}_0$, ⁕ certainly is associative in $\mathscr{T}$.

The existence of an identity in $(\mathscr{G}_0, ⁕)$ was shown in Subsection e. The identity was defined to be the geometric transformation I such that $I(P) = P$ for every point P of the plane. Does I belong to $\mathscr{T}$, or, in other words, is I a translation? Not according to our original definition of translation. But it is advantageous at this point to change this definition, from now on requiring the set $\mathscr{T}$ of translations (or "translations," if you prefer) to include I. Henceforth, we thus regard I as a translation, and on this understanding $(\mathscr{T}, ⁕)$ has an identity.

We shall now show that an arbitrary translation T has an inverse, completing the proof that $(\mathscr{T}, ⁕)$ is a group. If P denotes any point of the plane, $T(P)$ results from moving P a certain distance in a certain direction. Define the translation S as motion through an equal distance, but in the opposite direction. Then, as Figure 7-81 illustrates, $S(T(P)) = P$ and $T(S(P)) = P$. In other words,

$$(S ⁕ T)(P) = I(P), \quad (T ⁕ S)(P) = I(P),$$

and, these equalities holding for every point P, we have

$$S ⁕ T = I, \quad T ⁕ S = I.$$

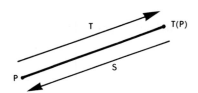

FIGURE 7-81   A translation and its inverse.

Therefore, S is an inverse of T: $S = T^{-1}$. Since inverses are unique (Theorem 2, Section 3, Chapter 6) S is *the* inverse of T. We conclude that $(\mathscr{T}, ⁕)$ is a group, as asserted.

We have associated a vector with every translation not equal to I, but what vector can we now associate with I? Recall that the vector assigned to an arbitrary transformation T is a *specification of length and direction* such that an arrow of the specified length pointing in the specified direction leads from any point P to its image $T(P)$. For I, such an arrow would have to be of zero length. Accordingly, now define the "zero" vector,

$$\vec{0},$$

to be the specification, zero length. (No direction is specified for $\vec{0}$.) The equality $\vec{PQ} = \vec{0}$ then means that $P = Q$, the new vector $\vec{0}$ thus corresponding to I in the same way that other vectors correspond to translations not the identity.

EXERCISES

1. Prove that the group $(\mathcal{T}, *)$ is commutative. (See Figure 7-82).

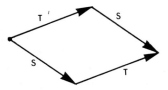

FIGURE 7-82 *The commutativity of translations.*

2. Suppose a point P is moved successively through four translations, all through the same distance, but each in a direction 90° clockwise from the direction of the previous translation. What single translation is the same as these four successive translations?

3. Suppose a point P is moved through four successive translations such that the first and third are through the same distance, and the second and fourth are through the same distance, and each translation is in a direction 90° clockwise from the direction of the previous translation. What single translation is the same as the composition of these four successive translations?

4. A fixed point of a transformation is a point in the plane that is its own image under the transformation. Do any translations have fixed points? Which translations? Which points? What are the fixed points of the geometric transformations in Examples 1 and 2, Subsection a?

5. A fixed line of a translation is a line that is left unchanged by the transformation. Do any translations have fixed lines? Which translations? Which lines?

6. Suppose T is a translation of the plane. By the symbol "T^{-1}" we mean the translation that is the inverse of the translation T under the operation of compounding. If we symbolize composition by $*$, prove the following:

    (a) $(T^{-1}) * (T^{-1}) = (T * T)^{-1}$

    (b) $(T^{-1})^{-1} = T$

7. If S and T are two translations and $*$ indicates compounding, prove:

    (a) $(T * S)^{-1} = (T^{-1}) * (S^{-1})$

    (b) $S * (T^{-1}) = (T^{-1}) * S = (T * (S^{-1}))^{-1} = ((S^{-1}) * T)^{-1}$

    (c) $S * T = I$ if and only if $S = (T^{-1})$

    (d) $T * T = I$ if and only if $T = I$

g. CENTRAL SYMMETRIES.†

Choose a point O of the plane. Then if P is any point of the plane, determine a companion point P' such that O is the midpoint of the segment PP' (Figure 7-83). The assignment of P' to P is a geometric transformation that we shall call a *symmetry about the point O*, O

---

†This section is largely an adaptation of I. M. Yaglom, *Geometric Transformations,* New York, Random House, 1962, Chapter 1, Section 2.

FIGURE 7-83 *Central symmetry.*

being the *center* of symmetry. We shall also refer to a symmetry about a point as a "central" symmetry.

Central symmetries have geometric and algebraic properties that are startlingly effective in certain types of problems. The following are the properties we shall need:

(1) *If O is the center of symmetry, then $O' = O$. No other point is its own image.*

(2) For any point *P*, $(P')' = P$. Hence, *if S denotes a central symmetry, we have*

$$S \circ S = I;$$

this means that *S has an inverse S^{-1} and that $S^{-1} = S$.* (Here, as usual, *I* is the identity transformation and $\circ$ the symbol for compounding two transformations.)

(3) *If A and B are distinct points not collinear with O, then $AB'A'B$ is a parallelogram* (Figure 7-84).

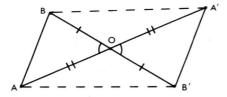

FIGURE 7-84 *Images of two points under a central symmetry.*

(4) *If A and B are distinct points not collinear with O, then the segment $A'B'$ is the image of the segment AB.* In fact, if *P* is a point of *AB* and *Q* the intersection of *PO* with $A'B'$ (see Figure 7-85), Property 3 implies that $\triangle AOP \cong \triangle A'OQ$. Hence, $OP = OQ$, and therefore $P' = Q$. Therefore, the images of the points of *AB* are among the points of $A'B'$. In the same way, it can be seen that every point of $A'B'$ is the image of some point of *AB*. We conclude that $A'B'$ is the image of *AB*, as asserted.

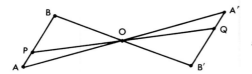

FIGURE 7-85 *The image of a segment under central symmetry.*

(5) *The composition of two central symmetries is a translation.* To prove this, let *R* and *S* denote any two central symmetries. If $R = S$, we have $R \circ S = R \circ R = I$ by Property 2, and our assertion is

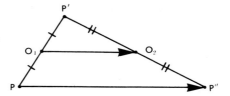

FIGURE 7-86   The composition of two central symmetries.

true. If $R \neq S$, then R and S have different centers of symmetry, say O_1 and O_2, respectively. Let P be any point, and set $P' = R(P)$, $P'' = S(P')$. From Figure 7-86 it is clear that $\triangle PP'P''$ and $\triangle O_1P'O_2$ are similar, the sides of the first being twice as long as those of the second. Hence, the vector $\overrightarrow{PP''}$ has the same direction as $\overrightarrow{O_1O_2}$, but twice the length. This being so for every P, the geometric transformation that associates P'' with P is a translation in the direction of $\overrightarrow{O_1O_2}$ through a distance that is twice the length of $\overrightarrow{O_1O_2}$. (We remark that, consequently, composition of central symmetries is in general noncommutative. In fact, $S * R$ is a translation in the direction of $\overrightarrow{O_1O_2}$, while $R * S$ is a translation in the direction of $\overrightarrow{O_2O_1}$.)

(6) *Given any translation T and central symmetry S, central symmetries R_1 and R_2 exist such that*

$$T = S * R_1 = R_2 * S.$$

In words: *any translation can be effected by compounding two central symmetries, one of which can be chosen arbitrarily.* In proof, we shall show how to find R_2, R_1 being obtainable by similar means. All that is needed to specify R_2 is its center O'. Let O denote the center of S, and let P be an arbitrary point. As in Figure 7-87, join P with its image P' under the translation T. (Thus, $\overrightarrow{PP'}$ is the vector corresponding to T.) Property 5 shows that O' is the point such that $\overrightarrow{OO'}$ has the direction of $\overrightarrow{PP'}$ and half its length.

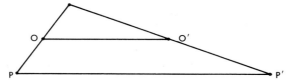

(7) *If T is a translation and S a central symmetry, then*

$$T * S \text{ and } S * T$$

are central symmetries. In fact, Property 6 assures us of a central symmetry R such that $T = R * S$. Then

$$
\begin{aligned}
T * S &= (R * S) * S \\
&= R * (S * S) \quad \text{(by associativity)} \\
&= R * I \quad\quad\ \text{(by Property 2)} \\
&= R.
\end{aligned}
$$

This justifies the first statement, and the second can be proved similarly.

EXERCISE

1. Prove Property 7 geometrically. HINT: Use Property 5.

Let H denote the set of geometric transformations that are either translations or central symmetries. The composition of two translations is a translation, the composition of two central symmetries is a translation, and the composition of a translation and a central symmetry (in either order) is a central symmetry. Hence, H is closed under the operation of compounding. Furthermore, this operation $*$ is associative, $(H, *)$ has an identity, and each member of H has an inverse (with respect to $*$). Consequently, $(H, *)$ is a group. This and the preceding relations make possible very elegant solutions of a certain kind of problem, as we now illustrate.

Problem 1.   Prove that the midpoints of the sides of an arbitrary quadrilateral (four-sided closed polygon) are the four vertices of a parallelogram.

SOLUTION: Let A, B, C, D be the vertices of the quadrilateral in order, and let M, N, P, Q be the midpoints of the sides DA, AB, BC, CD, respectively (see Figure 7-88). Denote by S_M, S_N, S_P, S_Q the symmetries about the points M, N, P, Q, respectively, as centers.

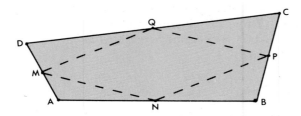

FIGURE 7-88   The parallelogram inscribed in an arbitrary quadrilateral.

Now consider the geometric translation T defined as follows:

$$T = (S_M * S_N) * (S_P * S_Q).$$

In the first place, T is a translation, since compounding two central symmetries produces a translation and then compounding two translations results in another translation. Secondly, note that

$$S_Q(D) = C,$$

that consequently

$$(S_P * S_Q)(D) = S_P(C) = B,$$

and that by a succession of such steps

$$T(D) = (S_M \ast S_N \ast S_P \ast S_Q)(D)$$
$$= D.$$

Thus, the translation T moves D into D. Therefore, this translation is the identity: $T = I$, or

$$(S_M \ast S_N) \ast (S_P \ast S_Q) = I.$$

Therefore,

$$S_M \ast S_N = (S_P \ast S_Q)^{-1}.$$

The left member of this equality represents translation in the direction from N to M through the distance $2\,NM$, the right member translation in the direction from P to Q through the distance $2\,QP$. We conclude that $\overrightarrow{NM} = \overrightarrow{PQ}$ and thus that $QMNP$ is a parallelogram.

Problem 2. Given five points in the plane, find a pentagon with these points as midpoints of its sides. (A pentagon is a five-sided closed polygon. Its sides are permitted to intersect at other points than the five vertices.)

SOLUTION: Call the given points M_1, M_2, M_3, M_4, M_5, and let S_1, S_2, S_3, S_4, S_5 denote the symmetries about these respective points. Supposing at first that the desired pentagon really exists, call its vertices in order A_1, A_2, A_3, A_4, A_5, stipulating, say, that M_1 be the midpoint of the side A_1A_2, M_2 the midpoint of A_2A_3, and so on, with M_5 the midpoint of A_5A_1. (See Figure 7-89.) We shall show that A_1 is determined as the center for the central symmetry S defined by

$$S = S_5 \ast S_4 \ast S_3 \ast S_2 \ast S_1.$$

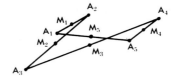

FIGURE 7-89 A pentagon reconstructed from the midpoints of its sides.

In the first place, we easily verify that S is a central symmetry, for $S_2 \ast S_1$ and $S_4 \ast S_3$ are translations, compounding two translations gives a translation, and compounding a translation and a central symmetry gives a central symmetry. Thus,

$$S = S_5 \ast (\text{translation} \ast \text{translation})$$
$$= S_5 \ast \text{translation}$$
$$= \text{central symmetry.}$$

To see that A_1 is the center for S, it suffices to show that $S(A_1) = A_1$, no point other than the center being its own image. We show this by direct calculation. Indeed, $S_1(A_1) = A_2$ (since M_1 is the midpoint of the segment A_1A_2), hence $(S_2 \circ S_1)(A_1) = S_2(A_2) = A_3$, and by a further succession of such steps we have ultimately

$$S(A_1) = (S_5 \circ S_4 \circ S_3 \circ S_2 \circ S_1)(A_1)$$
$$= A_1.$$

In sum: A_1 must be the center for the central symmetry S, as asserted. With this knowledge, it is easy to construct the pentagon required. First, define S as before. This requires knowledge only of the given midpoints. Secondly, find the center for S. This might be done, for instance, by taking an arbitrary point B and constructing $S(B)$. If, by good chance, $B = S(B)$, then B itself is the desired center of the symmetry. If $B \neq S(B)$, then the center for the symmetry S is of course the midpoint of the segment joining B with $S(B)$ (see Figure 7-90). In either case, we obtain the center of symmetry, which we shall

FIGURE 7-90   *Determining the center O of a central symmetry S.*

call A_1. Determine A_2 such that M_1 is the midpoint of the segment A_1A_2, determine A_3 such that M_2 is the midpoint of the segment A_2A_3, and so on, finally determining A_5 such that M_4 is the midpoint of the segment A_4A_5. In algebraic terms,

$$A_2 = S_1(A_1),\ A_3 = S_2(A_2),\ A_4 = S_3(A_3),\ A_5 = S_4(A_4),$$

and thus, in particular,

$$A_5 = (S_4 \circ S_3 \circ S_2 \circ S_1)(A_1).$$

We have still to check that M_5 is the midpoint of the segment A_5A_1, which is to say that

$$A_1 = S_5(A_5).$$

But this condition means

$$A_1 = (S_5 \circ S_4 \circ S_3 \circ S_2 \circ S_1)(A_1)$$
$$= S(A_1)$$

and is assured by the manner of selecting A_1. Thus, our construction is completely justified.

EXERCISES

2. Prove that compounding any even number of central symmetries results in a translation and that compounding any odd number of central symmetries produces a central symmetry. (See Chapter 10 on mathematical induction).

3. Let O_1, O_2, O_3 be any points in the plane. Now move an arbitrary point A by successive symmetries about O_1, O_2, O_3, and then by symmetries about O_3, O_2, O_1, in the order mentioned. Prove that A returns after the six central symmetries to its original position.

4. Let O_1, O_2, O_3 be any points in the plane. Move an arbitrary point A by successive symmetries about O_1, O_2, O_3, and then by symmetries about O_1, O_2, O_3 again, in the order mentioned. Prove that A returns after the six central symmetries to its original position.

5. Let O_1, O_2, O_3 be any points in the plane. Prove that to move an arbitrary point A by successive symmetries about O_1, O_2, O_3, in that order, is the same as to move the point by symmetries about O_3, O_2, O_1 in this order.

6. Let O_1, O_2, O_3, O_4 be four points in the plane. Move an arbitrary point A by successive symmetries about O_1, O_2, O_3, O_4, and then by successive symmetries about O_4, O_3, O_2, O_1, in the order mentioned. Does A return after the eight central symmetries to its original position? Explain.

7. Let O_1, O_2, O_3, O_4 be any points in the plane. Move an arbitrary point A by successive symmetries about these points in the order named and then again by successive symmetries about these points in the same order. Does A return to its original position after the eight central symmetries? Explain.

8. Let O_1, O_2, O_3, O_4 be points in the plane and AB an arbitrary straight line segment. Let A_1B_1 be the image of AB under the symmetry about O_1, A_2B_2 the image of A_1B_1 under the symmetry about O_2, A_3B_3 the image of A_2B_2 under the symmetry about O_3, and A_4B_4 the image of A_3B_3 under the symmetry about O_4. Then show that $\vec{AA_4} = \vec{BB_4}$. Is the corresponding result true with six given points, O_1, . . ., O_6, instead of four? Is it true with three points or with five?

9. Let O_1, O_2, O_3, O_4 be any four points in the plane. Prove that to move an arbitrary point A by successive symmetries about O_1, O_2, O_3, O_4, in that order, is the same as to move this point by symmetries about O_3, O_4, O_1, O_2, in this order.

10. Let O_1, O_2, O_3, O_4, O_5 be any five points in the plane. Move an arbitrary point A by successive symmetries about these points in the order mentioned. Prove that the result is the same as if A had been moved by successive symmetries about the same points taken in reverse order: O_5, O_4, O_3, O_2, O_1.

11. Let seven distinct points be given in the plane. Find the vertices of a seven-sided closed polygon whose sides have the seven given points as midpoints. HINT: See Problem 2.

12. Do any central symmetries have fixed points? Which points are fixed?

13. Do any central symmetries have fixed lines? Which central symmetries? Which lines are fixed?

14. Prove that the translation that is obtained by compounding central symmetries through four arbitrarily picked points O_1, O_2, O_3, O_4, in that

order, is a translation through a distance less than or at most equal to $2(O_1O_2 + O_2O_3 + O_3O_4)$.

15. Complete the steps of the following proof, which shows that if T is any translation, H any central symmetry, and "$*$" the operation of compounding, then $H * T = T^{-1} * H$. (See Exercises 6 and 7, Subsection f.)

PROOF: (See Figure 7-91.) Let A and B be any points in the plane. Let T be the translation through the distance AA' in the direction of

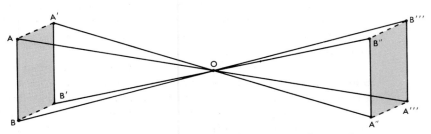

FIGURE 7-91 *Compounding a central symmetry and a translation.*

$\overrightarrow{AA'}$ and let H be the central symmetry about the point O. Also let $A'B'$ be the image of AB under T, $A''B''$ the image of $A'B'$ under H, and $A'''B'''$ the image of AB under H.

(a) To prove that $H * T = T^{-1} * H$, we must prove that $A''B''$ is the image under T^{-1} of $A'''B'''$. Why?

(b) $BO = OB'''$. (Why?)

(c) $B'O = OB''$. (Why?)

(d) $\angle BOB' = \angle B''OB'''$. (Why?)

(e) $\triangle BOB' \cong \triangle B''OB''$. (Why?)

(f) $BB' = B''B'''$.

(g) How may we now conclude that $H * T = T^{-1} * H$?

16. Prove that if H_1 and H_2 are any two central symmetries and $*$ indicates the operation of compounding, then $H_1 * H_2 = (H_2 * H_1)^{-1}$.

17. If H_1 and H_2 are any two central symmetries and T is any translation, show that $(H_1 * H_2) * T = I$ if and only if $T = H_2 * H_1$. HINT: See Exercise 7, Subsection f.

18. If H_1, H_2, H_3, and H_4 are any central symmetries, prove that $H_1 * H_2 * H_3 * H_4 = (H_2 * H_1 * H_4 * H_3)^{-1}$.

19. Can Exercise 18 be extended to any even number of central symmetries? What is the statement of this fact for $2n$ central symmetries?

20. Show algebraically that if any number of central symmetries are performed successively on an arbitrary point A in the plane, and then the same central symmetries are applied to the resulting point successively in reverse order, then the new point is again A. HINT: This amounts to proving that if H_1, H_2, ..., H_n are any n central symmetries, then $(H_1 * H_2 * ... * H_n) * (H_n * H_{n-1} * ... * H_2 * H_1) = I$.

21. Suppose that O_1 and O_2 are any points in the plane, and suppose some point A is transformed by the central symmetry H_1 about the point O_1 followed by the central symmetry H_2 about O_2 followed again by H_1 and H_2 in that order. Show that the resulting point A' will be the same as the point A if and only if $O_1 = O_2$.

22. Generalize Exercise 21 to any even number of central symmetries.

CHAPTER 8

COORDINATE GEOMETRY

1.

Functions

If the value of a certain quantity is wholly determined by the value of a second quantity x, we say that the first quantity is a *function of* x. Since, for instance, the value of the reciprocal of a number is wholly determined by the number, the reciprocal is a function of the number: $1/x$ is a function of x (for $x \neq 0$). Similarly, $x - 2$, x^2, x^3, $-x + 3$ are functions of x (for all values of x); sin x is a function of x we defined for x between $0°$ and $180°$ (Chapter 7). Since x can take any of various possible values, x is called a *variable*. For each particular value of the variable x, a given function of x has a corresponding value. This value is denoted by a symbol, such as $f(x)$ (read, "f of x"), displaying the value of x on which it depends. For instance, if $f(x)$ denotes the reciprocal of x, i.e., $f(x) = 1/x$, then $f(1) = 1, f(2) = 1/2$, $f(3/4) = 1/(3/4) = 4/3$. If $h(x) = 1 - x$, we have $h(0) = 1$, $h(10) = 1 - 10 = -9, h(a) = 1 - a, h(1 - x) = 1 - (1 - x) = x, h(x^2) = 1 - x^2$, $f(x)h(x) = (1/x)(1 - x) = 1/x - 1$. If

$$j(x) = 1 \text{ for } x > 0$$
$$= 0 \text{ for } x \leq 0,$$

then $j(1/2) = j(1) = j(10) = 1, j(0) = j(-1) = j(-80) = 0$.

EXERCISES

Suppose $f(x) = 1/(2x)(x \neq 0)$, $g(x) = 1 + x + x^2 + x^3$, $h(x) = 1 - x$.
1. Find $f(1)$, $g(0)$, $h(-1)$.

2. Find the functions $f(1/x)(x \neq 0)$, $g(x^2)$, $h(2-x)$.

3. Find $g(x)h(x)$, $(h(x))^2$.

4. If $s(x) = \sin x$, $c(x) = \cos x$, $t(x) = \tan x$, prove that $t(x)c(x)/s(x) = 1$ for positive values of x less than $90°$.

In describing a function of x, we must specify the values of x for which the function is defined. The function x^2, for instance, is defined for all values of x, the function $1/x$ for all values but zero, $1/(x+1)$ for all values but -1, $1/(x^2-1)$ for all except 1 and -1 (the denominators of the last three functions vanish for the values excluded).

Functions of x are not necessarily relatively simple mathematical expressions like those just listed. For instance, the temperature at a given place from 7 A.M. to 7 P.M. on a certain day can be regarded as a function of time. The height of a particular child is a function of his age. Any rule of correspondence that ascribes a definite number to each value of x lying within a specified set of values defines a function. The connection between the value of the variable x, which is arbitrary (but within the set of admitted values), and the corresponding value of the function may be complicated. Yet it can be depicted in its entirety by geometrical means we shall now describe.

2.

Cartesian frames

The geometrical means alluded to, to clarify the connection between the values of x and the corresponding values of a given function of x, are based on a scheme for labeling the points of a plane essentially devised in the 17th Century in France by Descartes and Fermat, a philosopher and a lawyer, respectively. This labeling scheme is natural to any city dweller who knows how to find, say, the intersection of East Twelfth Street and South Ninth Avenue. In fact, each point in the plane is given a similar description. To this end, we first

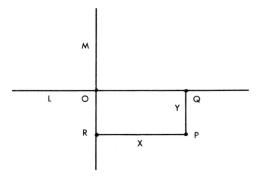

FIGURE 8-1 *Assignment of coordinates in a plane.*

select two perpendicular lines in the plane. Denoting them as L and M and their point of intersection as O, we may (if necessary, by turning the plane) think of L as being horizontal and M as vertical. Now consider an arbitrary point of the plane denoted by the symbol P. We shall associate with P two numbers, x and y, that will indicate its precise location. Construct perpendiculars from P to the lines L and M, letting Q denote the point in which the perpendicular to L intersects L, and R the point in which the perpendicular to M intersects M. This is illustrated in Figure 8-1.

Let X denote the length of the segment PR, and Y the length of the segment PQ: X is called the (perpendicular) distance between P and M, and Y the distance between P and L. Then set

$$x = X \text{ if } Q \text{ is to the right of 0,}$$
$$= -X \text{ if } Q \text{ is to the left of 0,}$$
$$= 0 \text{ if } Q \text{ coincides with 0.}$$

Similarly, set

$$y = Y \text{ if } R \text{ is above 0,}$$
$$= -Y \text{ if } R \text{ is below 0,}$$
$$= 0 \text{ if } R \text{ coincides with 0.}$$

One might call x the "signed" distance — the distance with a plus or a minus sign — of P from M, y the signed distance of P from L. Commonly, x is called the *abscissa* of P and y the *ordinate* of P. The abscissa x and ordinate y are both known as *coordinates* of P and usually are written together without further explanation as (x,y), the abscissa always being the first and the ordinate the second coordinate entered. The symbol (x,y) often is described as an *ordered pair of numbers*, since its meaning depends on the order in which the two numbers, x and y, constituting the symbol occur. L and M are both called *coordinate axes*, L being the *x-axis* and M the *y-axis*, and O is called the *origin* of the coordinate system. The two coordinate axes together constitute what is called, after Descartes, a *Cartesian frame.*

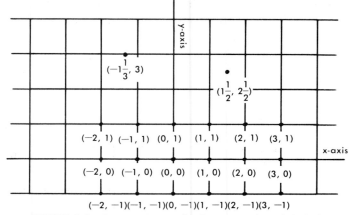

FIGURE 8-2   *Some points in the Cartesian plane labeled.*

A plane in which a Cartesian frame is installed may be called a *Cartesian plane.* In Figure 8-2, we illustrate the labeling of points in a Cartesian plane.

We have just assigned to each point P in the Cartesian plane an ordered pair of numbers (x,y) such that x is the signed distance of P from the y-axis and y is the signed distance of P from the x-axis. Every ordered pair of numbers was assigned by this rule to some point of the plane, and to one point only. We thus established a correspondence between points of the plane and ordered pairs of numbers under which each point corresponds to one and only one ordered pair, and each ordered pair corresponds to one and only one point. Such a correspondence is described as being 1-1 (one to one).

Several additional facts stand out: (1) The coordinates of the origin O are $(0,0)$. (2) The coordinates of an arbitrary point on the *x-axis* are all of the form $(x,0)$. In other words, $y=0$ on the x-axis. Similarly $x=0$ on the y-axis. (3) On any line parallel to the x-axis, y is constant. On any line parallel to the y-axis, x is constant. (4) The points with negative abscissas are to the left of the y-axis, those with negative ordinates are below the x-axis.

We also note that any line parallel to a coordinate axis can be regarded as a scale. When the line is parallel to the x-axis, the readings of the scale are the abscissas of its points; when the line is parallel to the y-axis, the readings are the ordinates of its points.

EXERCISES

Plot the following sets of points:

1. $(-2,-2)$, $(-1,-1)$, $(0,0)$, $(1,1)$, $(2,2)$, $(6,6)$.
2. $(-2,-6)$, $(-1,-3)$, $(0,0)$, $(1,3)$, $(2,6)$.
3. $(0,-6)$, $(1,-3)$, $(2,0)$, $(3,3)$, $(4,6)$.
4. $(-2,-3)$, $(-1,0)$, $(0,3)$, $(1,6)$, $(2,9)$.
5. $(-1,-5)$, $(0,-2)$, $(1,1)$, $(2,4)$, $(3,7)$.
6. Three vertices of a rectangle have the coordinates $(2,-8)$, $(2,-2)$, $(8,-2)$. Determine the coordinates of the fourth vertex and find the area of the rectangle.
7. What is the distance between:

$(1,1)$ and $(2,2)$, $(a,1)$ and $(a,2)$, (a,b) and $(a,b+1)$, (a,b) and (a,d), (a,b) and (c,d)?

8. Show that $(-1,3)$, $(4,1)$, and $(2,-4)$ are the vertices of a right triangle. HINT: Use the converse to the Theorem of Pythagoras.
9. Find the number k so that $(4,0)$, $(k,0)$ and $(0,-6)$ are the vertices of a right triangle with right angle at the third vertex.
10. If $(0,0)$ and $(a,0)$ are two vertices of an equilateral triangle, find the third vertex.

3.

Graphs

The geometrical means of studying functions to which we alluded can now be explained. Let us begin with a concrete case, say that of the function

(1) $$1 + x^2.$$

For each value of the variable x, this function has a certain corresponding value we shall denote by y. Thus,

(2) $$y = 1 + x^2.$$

We emphasize that the possible choices for x on the right side of equation (2) are unrestricted, but that each choice of x rigidly determines a corresponding value of y. For these reasons, x is called the *independent variable* in equation (2) and y the *dependent variable*. By the *graph* of equation (2)—or of the function (1)—we mean the set of points in a Cartesian plane with the coordinates (x,y), where x denotes the independent variable, and y the dependent variable, in (2). A good idea of the graph can be obtained simply by plotting (i.e., marking) a reasonable number of its points and connecting them by a smooth line. First, we would tabulate the values of y that correspond to various values of x, for instance, as follows:

x	−6	−5	−4	−3	−2	−1	0	1	2	3	4	5	6
y	37	26	17	10	5	2	1	2	5	10	17	26	37.

We would then plot the points with these coordinates and connect them by a smooth line to obtain such a result as is shown in Figure 8-3.

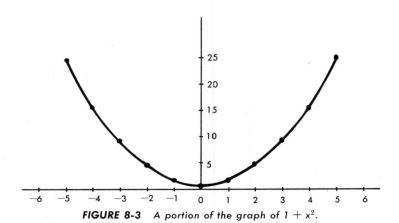

FIGURE 8-3   A portion of the graph of $1 + x^2$.

The graph idea carries over without change to any function. To graph an arbitrary function $f(x)$ we would set

(3) $$y = f(x).$$

Here, x again is called the independent variable and y, as defined from (3) in terms of x, the dependent variable. By the graph of equation (3) — or of the function $f(x)$ — is then meant the set of points in a Cartesian plane with the coordinates (x, y), where x denotes the independent variable in (3) and y the dependent variable. The graph can be approximated, just as in the special case we discussed, by plotting a reasonable number of its points and connecting them with a smooth line.

Graphs sometimes can be obtained with great accuracy by mechanical, or other instrumental, means. An example is the barograph, in which an inked needle is held at a height determined by the momentary atmospheric pressure to trace a line on a sheet of paper unwinding from one drum and wound up at a uniform rate on another. Thus the line traced by the needle is a continuous record of the atmospheric pressure as a function of time: within the limits of instrumental error, it thus is a graph. Figure 8-4 illustrates a barographic trace for a particular 24-hour period, time being measured in hours

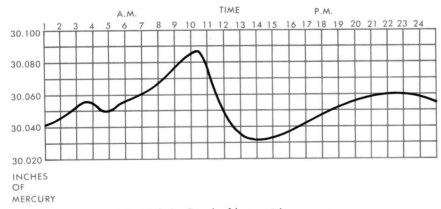

FIGURE 8-4 Graph of barometric pressure.

and atmospheric pressure in inches of mercury. At any desired time, say 10 A.M., we read from this graph the corresponding barometric pressure; for instance, at 10 A.M. barometric pressure was approximately 30.086 inches of mercury. The functional relationship depicted in this graph is not representable neatly by an algebraic formula. Algebraic formulas can be used, however, to approximate such relationships with great accuracy. Advanced methods are required, which we shall not discuss.

EXERCISES

Some of the following functions are divided into groups. Graph the polynomials of each group on the same sheet of paper for x, say, between 4 and -4, inclusive.

1. x, $1 + x$, $2 + x$, $-1 + x$.
2. x, $(1/2)x$, $2x$, $15x$, $-2x$.
3. x^2, $1 + x^2$, $-x + x^2$.
4. $10x + x^2 - x^3$.
5. $x - 10x^2 + x^4$.
6. $-1 + x$, x^2. On this graph, plot new points by adding, for each value of x, the two corresponding ordinates already plotted. The smooth curve joining these new points is a graph of $-1 + x + x^2$.
7. $1/x$, $1/(x - 1)$, $1/(x + 1)$.

4.

Polynomial graphs and algebraic equations

We know that two polynomials in x that are equal for all values of x are essentially the same, their respective coefficients being the same (Chapter 5, Section 4). Given two different polynomials in x, we may ask if they are equal for *any* values of x and, if so, for which. Before discussing the answer, we simplify the question by reducing it to the case in which one of the polynomials is zero. If $P(x)$ and $Q(x)$ are two polynomials, to ask if a value of x exists for which $P(x) = Q(x)$ is to ask the same question for the equation $P(x) - Q(x) = 0$. However, $P(x) - Q(x)$ is a polynomial, which we may call $R(x)$. The given problem thus reduces to asking whether a value of x exists such that $R(x) = 0$. Such a value of x, if it exists, is called a *solution,* or a *root,* of the *equation* $R(x) = 0$.

Returning to previous notation, consider an arbitrary polynomial

$$A(x) = a_0 + a_1 x + \ldots + a_k x^k,$$

not all of whose coefficients are zero. Our question is: Does a specific value x_1 exist such that

$$A(x_1) = a_0 + a_1 x_1 + \ldots + a_k (x_1)^k = 0?$$

If so, how many such values are there? What, in other words, are the solutions of the equation $A(x) = 0$?

The degree of the polynomial $A(x)$ is also called the degree of the equation $A(x) = 0$. It is easy to see that the number of real roots of an algebraic equation can be as high as its degree and, in fact, that k roots can be arbitrarily prescribed for a polynomial of degree k (i.e., that a polynomial of degree k can be found with the k stipulated roots). Let us ask, for example, for a polynomial of the fourth degree with the four roots $0, -1, 2, -3$. The trick in finding it is to realize that the product $x(x+1)(x-2)(x+3)$ is zero for the four indicated values (the first factor of the product vanishes for $x = 0$, the second factor for $x = -1$, and so forth), and the desired polynomial is obtainable by simply expanding this expression. It comes out to be

$$x^4 + 2x^3 - 5x^2 - 6x$$

(this may be multiplied by any constant not zero), as can be verified directly. A similar procedure will suffice in any other case. Moreover, it is possible to prove that the number of (real) roots of any algebraic equation is at most equal to its degree. (All algebraic equations thus resemble in this respect the equations of first and second degrees. See Chapter 2, Section 3, and Chapter 4, Section 2.) We shall not attempt to do so here nor to give general arithmetical procedures for finding the roots. We shall describe, however, a very serviceable graphical method by which the real solutions of an algebraic equation can be found approximately with very little calculation.

We recall that the graph of $A(x)$ consists of all points (x,y) in the Cartesian plane such that $y = A(x)$. To ask if the equation $A(x) = 0$ has a root thus is equivalent to asking: Is there a point on the graph of $A(x)$ whose second coordinate is zero; that is, does the graph of $A(x)$ intersect the x-axis (the line on which $y = 0$) and, if so, where? This question can be answered approximately for any polynomial by plotting and reading its graph with care. We illustrate this in Figure 8-5 for the three equations (a) $-2x + x^2 = 0$, (b) $1 - 2x + x^2 = 0$, and (c) $2 - 2x + x^2 = 0$, which are observed to have two solutions, one solution, and no solution, respectively.

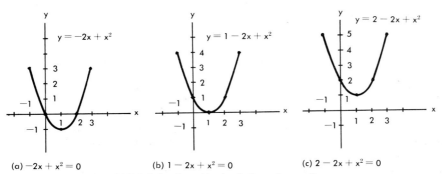

(a) $-2x + x^2 = 0$ (b) $1 - 2x + x^2 = 0$ (c) $2 - 2x + x^2 = 0$

FIGURE 8-5   *Graphical solution of equations.*

EXERCISES

1. Find by graphical means an approximate solution of the first problem discussed in Chapter 4, Section 4.

2. Find by graphical means an approximate solution of the second problem in Chapter 4, Section 4.

3. Find, by graphing, the number of (real) roots of each of the following
equations:

    (a) $x^3 + x^2 + x + 1 = 0$,

    (b) $x^3 - 4x^2 + x + 6 = 0$,

    (c) $x^4 + x^3 + x^2 + x + 1 = 0$.

4. Find a quadratic equation with the roots 3/2 and $-3/2$. Write the
equation with integral coefficients.

5. Let a, b, c, and d denote any four numbers.

    (a) Find a quadratic equation with the roots a and b.

    (b) Find an equation of the third degree with the roots a, b, c.

    (c) Find an equation of the fourth degree with the roots a, b, c, d.

5.

The equation of a straight line in the plane

Any line or curve in the Cartesian plane can be regarded as a
graph, the graph of an appropriate relation. Consider, for instance, a
curve like that sketched in Figure 8-6, which meets once and but
once any straight line parallel to the y-axis. To each abscissa x cor-

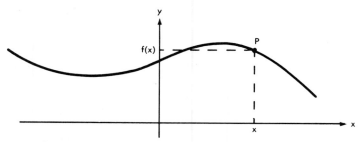

FIGURE 8-6   A curve defining a relation of the form $y = f(x)$.

responds one and but one point P of this curve; hence, the ordinate
of P is a function of x. If $f(x)$ denotes this function, P in Cartesian
coordinates is represented by the ordered pair $(x, f(x))$, and the curve
itself becomes identifiable as the graph of $f(x)$. The *equation* of the
curve, which also expresses the relation between the ordinate and
the abscissa of a variable point P, is

$$y = f(x).$$

For a curve that, as in Figure 8-7, meets once and only once any

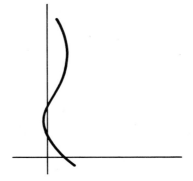

FIGURE 8-7 A curve defining a relation of
the form x = g(y).

straight line parallel to the *x*-axis, the abscissa is a function of its
ordinate. Its equation, therefore, is of the form

$$x = g(y),$$

y in this case taking the role of independent variable and *x* the role of
dependent variable.

Some curves are divisible into segments each of which has an
equation of either of the two preceding kinds. In Figure 8-8, for
instance, the segment *AB* is representable by $y = f_1(x)$, the segment *BC*
by $y = f_2(x)$, and the segment *CA* by $x = g(y)$; the functions f_1 and f_2
are, of course, quite different.

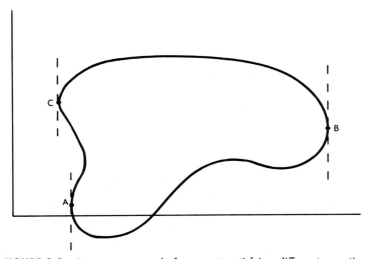

FIGURE 8-8 A curve composed of segments satisfying different equations.

Certain curves—the straight lines, circles, ellipses, and so forth
of Euclidean geometry, as well as many others—have simple equations, and knowledge of these has immeasurably benefited mathe-

matical science. We shall now investigate the most simple and most fundamental of the "curves" of the plane – straight lines. Our methods are based on the concept of the "slope" of a line. If, in the Cartesian plane, $A = (a,b)$ and $P = (x,y)$ denote different points of a given nonvertical line L, the ratio

(1) $$s = (y - b)/(x - a)$$

is called the *slope* of the line L. If L is horizontal, and thus of constant ordinate b, then $y = b$ and $s = 0$ for any choice of P along L. If L is oblique (nonhorizontal, as well as nonvertical), the graphs in Figure 8-9 show that $x - a$ and $y - b$ are the lengths, or the negatives of the lengths, of the two arms of a right triangle with acute angles at A and at P. Since the ratio of these lengths is independent both of A and of P

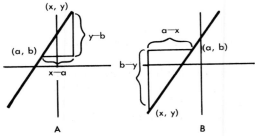

A   B

FIGURE 8-9   *Oblique lines with some selected points.*

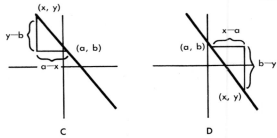

C   D

(Chapter 7, Section 5), the slope s similarly is independent of these choices. Thus the slope is a characteristic of the line itself, not merely of the particular points A and P used at first to define it. The slope, in fact, indicates the direction of the line. We have already noted that the slope is zero if and only if the line is horizontal. Now suppose the slope to be nonzero, the line then being oblique. Let $A = (a,b)$, as before, denote any point of the line, but select for $P = (x,y)$ a point of the line for which $x > a$: thus, $x - a > 0$. In the case in which $s > 0$, Definition (1) tells us that $y - b > 0$; thus, $x - a$ and $y - b$ are the lengths of the segments AB and BP (Figure 8-10A), and

$$s = (y - b)/(x - a) = BP/AB = \tan S$$

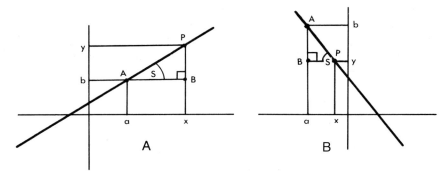

FIGURE 8-10   Lines of positive and negative slope.

(Chapter 7, Section 5). In the case in which $s < 0$, definition (1) tells us that $y - b < 0$; hence, $x - a$ and $b - y$ are the lengths of the segments BP and BA (Figure 8-10B), and

$$s = (y - b)/(x - a) = -(b - y)/(x - a) = -BA/BP = -\tan S.$$

The absolute magnitude of the slope s thus is equal to the tangent of the angle the line makes with the horizontal, the sign of s (whether s is positive or negative) indicating whether y increases or decreases as x increases. The magnitude of s and its sign together thus specify fully the direction of the line.

The fact previously developed that the slope of a line is characteristic of the line itself, not merely of the particular points A and P used at first to define it, puts equation (1) in a new light. Fix A at some definite position on L; as a result, its coordinates, a and b, may be considered constants. Since s, too, is a constant, the only variable quantities involved in equation (1) are x and y, the coordinates of P. But P is an arbitrary point of L (arbitrary, except that $P \neq A$). Hence, solving equation (1), say, for y as a function of x should give us an equation for L such as was discussed abstractly before. We shall see that it does.

Equation (1) presumes $P \neq A$, which means, since L is not vertical, that $x \neq a$. For any such value of x, multiplying the two members of this equation by $x - a$ results in the relation

$$y - b = s(x - a);$$

adding b to both members now gives, equivalently,

(2) $$y = b + s(x - a).$$

This, we maintain, is an equation for L: equation (2) is satisfied at each point of L, but at no other point of the plane. By its derivation, in fact, equation (2) holds at any point P of L other than A, while the substitution $x = a$ and $y = b$ shows the equation also to hold when $P = A$. Thus, this equation is satisfied at each point of L. It remains to be seen that the equation fails at any point not on L. If $Q = (p,q)$ is such a point, let $R = (p,r)$ be the point of L with the same abscissa as Q (Figure 8-11). Since R is subject to equation (2), we have

$$r = b + s(p - a).$$

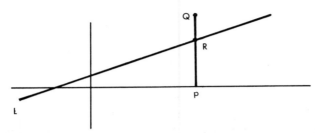

FIGURE 8-11   A point not on an oblique line in the Cartesian plane.

Since Q and R are distinct points with the same abscissa, their ordinates are different, i.e., $q \neq r$. This means, however, that

$$q \neq b + s(p - a),$$

or, in other words, that equation (2) does not hold at Q. Thus, all requirements are met that equation (2) be the equation for L, as asserted.

We have just seen that any nonvertical straight line has an equation of the form (2). Conversely, for any numbers a, b, s, equation (2) determines a nonvertical straight line L, which this equation represents. In fact, let d denote any number different from b, and then find a number c such that

$$s = (c - a)/(d - b).$$

The line joining the two points (a,b) and (c,d) is the line L demanded (Figure 8-12) (See Exercise 12.)

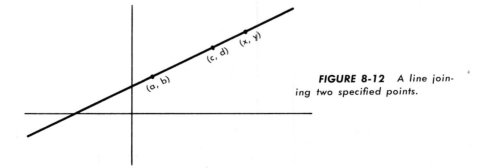

FIGURE 8-12   A line joining two specified points.

The equation of a vertical line with constant abscissa a is

(3)
$$x = a.$$

Such a line is said to have *infinite slope*, the denominator in the ratio for s (equation (1)) being zero. With this convention, every line passing through a given point has a slope, one and but one line having each particular slope. This is the algebraic counterpart of the geometrical fact that one and but one line passes through a given point in a given direction.

EXERCISES

1. Using a protractor, accurately plot angles of 70°, 85°, 89°. From these diagrams calculate as closely as possible the slopes of the lines making these angles to the horizontal.

2. Let (1,2) be one point of a vertical line. Give two other points of this line.

3. Let (2,1) be a point of a horizontal line. Give two other points of this line.

4. Let (2,−3) be a point of a line with slope 2. Give two other points of this line.

5. Let (−2,−1) be a point of a line with slope −1. Give the points with abscissas 2 and −2, respectively.

6. Draw a graph of the line through (−2,−1) with slope 3. Calculate the points of intersection of this line with the axes.

7. Let L denote the line through the origin with slope −2. Give the equation of a line parallel to L through the point (1,2). Graph both lines.

8. Find the equation of a line through the origin and (1,3). Graph the line. Do the same for a line through the origin and (a,b).

9. Let L denote a line through the point (a,b) with slope s. What is the equation of the line L?

10. Prove that r in the equation $y = sx + r$ equals the ordinate of the point at which L meets the y-axis.

11. Thermometers in the U.S. are commonly based on either of two scales, the Centigrade or the Fahrenheit. A Centigrade thermometer is calibrated to read precisely 0° (zero degrees) at the temperature at which pure water freezes and 100° at the temperature at which pure water boils, at sea level. A Fahrenheit thermometer is calibrated to read 32° and 212° on these respective occasions. Furthermore, when Fahrenheit readings for other temperatures are plotted against the corresponding Centigrade readings as in Figure 8-13, the resulting graph is a straight line.

(a) What is the equation of the line?

(b) What is its slope?

(c) If temperature Fahrenheit increases 9°, what is the change on the Centigrade scale? If temperature Fahrenheit increases x degrees, what is the change on the Centigrade scale?

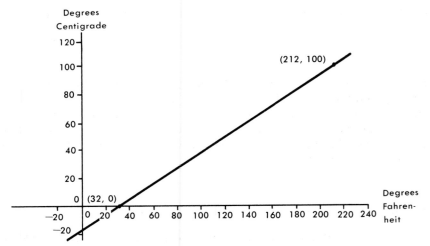

FIGURE 8-13   *Fahrenheit against Centigrade.*

(d) How are the answers to (b) and (c) related?

(e) At what temperature will Centigrade and Fahrenheit thermometers read the same?

12. Given an arbitrary equation of the form (2), we have indicated (p. 280) how to find the line *L* this equation represents. Prove that this equation really does represent *L*, as asserted.

13. Let *A, B, C* be different points of the same straight line, and let the coordinates of these points be

$$(a, b), (u, v), (c, d),$$

respectively. Prove that

$$AB/AC = p$$

if and only if

$$\left| (u - a)/(c - a) \right| = \left| (v - b)/(d - b) \right| = p.$$

14. A median of a triangle is a line segment from a vertex to the midpoint of the opposite side. Consider the triangle with the vertices $(-1, 2)$, $(3, 4)$, $(1, -6)$. Show that the medians of this triangle intersect at a point two thirds of the distance from each vertex to the midpoint of the opposite side (Figure 8-14). HINT: First find the midpoints of the sides. Use Exercise 13 to find the point on each median that is two thirds of the distance from the vertex to the midpoint of the side opposite this vertex. Verify that the three points for the three medians thus calculated are in fact one and the same.

15. Let the points *A, B, C, D* have the coordinates $(0, 0)$, $(0, b)$, (a, b), $(a, 0)$, respectively.

(a) Prove that *ABCD* is a parallelogram.

(b) Prove that the diagonals of a parallelogram bisect each other.

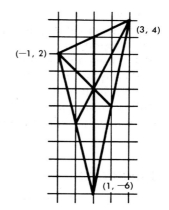

FIGURE 8-14 *A triangle and its medians.*

We have seen that any nonvertical straight line has an equation of the form

(4) $$y = sx + r$$

with suitable choices of s and r, while any vertical line has an equation of the form

(5) $$x = a$$

with appropriate a. Both these forms are special cases of the equation

(6) $$px + qy + r = 0.$$

In fact, form (4) is equivalent to

$$sx - y + r = 0,$$

and thus results from (6) for $p = s$, $q = -1$; form (5) results from (6) for $p = 1$, $q = 0$, $r = -a$.

Conversely, if p and q are not both zero, equation (6) has a straight line graph. Indeed, if $q \neq 0$, equation (6) is equivalent to an equation of the form (4), which we already know to have a straight line as its graph. On the other hand, if $q = 0$, then $p \neq 0$ and equation (6) reads

$$px + r = 0 \quad (p \neq 0).$$

Hence,

$$x = -r/p.$$

This is an equation of the form (5), and its graph is a vertical line with abscissa $-r/p$. Thus, the graph of equation (6) always is a straight line, while, as previously noted, every straight line has an equation of the form (6). Equations of this form, which algebraically are of the first degree, are therefore also called *linear equations*; *p* and *q* are called the *coefficients of x and y*, respectively, and *r* the *constant term* of the equation.

Such an expression as: "the straight line represented by equation (6)" is commonly shortened to: "the straight line (6)," although (6), of course, is really an equation, not the graph of an equation.

EXERCISES

16. Plot the graphs of the following equations, and give their slopes:
(a) $x + y = 0$
(b) $x - y = 0$
(c) $x + y = -1$
(d) $2x = x + 2y$
(e) $x + 5y + 2 = 0$
(f) $x + 5y - 3 = 0$
(g) $5x + y = 2$
(h) $5x = -y - 1$

17. Find the equation of the line through the two points, (1,3) and $(-6, -1)$. If $P = (a,b)$ and $Q = (c,d)$ are any points in the plane, find the equation of the line PQ.

18. The *x-intercept* of a line is its point of intersection with the x-axis; the *y-intercept* is its point of intersection with the y-axis. Does every line have an x-intercept and a y-intercept? Find the x- and y-intercepts, if they exist, of the lines in Exercise 16 and, in addition, of the lines $x = 2$ and $y + 1 = 0$. Find the intercepts for the line corresponding to equation (6).

19. Let a denote the x-intercept of a line L and b the y-intercept. Prove that the equation of L can be written as

$$x/a + y/b = 1.$$

20. If $2y + kx = 6$ is the equation of a line passing through (2,1), find k.

21. Find the midpoint of the line segment AB, where $A = (-3,8)$ and $B = (5,2)$. Then prove that if $P = (x,y)$ and $Q = (x',y')$, then the midpoint of the line segment PQ has abscissa $(x + x')/2$ and ordinate $(y + y')/2$.

22. Is there a one-to-one correspondence between straight lines in the Cartesian plane and equations of the form (6)?

Appendix to Section 5: Parametric equation of straight lines

The algebraic methods so successful in two dimensions can be extended with great benefit to (three-dimensional) space. In the resulting more general treatment, both planes and straight lines, in different ways, play roles fulfilled in two dimensions by straight lines

alone. Planes in space can be treated by extending the method discussed in Section 5. Straight lines in space are more easily handled,
however, by a modification of this method, which we shall now describe. We shall take up the three-dimensional case and apply it to
perspective drawing in Chapter 9.

Let L again denote any straight line in the Cartesian plane, and
consider any point $A = (a,b)$ of L, which we shall hold fixed in the
following discussion. This point separates L into two parts, called
"half-lines," or "rays" issuing (or emanating) from A. (The positive
x-axis, for instance, is a ray that issues from the origin.) Let $P = (x,y)$
be an arbitrary point confined to a particular one of these rays. If L is
oblique, we have already seen (Figure 8-9) that $x - a$ and $y - b$ are
the lengths, or the negatives of the lengths, of the two arms of a right
triangle with acute angles at A and at P. Denote the distance between
A and P, the hypotenuse of this triangle, by d. While the triangle
depends on the choice of P, which is permitted to vary on one ray,
the ratios of the arms to the hypotenuse of the triangle are independent of P (Chapter 7, Section 5). These ratios are the absolute
values of

(1) $$l = (x - a)/d, \; m = (y - b)/d.$$

Hence, $|l|$ and $|m|$ are independent of the position of P on L $(P \neq A)$.
Furthermore, the signs of l and m are independent of P on either ray
of L issuing from A but are reversed on the opposite ray. We conclude
that l and m are independent of P on either ray of L issuing from A and
simply reverse their signs on the opposite ray.

By Pythagoras's theorem,

$$(x - a)^2 + (y - b)^2 = d^2$$

(Figure 8-9). Hence,

$$l^2 + m^2 = 1.$$

If we solve equations (1) for x and y, the coordinates of P, we
obtain

(2) $$x = a + ld, \; y = b + md.$$

Unlike (1), equations (2) hold when $P = A$, in which case $d = 0$.
Equations (2) also can be freed from the restriction under which we
derived (1) that L be oblique. If nonoblique, L is either horizontal or
vertical. If L is horizontal, then $y = b$ and $d = |x - a|$; hence, equa-
tions (2) hold with $m = 0$ and

$$l = 1 \text{ on the ray to the right of } A,$$
$$= -1 \text{ on the ray to the left of } A.$$

If L is vertical, then $x = a$ and $d = |y - b|$; hence, equations (2) hold with $l = 0$ and

$$m = 1 \text{ on the ray extending upwards from } A,$$
$$= -1 \text{ on the ray extending downwards from } A.$$

We conclude that equations (2) hold for all points P of the given ray of L, whatever may be the direction of L. These equations give P in terms of the distance $d = AP$. In the right members of these equations, only d may vary, P varying along the ray as a result, its distance from A always being equal to d. Both coordinates of P are thus specified by the single variable d in manifestation of the one-dimensionality of a straight line. Such a variable, whose value determines the position of a point, is called a *parameter*. Thus, d is a parameter determining P; equations (2) are called *parametric equations* for P.

Permitting the parameter d in equations (2) to assume negative values has the effect of allowing P to leave the originally specified ray for the opposite ray of L emanating from A. As d runs through positive values, P describes one of the rays of L issuing from A; as d runs through negative values, P describes the other ray.

6.

The mutuality of geometry and algebra: intersections, parallelism, and perpendicularity

Through the correspondence discussed in Section 5, linear equations in all their aspects are mirrored by straight lines and straight lines, reciprocally, by linear equations. Several instances will illustrate this mutuality. Consider first the purely algebraic problem of determining two numbers x and y satisfying the two linear equations

(1)
$$x + 2y = 4$$
$$2x - y = 6$$

simultaneously. Plot the graphs of the two equations, which are straight lines (Figure 8-15). If x and y satisfy both the equations, then the point (x,y) occurs on both the graphs and thus is the point at which the two graphs intersect. In fact, solving simultaneous equations always has the effect of finding the intersection of the corresponding graphs. Thus, in principle, two simultaneous equations could be solved without calculation by reading off the coordinates of the point of intersection of the two corresponding graphs, accurately plotted. In practice, arithmetical methods, however, are generally superior. In an arithmetical approach, the two equations are combined in such a way as to eliminate one of the unknown numbers and, thus, to give

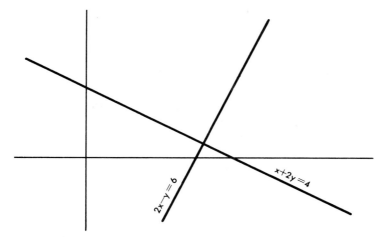

FIGURE 8-15 *The graphs of two simultaneous linear equations.*

the value of the other. Once this is known, the first number is also obtainable. In the present problem we can, for instance, eliminate y by adding the first equation to twice the second, thereby obtaining

$$5x = 16,$$

or $x = 16/5$. Now knowing x, we can find y from either of the original equations. From the first equation, for instance, we would have

$$16/5 + 2y = 4,$$

and, hence, $2y = 4/5$ and $y = 2/5$; using the second equation would give the same result. Substitution in (1) of the values of x and y thus discovered checks our answer:

$$16/5 + 2 \cdot 2/5 = 4,$$
$$2 \cdot 16/5 - 2/5 = 6.$$

The same answer would have been found had we first eliminated x (by subtracting the second equation from twice the first equation), instead of y.

Similar algebraic methods enable us to calculate the intersection of any pair of intersecting lines whose equations are known. Moreover, the algebraic form of the equations of two given lines will tell us if these lines intersect or not. Let

(2) $$px + qy + r = 0, \qquad Px + Qy + R = 0$$

be the equations of two given straight lines. We shall see that the lines coincide or are parallel if and only if the coefficients of x and y are proportional. The proportionality condition means that a constant k, not zero, exists such that

(3) $$p = kP, \ q = kQ.$$

The reader may check the plausibility of the foregoing assertion by plotting, for instance, the graphs of the equations:

$$x - y + 2 = 0,$$
$$2x - 2y - 5 = 0,$$
$$10x - 10y = 0.$$

Note, incidentally, that each of the last equations can be rewritten as

$$x - y + m = 0,$$

where m is a constant ($m = 2$ for the first equation, $-5/2$ for the second, and 0 for the third). This parallelism of form is observable whenever the coefficients of x and y are proportional, since substitution from (3) shows that

$$px + qy + r = kPx + kQy + r$$
$$= k(Px + Qy + r/k);$$

the first equation of (2) thus can be written as

$$Px + Qy + r/k = 0,$$

a result differing from the second equation, if at all, in the constant term alone. Our criterion for coincidence or parallelism thus amounts to the condition that it be possible to write the two equations in such a way that they differ, if at all, in their constant terms alone. (If the constant terms, too, are alike, the two lines coincide; otherwise, they are parallel.)

In justifying (3) as a necessary and sufficient condition that the straight lines (2) be parallel or coincide, we distinguish the case in which at least one of the lines is vertical from that in which neither is vertical. Any vertical line has an equation of the form

$$x = a.$$

Conversely, a line with such an equation or, more generally, with an equation of the form

(4) $$px + r = 0 \ (p \neq 0),$$

reducible to this by dividing by p and setting $a = -r/p$, is vertical. Thus, a line is vertical if and only if it admits an equation of the form

(4). A second line is parallel to a given vertical line if and only if it too is vertical and, hence, if and only if it too has an equation of the form (4), say

(5)
$$Px + R = 0$$

with $P \neq 0$. For equations (4) and (5), the conditions (3), however, are obviously valid with $k = P/p$. Our discussion of the first case thus is complete.

The other case is that in which neither line is vertical so that, in particular,

(6)
$$q \neq 0, \ Q \neq 0.$$

In this case, we can divide the two members of the first equation of (2) by q to obtain

$$(p/q)x + y + r/q = 0;$$

this equation can be written as

(7)
$$y = sx + b,$$

where

$$s = -p/q, \ b = -r/q.$$

Similarly, dividing the members of the second equation of (2) by Q, we obtain

(8)
$$y = Sx + B$$

as an alternative form, where

$$S = -P/Q, \ B = -P/Q.$$

If the lines have a common point, which we denote by (x_0, y_0), we have

$$y_0 = sx_0 + b$$

by substitution into (7) and

$$y_0 = Sx_0 + B$$

by substitution into (8). Hence, $Sx_0 + B = sx_0 + b$, or

$$(S - s)x_0 = b - B.$$

This is a necessary condition if the two lines meet at a point with the abscissa x_0. Conversely, if c is any number such that

(9) $$(S - s)c = b - B,$$

then the two lines meet at a point with the abscissa c; the ordinate of this point will be

(10) $$d = sc + b.$$

Indeed, the point (c,d) is on the line (7), by definition (10), and also is on the line (8), because

$$d = sc + b = Sc + B,$$

by condition (9). We conclude that the two lines (7) and (8) have a common point for every value c satisfying (9) and that c is the abscissa of the point. The lines intersect in just one point if just one value of c satisfies (9), coincide if all values satisfy (9), and are parallel if no value satisfies (9). As to the existence of values of c that satisfy (9), three cases are to be distinguished:

Case (i): $s - S \neq 0$. In this case, c has one and only one value that will satisfy (9), and the lines therefore intersect in one point only.

Case (ii): $s - S = 0$, $b - B = 0$. In this case, every value of c will satisfy (9), and the two lines coincide.

Case (iii): $s - S = 0$, $b - B \neq 0$. No value of c satisfies (9), and the two lines are parallel.

From this discussion of cases, it is clear that the lines coincide or are parallel if and only if

$$s - S = 0.$$

Since $s - S = p/q - P/Q$, this condition can be written also as

$$pQ = Pq.$$

This is equivalent to the two conditions:

$$p = kP$$
$$q = kQ$$

with $k = q/Q$. Thus, condition (3) is seen to be necessary and sufficient that the lines (2), when not vertical, be parallel or coincide. Since the condition already was justified for vertical lines, we recognize that it is entirely general, as asserted.

As a final instance in this section of the reciprocity between geometry and algebra, we now discuss the algebraic counterpart of perpendicularity. Let A be the intersection of two oblique, perpendicular lines, AB and AC (Figure 8-16). Draw a line through A parallel

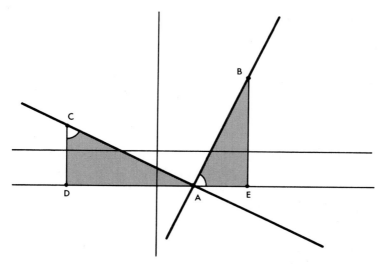

FIGURE 8-16   *Perpendicular lines.*

to the *x*-axis, and draw *CD* and *BE* perpendicular to this line. For definiteness, assume as in the diagram that *AB* has positive slope and *AC*, therefore, negative slope. Then

(11)   slope of $AB = BE/AE$
                               slope of $AC = -CD/DA$.

Since $\angle CAB = 90°$, we have $\angle EAB = 90° - \angle CAD$ and, consequently, $\angle EAB = \angle ACD$. Therefore, the two right triangles *ACD* and *BAE* are similar, so that, in particular,

$$CD/AD = AE/BE.$$

This and (11) imply that

(12)   (slope of AB) $\cdot$ (slope of AC) $= -1$.

We have proved that if two oblique lines are perpendicular, the product of their slopes equals -1.

Conversely, if two oblique lines, *L* and *M*, satisfy this condition, then they are perpendicular, as we see in the following way. First, the lines, having different slopes, must intersect. Call the point of intersection *A*. Secondly, let *M'* denote the perpendicular to *L* through *A*. By the foregoing, the slope of *M'* equals $-1/s$, *s* denoting the slope of *L*. Hence, *M'* passes through *A* with the same slope as *M*. Hence, *M'* coincides with *M*, which thus is perpendicular to *L*.

Condition (12) can be stated in a particularly symmetric, general form. Suppose the given lines are represented by equations (2). If the lines are oblique, their equations can be reduced to the forms

$y = sx + m$ and $y = Sx + M$, respectively, with

$$s = -p/q, \qquad S = -P/Q.$$

Condition (12) says that $sS = -1$, and thus that $pP/qQ = -1$ or, equivalently, that

(13) $$pP + qQ = 0.$$

This is the symmetrical condition for perpendicularity referred to. Unlike (12), this condition is not restricted to oblique lines but is also satisfied when one line is horizontal and the other vertical. Since the coefficient of x vanishes for a horizontal line, and the coefficient of y vanishes for a vertical line, the sum of the products of the two x-coefficients and the two y-coefficients in fact is zero for such a pair of lines, as demanded in (13). Thus, condition (13) characterizes perpendicular lines without exception.

EXERCISES

1. Graph the two lines with the equations

$$x - y = 1,$$
$$x + y = 2.$$

Find their point of intersection algebraically. Prove algebraically that these lines are perpendicular.

2. Can any pair of simultaneous equations be solved? Consider these:

$$-2x + y = 6$$
$$6x - 3y = 2.$$

Explain in both algebraic and geometric terms.

3. Find the line through $(1,2)$ perpendicular to the line $y = 2x$. Find the parallel to this line through $(2,2)$.

4. Which of the following lines are parallel?
   (a) $y = 4x/3 - 7$
   (b) $3y = 2x + 3$
   (c) $3y = 4x + 6$
   (d) $18 - 9y + 12x = 0$.

5. If L is the line given by $y = 3x + 1$, find the perpendicular to L through the point $P = (-3,4)$. Then calculate the distance from P to L. (This is the distance from P to the point of intersection with L of the perpendicular that goes through P.)

6. Find the distance from $(0,0)$ to the line $ax + by + c = 0$.

7. Let a, b, A, B denote four numbers such that $B \neq 0$. Prove that

$$aB - Ab = 0$$

if and only if a number k exists such that

$$a = kA, \ b = kB.$$

8. Prove that two linear equations,

$$px + qy + r = 0,$$
$$Px + Qy + R = 0,$$

have the same graph if and only if their coefficients and constant terms are proportional. This means that a constant k, not zero, exists such that

$$p = kP, \ q = kQ, \ r = kR.$$

9. Prove that parallel lines have equal slopes.

10. A farmer propounded the following question: "That ten-acre meadow of mine will feed twelve bullocks for sixteen weeks or eighteen bullocks for eight weeks. How many bullocks could I feed on a forty-acre field for six weeks, the grass growing regularly all the time?"[†] HINT: Let us agree to measure grass for simplicity in such units that 1 bullock eats 1 unit of grass per week. Let A denote the amount of grass (in such units) on one acre of the farmer's land; let r denote the amount of new growth per week. Over a period of t weeks, the total amount of grass per acre available for grazing thus is

$$A + rt.$$

The amount of grass per acre available over a period of 16 weeks, in particular, is $A + 16r$, and the amount of grass available from 10 acres over this period is $10(A + 16r)$. The total grass consumed by 12 bullocks in 16 weeks, however, is $12 \cdot 16 = 192$ units. Hence,

$$10(A + 16r) = 192.$$

A second equation also can be obtained from the information given, the two equations together permitting one to calculate the actual values of A and r. After finding these, calculate the total amount of grass available in 40 acres over a 6-week period. This must be equal to the (unknown) number of bullocks to be accommodated multiplied by the number of weeks.

11. Prove by coordinate geometry that the line segment joining the midpoints of two sides of a triangle is parallel to and one-half the length of the third side.

12. Prove that the line segment joining the midpoints of the nonparallel sides of a trapezoid is parallel to the bases and equal to half the sum of their lengths.

13. Prove that the line segments joining the midpoints of opposite sides of any quadrilateral[‡] bisect each other.

[†] Dudeney, Henry E., The Canterbury Puzzles, Fourth Edition, New York, Dover Publications, Inc., 1958, p. 157.

[‡] A quadrilateral is a four-sided closed polygon.

14. Prove that the midpoints of two opposite sides of any quadrilateral and the midpoints of the diagonals are the vertices of a parallelogram.

15. Prove that the two lines from a vertex of a parallelogram to the midpoints of the opposite sides trisect the diagonal that they cross.

7.

Price determination in a free market

Economists put the idea of a graph to good use in their curves of supply and demand. Alfred Marshall explains the background thus:

Let us . . . take an illustration from a corn-market in a country town, and let us assume for the sake of simplicity that all the corn in the market is of the same quality. The amount which each farmer or other seller offers for sale at any price is governed by his own need for money in hand, and by his calculation of the present and future conditions of the market with which he is connected. There are some prices which no seller would accept, some which no one would refuse. There are other intermediate prices which would be accepted for larger or smaller amounts by many or all of the sellers. Everyone will try to guess the state of the market and to govern his actions accordingly. Let us suppose that in fact there are not more than 600 quarters, the holders of which are willing to accept as low a price as 35s.; but that holders of another hundred would be tempted by 36s.; and holders of yet another three hundred by 37s. Let us suppose also that a price of 37s. would tempt buyers for only 600 quarters; while another hundred could be sold at 36s., and yet another two hundred at 35s. These facts may be put out in a table thus: —

At the price	Holders will be willing to sell	Buyers will be willing to buy
37s.	1000 quarters	600 quarters
36s.	700 quarters	700 quarters
35s.	600 quarters	900 quarters

Of course some of those who are really willing to take 36s. rather than leave the market without selling, will not show at once that they are ready to accept that price. And in like manner buyers will fence, and pretend to be less eager than they really are. So the price may be tossed hither and thither like a shuttlecock, as one side or the other gets the better in the "haggling and bargaining" of the market. But unless they are unequally matched; unless, for instance, one side is very simple or unfortunate in failing to gauge the strength of the other side, the price is likely to be never very far from 36s.; and it is nearly sure to be pretty close to 36s. at the end of the market. For if a holder thinks that the buyers will really be able to get at 36s. all that they care to take at that price, he will be unwilling to let slip past him any offer that is well above that price.

Buyers on their part will make similar calculations; and if at any time the price should rise considerably above 36s. they will argue that the supply will be much greater than the demand at that price: therefore even those of them who would rather pay that price than go unserved, wait; and by waiting they help to bring the price down. On the other hand, when the price is much below 36s., even those sellers who would rather take the price than leave the market with their corn unsold, will argue that at that price the demand will be in excess of the supply: so they will wait, and by waiting help to bring the price up.

The price of 36s. has thus some claim to be called the true equilibrium price: because if it were fixed on at the beginning, and adhered to throughout, it would exactly equate demand and supply (i.e., the amount which buyers were willing to purchase at that price would be just equal to that for which sellers were willing to take that price); and because every dealer who has a perfect knowledge of the circumstances of the market expects that price to be established. If he sees the price differing much from 36s. he expects that a change will come before long, and by anticipating it he helps it to come quickly.

It is not indeed necessary for our argument that any dealers should have a thorough knowledge of the circumstances of the market. Many of the buyers may per-haps underrate the willingness of the sellers to sell, with the effect that for some time the price rules at the highest level at which any buyers can be found; and thus 500 quarters may be sold before the price sinks below 37s. But afterwards the price must begin to fall and the result will still probably be that 200 more quarters will be sold, and the market will close on a price of about 36s. For when 700 quarters have been sold, no seller will be anxious to dispose of any more except at a higher price than 36s., and no buyer will be anxious to purchase any more except at a lower price than 36s. In the same way if the sellers had underrated the willingness of the buyers to pay a high price, some of them might begin to sell at the lowest price they would take, rather than have their corn left on their hands, and in this case much corn might be sold at a price of 35s.; but the market would probably close on a price of 36s. and a total sale of 700 quarters.†

In any situation such as that described, graphs have visual ad-vantages over tables. Accordingly, we have plotted Marshall's supply schedule (the first two columns of his table) in Figure 8-17A and inter-polated a smooth curve between the separate points. The demand schedule (first and third columns) is plotted in Figure 8-17B with a smooth curve again interpolated between the separate points. In Figure 8-17C, the two curves are brought together. Representing the schedules of supply and demand, they are called the "supply curve" and the "demand curve," respectively. The point at which they cross

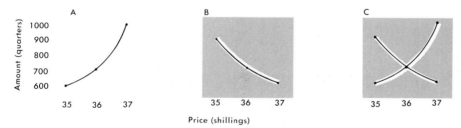

FIGURE 8-17 *Curves of supply and demand. A, Supply schedule: amounts holders are willing to sell. B, Demand schedule: amounts buyers are willing to purchase. C, Supply and Demand curves.*

tells the price at which demand and supply are equal, Marshall's "equilibrium" price. At a higher price, purchasers are more reluctant and sellers more eager. At a lower price, sellers hold back and buyers show zeal. Competition among buyers thus tends to keep the price at least as high as the equilibrium value and competition among sellers

†Alfred Marshall, *Principles of Economics*, 9th Ed., Vol. 1, Macmillan, New York, 1961, pp. 332-334.

at least as low. Therefore, according to Marshall, the intersection of the supply curve and the demand curve determines rather closely the actual price.

8.

The graphs of inequalities

The graph of a relation between x and y is the set of all points (x,y), in the xy-plane, at which the relation is satisfied. The graphs of inequalities, in particular, usually are regions rather than lines or curves. For instance, the graph of the inequality

$$x > 1,$$

i.e., the set of all points (x,y) such that $x > 1$, is the region to the right of (and not on) the vertical line $x = 1$; in Figure 8-18 this region is hatched. The graph of the inequality

$$x < 1$$

is the region to the left of (and not on) the line $x = 1$; this region, in Figure 8-18, is stippled. Thus, the graph of the line $x = 1$ separates the two regions that are the graphs of the opposite inequalities $x < 1$ and $x > 1$, the three graphs together covering the entire plane.

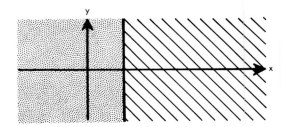

FIGURE 8-18   *The region $x > 1$.*

For any constant q, we see similarly that the graph of the inequality

$$x > q$$

is the region to the right of (and not on) the line

$$x = q,$$

and the graph of the inequality

$$x < q$$

is the region to the left of (and not on) this vertical line.
    Let us now find the graph of the inequality

(1) $y > x + 2.$

Our previous example suggests that we start with the graph of the
line

(2) $y = x + 2$

(Figure 8-19). Let x_0 denote any abscissa, and let $y_0 = x_0 + 2$. Thus,
the point (x_0, y_0) is on the line (2), while (x_0, y) is above the line (2)
if $y > y_0$ and below the line (2) if $y < y_0$. The last two assertions mean
that the graph of the inequality

$$y > x + 2$$

is the region above the line (2) (hatched, in Figure 8-19), and the
graph of the opposite inequality

$$y < x + 2$$

is the region below. The graphs of the two inequalities are separated
by line (2), their common boundary.

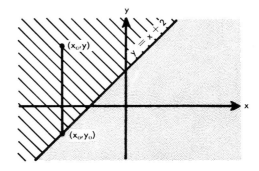

FIGURE 8-19 *The regions*
$y > x + 2$ *and* $y < x + 2$.

    For any constants p and q, we see similarly that the graph of the
inequality $y > px + q$ is the region above (and not on) the line
$y = px + q$, and the graph of the inequality $y < px + q$ is the region
below (and not on) this line.

EXERCISES

1. Sketch the graphs of the following inequalities:
    (a) $y > 2x,$ (c) $y > -x + 1,$ (e) $x > y.$
    (b) $y < 0,$ (d) $x + y > 0,$

We are now ready to consider a general "linear" inequality, such as

$$(3) \qquad\qquad ax + by + c > 0.$$

This inequality is degenerate unless

$$(4) \qquad\qquad a \neq 0 \quad \text{or} \quad b \neq 0.$$

(If $a = b = 0$, the inequality degenerates to the statement that $c > 0$, a statement that holds, if true, for all points (x,y) and, if false, for none. The graph of the inequality in the first case is the entire xy-plane and in the second case is void, i.e., does not contain any points.) We shall only consider nondegenerate inequalities or, in other words, assume conditions (4) to be satisfied.

It will appear that the graph of (3) is the region to one side or the other of the line

$$(5) \qquad\qquad ax + by + c = 0.$$

To show this, first consider the case in which $b = 0$, the inequality in this case reducing simply to

$$ax + c > 0,$$

or

$$ax > -c,$$

with $a \neq 0$. If $a > 0$, dividing by a preserves the inequality (Chapter 2, Section 5), and we have

$$(6)_+ \qquad\qquad x > -c/a.$$

If $a < 0$, dividing by a reverses the inequality, and we have

$$(6)_- \qquad\qquad x < -c/a.$$

Inequality $(6)_+$ or $(6)_-$, whichever is correct, is equivalent to (3) and thus has the same graph. The graph of $(6)_+$, by our previous discussion, however, is the region to the right of the vertical line $x = -c/a$, the graph of $(6)_-$ being the region to the left. Since the line $x = -c/a$ is also represented by equation (5) ($b = 0$), we conclude that the graph of (3) is the region to the right of the line (5) (which is vertical) when $a > 0$ and $b = 0$, and is the region to the left of this line when $a < 0$ and $b = 0$.

Next consider the case in which $b \neq 0$. In this case, we can write inequality (3) as

$$by > -ax - c$$

and thus as

(7)$_+$ $$y > -(a/b)x - c/b$$

if $b > 0$ and as

(7)$_-$ $$y < -(a/b)x - c/b$$

if $b < 0$. The previous discussion shows that the graph of (7)$_+$ is the region above the line

$$y = -(a/b)x - c/b$$

and the graph of (7)$_-$ is the region below the line. Since this line is also represented by equation (5), we conclude that the graph of (3) is the region above the line (5) when $b > 0$ and is the region below this line when $b < 0$. Our contention that the graph of (3) is the region to one side or the other of the line (5) is thus completely proved.

For brevity, we shall often refer to the *graph of an inequality*, such as (3), as the *region* (3) and to the *graph of an equation*, such as (5), as the *line* (5).

The graph of the inequality

$$ax + by + c \geq 0$$

consists of all the points (x,y) such that $ax + by + c > 0$, as well as those for which $ax + by + c = 0$. In our abbreviated terminology, the region

$$ax + by + c \geq 0$$

thus consists of both the region

$$ax + by + c > 0$$

and its boundary, the line

$$ax + by + c = 0.$$

EXERCISE

2. Sketch the graphs of the following inequalities:
   (a) $-x + y - 1 \geq 0$,
   (b) $x \geq 2y - 3$,
   (c) $4 > x + 2y$,
   (d) $2 - x \leq 1 + y$,
   (e) $x + y > -(x + y) - 2$.

Inequalities of any kind have graphs. As an instance of a non-linear inequality, consider

(8) $$x^2 + y^2 < 4.$$

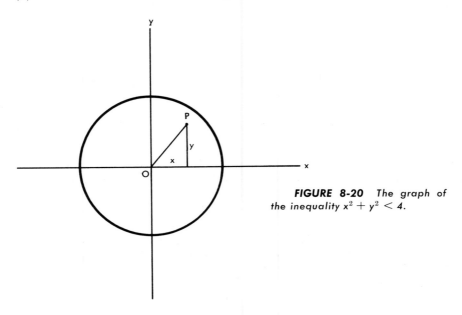

FIGURE 8-20 *The graph of the inequality* $x^2 + y^2 < 4$.

This inequality has a geometrical interpretation, which makes its graph (Figure 8-20) at once evident. In fact, $\sqrt{x^2 + y^2}$ represents the distance between the origin O and the point $P = (x,y)$. Hence, inequality (8), which may be rewritten as

$$\sqrt{x^2 + y^2} < 2,$$

states that the distance between O and P is less than 2. Since this condition means simply that P is in the interior of the circle of radius 2 about O, the interior of this circle is the graph of the inequality. The exterior of the circle is seen in the same way to be the graph of the opposite inequality,

$$x^2 + y^2 > 4.$$

The two graphs are separated by the circle,

$$x^2 + y^2 = 4.$$

A second example of a nonlinear inequality is the relation

(9) $$y > 1 - x^2.$$

We shall find its graph by the means used previously for inequality (1),

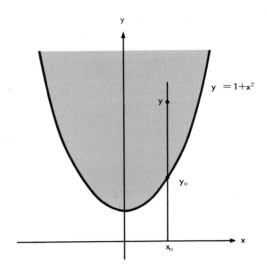

FIGURE 8-21 The region $y >$ $1 + x^2$.

this time starting with the graph (Figure 8-21) of the curve

(10) $y = 1 + x^2.$

Let x_0 denote any abscissa, and let $y_0 = 1 + x_0^2$. Thus, the point (x_0, y_0) is on the curve (10), while (x_0, y) is above the curve (10) if $y > y_0$ and below the curve (10) if $y < y_0$. The last two assertions mean that the graph of the inequality (9) is the region shaded, in Figure 8-21), above the curve (10), and the graph of the opposite inequality,

(9') $y < 1 + x^2,$

is the region below. The graphs of the two inequalities are separated by the curve (10), their common boundary.

EXERCISE

3. Indicate by shading, in appropriate figures, graphs of the following inequalities:

    (a) $x + y > 0,$
    (b) $x^2 + y > 0,$
    (c) $(x - 1)^2 + y \leq 0,$
    (d) $(x - 1)^2 + (y + 2)^2 < 1,$
    (e) $x^2 + y^2 < 0.$

On occasion, as in the economic problems of the following section, x and y may be subjected to several conditions required to hold simultaneously. The graph of a set of simultaneous relations is the assemblage of points (x,y) at which the individual relations are all satisfied simultaneously. Thus, the graph of a set of relations is the common part (if any) of all the graphs of the individual relations. To illustrate, we shall find the graph of the following set of three inequalities:

$$(11) \qquad 2x + y - 1 > 0,$$

$$(12) \qquad x - 2y - 2 > 0,$$

$$(13) \qquad -5x + 3y + 24 \geq 0.$$

We must first find the graph of each inequality individually, and to this end rewrite the inequalities as

$$(11') \qquad y > -2x + 1,$$

$$(12') \qquad y < (1/2)x - 1,$$

$$(13') \qquad y \geq (5/3)x - 8.$$

From these forms, it is clear that the graph of (11) is the region above (but not including) the line

$$(14') \qquad y = -2x + 1$$

or, in other words, the region above the line

$$(14) \qquad 2x + y - 1 = 0;$$

the graph of (12) is the region below (but not including) the line

$$(15') \qquad y = (1/2)x - 1,$$

i.e., the region below the line

$$(15) \qquad x - 2y - 2 = 0;$$

the graph of (13) is the region above, and including, the line

$$(16') \qquad -5x + 3y + 24 = 0.$$

The points (x,y) common to these three regions are the points at which the three inequalities (11), (12), and (13) are all fulfilled. These points thus constitute the graph of this set of inequalities. In Figure 8-22, they fill the shaded area, including the darkened line segment.

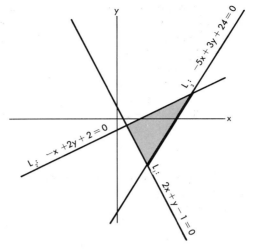

FIGURE 8-22 *The graph of a system of simultaneous inequalities.*

A system of relations may be such as to be satisfied at no point (x,y). Such a system is called *inconsistent,* and its graph *empty, void,* or *vacuous.* We obtain an inconsistent system, for example, by adding the fourth inequality,

(17) $$-x + 3y - 6 > 0,$$

to the three inequalities, (11), (12), (13), previously considered.

EXERCISES

4. Prove the inequalities (11), (12), (13), and (17) to be inconsistent.
5. Find the graphs of the following sets of simultaneous conditions:
   (a) $x + y = 2$
   $x - y = 0.$
   (b) $y \leq 0$
   $-2x + y - 3 \geq 0$
   $3x + y - 3 \geq 0.$
   (c) $x > 1$
   $x < 2$
   $y > 1$
   $y < 2.$
   (d) $y \leq -x + 1$
   $y \geq x - 1$
   $y \leq x + 1$
   $y \geq -x - 1$
   $x^2 + y^2 < 1/4.$
   (e) $x^2 + y^2 \leq 9$
   $x^2 + y^2 > 4.$
6. Find the graphs of the following inequalities or sets of inequalities:
   (a) $1 < x < 2$
   (b) $1 < |x| < 2$
   (c) $1 < x - y < 2$
   (d) $|x - y| < 1$
   (e) $|x - y| < |x|$

7. A region R is *bounded* if there exists some constant M such that the distance between every point (x,y) in R and $(0,0)$ is less than M. Determine which of the given regions are bounded:

(a) $x \leq 7$
  $2y \geq x - 6$
  $y \leq 2x + 5$
  $y \leq 4x + 20.$

(b) $y \geq x + 1$
  $y \geq -4x - 11$
  $y \geq 3x - 6.$

(c) $y \leq 3x + 3$
  $y \geq 2x + 1$
  $4y \geq x - 3$
  $3y \geq x - 3$
  $2y \geq x - 3$
  $y \geq 2x - 6$
  $y \geq 3x - 9$
  $y \geq 5x - 15.$

8. Determine by graphing whether these systems of inequalities are consistent or not:

(a) $3y \leq x + 4$
  $y \geq -2x + 5$
  $y \geq 4x + 10.$

(b) $2y - 3x - 4 \geq 0$
  $4y \leq 6x + 3.$

(c) $y \geq 2$
  $x + 2 \leq 0$
  $y + 2 \leq 0$
  $x \geq 2.$

9. Find the perimeter and area of each of the following figures:

(a) The triangle determined by
  $y \geq 0$
  $y - 2x \leq 2$
  $2y + x \leq 10.$

(b) The sector of the circle determined by
  $x^2 + y^2 \leq 9$
  $y - 4x \leq 0$
  $y - x \geq 0.$

(c) The square determined by
  $y + x - 4 \geq 0$
  $y - x + 2 \geq 0$
  $y + x - 8 \leq 0$
  $y - x - 2 \leq 0.$

9.

Some economic problems: linear programming

Geometrical considerations such as those we have presented have inspired methods of solutions of a certain type of problem very prominent in economics. Suppose, for instance, that an alloy, or mixture of metals, requires *at least* certain proportions, and *at most* certain other proportions, of its constituents, these proportions not being more exactly prescribed. The composition most profitable to the fabricator will depend on the prices he must pay for the raw

materials. The problem is to determine this most profitable composition, meeting the specifications at minimum cost, given the
prices of the raw materials. We illustrate with the following (artificial)
example:

A manufacturer wishes to produce at minimum cost 3 pounds of
an alloy required to contain at most 53 1/3 per cent lead, at most
33 1/3 per cent tin, and at least 23 1/3 per cent zinc, no other requirements being specified. Lead, tin, and zinc are available to the manufacturer in three other alloys, denoted by A, B, and C, which are
mixtures in the proportions listed in Table 8-1. (Thus, for instance,
alloy B contains 40 per cent lead, 40 per cent tin, and 20 per cent
zinc.) The costs to the manufacturer of A, B and C are \$4, \$5, and \$6
per pound, respectively. How many pounds of these alloys will produce a composition meeting the specifications at minimum cost?

	% of lead	% of tin	% of zinc
A	60	10	30
B	40	40	20
C	30	30	40

Table 8-1 Constitution of available alloys

To formulate this problem more succinctly, let x, y, z represent
the (unknown) quantities, in pounds, of alloys A, B, C, respectively,
that we need. In terms of x, y, z, the specifications read as follows:

(1) $$x + y + z = 3$$

(2) $$(.60x + .40y + .30z)/3 \leq .53\ 1/3$$

(3) $$(.10x + .40y + .30z)/3 \leq .33\ 1/3$$

(4) $$(.30x + .20y + .40z)/3 \geq .23\ 1/3$$

Equality (1) states that the amount of the product (three) is the sum
of the amounts (x, y, and z) of its constituents.

In inequality (2), the numerator of the fraction on the left represents the percentage of lead in A multiplied by the quantity of A,
plus the percentage of lead in B multiplied by the quantity of B, plus
the percentage of lead in C multiplied by the quantity of C, and thus
is the total amount of lead in the alloy produced. Dividing this total
amount by 3 gives the percentage of lead in the new alloy, which, by
specification, must be less than or equal to 53 1/3 per cent. Inequality
(2) states this specification. Inequalities (3) and (4) similarly state the

two other specifications. To these we may add the obvious requirements that x, y, z be non-negative:

(5) $x \geq 0,$

(6) $y \geq 0,$

(7) $z \geq 0.$

The problem is to find values for x, y, z that satisfy the previous
seven requirements at as small a total cost as possible. This total
cost is

(8) $4x + 5y + 6z.$

   An expression like (8) of the form

$$ax + by + cz + d$$

with fixed (but not necessarily explicitly stated) "coefficients" a, b, c,
d (in (8), $d = 0$), is called a *linear function* of the variables x, y, z; an
equality like (1) of the form

$$ax + by + cz + d = 0$$

is called a *linear equality*, or *equation*, in the variables x, y, z; an
inequality like (2), (3), or (4) of the form

$$ax + by + cz + d \leq 0$$

or

$$ax + by + cz + d \geq 0,$$

is called a *linear inequality* in the variables x, y, z. Similar terminology
is used with more than three variables.
   In this language, the preceding problem may be described, in
general terms, as follows. A linear function (in the preceding problem,
total cost) of several variables is given. The variables are partially
restricted by linear equalities and inequalities. What is the least
value of the linear function possible under these restrictions, and
how may this least value be realized? The second question means:
Of all the sets $(x,y,z,\ldots)$ of values of the several variables satisfying
the specified linear equalities and inequalities, which set (or sets)
allows (or allow) the least value of the given linear function?
   The terms of this problem are algebraic; hence, the logic of solution must ultimately be algebraic. The most effective calculation
procedures, using high speed electronic computers, also are algebraic.
These methods are beyond our scope, but they are based, as we

previously remarked, on a geometrical idea, which we shall now explain in connection with the previous problem.

Because of (1) we can eliminate one of the variables from the inequalities. Let us eliminate z. Solving (1) for z, we have

$$(9) \qquad\qquad z = 3 - x - y,$$

and substituting this in (2) to (7) results in

$$(10) \qquad .60x + .40y + .30(3 - x - y) \le (.53\ 1/3)\ (3)$$

$$(11) \qquad .10x + .40y + .30(3 - x - y) \le (.33\ 1/3)\ (3)$$

$$(12) \qquad .30x + .20y + .40(3 - x - y) \ge (.23\ 1/3)\ (3)$$

$$(13) \qquad\qquad\qquad\qquad x \ge 0$$

$$(14) \qquad\qquad\qquad\qquad y \ge 0$$

$$(15) \qquad\qquad\qquad 3 - x - y \ge 0.$$

We can simplify (10), (11), (12) by multiplying by 10 to obtain

$$6x + 4y + 3(3 - x - y) \le (5\ 1/3)\ (3)$$
$$x + 4y + 3(3 - x - y) \le (3\ 1/3)\ (3)$$
$$3x + 2y + 4(3 - x - y) \ge (2\ 1/3)\ (3).$$

Further simplification reduces these to

$$(16) \qquad\qquad\qquad 3x + y \le 7$$

$$(17) \qquad\qquad\qquad -2x + y \le 1$$

$$(18) \qquad\qquad\qquad -x - 2y \ge -5.$$

Also substituting for z in (8), we obtain for the total cost the expression

$$4x + 5y + 6(3 - x - y) = -2x - y + 18.$$

If we denote this total cost by c, we thus have

$$(19) \qquad\qquad\qquad c = -2x - y + 18.$$

Our problem is reduced to finding the least value of c for which quantities x and y exist that satisfy the constraining conditions (13) to (18), inclusive. We also wish to know which pair (or pairs) (x,y) satisfying the constraining conditions thus minimize c.

To require that x and y satisfy the inequalities (13) to (18) is to require geometrically that (x,y) in the Cartesian plane be a point of the graph of these six simultaneous inequalities. To find this graph (Section 8), we must find the graphs of the six inequalities individually. The graph of (13) consists of the points to the right of (and on) the y-axis, the graph of (14) of the points above (and on) the x-axis. Rewriting (15) as

$$y \leq -x + 3,$$

we see that its graph comprises the points below (and on) the line

$$y = -x + 3;$$

the equation of this line also can be written as

(15′) $3 - x - y = 0.$

The graph of (16) is the region to the left of (and including) the line

(16′) $3x + y = 7,$

the graph of (17) is the region to the right of (and including) the line

(17′) $-2x + y = 1,$

and the graph of (18) is the region below (and including) the line

(18′) $-x - 2y = -5.$

The graph of the six simultaneous inequalities, by definition, is the region common to the six individual graphs just described and thus is represented by the shaded region in Figure 8-23. The points of this region (including the boundary of the region) satisfy the six constraining conditions of the problem, while any point not in this region violates at least one of the constraints. We shall call this region the "constraint graph."

Our ultimate object is to find the point or points of the constraint graph for which c, defined by (19), is least (i.e., is not greater than the value c takes at any other point of the region). To this end, we now raise the following simpler question: What values of x and y, if any, will satisfy the constraining conditions at *given* cost c? According to (19), one and the same cost c is incurred for any values of x and y satisfying the linear relation

(20) $2x + y = 18 - c.$

Hence, for any point (x,y) on the straight line with this equation, and for no other point, the total cost will be c. Only the points of the constraint graph, however, obey the six constraints. It follows that the values of x and y that satisfy the restraining conditions and also result in cost c are just those for which (x,y) belongs both to the constraint graph and also to the cost line (20).

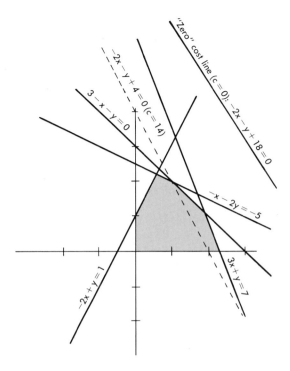

FIGURE 8-23

For $c = 0$, equation (20) reducing to

$$2x + y = 18,$$

the cost line does not touch the constraint graph (Figure 8-23). For any value of c, the cost line occupies a position parallel to that for $c = 0$ (Section 6) and, as c increases, moves to the left. (For larger c, the right side of equation (20) is smaller, and, at any fixed ordinate, $y = $ constant, the abscissa x determined by this equation is smaller as a result.) For $c = 14$, for which value equation (20) becomes

$$2x + y = 4,$$

the cost line is so far to the left as to cut inside the constraint graph, with which it has a segment in common. The value of c we desire, however, is the least value for which the cost line and the constraint graph meet. Geometrically, it is plain that this desired least value, less than 14 and greater than zero, is that for which the cost line just touches the boundary of the constraint graph, or lies along a segment of the boundary, not cutting inside. From the shape of the constraint graph and the direction of the cost line in the present problem (Figure 8-23), the desired value of c is that for which the cost line meets the boundary of the constraint graph in the point, a vertex, at which the lines

(21)
$$3 - x - y = 0$$
$$3x + y = 7$$

intersect. Let us find this vertex, which means to find x, y satisfying equations (21) simultaneously. To do this, we may, for instance, solve the first equation for y, obtaining

$$y = 3 - x,$$

and substitute this expression for y in the second equation. We thereby have

$$3x + (3 - x) = 7,$$

and, therefore,

$$x = 2.$$

This, substituted in either equation of the pair (21) gives

$$y = 1.$$

Hence, the vertex is $(2,1)$. The value of c at this point is the least for which any cost line and the constraint graph meet and thus is the least cost for which the six constraining conditions are satisfied. This value is given by (19) as

$$c = -2(2) - 1 + 18 = 13.$$

The alloy composition resulting in this minimum cost is:

$$x = 2, \ y = 1, \ z = 3 - x - y$$
$$= 0.$$

These results are the solution of the problem.

EXERCISES

1. Another industrial problem to which linear programming methods are applicable is that of allocating scarce raw materials to products which are mixtures of these raw materials. The scarcity of the raw materials restricts the amounts available each day. Profit margins may be different for the different finished products. The problem is to find an optimum allocation of the raw materials such that the total profit on all of the mixtures produced is maximum. (Note that in this case we must maximize rather than minimize, but the method of solution is essentially the same.) We give the following hypothetical ex-

ample: An oil company produces two grades of gasoline by blending three raw materials in the proportions $2 : 1 : 2$ for one gasoline and $1 : 1 : 3$ for the other. Scarcity limits the maximum quantities available of the raw materials to 10, 6, and 15 units per day. The profit per unit of each of the two gasoline blends are \$3 and \$2 respectively. Find the quantities of each of the two gasolines which will maximize the profit and at the same time conform to the scarcity restrictions. What is the maximum profit?[†]

2. A gambler, dissatisfied with his record of profligacy, becomes cautious in his betting on a forthcoming heavyweight boxing match. The odds are 5 to 1 in favor of the champion. Expecting to place money on both the champion and the challenger, the gambler wishes to determine the smallest sum of money that he need wager in order to insure himself a return of at least \$10, no matter who wins the bout. With this restriction in mind, what amounts should the gambler bet on each man? HINT: Use linear programming to find the answer.

3. A certain automobile manufacturing plant makes both trucks and automobiles. This plant has four departments: the sheet metal department, the engine assembly department, the automobile final-assembly department, and the truck final-assembly department. Each department has a limited capacity per month: the first is either 30,000 automobiles or 20,000 trucks, the second 40,000 automobiles or 20,000 trucks, the third 22,500 automobiles, and the fourth 15,000 trucks. The amount of profit (the selling price minus the cost) made is \$200 per automobile and \$300 per truck. Determine the maximum possible profit per month and the number of automobiles and the number of trucks which realize this maximum. Assume that, since the sheet metal department can produce either 30,000 automobiles or 20,000 trucks, the production of one automobile utilizes 1/30,000-th and the production of one truck 1/20,000-th of its capacity. Make a similar assumption concerning the engine assembly department. HINT: Let x represent the number of automobiles and y the number of trucks produced per month. Then x automobiles and y trucks utilize $x/30,000$-th and $y/20,000$-th of the sheet metal capacity. Since the production of x automobiles and y trucks cannot exceed the whole capacity of the sheet metal department, we have

$$x/30,000 + y/20,000 \leq 1.$$

Three other inequalities are obtained from the other three departments. The x and y obtained as a solution to such a problem may not be unique.[‡]

[†]This problem is similar to one in *Linear Programming in Industry, Theory and Applications*, p. 36-37, by Sven Danø, Springer-Verlag, 1963.

[‡]This problem is similar to one in Danø, *op. cit.*, p. 53.

CHAPTER 9

THREE-DIMENSIONAL SPACE AND PERSPECTIVE DRAWING

Space geometry was a natural outgrowth of plane geometry, indispensable to mathematics and also eventually to other fields, such as navigation, astronomy, and mechanics. Here we shall develop some of the basic properties of three-dimensional space, first intuitively (Section 1), and then logically in the Euclidean style (Section 2), enough to enable us to establish Cartesian coordinates in three dimensions (Section 3). Then we shall obtain parametric representations of straight lines (Section 4), examine some of their mathematical consequences (Section 5), apply them to the theory of perspective drawing (Sections 6, 7), and deduce additional results in geometry this theory suggests (Section 8).

1.

An intuitive description of three-dimensional space. Definitions.

In this section, we shall consider some of the most fundamental attributes of points, lines, and planes. These attributes seem intuitively obvious; most people are inclined to accept them without proof. Here we shall introduce appropriate terminology and define the properties and relations we shall have to consider, developing them systematically in the following section. The properties and relations discussed fall under five headings: (i) the determination of planes in space; (ii) the nature of three-dimensionality; (iii) intersection properties; (iv) parallelism; (v) perpendicularity.

(i) *The determination of planes in space*: (1) Any three points not on a straight line determine one and just one plane containing them all. This is the principle by which a tripod's three legs always rest on the floor, while a table with four uneven legs may wobble (Figure 9-1).

FIGURE 9-1 *Steady and wobbly.*

(2) Infinitely many planes contain the same straight line. In fact, if a plane is regarded as hinged along the line (Figure 9-2), it is seen to be capable of infinitely many positions obtained by turning the hinge. Since only one of these planes will pass through a given point

FIGURE 9-2   *A hinged plane.*

not on the hinge line, we see also that (3) only one plane contains both the given line and a prescribed point outside the line. The latter is the principle of the door stop (Figure 9-3). (4) Two intersecting straight lines determine one and only one plane containing them both.

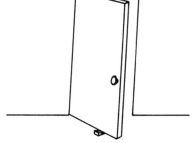

FIGURE 9-3   *A plane determined by a line (of the door's hinges) and a point (the doorstop).*

(ii) *The nature of three-dimensionality*: (1) No single plane fills (three-dimensional) space. (2) Any plane, like a wall, divides space into two parts, one part on either side (Figure 9-4).

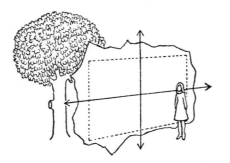

FIGURE 9-4   *A plane dividing space like a continuation of a wall.*

The reader will note how these parts are characterized mathematically in the next section.

Definition.   The *intersection* of two figures (such as lines, planes, a line and a plane, a pyramid and a sphere, a plane and a prism) is their common part.

(iii) *Intersection properties*: (1) If a straight line has two distinct points in common with a plane, it lies wholly in the plane. (2) If two different planes meet, their intersection is a straight line (Figure 9-5).

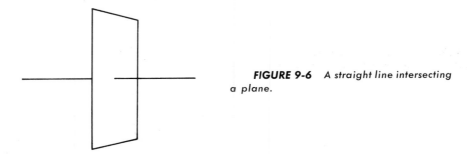

FIGURE 9-5   *Intersecting planes.*

Wall and ceiling thus join in a straight line. (3) If a straight line intersects a plane but does not lie in the plane, then the intersection is a single point (Figure 9-6). This is illustrated by a pin prick.

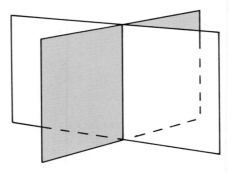

FIGURE 9-6   *A straight line intersecting a plane.*

Definitions. Two straight lines are *parallel* if they are in the same plane but do not meet. Two lines are *skew* if they are not in the same plane (Figure 9-7A). A line and a plane are *parallel* if they do not meet (Figure 9-7B). Two *planes* are *parallel* if they do not meet (Figure 9-7C).

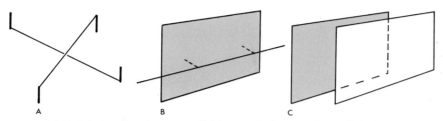

FIGURE 9-7 *Skew lines, parallel line and plane, and parallel planes.*

(iv) *Parallelism*: (1) A plane containing either of two parallel lines and not the other is parallel to the other line. (2) Two straight lines that are parallel to a third line are parallel to each other. The two lines, in particular, thus lie in a single plane, as we illustrate (Figure 9-8) with opposite edges of a box.

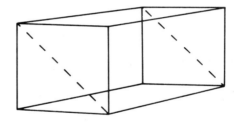

FIGURE 9-8 A box.

Definition. A line l is perpendicular to a plane H if l and H intersect in a point P, and l is perpendicular to every line in H through P.

(v) *Perpendicularity*: (1) A line perpendicular to two intersecting lines is perpendicular to the plane containing them (Figure 9-9).

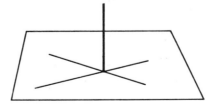

FIGURE 9-9 A perpendicular to intersecting lines.

(This means that the line is perpendicular to every straight line lying in the plane of the two given lines and passing through their intersection.) (2) All the perpendiculars to a given line at a given point lie in a plane perpendicular to the given line at that point. (3) One and only one plane perpendicular to a given line contains a given point. This is the principle of the instrument used in shoe stores to measure foot length (Figure 9-10). (4) One and only one line perpendicular to a

FIGURE 9-10 *A plane perpendicular to a given line and passing through a given point.*

given plane passes through a given point. A good example is a plumb line, which is perpendicular to the horizontal (Figure 9-11). (5) Two lines perpendicular to the same plane are parallel. For instance,

FIGURE 9-11 *A plumb line, perpendicular to a horizontal plane.*

telephone poles are (approximately) parallel (Figure 9-12). (6) Parallel lines have the same perpendicular planes. This means that a plane is perpendicular to either of two parallel lines if and only if the plane is perpendicular to the other line.

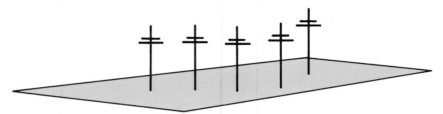

FIGURE 9-12   *Lines perpendicular to the same plane are parallel.*

The fourth perpendicularity property (the uniqueness of the line perpendicular to a given plane and passing through a given point) has an analogue for perpendicular lines of the same plane. These

properties justify some additional definitions relating to perpendicular projections.

Definitions.   Let P be any point, H any plane, and l the perpendicular to H through P. The point P_H in which l and H intersect is
called the *perpendicular projection of P upon H*. Analogously, let a
be any line and k the perpendicular to a (in the plane of P and a)
through P. The point P_a in which a and k intersect is called the
perpendicular projection of P upon a. (See Figure 9-13.) Property (4)

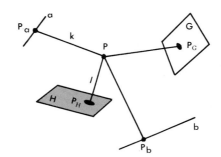

FIGURE 9-13   *Perpendicular projections of a given point P upon lines a and b
and upon planes G and H.*

is equivalent to the contention that each point has one and only one
perpendicular projection upon any plane; from plane geometry, it is
known that each point has one and only one perpendicular projection
upon any line. Moreover: if m is a line belonging to plane F, the perpendicular projection of P_F upon m coincides with P_m (the perpendicular projection of P upon m) (Figure 9-14).

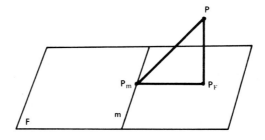

FIGURE 9-14   *The perpendicular projection upon a line of
a perpendicular projection upon
a plane that contains the line.*

We conclude this section with some common conventions as to
the "distance" from a point to a line, from a point to a plane, between
two parallel lines, and so forth.

Definitions.   *The distance from a point to a line* or *from a point
to a plane* is defined to be the distance between the point and its
perpendicular projection upon the line or plane, respectively. *The
distance between two parallel lines* is defined as the distance between
any point of one of the lines and its perpendicular projection upon the
other line. *The distance between a straight line and a plane to which*

it is parallel is defined as the distance between any point of the line and its perpendicular projection upon the plane. *The distance between two parallel planes* is defined to be that between any point on one plane and its perpendicular projection on the other. (The distance is the same, no matter how the point is chosen. A similar remark applies to the previous two definitions.)

2.

Three-dimensional Euclidean geometry†

In space, as in the plane, geometry is based on a very small number of principles with strong intuitive appeal. We formulate them here as follows:

(1) Any three points not on a straight line determine a plane containing them all; only one such plane exists.

(2) If a straight line has two distinct points in common with a plane, it lies wholly in the plane.

(3) Two planes that meet have at least two points in common.

(4) Four points exist that are not in any single plane.

(5) Any plane divides space outside the plane itself into two parts, called the two sides of the plane. Two points P and Q are on the *same* side if the line segment PQ does not intersect the plane and are on *opposite* sides if PQ does intersect the plane.

(6) Euclidean plane geometry is valid in each individual plane of space. Furthermore, comparisons (as to equality or congruence) of segments and angles apply whether or not the segments and angles are in the same plane.

These principles are all (the sixth, implicitly) among the intuitively founded assertions of Section 1; the fourth and fifth, in particular, are those that express the three-dimensionality of space. All solid geometry follows from these principles by deduction, but we shall be concerned only with the remaining assertions of Section 1, which will enable us to build Cartesian coordinate systems in space (Section 3). These assertions are proved in a different order from that in which it was convenient to list them.

(7) Any point and a line not passing through it determine a plane containing them both; only one such plane exists.

PROOF: The given point plus any two points of the given line

---

†This presentation in some aspects is based on C. F. Brumfiel, R. E. Eicholz, and M. E. Shanks' *Geometry*, published by Addision-Wesley Publishing Company, Inc., Reading, Mass., 1960, pp. 237-242, and on F. M. Morgan and W. E. Breckenridge's *Solid Geometry*, revised edition, published by Houghton Mifflin Company, Boston, 1957, pp. 15-40.

determine one and only one plane (by (1)) that contains the given line (by (2)).

(8) Any two intersecting lines that do not coincide determine a plane containing them both; only one such plane exists.

PROOF: Denote the two lines by l and m, their intersection by P, and a different point of m by Q (Figure 9-15). One and only one plane (by (7)) contains both l and Q. This plane contains P, which is on l, and therefore (by (2)) contains the line m joining P and Q.

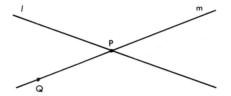

FIGURE 9-15 The plane determined by two intersecting lines.

(9) If two planes meet, their intersection is a straight line.

PROOF: The planes have at least two points in common (by (3)), while the line joining the two points belongs to each plane (by (2)) and thus to their intersection. If both planes contained a point not on this line, the planes would coincide (by (7)). Hence, this line is their entire intersection.

(10) If a straight line meets a plane, but is not wholly contained in the plane, the intersection is a single point.

PROOF: If the line had (at least) two points in common with the plane, the line would lie wholly in the plane (by (2)).

(11) Two straight lines that are parallel to a third line are parallel to each other.

PROOF: Let a and b denote two lines, each of which is parallel to a third line c. Our aim is to prove that a and b are parallel. If a, b, and c happen to be in the same plane, the assertion is one of plane geometry and is known to be true. We shall only consider the case, therefore, in which a, b, and c do not lie in a single plane (Figure 9-16). Then the plane F of a and c is different from the plane G of b and c, F and G intersecting in c. Let H denote the plane through a and any point P of b. Thus, H contains a point (namely, P) not in F; hence, H meets F only in a (by (9)), and H therefore does not meet c at all. Similarly, G does not meet a. Since G and H meet (at P), their intersection is a line (by (9)), which we shall denote by b'. Belonging to G, b' is in a plane containing c, and, belonging to H, b' does not

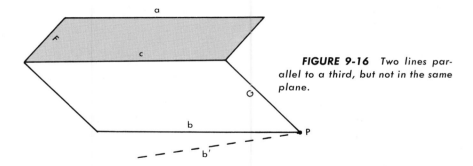

FIGURE 9-16 *Two lines parallel to a third, but not in the same plane.*

meet c. Hence, b' is a line in G parallel to c; by construction, b' passes through the point P. But b also is a line in G, passing through P, parallel to c. Therefore, b and b' coincide (by (6)), so that b, in particular, is in H, a plane containing a. Furthermore, b, lying in G, does not meet a. Hence, b is parallel to a, as contended.

(12) A line perpendicular to two intersecting lines is perpendicular to the plane containing them.

PROOF: Let a and b denote intersecting lines, P their point of intersection, and l a line perpendicular to a and b at P. Our aim is to prove that l is perpendicular to any line c through P in the plane of a and b (Figure 9-17). Choose points Q on l, A on a, and B on b, all distinct from P. Denote by Q' the point of l on the opposite side to Q of the plane of a and b (see (5)) such that $PQ = PQ'$. The side-angle-side criterion shows that $\triangle QPA \cong \triangle Q'PA$ and that $\triangle QPB \cong \triangle Q'PB$. Hence, $QA = Q'A$ and $QB = Q'B$. Then by the side-side-side criterion, $\triangle QAB \cong \triangle Q'AB$. This implies that $\angle QAC = \angle Q'AC$, where C denotes the intersection of AB with c. The previous result and the

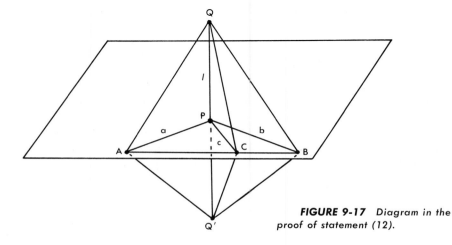

FIGURE 9-17 *Diagram in the proof of statement (12).*

side-angle-side criterion show that $\triangle QAC \cong \triangle Q'AC$. Therefore, $QC = Q'C$. The side-side-side criterion now shows that $\triangle QPC \cong \triangle Q'PC$ and thus, in particular, that $\angle QPC = \angle Q'PC$. Since these two angles fill a straight angle, they are individually right angles so that l is perpendicular to c, as was to be proved.

(13) All the perpendiculars to a given line at a given point lie in a single plane perpendicular to the given line at that point.

PROOF: Suppose three lines, a, b, l, intersect at a point P and that a and b are perpendicular to l (Figure 9-18). We intend to show that any fourth line c perpendicular to l at P lies in the plane of a and

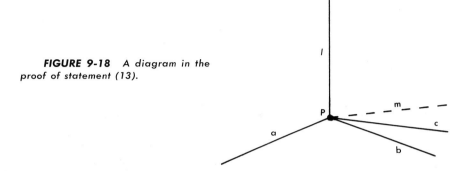

FIGURE 9-18 A diagram in the proof of statement (13).

b. Denote by m the straight line in which the plane of a and b and the plane of l and c intersect. Since m thus lies, in particular, in the plane of a and b, m is perpendicular to l (by (12)); also, m passes through P and lies in the plane of l and c. Thus, m and c are in a single plane with l, pass through P, and are perpendicular to l. Therefore, m and c are the same, c consequently lying in the plane of a and b, as was to be proved.

(14) One and only one line is perpendicular to a plane at a given point of the plane.

PROOF: Let P denote any point of a plane H, and consider any two perpendicular lines a and b lying in H and intersecting at P (Figure 9-19). By (13), planes F and G exist perpendicular to a and b,

FIGURE 9-19 A diagram in the proof of statement (14).

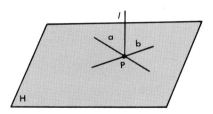

respectively, at P. The intersection of these planes is a line l, which, therefore, also is perpendicular both to a and to b. We must show there is no other perpendicular to a and b. Let m, therefore, denote any perpendicular to a and b at P; we shall prove m to coincide with l. Since a is perpendicular to b, l, and m, the last three lines all lie in the same plane. But l and m are both perpendicular to b at the same point P. Hence, l and m coincide, as was to be proved.

(15) One and only one plane perpendicular to a given line contains a given point not on the line.

PROOF: Let l denote any line and P any point not on this line (Figure 9-20); let H denote the plane of P and l. Draw the perpendicu-

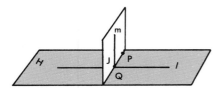

FIGURE 9-20   A diagram in the proof of statement (15).

lar (in H) from P to l. Call the intersection of l with the perpendicular Q. Let m denote any other line through Q perpendicular to l. The plane of m and PQ is perpendicular to l and contains P. Call this plane J. We must prove that J is the only plane through P perpendicular to l. In fact, letting K denote any plane through P perpendicular to l, we shall show that K is the same as J. If K intersects l in the point R, then PR is perpendicular to l. However, both PR and PQ are in the plane of l and P, both lines pass through P, and both lines are perpendicular to l. Therefore, the lines are the same. Hence, their intersections with l, in particular, are the same: i.e., Q and R coincide. Only one plane, however, is perpendicular to l at Q (by (13)). Therefore, J and K are the same, as asserted.

(16) Parallel lines have the same perpendicular planes.

PROOF: Let l and m denote any two parallel lines, and suppose F to be a plane perpendicular to l at a point P (Figure 9-21). In the

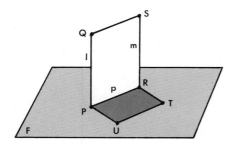

FIGURE 9-21   A diagram in the proof of statement (16).

plane of l and m, let p be a line perpendicular to l at P; thus, p is in F. Since l and m are parallel, p intersects m and is perpendicular to m at the point of intersection, which we shall denote by R. Our aim is to show that m is perpendicular to F at R. Since m is known to be perpendicular to p, it suffices to prove m to be perpendicular to another line through R in the plane F. Let PQ and RS be equal segments of l and m, respectively, on the same side of F. Since l and m lie in a plane, $PQSR$ is a parallelogram (and, more precisely, a rectangle, owing to the right angles at P and R). Hence, PR and QS are equal and parallel. Now let RT be a line segment in the plane F not collinear with (i.e., not along the same line as) RP, and let PU be an equal and parallel segment on the same side (in the plane F) of PR. Then $PRTU$ is a parallelogram, and UT and PR, in particular, are equal and parallel. As we saw, PR and QS also are equal and parallel. We conclude immediately that UT and QS are equal, and we conclude from (11) that UT and QS are parallel. Therefore, $QSTU$ is a parallelogram, and, consequently, $QU = ST$. The side-side-side criterion now shows that $\triangle QPU \cong \triangle SRT$; therefore, $\angle SRT = \angle QPU = 90°$. Thus, m is perpendicular to RT, as well as to PR, and thus is perpendicular to F, as we had desired to prove.

(17) Lines perpendicular to the same plane are parallel.

PROOF: Let l and m denote straight lines perpendicular to a plane F at points P and Q, respectively (Figure 9-22). Let m' denote the line parallel to l through Q. Since l is perpendicular to F, assertion (16) shows that m' is perpendicular to F. A plane (by (14)) has but one perpendicular, however, at a given point. Hence, m and m' coincide, and m is seen to be parallel to l, as asserted.

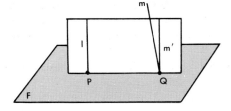

FIGURE 9-22 A diagram in the proof of assertion (17).

(18) One and only one straight line passing through a given point is perpendicular to a given plane.

PROOF: Let P denote any point and F any plane. The case in which P is on F has been already considered in assertion (14). Thus, we shall now assume that P does not lie on F. In this case, let Q denote any point of F (Figure 9-23). By assertion (14), a line m through Q exists perpendicular to F. Let l denote the line parallel to m through P. By assertion (16), l is perpendicular to F. Thus, l is the line required.

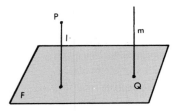

FIGURE 9-23   A diagram in the proof of assertion (18).

We must still show that no other perpendicular to F through P exists. Suppose, to the contrary, that there were such a line; denote it by l'. Then l and l' intersect F in different points, which we shall denote by R and R', respectively (Figure 9-24). Since l and l' are both supposed to be perpendicular to F, they are perpendicular, in par-

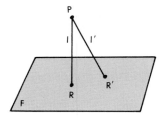

FIGURE 9-24   Second diagram in proof of assertion (18).

ticular, to RR'. But it is known from plane geometry that two perpendiculars from a given point to a specified straight line do not exist. Thus, the supposition that l and l' are distinct leads to a contradiction and must be abandoned. We conclude that only one perpendicular to F through P exists, as asserted.

(19) Let F denote any plane containing a given line a. If P is any point, denote by P_F the perpendicular projection of P upon F and by P_a the perpendicular projection of P upon a. Then P_a is the perpendicular projection of P_F upon a.

PROOF: Let G denote the plane through P_a perpendicular to a. Since PP_a is perpendicular to a, PP_a is contained within G. Since G and F have the point P_a in common, they intersect in a straight line we shall denote by b (Figure 9-25). Let Q denote the perpendicular projection of P upon b. Since P_aQ is perpendicular to a, P_a is the perpendicular projection of Q upon a. Thus, we need only prove that Q and P_F are the same. We shall do so by proving PQ to be perpendicular to each of two lines in F passing through Q, recognizing from (12) that PQ therefore is perpendicular to F, and relying on (14) for the assurance that no other perpendicular to F from P exists; PQ being that perpendicular, Q will be identified as the perpendicular projection of P upon F, as asserted. We have still to find two lines through Q and lying in F that are perpendicular to PQ. By construction, P_aQ is one such line. By assertion (16), the line through Q parallel to a (this

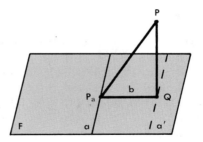

FIGURE 9-25 A diagram in the proof of assertion (19).

line is labeled a' in Figure 9-25) is a second such line. Exhibiting these two lines completes the proof.

EXERCISES

Prove the following statements:

1. Let P denote any point, and l any line not containing P, in space. Only one line through P is parallel to l.

2. If a given line is parallel to a plane, the plane meets any plane containing the line (if it meets the plane at all) in a line that is parallel to the given line.

3. If a line intersects one of two parallel planes, it intersects the other.

4. If a plane intersects one of two parallel planes, it intersects the other.

5. If two straight lines are parallel, every plane containing one and only one of the lines is parallel to the other line.

6. Two planes parallel to a third plane are parallel to each other.

7. If each of two intersecting planes is parallel to a given line, the intersection of the planes is parallel to that line.

8. If two intersecting lines are each parallel to a given plane, the plane determined by these lines is parallel to the given plane.

9. Through either of two skew lines, one plane and only one can be passed parallel to the other line.

10. The intersections of two parallel planes by a third plane are parallel lines.

11. If a line is perpendicular to one of two parallel planes, it is perpendicular to the other.

12. Two planes perpendicular to the same line are parallel.

13. Suppose two different points P and Q have the same projection on a given plane F. Then the line PQ is perpendicular to F.

14. Let P and Q have projections P_F and Q_F, respectively, on a given plane F. If P and Q are distinct and $P_F Q_F = PQ$, then $P_F Q_F$ and PQ are parallel.

15. All points in any plane which is perpendicular to a given line have the same perpendicular projection upon the line.

16. The perpendicular projection of a point P upon a plane F can be obtained as follows. Let l denote any line of the plane F and P_l the perpendicular projection of P upon l. Let G denote the plane through P_l perpendicular to l; let m be the line of intersection of F and G. Then the perpendicular projection of P upon m is the desired perpendicular projection of P upon F.

3.

Coordinates in space. The distance between two points.

In this and the following sections, we shall develop enough of the coordinate geometry of three-dimensional space to be able to treat the theory of perspective, to which the later part of the chapter is devoted.

We must first describe an appropriate scheme for labeling and referring to the points of space; it will generalize the previous scheme for a plane. Select three mutually perpendicular straight lines, l, m, and n, intersecting in a common point O. (Thus, l is perpendicular to m and to n, and m and n are also perpendicular.) We may think of l as east-west and of m as north-south, l and m both lying in a horizontal plane; n then will be vertical, i.e., perpendicular to this plane. On l, m, and n establish scales with the same unit distance and with origins at O. We shall assume, as is customary, that the positive half of the scale on l is to the east of the origin, on m is to the north of the origin, and on n is above the origin. Now consider an arbitrary point of space denoted by P. Let P_l, P_m, P_n denote the perpendicular projections of P on l, m, n, respectively (Figure 9-26). Denote by x the number assigned to P_l in the scale impressed upon l; thus, x is the distance of P_l from O if P_l is east of O and is the negative of this distance if P_l is west of O: in other words, x is the signed distance of P_l from O as read off from the impressed scale on l. Similarly, denote by y the number assigned to P_m in the scale adopted for m and by z the number assigned to P_n in the scale adopted for n; y and z are the signed distances from O of P_m and P_a, respectively, each as read from the appropriate scale. The three numbers, x, y, and z, thus associated with P are called the *coordinates* of P; l, m, and n are called *coordinate axes*, l being the *x-axis*, m the *y-axis*, and n the *z-axis*; O is called the *origin* of the coordinate system. The plane of l and m is called the *xy-plane*, the plane of l and n the *xz-plane*, and the plane of m and n the *yz-plane*; these three planes are called the *coordinate planes*. The coordinate axes together constitute what is called a three-dimensional *Cartesian frame* and (three-dimensional) space with a Cartesian frame, *Cartesian space*. The coordinates of P are usually

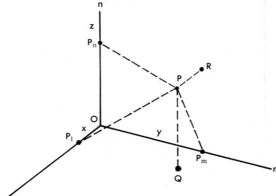

FIGURE 9-26 *Perpendicular projections P_l, P_m, and P_n of point P on lines l, m, and n (x, y, and z axes) respectively. Points Q and R are perpendicular projections of P onto the xy and yz coordinate planes respectively.*

written together in an *ordered triple* (x,y,z), the x-coordinate (the signed distance from O of the perpendicular projection of P upon the x-axis) being the *first* entry in the list, the y-coordinate the *second*, and the z-coordinate the *third*. One and only one such ordered triple of numbers is associated with every point.

The ordered triple of coordinates corresponding to an arbitrary point of the x-axis is $(u,0,0)$, u denoting the signed distance of the point from the origin. Similarly, the ordered triple of coordinates corresponding to an arbitrary point of the y-axis is of the form $(0,v,0)$, and that corresponding to an arbitrary point of the z-axis of the form $(0,0,w)$. A point of the xy-plane is described by an ordered triple of coordinates of the form $(u,v,0)$, the z-coordinate being zero for such a point, a point of the xz-plane by an ordered triple of the form $(u,0,w)$, and a point of the yz-plane by $(0,v,w)$.

If P is an arbitrary point with the ordered triple of coordinates (u,v,w), its perpendicular projections upon the coordinate axes are the points with the coordinate triples $(u,0,0)$, $(0,v,0)$, and $(0,0,w)$. The perpendicular projection of P upon the xy-plane is a point Q having the ordered coordinate triple $(u,v,0)$ (Figure 9-27). First, the z-coordinate of Q is 0, because Q is in the xy-plane. Secondly, the x-coordinate of Q is the same as that of P because of assertion (19), Section 2. For the same reason, the y-coordinates of Q and P coincide. Therefore, Q determines the ordered coordinate triple $(u,v,0)$, as asserted. Similarly, the perpendicular projections of P upon the xz- and yz-planes have the coordinate triples $(u,0,w)$ and $(0,v,w)$, respectively.

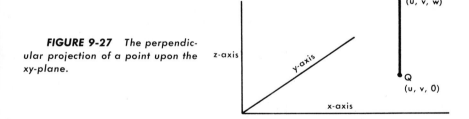

FIGURE 9-27 *The perpendicular projection of a point upon the xy-plane.*

If (u,v,w) is the coordinate triple for P, it is apparent that u is positive when P is east of the yz-plane, zero when P is on this plane, and negative when P is west of this plane. We shall see also that $|u|$ measures the distance of P from the xy-plane. Thus, u can be described as the *signed distance* of P *from this plane:* the sign of u tells which side of the plane p is on, and the absolute value of u the actual distance of P from the plane. Similarly, v is the signed distance of P from the xz-plane and w the signed distance of P from the xy-plane. To prove our contention respecting $|u|$, recall that, in the terminology of Figure 9-28, $|u|$ is the distance of P_l from O. But O

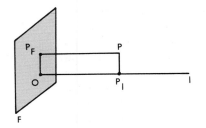

FIGURE 9-28   A point P, its perpendicular projection P_l upon a line l, and the projections of P and P_l upon a plane perpendicular
to l.

is the projection of P_l upon the yz-plane; hence, the distance of P_l
from O is the distance of P_l from this plane. Our aim is to show that
this is also the distance of P from this plane. Denote the plane by F
(Figure 9-28) and the perpendicular projection of P upon F by P_F.
Our contention is that $PP_F = OP_l$. Assertion (17) of Section 2 shows that
PP_F and P_lO are parallel; since F is perpendicular to l, it follows that
P_FO also is perpendicular to l; by construction, PP_l is perpendicular to
l. Hence, OP_lPP_F is a rectangle, and therefore $PP_F = P_lO$, as contended.
Since $|u| = OP_l$, this means that $|u|$ is indeed the distance of P from
the yz-plane and thus, as we asserted, that u is the signed distance of P
from this plane. As we mentioned, v and w have similar interpretations.

Assigning to each point in the Cartesian plane the ordered pair of
numbers consisting of its coordinates resulted (Section 2, Chapter 8)
in a one-to-one correspondence between the set of all points in the
plane and the set of all ordered pairs of numbers. In other words, each
point was assigned one and only one ordered pair of numbers, and
each ordered pair of numbers was assigned to one and only one point,
in the indicated manner. The xy-plane is a Cartesian plane, and these
remarks apply in particular to it. Hence, assigning the ordered pair
(u,v) to the point Q in the xy-plane whose x-coordinate is u and
y-coordinate is v establishes a one-to-one correspondence between
the set of all points in the xy-plane and the set of all ordered pairs of
numbers. Therefore, assigning the ordered *triple* $(u,v,0)$ to Q gives
a one-to-one correspondence between the set of all points in the
xy-plane and the set of all ordered triples of numbers having 0 in the
third place. We shall use this fact to prove the corresponding statement in space: assigning to each point in Cartesian space its ordered
coordinate triple results in a one-to-one correspondence between the
set of all points in space and the set of all ordered triples of numbers.
This means that each point in Cartesian space is assigned one and
only one ordered triple of numbers, and each ordered triple of
numbers thereby is assigned to one and only one point.

We have already seen that one and but one ordered triple of
coordinates is associated with every point. Now we shall prove that
every ordered triple of numbers corresponds under this association
to one and but one point (of which it is the coordinate triple). Let
(a,b,c) denote any ordered triple of numbers. Our remarks in the
previous paragraph show that the ordered triple $(a,b,0)$ defines a
point in the xy-plane; we shall denote this point by Q. Let h denote

the straight line through Q perpendicular to the xy-plane, and now define P as the point on h that is c units above Q if c is positive, $|c|$ units below Q if c is negative, and coincident with Q if $c=0$. We have already shown that, in any case, c is the z-coordinate of P and that a and b are the x- and y-coordinates of P. Thus, (a,b,c) is the coordinate triple for P. We must show P is the only point with this coordinate triple. A point with the coordinate triple (a,b,c) has Q (whose coordinate triple is $(a,b,0)$) as its perpendicular projection upon the xy-plane and thus is on h; read from its z-coordinate, the signed distance of this point from Q is equal to c. Thus, this point is uniquely determined, coinciding with P. We conclude that an arbitrary ordered triple of numbers serves as coordinate triple for one and only one point, as asserted. It follows that the assignment to each point in Cartesian space of its ordered triple of coordinates defines a one-to-one correspondence between the set of all points in space and the set of all ordered triples of numbers. Every ordered triple of numbers therefore represents a point, and every point is so representable.

An ordered triple of numbers (a,b,c) thus can be used to *name* the point it represents. If we intend also to use another symbol, such as A, for this point, we may then write $A = (a,b,c)$ to signify that both symbols denote the same point.

We end this section with the generalization to three-dimensional space of the Pythagorean law. Let P and Q denote any two points of Cartesian space with coordinate triples (x,y,z) and (X,Y,Z), respectively. Then, if d_{PQ} denotes the distance between P and Q, the generalization to space of the Pythagorean law states:

$$d_{PQ}^2 = (X - x)^2 + (Y - y)^2 + (Z - z)^2.$$

The proof depends upon Pythagoras' law in the plane. Through P construct straight lines l, m, n parallel to the x-axis, y-axis, and z-axis, respectively (Figure 9-29). Let R denote the perpendicular projection of Q upon the plane of l and m, T the perpendicular pro-

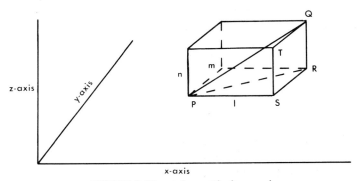

FIGURE 9-29 A box with diagonal.

jection of Q upon the plane of l and n, and S the fourth vertex of the rectangle for which Q, R, and T are the three other vertices. This rectangle is one face of a box, the other vertices of which may be constructed by similar processes, and our problem is to express the diagonal PQ of this box in terms of its edges. Pythagoras' theorem in the plane shows that

$$PQ^2 = QR^2 + PR^2$$

and also that

$$PR^2 = PS^2 + SR^2.$$

Therefore,

$$PQ^2 = QR^2 + PS^2 + SR^2,$$

and substitution from the obvious relations

$$QR = |Z - z|, \ PS = |X - x|, \ SR = |Y - y|$$

gives the desired result.

The *sphere of radius r and center A* is defined to be the set, or aggregation, of points P such that the distance between P and A is equal to r. If $P = (x,y,z)$ and $A = (a,b,c)$, this distance is given by the formula

$$d_{AP}^2 = (x - a)^2 + (y - b)^2 + (z - c)^2.$$

Hence, every point of the sphere of radius r and center A satisfies the condition

(1) $$(x - a)^2 + (y - b)^2 + (z - c)^2 = r^2;$$

conversely, a point satisfying this condition belongs to the sphere. Hence, equation (1) is an equation for the sphere.

A sphere of unit radius is called a *unit sphere*. The unit sphere about the origin, in particular, has the equation

$$x^2 + y^2 + z^2 = 1.$$

EXERCISES

1. What plane is determined by the three points (1,2,0), (3,1,0), (2,2,0)? What plane by (1,2,7), (3,1,7), (2,2,7)?

2. What line is determined by the two points (0,0,0), (0,0,2)? What line by (0,1,0), (0,1,2)? (Describe the lines in relation to the Cartesian frame.)

3. (a) Letting $P = (1,2,3)$, name a second point Q such that the line PQ is parallel to the x-axis and a third point R such that P, Q, and R determine a plane parallel to the xy-plane. What is the distance between this plane and the xy-plane?

(b) Find a fourth point S such that P, Q, and S determine a plane parallel to the xz-plane.

(c) Find equations for the planes determined by P, Q, R and by P, Q, S, respectively.

Prove the following statements:

4. The set of all points of the form (x,y,c), where c is a constant and x and y assume arbitrary values, constitutes a plane. Denote this plane by Z_c. If $c = 0$, Z_c coincides with the xy-plane, and if $c \neq 0$, Z_c is parallel to the xy-plane at a distance equal to $|c|$. If $c > 0$, the plane Z_c is above the xy-plane and, if $c < 0$, Z_c is below the xy-plane. The equation

$$z = c$$

is an equation for the plane Z_c.

5. If $a > b$, then Z_a is above Z_b. The distance between the two (parallel) planes with the equations

$$z = a$$

and

$$z = b,$$

respectively, is equal to $|a - b|$.

6. Give algebraic equations for the planes parallel to the yz-plane.

7. The set of all points of the form (x,b,c), where b and c are constants and x assumes arbitrary values, constitutes a straight line. This line coincides with the x-axis if $a = b = 0$, but otherwise is parallel to the x-axis at a distance from it equal to $\sqrt{b^2 + c^2}$. The equations

$$y = b$$

$$z = c,$$

holding simultaneously, are equations for this line.

8. Characterize similarly the lines parallel to the z-axis.

4.

Parametric equations for a straight line in space

A straight line in the plane has been characterized by two parametric equations (Appendix to Section 5, Chapter 8). A straight line in space is represented by three parametric equations, which we shall obtain by means like those employed in the plane. Let k denote any straight line of Cartesian space; let A and P be any two points of k, which we represent as $A = (a,b,c)$ and $P = (x,y,z)$, respectively, and let d denote their distance apart. Thus (Section 3),

(1) $$d^2 = (x - a)^2 + (y - b)^2 + (z - c)^2.$$

We will regard A — and thus the coordinates a,b,c — as fixed throughout the following discussion; P, however, will be permitted to vary on k. If l denotes the line through A parallel to the x-axis, and P_l the perpendicular projection of P upon l (Figure 9-30), then the ratio

$$AP_l/AP$$

is the same for all positions of P on k different from A (Section 5a, Chapter 7).

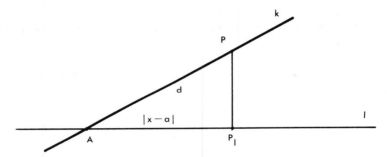

FIGURE 9-30   A variable point $P = (x,y,z)$ on a given line k and its perpendicular projection upon the line l parallel to the x-axis and intersecting k in $A = (a,b,c)$.

Since $AP_l = |x - a|$ and $AP = d$, this ratio is equal to

$$|x - a|/d.$$

Hence, $|x - a|/d$ is the same for all positions of P on k different from A. Similarly, $|y - b|/d$ is the same for all positions of P on k different from A, and an analogous statement is true of $|z - c|/d$. Let k_1 and k_2 denote the two rays of k that issue from A (Figure 9-31). Figure 9-32

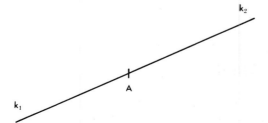

FIGURE 9-31   A line k and its two rays, k_1 and k_2, that issue from one of its points A.

shows that $x - a$ is of one sign on k_1 and of the opposite sign on k_2, vanishing of course for $P = A$. (If k is perpendicular to the x-axis, $x - a = 0$ at every point of k.) Since d is positive when P is different from A, the ratio $(x - a)/d$ thus is of one sign on k_1 and is of the opposite sign on k_2, and the same is true of $(y - b)/d$ and $(z - c)/d$. (The intersection with lines parallel to the y- and z-axis is not shown on Figure 9-32, for simplicity.) The absolute values of these ratios being constant on k, we can conclude that these ratios themselves, namely,

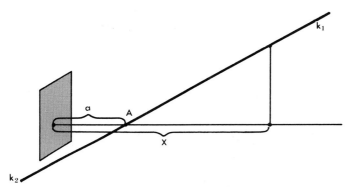

FIGURE 9-32   A line intersecting a line l parallel to the x-axis and a plane m parallel to the yz-plane.

(2) $$(x - a)/d, \ (y - b)/d, \ (z - c)/d,$$

are constant, in particular, on k_1, i.e., have the same values, respectively, for all positions of P on k_1. For the same reason, the ratios also are constant on k_2, on which their values are the negatives of the respective values assumed on k_1. Thus, if p, q, r denote the values of these ratios, respectively, on k_1, i.e., if

(3) $$(x - a)/d = p, \ (y - b)/d = q, \ (z - c)/d = r$$

when (x,y,z) is a point other than A on k_1,

then

(3') $$(x - a)/d = -p, \ (y - b)/d = -q, \ (z - c)/d = -r$$

when (x,y,z) is a point other than A on k_2.

The constants p, q, r satisfy the condition

(4) $$p^2 + q^2 + r^2 = 1,$$

which follows when we divide the two sides of (1) by d^2 and substitute from (3) or (3').

EXERCISES

In the following exercises, A and B will denote specified points. In each case, let k be the straight line AB, k_1 the ray issuing from A passing through B, and k_2 the opposite ray of k that issues from A. In each exercise, answer the following questions for the indicated choices of A and B:

(a) What is the distance AB?

(b) What are p, q, r (equations (3)) in this problem?

(c) Find the points on k_1 and k_2 that are at unit distance from A. Denote these points by P_1 and Q_1, respectively.

(d) Find the two points of k that are at unit distance from B.

(e) For each A and B, find the points of k_1 and k_2 that are twice as far from A as is B.

1. $A = (0,0,0)$, $B = (1,2,3)$.
2. $A = (1,2,3)$, $B = (0,0,0)$.
3. $A = (-1,-2,5)$, $B = (0,1,3)$.
4. $A = (0,1,3)$, $B = (-1,-2,5)$.

Under our assumption that A and P are distinct, in which case $d \neq 0$, equations (3) are equivalent to

$$(5) \qquad \begin{aligned} x &= a + pd \\ y &= b + qd \quad \text{on } k_1 \\ z &= c + rd \end{aligned}$$

and equations (3') to

$$\begin{aligned} x &= a - pd \\ y &= b - qd \quad \text{on } k_2. \\ z &= c - rd \end{aligned}$$

We find it worthwhile to rewrite the last equations as

$$\begin{aligned} x &= a + p(-d) \\ y &= b + q(-d) \quad \text{on } k_2 \\ z &= c + r(-d) \end{aligned}$$

and, making the substitution

$$-d = d',$$

as

$$(5') \qquad \begin{aligned} x &= a + pd' \\ y &= b + qd' \quad \text{on } k_2. \\ z &= c + rd' \end{aligned}$$

Note that d' always represents a negative number, d' being in fact the negative of the distance from P to A.

We have just seen that any point P of k_1 determines a positive number d (the distance of the point from A) in terms of which the coordinates of P are ascertainable from equations (5) and that any point P' of k_2 determines a negative number d' (the negative of the distance from P' to A) in terms of which the coordinates of P' are ascertainable from equations (5'). We now assert that, conversely, the point determined from equations (5) for an arbitrary positive value of d lies on k_1, and the point determined from equations (5') for an arbitrary negative value of d' lies on k_2. If u is, for instance, any positive number, we thus contend that one and only one point of k_1 exists whose coordinates result from equations (5) for $d = u$. Indeed, just one point fits this description, and the point of k_1 with distance u from A is this point. Thus, our contention respecting equations (5) is proved, and the analogous contention respecting equations (5') is similarly proved. We conclude that equations (5) give all points of k_1, and no other points, as d runs through the positive numbers, equations (5') similarly giving all points of k_2, and no other points, as d' runs through the negative numbers. Each positive value of d determines one and but one point of k_1, and each point of k_1 thereby is determined by one and but one positive value of d; each negative value of d' determines one and but one point of k_2, and each point of k_2 thereby is determined by one and but one negative value of d'. Therefore, equations (5) are parametric equations for k_1 and equations (5') parametric equations for k_2; d is the parameter in equations (5) and d' that in equations (5'). These two systems of equations can, however, be combined, for both are of the form

(6)
$$\begin{aligned} x &= a + ps \\ y &= b + qs \\ z &= c + rs, \end{aligned}$$

equations (5) resulting when s is a positive number, such as we previously denoted by d, and equations (5') resulting when s is a negative number such as was denoted by d'. Every positive value of s in equations (6) thus determines one and only one point of k_1, and every negative value of s determines one and only one point of k_2. Every point of k except A thereby corresponds to one and only one positive or negative value of s. For $s = 0$, a hitherto excluded value, equations (6) give A. Thus, equations (6) determine one and only one point of k for every (positive, negative, or zero) value of s, and every point of k thereby corresponds to one and only one such value of s. Equations (6) are therefore called *equations for k* and, more particularly, parametric equations for k, the parameter being s. The other quantities in the right members of (6) are regarded as constants, a, b, and c because A was fixed at the outset, and p, q, and r by demonstration.

If $P = (x,y,z)$, s is equal to the distance from A to P when P is on one of the rays of k emanating from A and is the negative of this distance when P is on the other ray. Hence, we shall refer to s as the *signed* distance from A to P.

EXERCISE

5. In the notation of the previous exercises:
   (f) Find s for P_1, P_2, Q_1, Q_2 in Exercises 1 to 4.

Equations (6) tell us, in the light of the previous considerations, that any point of k can be represented as

(7) $(a + up, b + uq, c + ur)$

in terms of an appropriate value of u and that, conversely, for any (positive, negative, or zero) value of u the point represented by (7) is a point of k. It follows, in particular, that the point S such that $S = (a + p, b + q, c + r)$ is a point of k. The distance between A and S being given by

$$d_{AS}{}^2 = [(a + p) - a]^2 + [(b + q) - b]^2 + [(c + r) - c]^2$$
$$= p^2 + q^2 + r^2$$
$$= 1,$$

S lies on the unit sphere with center at A. (Recall that the unit sphere is that with radius equal to 1.) When k is required to pass through A, to specify p, q, and r thus is to say where k pierces the unit sphere with center at A and hence is to specify the *direction* of k (Figure 9-33). In this remark, all six constants in equations (6) are given geometrical interpretations.

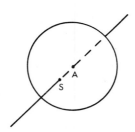

FIGURE 9-33   A line passing through a given point A with its direction determined by its intersection S with a sphere centered at A.

EXERCISES

6. Let $A = (1,2,-1)$, $B = (-1,3,0)$.
   (a) Find parametric equations for the straight line AB.
   (b) Find where AB intersects the unit sphere with center at A.
   (c) Find where AB intersects the unit sphere with center at B.
   (d) Find parametric equations for the projection of AB upon the xy-plane, upon the xz-plane, and also upon the yz-plane.

7. Let k be the straight line with the parametric equations:

$$x = 1 - (1/\sqrt{6})\,s$$
$$y = -3 + (1/\sqrt{6})\,s$$
$$z = 2 + (2/\sqrt{6})\,s.$$

(a) Find where k intersects the unit sphere with center at $(1,-3,2)$.

(b) Find where k intersects the unit sphere with center at $(0,-2,4)$.

(c) Find parametric equations for the projection of k upon the xy-plane, upon the xz-plane, and also upon the yz-plane.

We have seen that every straight line has parametric equations of the form (6), where a, b, c are the coordinates of an arbitrary point of the line, p, q, r are numbers satisfying condition (4), and the parameter s represents the signed distance between (a, b, c) and (x, y, z). The converse of this statement also is true. We formulate it as follows: if a, b, c are any numbers, and if p, q, r are any numbers satisfying (4), then a straight line exists for which equations (6) are parametric equations; the line passes through the point (a,b,c), and s is the signed distance between (a,b,c) and (x,y,z). To prove this, we must find a line with the stipulated properties, and from the previous paragraph it is natural to surmise that this line is AA_1, where

$$A = (a,b,c),\ A_1 = (a + p,\ b + q,\ c + r).$$

(The line is required to contain A and should be expected to contain (7) for each value of u, in particular $u = 1$.) Indeed, what are the equations of the line AA_1, which we shall denote by k? If P and P_1 are two points different from A on the same ray of k emanating from A (Figure 9-34), and if $P = (x,y,z)$ and $P_1 = (x_1,y_1,z_1)$, the constancy of the ratios (2) implies that

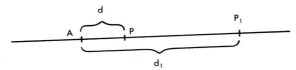

Figure 9-34 Two points, P and P_1, on the same ray of a line k emanating from A.

(8)
$$(x - a)/d = (x_1 - a)/d_1,$$
$$(y - b)/d = (y_1 - b)/d_1,$$
$$(z - c)/d = (z_1 - c)/d_1;$$

here, d denotes the distance of P from A and d_1 the distance of P_1 from A. We apply these formulas with A_1 in place of P_1 and with P therefore restricted to the ray containing A_1. In this application,

$$x_1 = a + p,\ y_1 = b + q,\ z_1 = c + r,$$

and

$$d_1^2 = (x_1 - a)^2 + (y_1 - b)^2 + (z_1 - c)^2$$
$$= p^2 + q^2 + r^2$$
$$= 1,$$

since p, q, r satisfy condition (4). Thus, $d_1 = 1$, and equations (8) reduce to the equations

$$(x - a)d = p, \ (y - b)/d = q, \ (z - c)/d = r.$$

These are identical with (3), and the reasoning applied to (3) will show that the parametric equations for k therefore are identical with (6). This contention is thus proved.

What we have just shown implies without further calculation that if B_1 is any point of the line represented by equations (6), and if $B_1 = (a_1, b_1, c_1)$, then the equations

(9)
$$x = a_1 + pu$$
$$y = b_1 + qu$$
$$z = c_1 + ru$$

also are parametric equations of this line, the new parameter u indicating the signed distance from P to B_1. We can verify this fact by direct calculation, however, as follows. Since B_1 is a point of k, a parameter value s_1 exists such that

$$a_1 = a + ps_1, \ b_1 = b + qs_1, \ c_1 = c + rs_1.$$

Hence, in particular, $a_1 - a = ps_1$, and thus for an arbitrary point P with parameter value s, we have

$$x = a + ps$$
$$= a_1 + (a - a_1) + ps$$
$$= a_1 - ps_1 + ps$$
$$= a_1 + p(s - s_1).$$

The second and third equations of (6) take similar forms: thus, equations (6) are equivalent to the equations

$$x = a_1 + p(s - s_1)$$
$$y = b_1 + q(s - s_1)$$
$$z = c_1 + r(s - s_1),$$

and these reduce to (9) if we substitute u for $s - s_1$. All that remains to prove is that u in (9) is the signed distance between P and B_1. We might do this solely from the equality $u = s - s_1$, but we prefer the following method. For $u \neq 0$, equations (9) imply that

$$p = (x - a_1)/u, \ q = (y - b_1)/u, \ r = (z - c_1)/u,$$

and substitution into (4) proves that

$$((x - a_1)/u)^2 + ((y - b_1)/u)^2 + ((z - c_1)/u)^2 = 1.$$

Therefore,

$$u^2 = (x - a_1)^2 + (y - b_1)^2 + (z - c_1)^2,$$

and by (1)

$$|u| = d_{B_1 P}.$$

Since $u = s - s_1$, u is positive on one ray emanating from B_1 and negative on the other. Hence, u is the signed distance from B_1 to P, as
asserted. In conclusion, equations (9) represent the same line as do
equations (6) with u equal to the signed distance between B_1 and P,
as we had stated.

EXERCISE

8. Let k be the straight line represented in Exercise 7.
   (a) Let A_1 denote the point of k corresponding to $s = 1$. Then, for this
   choice of A_1, carry out the calculations necessary to put the parametric equations for k into the form (9).
   (b) Do the same when A_1 is the point of k corresponding to $s = -1$.

If we relax condition (4), equations (6) still may represent a
straight line, but s no longer is the signed distance from P to A. We
shall discuss this matter generally, but we shall first illustrate it in an
interesting special case. Given two points A and B with $A = (a,b,c)$
and $B = (e,f,g)$, we ask parametric equations for the line AB. Again
let d denote distance between A and an arbitrary point P of the line;
let d_{AB} denote the distance between A and B. Let $P = (x,y,z)$. We
know that if P is confined to either ray emanating from A of the line
AB, then the ratios

(10) $(x - a)/d, \ (y - b)/d, \ (z - c)/d$

have constant values. Moreover, if these values are denoted by
p, q, r, respectively, then the line AB has the parametric equations

(11)
$$\begin{aligned} x &= a + ps \\ y &= b + qs \\ z &= c + rs, \end{aligned}$$

in which s is the signed distance between A and P. When P coincides with B $(x = e, y = f, z = g)$, the ratios (10) have the values

$$(e - a)/d_{AB}, \quad (f - b)/d_{AB}, \quad (g - c)/d_{AB}$$

respectively. Hence, we can take

$$p = (e - a)/d_{AB}, \quad q = (f - b)/d_{AB}, \quad r = (g - c)/d_{AB}$$

in equations (11). We shall, however, slightly reform these equations, writing

$$\begin{aligned} ps &= ((e - a)/d_{AB}) \, s \\ &= (e - a) \, (s/d_{AB}) \\ &= Pt, \end{aligned}$$

where

$$P = e - a$$

and

$$t = s/d_{AB}.$$

Similar manipulations give us

$$qs = Qt, \quad rs = Rt,$$

where

$$Q = f - b, \quad R = g - c.$$

Thus, equations (11) are equivalent to

(12)
$$\begin{aligned} x &= a + Pt \\ y &= b + Qt \\ z &= c + Rt, \end{aligned}$$

where

$$\begin{aligned} P &= pd_{AB} = e - a \\ Q &= qd_{AB} = f - b \\ R &= rd_{AB} = g - c, \end{aligned}$$

and where $t = (1/d_{AB})s$. Because of the equivalence, equations (12) again are parametric equations for the line AB, but the parameter t is *proportional*, not ordinarily equal, to the signed distance from A to P. The new coefficients P, Q, R are the respective differences

$$e - a, f - b, g - c,$$

that were the numerators in the ratios defining p, q, r.

9. Find equations for the lines AB in Exercises 1, 3, 6.
10. Find parametric equations for the line passing through the origin and a given point (a,b,c).

This result suggests that we investigate how, in general, equations of the form

(13)
$$x = a + Pt$$
$$y = b + Qt$$
$$z = c + Rt$$

may represent a straight line *in the absence* of the condition $P^2 + Q^2 + R^2 = 1$ analogous to (4). We shall assume that a, b, c, P, Q, R are constants, t being the parameter. (Thus, t alone in the right members of (13) is permitted to vary, x, y, z on the left then varying accordingly.) We contend that equations (13) represent a straight line if, merely, P, Q, R are not all zero and that in this case the parameter t is proportional to the signed distance from (a,b,c) to (x,y,z). To prove this, we first note that

$$P^2 + Q^2 + R^2 \neq 0,$$

since P, Q, R are not all zero. Hence, the quantities

$$P/\sqrt{P^2 + Q^2 + R^2}, \; Q/\sqrt{P^2 + Q^2 + R^2}, \; R/\sqrt{P^2 + Q^2 + R^2},$$

having nonzero denominators, exist. Furthermore, the sum of the squares of these quantities is equal to 1. In fact, denoting these quantities by p, q, r, respectively, we have

$$p^2 + q^2 + r^2 = (P/\sqrt{P^2 + Q^2 + R^2})^2 + (Q/\sqrt{P^2 + Q^2 + R^2})^2$$
$$+ (R/\sqrt{P^2 + Q^2 + R^2})^2$$
$$= P^2/(P^2 + Q^2 + R^2) + Q^2/(P^2 + Q^2 + R^2)$$
$$+ R^2/(P^2 + Q^2 + R^2)$$
$$= (P^2 + Q^2 + R^2)/(P^2 + Q^2 + R^2)$$
$$= 1.$$

Thus, if we rewrite equations (13) as

$$x = a + Pt = a + (P/\sqrt{P^2 + Q^2 + R^2})\,(\sqrt{P^2 + Q^2 + R^2}\, t)$$
$$y = b + Qt = b + (Q/\sqrt{P^2 + Q^2 + R^2})\,(\sqrt{P^2 + Q^2 + R^2}\, t)$$
$$z = c + Rt = c + (R/\sqrt{P^2 + Q^2 + R^2})\,(\sqrt{P^2 + Q^2 + R^2}\, t),$$

the result is an equivalent system of equations of the form

(14)
$$x = a + ps$$
$$y = b + qs$$
$$z = c + rs,$$

in which $s = \sqrt{P^2 + Q^2 + R^2}\, t$ and $p^2 + q^2 + r^2 = 1$. Since equations (14) thus satisfy condition (4), they represent a straight line passing through (a,b,c), and s is the signed distance from (a,b,c) to (x,y,z). Equations (13) being equivalent to Equations (14) represent the same straight line with t proportional to s. (In fact, $t = s/\sqrt{P^2 + Q^2 + R^2}$.) Thus, our contention is proved.

EXERCISE

11. A line k has parametric equations:

$$x = 4t$$
$$y = -1 + 2t$$
$$z = 2 - 2t.$$

(a) Give parametric equations for k of the form

$$x = ps$$
$$y = -1 + qs$$
$$z = 2 + rs$$

with

$$p^2 + q^2 + r^2 = 1.$$

(b) If d denotes the distance of (x,y,z) from $(0,-1,2)$, express the parameter t in terms of d on each of the two rays of k that issue from $(0,-1,2)$.

(c) If D denotes the distance of (x,y,z) from $(4,1,0)$, express t in terms of D on each of the two rays of k that issue from $(4,1,0)$.

When do two sets of equations of the respective forms

(15a)
$$\begin{array}{l} x = a + ps \\ y = b + qs \\ z = c + rs \end{array} \quad \text{and} \quad (15b) \quad \begin{array}{l} x = a + Pt \\ y = b + Qt \\ z = c + Rt, \end{array}$$

with p, q, r not all zero (condition (4) is not assumed) and P, Q, R not all zero, represent the same straight line? The answer is: they do so if p, q, r are proportional to P, Q, R, respectively. This means that a nonzero constant u exists such that

(16) $p = uP,\ q = uQ,\ r = uR.$

In fact, if the proportionality condition is satisfied, equations (15a) become

$$x = a + Pus$$
$$y = b + Qus$$
$$z = c + Rus$$

and reduce to (15b) when us is replaced by t. When the proportionality condition is satisfied, therefore, equations (15a) and (15b) are equivalent and thus certainly represent the same line, as contended. Conversely, if equations (15a) and (15b) represent the same straight line, we assert that the proportionality conditions (16) are satisfied. Let (A,B,C) denote a point of the line other than (a,b,c). If the parameters s and t take the values u and v, respectively, at this point, we have $u \neq 0$, $v \neq 0$, and

$$A = a + pu \qquad A = a + Pv$$
$$B = b + qu \qquad B = b + Qv$$
$$C = c + ru \qquad C = c + Rv.$$

Hence,

$$pu = Pv$$
$$qu = Qv$$
$$ru = Rv.$$

Since u, in particular, is not zero,

$$p = (v/u)\,P$$
$$q = (v/u)Q$$
$$r = (v/u)\,R.$$

relations that are of the form (16) with u replaced by v/u, a nonzero constant since $v \neq 0$. Thus, the converse proposition is proved. Therefore, the proportionality conditions (16) are both necessary and sufficient conditions that both sets of equations (15a) and (15b) represent the same straight line.

This result and our comments after equation (7) justify the name of *direction numbers* for the triple

$$P, Q, R$$

in equations (13) and for any proportional triple, i.e., for

$$mP, mQ, mR$$

with $m \neq 0$. In the next section, it will appear, as we should expect, that lines with the same direction numbers are parallel and that parallel lines have the same direction numbers.

EXERCISES

12. Let k denote the line with the parametric equations:

$$x = 4t$$
$$y = -1 + 2t$$
$$z = 2 - 2t.$$

Prove that this line also has the parametric equations:

$$x = 4 + 2u$$
$$y = 1 + u$$
$$z = -u.$$

13. What geometrical object do equations (15a) represent when $p = 0$, $q = 0$, $r = 0$?

14. (a) Give parametric equations for the line passing through $(1,2,0)$ and $(4,5,0)$.

(b) What is true of all lines represented by equations of the form (15a) with $r = 0$? With $p = 0$? With $q = 0$?

(c) What is true of all lines represented by equations of the form (15a) with $p = q = 0$?

The principal results of this section may be summarized as follows:

(1) Any straight line in space can be represented by a set of parametric equations of the form

(17)
$$x = a + ps$$
$$y = b + qs$$
$$z = c + rs,$$

in which a, b, c, p, q, r are constants, the last three of which cannot all be zero, and s is a parameter. As s varies over all (positive, negative, and zero) numbers, the point (x,y,z) describes the line, each point of the line occurring for one and only one value of s and each value of s determining one and only one point of the line. The line passes through the point (a,b,c) in a direction determined by p, q, r. If (e,f,g) denotes any point of the line other than (a,b,c), the direction numbers p, q, r are proportional to the differences

$$e - a, f - b, g - c,$$

respectively. This means that we can take

(18)
$$p = m(e - a), q = m(f - b), r = m(g - c)$$

with any nonzero m. When m is so selected that $p^2 + q^2 + r^2 = 1$, the parameter s represents the signed distance from (a,b,c) to (x,y,z)

(s is positive on one side of (a,b,c) and negative on the other with absolute value equal to the distance). When m is not so selected, s is proportional to the signed distance from (a,b,c) to (x,y,z). If (A,B,C) is an arbitrary point of the line, the equations

$$x = A + pt$$
$$y = B + qt$$
$$z = C + rt$$

also represent the line parametrically, the parameter t being equal, or proportional to, the signed distance from (A,B,C) to (x,y,z).

(2) Let a, b, c, p, q, r denote constants the last three of which are not all zero. Let s denote a parameter, which is permitted to vary over all (positive, negative, and zero) numbers. Then, as s varies, the point (x,y,z) whose coordinates are defined in terms of s by the equations

$$x = a + ps$$
$$y = b + qs$$
$$z = c + rs$$

describes a straight line passing through the point (a,b,c) with direction numbers p, q, r.

Remark: Let (a,b,c) be any point other than the origin, and let l denote the line with the parametric equations:

(19)
$$x = a + ps$$
$$y = b + qs$$
$$z = c + rs.$$

If l passes through the origin, then a, b, c are proportional to p, q, r: more specifically, a constant h exists such that

(20)
$$a = hp, \; b = hq, \; c = hr.$$

Conversely, if condition (20) is satisfied with some constant h, then l passes through the origin. The first of these statements follows from the fact that, $(0,0,0)$ belonging to l, a value S exists such that

$$0 = a + pS, \; 0 = b + qS, \; 0 = c + rS;$$

hence, (20) holds with $h = -S$. The converse statement is obtained by substituting from (20) into (19) to obtain:

$$x = a + ps = hp + ps = p(h + s),$$
$$y = b + qs = hq + qs = q(h + s),$$
$$z = c + rs = hr + rs = r(h + s);$$

from this it is clear that $x = 0$, $y = 0$, $z = 0$ for $s = -h$; thus, $(0,0,0)$ lies on l in consequence of (20), as asserted.

We further remark that, p, q, r being not all zero, the proportionality condition (20) is equivalent to the system of equalities

(21) $$aq - bp = 0, \; ar - cp = 0, \; br - cq = 0.$$

Indeed, equations (20) tell us that $aq = hpq$, $ar = hpr$, $bp = hqp$, $cp = hrp$, $br = hqr$, $cq = hrq$; hence, equations (20) imply equations (21). It remains to be proved that when equations (21) are assumed, a constant h exists satisfying the three equations (20). Since p, q, r are not all zero, suppose, in particular, that $r \neq 0$. The second and third equations of (21) then show that

$$a = (c/r) \; p, \; b = (c/r) \; q.$$

In addition,
$$c = (c/r) \; r.$$

Hence, conditions (20) hold with $h = c/r$. While this result presupposed that $r \neq 0$, the supposition that $p \neq 0$ or that $q \neq 0$ would have produced a similar outcome. In any case, therefore, a constant h exists that satisfies (20), as asserted. Having already remarked that equations (20) imply equations (21), we conclude that these two systems of equations are equivalent, as previously contended.

It follows that if no constant h exists satisfying (20), then

(22) $$aq - bp \neq 0, \; \text{or} \; ar - cp \neq 0, \; \text{or} \; br - cq \neq 0.$$

Similarly, condition (22) implies that no constant h exists satisfying (20).

5.

Intersection, parallelism, and perpendicularity. The representation of planes.

How are geometrical relations among lines manifested algebraically? How, in particular, can we tell from the equations of lines whether they intersect, are perpendicular, are parallel, are skew? We shall answer these questions in this section. We shall see that the criterion for perpendicularity leads to an algebraic mode of representing planes.

a. THE INTERSECTIONS OF LINES

Let
(1a)
$$\begin{aligned} x &= a + ps \\ y &= b + qs \\ z &= c + rs \end{aligned}$$

(1b)
$$\begin{aligned} x &= e + Pt \\ y &= f + Qt \\ z &= g + Rt \end{aligned}$$

be sets of parametric equations for two straight lines, which we shall denote by k and l. The parameters in these sets of equations are s and t, respectively, $a, b, c, e, f, g, p, q, r, P, Q, R$ all being constants; p, q and r are not all to be zero; P, Q, and R are not all to be zero. The lines k and l intersect if and only if a point (X,Y,Z) exists common to both. For such a point, values u and v of the parameters s and t, respectively, exist such that

$$X = a + pu \qquad X = e + Pv$$
$$Y = b + qu \qquad Y = f + Qv$$
$$Z = c + ru \qquad Z = g + Rv$$

and thus that

$$(2) \qquad \begin{aligned} a + pu &= e + Pv \\ b + qu &= f + Qv \\ c + ru &= g + Rv. \end{aligned}$$

Therefore, if k and l intersect, numbers u and v exist that satisfy the three conditions (2). Conversely, if such numbers exist, then k and l intersect. In fact, the point

$$(a + pu, b + qu, c + ru)$$

occurs on k for $s = u$ (in equations (1a)) and occurs on l for $t = v$ (in equations (1b)), in view of the equalities (2); hence, this point is common to both lines, which, therefore, intersect. We conclude that k and l intersect if and only if two numbers u and v exist that together satisfy the three equalities (2).

It is worthwhile to see how this criterion works out when k and l belong to the xy-plane, in which case $c = g = r = R = 0$; we will write (x,y) in place of $(x,y,0)$. The third equation of (2) is of no interest in this case, but the remaining two equations lead to a simple condition necessary and sufficient in order that k and l shall intersect. To derive this condition, exclude for the moment the case in which at least one of the lines is parallel to, or coincides with, a coordinate axis. Thus, assume that k and l both intersect either the x-axis or the y-axis, say the former, but do not coincide with it. Under this assumption, $q \neq 0$ and $Q \neq 0$, since y varies on these lines as s and t vary. Since (a,b) is an arbitrary point of k (Section 4), we may take it as the point in which k intersects the x-axis, in which case $b = 0$. Similarly, we may take (e,f) as the intersection of l with the x-axis, so that $f = 0$. With these choices, conditions (2) become

$$(3) \qquad \begin{aligned} a + pu &= e + Pv \\ qu &= Qv. \end{aligned}$$

Since $Q \neq 0$, the second of these equations is equivalent to

$$(4a) \qquad v = qu/Q$$

and the first equation, under substitution for v, to

$$a + pu = e + Pqu/Q;$$

this is equivalent to

$$(p - Pq/Q)u = e - a$$

and thus to

(4b) $$(Qp - Pq)u = Q(e - a).$$

Since equations (4a) and (4b) are equivalent to equations (3), any point possessed in common by k and l determines a pair of numbers, u and v, satisfying equations (4a) and (4b); furthermore, every such pair of numbers is determined in this way by a point common to k and l. Equation (4b) has one and only one solution if

$$pQ - Pq \neq 0,$$

this solution u leading at once to a corresponding v such that equation (4a) also holds. Hence, k and l have one and only one point of intersection if $pQ - Pq \neq 0$. If, to the contrary,

$$pQ - Pq = 0,$$

then equation (4b) is satisfied by no value of u, and k and l thus do not meet, unless

$$e - a = 0.$$

If, finally,

$$pQ - Pq = 0 \text{ and } e - a = 0,$$

then equation (4b) is satisfied for all values of u, each value determining a value of v for which equation (4a) also is satisfied. In this case, k and l have more than one point in common and, hence, coincide. (Note also that the equations for k—the first two equations of (1a)— reduce to

$$x = a + ps = e + mPs,$$
$$y = b + qs = f + mQs,$$

where $m = q/Q$. These reduce further to the first two equations of (1b) if we set $t = ms$, and thus are equivalent to the equations for l. For this equivalence, see also Section 4.) In summary, we conclude: if $pQ - Pq \neq 0$, then k and l intersect (in only one point); if $pQ - Pq = 0$, then k and l coincide or are parallel.

This conclusion was arrived at on the supposition that both k and l

intersect the x-axis, neither coinciding with this axis. The conclusion is true in general, however, as we now see by considering the other possibilities, which are as follows:

(i) both k and l intersect the y-axis (and not the x-axis);
(ii) k intersects only one coordinate axis, and l intersects only the other.

In case (i), exactly the same kind of reasoning as that used before will justify the same conclusion. In case (ii), k and l are parallel to (or coincident with) the coordinate axes, respectively, and we can assume for definiteness that k is parallel to (or coincident with) the x-axis, l parallel to (or coincident with) the y-axis. Since horizontal lines have the equations

$$y = \text{constant}$$

and vertical lines the equations

$$x = \text{constant},$$

we see that $p = 0$, $q \neq 0$, $P \neq 0$, $Q = 0$. Therefore, $pQ - Pq \neq 0$, while k and l of course intersect, and again the criterion fits. Thus, the criterion stated at the end of the last paragraph for the intersection or parallelism of two lines in the plane is true without exception.

We shall now show that parallel lines in the xy-plane have the same direction numbers. If k and l, in particular, are parallel, we thus shall show that they have the same parametric equations

(5) $$\begin{aligned} x &= a + ps \\ y &= b + qs \end{aligned} \quad \text{and} \quad \begin{aligned} x &= e + pS \\ y &= f + qS, \end{aligned}$$

respectively, s and S denoting the respective parameters. The parametric equations given for these lines were:

(6) $$\begin{aligned} x &= a + ps \\ y &= b + qs \end{aligned} \quad \text{and} \quad \begin{aligned} x &= e + Pt \\ y &= f + Qt, \end{aligned}$$

respectively, both lines also satisfying the third condition $z = 0$. Since the lines are assumed here to be parallel, we have

(7) $$pQ - Pq = 0.$$

In case k and l are parallel to the x-axis, we have $q = Q = 0$, equations (6) thus reducing to

$$\begin{aligned} x &= a + ps \\ y &= b \end{aligned} \quad \text{and} \quad \begin{aligned} x &= e + Pt \\ y &= f, \end{aligned}$$

respectively. Since p and q cannot both be zero,

$$p \neq 0$$

(similarly, $P \neq 0$). Hence,

$$Pt = p((P/p)t),$$

and if we introduce a new quantity S, related to t, by the definition

$$S = (P/p)t,$$

we have

$$Pt = pS.$$

The parametric equations for l (the second pair in (6)) thus become

$$
\begin{aligned}
x &= e + pS \\
y &= f.
\end{aligned}
$$
(8)

Through equations (8), each value of S determines a point (x,y) of l, and each point of l is determined by an appropriate value of S. Hence, S is a parameter for l as good as t. Furthermore, equations (8) are of the form indicated in (5). Thus, the case in which k and l are parallel to the x-axis is complete.

The case in which k and l are parallel to the y-axis is handled in an exactly similar way.

The case in which k and l are parallel to neither axis remains. In this case p, P, q, Q are all nonzero. Hence, (7) is equivalent, in particular, to the relation

$$P = (Q/q)p,$$

and we have

$$Pt = p((Q/q)t).$$

Here we introduce S by the definition

$$S = (Q/q)t$$

and thus have

$$Pt = pS, \; Qt = qS,$$

the parametric equations for l becoming

$$
\begin{aligned}
x &= e + pS \\
y &= f + qS.
\end{aligned}
$$
(9)

Through equations (9), each value of S determines a point (x,y) of l, and each point of l is determined by an appropriate value of S. Hence,

S is a parameter for l, and equations (9) in this case are parametric equations for l. They are of the form required in (5). This form is thus justified in every case, as asserted.

It does not matter what symbol we use to denote a parameter. Hence, forgetting or discarding our original usage of t, we can just as well use this symbol (or any other) in place of S in (9). If we replace S by t, these equations become:

$$x = e + pt$$
$$y = f + qt.$$

Remark: Suppose two parallel lines intersect the x-axis in the plane (Figure 9-35), and let a and e denote the abscissas of the respective intersections. Let x and X be the abscissas of intersection of the two lines, respectively, with an arbitrary horizontal line. Plane geometry tell us that the horizontal distance between the two lines is the same at every ordinate and thus that

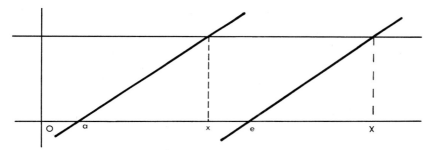

FIGURE 9-35   *Parallel lines intersecting parallels to the x-axis.*

$$|X - x| = |e - a|.$$

We shall require, however, the more informative equality

$$X - x = e - a.$$

This is easily obtained from the parametric equations for the two lines, which, according to the foregoing, can be taken as

$$x = a + ps \qquad \qquad x = e + pt$$
$$y = \quad qs \qquad \text{and} \qquad y = \quad qt,$$

respectively, with $q \neq 0$. For points on these lines with the same ordinate, the parameters s and t satisfy the condition

$$qs = qt;$$

hence, for these points,

$$s = t.$$

Thus,

$$x = a + ps, \ X = e + ps.$$

and $X - x = e - a$, as asserted.

EXERCISES

1. Find the intersection of the two lines represented parametrically as

$$
\begin{aligned}
x &= s \\
y &= 2s \\
z &= 3s
\end{aligned}
\quad \text{and} \quad
\begin{aligned}
x &= -1 + 2t \\
y &= 1 + t \\
z &= 2 + t.
\end{aligned}
$$

2. Relate condition (3) of Section 6, Chapter 8 to the foregoing criterion that two lines in the plane be parallel.

b. PARALLEL LINES IN SPACE

We have shown that two lines in the plane coincide or are parallel if and only if they have the same direction numbers. A similar criterion is true in space. First we shall prove that any two parallel lines in space have the same direction numbers. Purely algebraic methods could be used, but at this stage we prefer a geometrical approach and shall rely on the following geometrical lemma.†

Geometrical Lemma. Let two pairs of intersecting lines be given, each line of one pair being parallel to a line of the other. Then the angles made by the intersecting lines are equal.

PROOF: Let k, l and m, n be two pairs of parallel lines; let k and m intersect at A, l and n intersect at B (Figure 9-36). Denote the smaller angle between k and m by $\angle A$, the smaller angle between l and n by $\angle B$. We are to show that $\angle A = \angle B$. Let F denote the plane of k and l, and let G denote the plane of m and n. If F and G coincide,

---

†A "lemma" is a helping theorem.

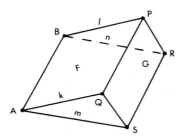

FIGURE 9-36   A diagram for a geometrical lemma.

the four lines are in one plane, and the contention is evident from plane geometry. Therefore, consider the case in which F and G are different planes. Let $ABPQ$ be a parallelogram in F and $ABRS$ a parallelogram in G such that $\angle A = \angle QAS$ and $\angle B = \angle PBR$. Since $PQ = AB$ and $AB = RS$, we have $PQ = RS$; since PQ is parallel to AB, and AB is parallel to RS, we infer that PQ is parallel to RS (Assertion (11), Section 2). Therefore, $PQSR$ is a parallelogram, and we have, in particular, that $PR = QS$. Furthermore, $BP = AQ$ and $BR = AS$, both equalities by construction. Hence, $\triangle PBR \cong \triangle QAS$, from which congruence we conclude that $\angle PBR = \angle QAS$, as contended.

We are now ready to prove our assertion that any two parallel lines have the same direction numbers. Denote the lines by k and l. They must intersect (neither lying within) at least one of the coordinate planes, and we shall suppose, to be definite, that they intersect the xy-plane; let A then denote the intersection of k with the xy-plane, and let B denote the intersection of l with the xy-plane. Suppose $A = (a,b,0)$ and $B = (e,f,0)$ Let P be a point of l and Q a point of k such that $ABPQ$ is a parallelogram (Figure 9-37). Let m and n denote the lines through A and B, respectively, that are parallel to

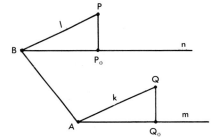

FIGURE 9-37 *Parallel lines intersecting the xy-plane and their perpendicular projections upon lines through the intersections parallel to (or coincident with) the x-axis.*

(or, possibly, coincident with) the x-axis, let P_0 be the perpendicular projection of P upon n and Q_0 the perpendicular projection of Q upon m. Thus, if $P = (U,V,W)$ and $Q = (u,v,w)$ we have $P_0 = (U,f,0)$ and $Q_0 = (u,b,0)$. Furthermore, $\angle PP_0B$ and $\angle QQ_0A$ are right angles. The lemma tells us that $\angle PBP_0 = \angle QAQ_0$, while $BP = AQ$ by construction. Therefore, $\triangle BPP_0 \cong \triangle AQQ_0$, and we have, in particular, $AQ_0 = BP_0$. Since AQ_0 and BP_0 are parallel (by construction), it follows that ABP_0Q_0 is a parallelogram. Consequently, AB is parallel to Q_0P_0, and the remark at the end of Subsection 5a (where we proved that if two parallel lines in the xy-plane intersect the x-axis, then at every ordinate the difference between their abscissas is the same) shows that the difference between the x-coordinates of B and P_0 is equal to the difference between the x-coordinates of A and Q_0:

$$U - e = u - a.$$

Similarly,

$$V - f = v - b$$

and, the z-coordinates of A and B being zero,

$$W = w.$$

But the differences between the corresponding coordinates of two arbitrary points on a line determine the direction numbers of the line (Section 4). We see by comparing A and Q that

$$u - a, \; v - b, \; w$$

are direction numbers for k and by comparing B and P that

$$U - e, \; V - f, \; W$$

are direction numbers for l. The previous equalities show these pairs of direction numbers to be identical, which is what we had desired to prove.

We shall now prove, conversely, that two lines with the same direction numbers must coincide or be parallel. Let k and l denote any two lines with common direction numbers, which we denote by

$$p, \; q, \; r.$$

Then k and l are represented by parametric equations of the forms

$$
\begin{array}{lll}
& x = a + ps & \qquad\qquad x = e + pt \\
(10a) & y = b + qs \quad \text{and} \quad (10b) & y = f + qt \\
& z = c + rs & \qquad\qquad z = g + rt,
\end{array}
$$

in which s and t are the respective parameters, (a,b,c) is an arbitrary point of k, and (e,f,g) is an arbitrary point of l. Not all the direction numbers can be zero; thus, we can assume for definiteness that

$$r \neq 0.$$

On this assumption, equations (10a) and (10b) show that k and l both pierce the xy-plane. (In fact, the z-coordinate is zero on k when $c + rs = 0$, i.e., when $s = -c/r$, and only then, and is zero on l when $g + rt = 0$ and only then.) Letting A and B denote the respective intersections of k and l with the xy-plane, now demand that (a,b,c) represent A and that (e,f,g) represent B (Section 4). Under these requirements, we have

$$c = 0, \; g = 0.$$

If k and l have a common point, let it occur for the values u and v of the parameters, i.e., let $s = u$ specify the point on k and $t = v$

specify it on l. If (X,Y,Z) denotes the common point, we thus have

$$
\begin{array}{ll}
X = a + pu & X = e + pv \\
Y = b + qu & Y = f + qv \\
Z = \quad ru & Z = \quad rv
\end{array}
$$

(recall $c = g = 0$) and, therefore,

$$
\begin{aligned}
a + pu &= e + pv \\
b + qu &= f + qv \\
ru &= \quad rv.
\end{aligned}
$$

Since $r \neq 0$, we infer from the last equation that $u = v$. The previous two equations show, when u now is substituted for v, that

$$
\begin{aligned}
a &= e \\
b &= f
\end{aligned}
$$

and thus that equations (10a) and (10b) are identical (except that different symbols are used for the two parameters). Hence, k and l coincide. We have proved that if k and l meet at all, they coincide.

Suppose, then, that k and l do not intersect. We shall show that they are in the same plane and, thus, are parallel. Recall that k passes through the point $(a,b,0)$, which we have also denoted by A, and l through the point $(e,f,0)$, which was denoted by B. In equations (10a) and (10b) (with $c = g = 0$), A corresponds to $s = 0$ and B to $t = 0$. Let C denote the point of k corresponding to $s = 1$; thus, $C = (a + p, b + q, r)$. Let D denote the point of l corresponding to $t = 1$: thus, $D = (e + p, f + q, r)$ (Figure 9-38). We shall prove that the lines BC and AD intersect, both k and l then lying in their common plane.

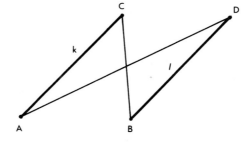

FIGURE 9-38 *Two supposedly parallel segments with their ends connected.*

The property of intersection can be established from parametric equations of the lines in question (Section 5a). We have seen how to formulate parametric equations for any line when we know two of its points (Section 4). Knowing $A = (a,b,0)$ and $D = (e + p, f + q, r)$, for instance, we deduce that AD has the direction numbers

$$
e + p - a,\ f + q - b,\ r
$$

and thus has the parametric equations

$$x = a + (e + p - a)u$$
$$y = b + (f + q - b)u$$
$$z = \qquad\qquad ru,$$

in which u represents the parameter. Similarly, BC has the parametric equations

$$x = e + (a + p - e)v$$
$$y = f + (b + q - f)v$$
$$z = \qquad\qquad rv,$$

in which v is the parameter. As we have already noted (Section 5a), the lines BC and AD have a common point (X, Y, Z) if and only if values U and V of the parameters u and v, respectively, exist such that

$X = a + (e + p - a)U$	$X = e + (a + p - e)V$
$Y = b + (f + q - b)U$	$Y = f + (b + q - f)V$
$Z = \qquad\quad rU$	$Z = \qquad\quad rV.$

Thus (Section 5a), BC and AD intersect if and only if values U and V exist such that

$$a + (e + p - a)U = e + (a + p - e)V$$
(11) $$b + (f + q - b)U = f + (b + q - f)V$$
$$rU = \qquad\qquad rV.$$

Such values, namely

$$U = 1/2, \; V = 1/2,$$

do exist. Therefore, BC and AD intersect, as contended.

While easily verifying these values of U and V, the reader may still wonder how they are known. They might have been found from the following reasoning. The third equation of (11) tells us that

$$U = V,$$

since $r \neq 0$. Now substituting U for V in the previous two equations gives after obvious cancellations:

$$a + (e - a)U = e + (a - e)U$$
$$b + (f - b)U = f + (b - f)U.$$

These equalities can be rewritten as

$$(a - e)(1 - 2U) = 0$$
$$(b - f)(1 - 2U) = 0,$$

which certainly are both satisfied by the value $U = 1/2$. Furthermore, the equations require $U = 1/2$, for otherwise $1 - 2U \neq 0$, and the equations imply that $a - e = 0$ and $b - f = 0$. These conditions mean that A and B coincide, while we had assumed explicitly that k and l do not meet. The contradiction is avoided only if $U = 1/2$.) We conclude that equations (11) are satisfied for $U = 1/2$ and $V = 1/2$, as remarked.

The contention stated at the beginning of this subsection is now fully proved. It is that two lines (in space) coincide or are parallel if and only if they have the same direction numbers.

EXERCISES

1. Which of the following pairs of lines are in the same plane?

(a)
$$\begin{matrix} x = s \\ y = s \\ z = s \end{matrix} \quad \text{and} \quad \begin{matrix} x = 1 \\ y = t \\ z = 0 \end{matrix}$$

(b)
$$\begin{matrix} x = -s \\ y = 1 + s \\ z = 2 + 2s \end{matrix} \quad \text{and} \quad \begin{matrix} x = 5 - 2t \\ y = 1 + 2t \\ z = 4t \end{matrix}$$

(c)
$$\begin{matrix} x = 2 - 3s \\ y = 3 + 2s \\ z = 1 - s \end{matrix} \quad \text{and} \quad \begin{matrix} x = t \\ y = (1/3)(13 - 2t) \\ z = (1/3)(1 + t) \end{matrix}$$

(d)
$$\begin{matrix} x = 2 - 3s \\ y = 3 + 2s \\ z = 1 - s \end{matrix} \quad \text{and} \quad \begin{matrix} x = t \\ y = 3 - 2t \\ z = 1 + t. \end{matrix}$$

2. Find a value g such that the two following lines will be in the same plane:

$$\begin{matrix} x = -2 + s \\ y = 4 - s \\ z = 1 + 2s \end{matrix} \quad \text{and} \quad \begin{matrix} x = -t \\ y = 4 - t \\ z = g - t. \end{matrix}$$

C. PERPENDICULARITY. PLANES.

Suppose two lines, which we shall denote by k and l, intersect at a point A. Let

$$p, q, r$$

be direction numbers for k and

$$P, Q, R$$

direction numbers for l. We shall show that k and l are perpendicular if and only if

(12) $$pP + qQ + rR = 0.$$

This criterion generalizes the algebraic criterion given in the plane case (condition (13), Section 6, Chapter 8).

Our simple proof of this criterion is adapted from E. Artin.[†] It is based on the distance formula (Section 3) and the following elementary geometrical proposition: If k and l are noncoincident lines intersecting at A, let B and C denote two points of k other than A such that $BA = AC$ (Figure 9-39). Let D denote any point of l other than A. Then k and l are perpendicular if and only if $BD = CD$.

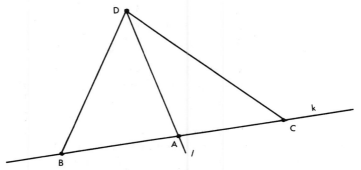

FIGURE 9-39 A geometrical criterion for perpendicularity.

Our aim is to prove that Artin's condition, $BD = CD$, is logically equivalent to (12). To do so, we must first describe the points in question by their coordinates; this requires algebraic representations of the two lines. Let $A = (a,b,c)$. Since k and l both pass through A, the first with direction numbers p, q, r and the second with direction numbers P, Q, R, these lines are represented by the two sets of parametric equations

(13a)
$$\begin{aligned} x &= a + ps \\ y &= b + qs \\ z &= c + rs \end{aligned}$$
(parametric equations for k),

(13b)
$$\begin{aligned} x &= a + Pt \\ y &= b + Qt \\ z &= c + Rt \end{aligned}$$
(parametric equations for l),

[†] E. Artin, *A Freshman Honors Course in Calculus and Analytic Geometry Taught at Princeton University.* Prepared under the auspices of the Committee on the Undergraduate Program, Mathematical Association of America, 518 Cabell Hall, University of Virginia, Charlottesville, Virginia, 1957, pp. 13-14.

respectively, s and t denoting the respective parameters. Recall that the parameter in either of these systems of equations is proportional to the signed distance from A (Section 4). Hence, in particular, the points of k determined by $s=1$ and $s=-1$ are equally distant from A. Taking these points as B and C, we thus have

$$B = (a + p, b + q, c + r)$$
$$C = (a - p, b - q, c - r).$$

Select as D the point of l for which $t = 1$. Thus,

$$D = (a + P, b + Q, c + R).$$

By the distance formula,

$$
\begin{aligned}
(BD)^2 &= [(a + P) - (a + p)]^2 + [(b + Q) - (b + q)]^2 \\
&\qquad + [(c + R) - (c + r)]^2 \\
&= (P - p)^2 + (Q - q)^2 + (R - r)^2 \\
&= P^2 - 2pP + p^2 + Q^2 - 2qQ + q^2 + R^2 - 2rR + r^2
\end{aligned}
$$

and

$$
\begin{aligned}
(CD)^2 &= [(a + P) - (a - p)]^2 + [(b + Q) - (b - q)]^2 \\
&\qquad + [(c + R) - (c - r)]^2 \\
&= (P + p)^2 + (Q + q)^2 + (R + r)^2 \\
&= P^2 + 2pP + p^2 + Q^2 + 2qQ + q^2 + R^2 + 2rR + r^2.
\end{aligned}
$$

The condition $BD = CD$ thus is equivalent to

$$
\begin{aligned}
P^2 - 2pP &+ p^2 + Q^2 - 2qQ + q^2 + R^2 - 2rR + r^2 \\
&= P^2 + 2pP + p^2 + Q^2 + 2qQ + q^2 + R^2 + 2rR + r^2.
\end{aligned}
$$

All squares in this equation cancel, and moving the other terms to the right member gives, after combining,

$$
\begin{aligned}
0 &= 4pP + 4qQ + 4rR \\
&= 4(pP + qQ + rR).
\end{aligned}
$$

This equation being equivalent to (12), this criterion is proved.

As previously remarked, criterion (12) gives us an algebraic mode of representing planes. Let F denote any plane and A an arbitrary point upon it; let $A = (a,b,c)$. One and only one line l is perpendicular to F at A (Assertion (14), Section 2), and all lines perpendicular to l at A lie in F (Assertion (13), Section 2). Let

$$p, q, r$$

be direction numbers for l. If P is an arbitrary point with $P = (x,y,z)$, the line AP (Figure 9-40) has the direction numbers

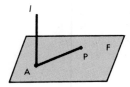

FIGURE 9-40 A perpendicular to a plane intersecting a line in the plane.

$$x - a, \, y - b, \, z - c$$

(Section 4). By criterion (12), l is perpendicular to AP if and only if

(14) $$p(x - a) + q(y - b) + r(z - c) = 0.$$

Hence, condition (14) is satisfied when P is a point of F and is not satisfied when P is not a point of F. Condition (14), therefore, is an equation for F.

We have proved that any plane has an equation of the form (14) in which a, b, c, p, q, r are constants such that (a,b,c) is a point of the plane, and p, q, r do not all vanish; in fact, p, q, r are direction numbers for the lines that are perpendicular to the plane. The following converse to this result also is true: if a, b, c, p, q, r are any constants such that p, q, r are not all zero, then a plane exists with the equation (14). This plane is that which passes through the point (a,b,c) and is perpendicular to all lines with the direction numbers p, q, r.

EXERCISES

1. What is the equation of the plane passing through the origin perpendicular to the line:

$$x = s$$
$$y = s$$
$$z = s?$$

2. What is the equation of the plane passing through the origin perpendicular to the line:

$$x = 1 + s$$
$$y = -2 + s$$
$$z = s?$$

3. Find a point on the plane with the equation: $x + y + z = 1$. With (a,b,c) representing this point, write the equation of the plane in the form (14). HINT: Any point (x,y,z) satisfying the condition $x + y + z = 1$ is a point of the indicated plane.

4. Find the intersection of the plane

$$x + y + z = 0$$

with the straight line

$$x = 1 + s$$
$$y = 2 - s$$
$$z = 2s \quad .$$

HINT: If a point of intersection exists, it corresponds to a value of s that can be determined by substituting $1 + s$ for x, $2 - s$ for y, and $2s$ for z in the equation of the plane.

5. Find the intersection of the line in Exercise 4 with the sphere

$$x^2 + y^2 + z^2 = 9$$

(see the end of Section 3).

6.

Perspective in drawing and painting

Algebra permeates geometry today, and geometrical insights have revolutionized algebra, the interaction between the two fields having been a spreading wave in the ocean of modern mathematics and its applications. The craft in which we voyage is too slight to ride the crest of this wave, but it can afford us an engaging cruise within a convenient sheltered bay. Such a bay is the art of painting, the cruise we propose a short study of perspective.

Reality often is distorted in its appearance. A tiny hill close at hand seems to tower over vast mountains in the distance. A broad stream extending to the horizon seems to taper to a point. Colors bright at close range appear less brilliant when viewed from afar, contrasts are weaker, and light and shadow are less clear-cut. Experience teaches us to judge distances from such distortions and thus to perceive depth, or three-dimensionality. Consciousness of depth is accentuated when objects in the foreground stand in the way of those behind. Sensations of roundness or solidity may be enhanced by the play of light and shadow. All the effects contributing to our awareness of depth may be heightened by binocular (two-eyed) vision, our two eyes, viewing from slightly different places, receiving slightly different impressions of a scene. These, fused in the mind, make our sensations of depth and distance particularly vivid at close range.

A depiction of a scene upon a flat surface can be realistic only if it conveys the illusion of three-dimensionality. This illusion is called perspective. The ambition to achieve it by accurately imitating the distortions and other effects that underlie our natural perceptions of depth, solidity, and roundness fired artists of the 14th, 15th, and 16th

Centuries. They did not, however, master the geometrical elements of perspective, the influence of distance from the observer upon apparent sizes, proportions, and directions, until they approached the question mathematically. It was prudent in this mathematical study to ignore the effects of binocular vision, these being inappreciable at large distances, rarely (as we are aware from countless photographs) fully essential to perspective, and difficult to treat mathematically. The artist mathematicians in any case limited themselves to the following question: how can a painting be made to convey the same impression to a *monocular* (one-eyed) observer as would the scene? Ultimately, they answered this question in its geometrical aspects with a system of rules that reduced perspective almost to a mechanical art, immensely simplifying the task of drawing an observed or imagined scene. The rules were outcomes of the following approach: Suppose a transparent, flat screen to be interposed between the observer and the scene he views. Denote the position of the observer's eye by O. (As noted before, the observer's second eye is disregarded.) If P is any point of the scene, let P' denote the intersection with the screen of the straight line OP (Figure 9-41). Since light travels in straight

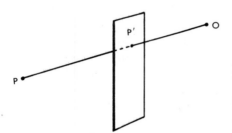

FIGURE 9-41   A point projected upon a screen.

lines, the observer's gaze penetrates the screen at P' when he looks at P. We shall refer to P' as the *image* of P on the screen and also as the *projection* of P upon the screen through the *viewing point O*. As P describes any figure — a line or a curve, such as the outline of a house, or several parallel lines — the projection of P upon the screen also describes a figure, which we shall call the *projection* upon the screen of the original. The projection makes exactly the same impression upon the eye, viewing from O, as does the original figure. Hence, the projection realistically depicts upon the screen the original figure as viewed from O: an artist with his eye placed at O, drawing the scene upon the screen as a canvas, would realistically represent the original figure by its projection upon this screen. The problem of perspective in its geometrical aspects is thus reduced to that of finding the projections of figures upon a fixed plane (the screen) through a fixed point O.

The simplest figures are straight lines. Next are families of parallel lines, such as may occur as the two sides of a road, the banks of a stream, tree trunks in a forest, parallel ditches, furrows, roof edges,

the intersections of walls with ceiling and floor, moldings, edges and
crevices between beams, and lines occurring in tile patterns. Such
parallel lines occurring in a scene often are essential to the composition of a picture, but even in scenes poor in this resource, knowledge
of perspective for parallel lines can be useful. If, for instance, a
rectangular grid is placed—or imagined—as an overlay upon a horizontal plane in the original scene, the artist may be guided by a correct
projection of this grid upon the screen. We illustrate by drawing a
circle and a circular cylinder in correct perspective. Figure 9-42A
shows a circle overlaid by a square grid—squares formed by equally
spaced vertical and horizontal lines—viewed from a point directly
above the center of the circle. To draw the circle in correct perspective from a different viewing point, it is helpful to know how the grid
projects through O upon the screen. This is indicated for a vertical
screen in Figure 9-42B, in which the image of each grid square is
apparent. Seeing how a small grid square projects upon the screen
indicates approximately how a piece of the circle within the square
projects. Thus, we are greatly aided in drawing the circle as viewed
from O by knowing exactly how the overlying grid should be drawn.
Figure 9-42C shows the result, obtained in this case by interpolating
a smooth curve between the images on the projected grid (Figure
9-42B) of closely spaced, selected points marked on the original circle
(Figure 9-42A). In Figure 9-42D, the perspective effect is enhanced
by shading.

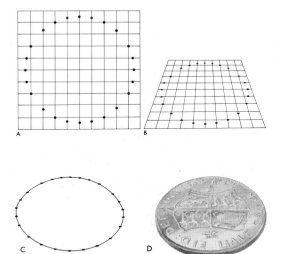

FIGURE 9-42 *A, A circle overlaid by a square grid.
Certain points of the circle
are marked. B, Projection of
the grid in Figure 9-42A with
approximate projections of
the marked points. C, Ap-
proximate projection of the
circle in Figure 9-42A obtained by drawing a smooth
curve through the points indicated in Figure 9-42B. D,
A horizontal circle drawn in
perspective and shaded.*

As a further example of the use of a grid, consider the problem of
drawing a cylindrical object in perspective. The top and the bottom
of the cylinder are circles, each of which can be drawn correctly by
means of appropriate grids by the preceding method. Vertical lines
joining corresponding points of the vertically separated circles

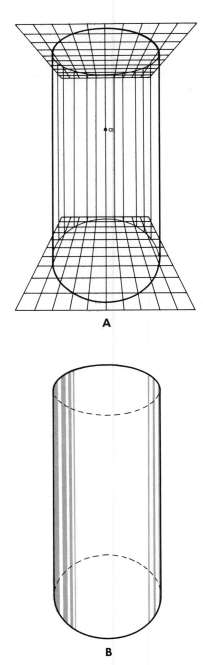

A

B

FIGURE 9-43   A, Projections of grids overlying top and base of circular cylinder.
a is the vanishing point of lines perpendicular to the screen; horizontal lines making an
angle of 45° with these have the vanishing point b or c. B, Cylinder with shading.

indicate the body of the cylinder (Figure 9-43A), and shading finally
accentuates its fullness (Figure 9-43B).

Now we shall see how correct grid projections are to be obtained.
(See, in particular, Exercises 5, 6, 7.)

We often refer to the screen as a *canvas*, to the plane of the screen
or canvas as the *picture plane*, to the projection of a figure upon the
screen as the *image*, or the *picture*, of the figure, and to O as the
viewing point. If a line *l* is parallel to the picture plane, its image *m*
is parallel to *l* (Figure 9-44). (But the line that is parallel to the picture

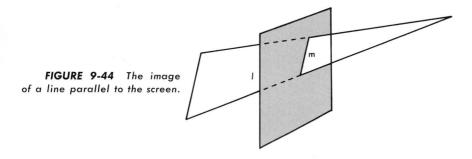

FIGURE 9-44   The image
of a line parallel to the screen.

plane and also passes through O does not have any image.) What is
the image of a line not parallel to the picture plane? If the line passes
through O, its image is a single point. In any case, the part of the line
extending behind the observer, out of the scene being depicted, is of
no interest. Hence, we rather ask this: if a line is not parallel to the
picture plane and does not pass through O, what is the image of one of
its rays contained within the scene? Let A denote the point at which
such a ray originates and A' the image of A. We shall see that the image
of the ray is a finite line segment A'B' (Figure 9-45), where B' is not
the image of a point on the ray but has the following property: as a
point P travels away from A along the ray, its image P' moves towards
B' along the straight line A'B'; P' never quite reaches B', but approaches B' more and more closely as P travels on and on away from
A. The image of an object attached to P dwindles, eventually seeming
practically to disappear, as P thus continues to recede along the ray.
For this reason, B' is called the *vanishing point* for the ray. This
vanishing point is the point the artist, standing at O, sees when looking at the canvas in the direction of the ray. Parallel rays have the same
vanishing point.

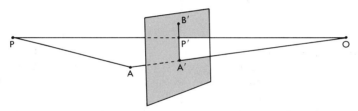

FIGURE 9-45   The image of a ray.

The last statement is one of the most important rules in drawing. Hence, we pause to illustrate it in a sketch (Figure 9-46), in which two

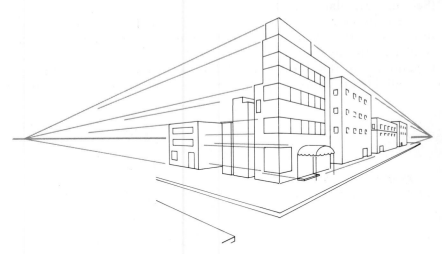

FIGURE 9-46   *A drawing in perspective.*

families of parallel lines are manifest, segments of these lines occurring as edges of roads, sidewalks, roofs, window frames, and so forth. The vanishing points for the two families of lines are the points to which the lines of the families converge. A second figure (Figure 9-47) shows in the case of a cube how the location of the vanishing point declares the viewing point of the observer.

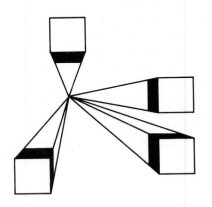

FIGURE 9-47   *Drawing of cubes with different relations to a vanishing point.*

The theory of perspective can be developed very simply with the aid of coordinate geometry. (This tool was of course unavailable prior to the 17th Century; the mathematician artists of the Renaissance had had only Euclidean methods in addition to the strings and sighting devices with which some of them had experimented.) Introduce a

Cartesian frame with the origin at the artist's eye and with the x-axis perpendicular to the screen. The x-axis then intersects the screen in a point we may represent as $(X_0,0,0)$ with $X_0 \neq 0$; take the positive direction of the x-axis such that $X_0 > 0$. If (x,y,z) denotes any point of the screen, we have

$$(1) \qquad\qquad x = X_0.$$

Conversely, any point (x,y,z) belongs to the screen if $x = X_0$. Hence, equation (1) is the equation of the screen.

To justify our statements concerning perspective, we must first find the image on the screen of an arbitrary line in space. Such a line, which we shall denote by l, has equations of the form

$$(2) \qquad\qquad \begin{aligned} x &= a + ps \\ y &= b + qs \\ z &= c + rs, \end{aligned}$$

in terms of a parameter s, (a,b,c) being an arbitrary point of l and p, q, r direction numbers. The first of equations (2) shows that if $p \neq 0$ the line penetrates the screen ($x = X_0$ occurring for the value $s = (X_0 - a)/p$) and that if $p = 0$ the line either is in the screen (in which case $a = X_0$) or is parallel to the screen (in which case $a \neq X_0$). The vanishing or nonvanishing of p will later have to be taken into account.

Let P denote an arbitrary point of l behind the screen (see Figure 9-45). If $P = (u,v,w)$, a value h of the parameter on l exists such that

$$(3) \qquad\qquad \begin{aligned} u &= a + ph \\ v &= b + qh \\ w &= c + rh. \end{aligned}$$

Since P is behind the screen, $u > X_0$, and, therefore, in particular, $u > 0$. Let P' denote the image of P, i.e., the intersection of OP with the screen. Since P' thus is a point of the screen, by condition (1) its first coordinate is X_0, and we can write

$$P' = (X_0,V,W)$$

with V and W still to be determined. We shall find V and W by use of equations for OP, which we write as

$$(4) \qquad\qquad \begin{aligned} x &= tu \\ y &= tv \\ z &= tw \end{aligned}$$

in terms of a parameter t having the value 0 at the point $(0,0,0)$ and the value 1 at the point P (Section 4). Denoting by T the value of t at P', we have from these equations

(5)
$$\begin{aligned} X_0 &= Tu \\ V &= Tv \\ W &= Tw, \end{aligned}$$

since $x = X_0$, $y = V$, $z = W$ at P'. The first equation of (5) shows that

$$T = X_0/u$$

and the second and third equations of (5) that

$$V = Tv = X_0 v/u, \quad W = Tw = X_0 w/u.$$

Substitution for u, v, w from (3) gives now

(6)
$$\begin{aligned} V &= X_0 v/u = X_0(b + qh)/(a + ph) \\ W &= X_0 w/u = X_0(c + rh)/(a + ph). \end{aligned}$$

Equations (6) indicate the y- and z-coordinates of P' in terms of the value h of the parameter for l at P. These equations thus say algebraically exactly how P' depends upon P when P is restricted to l.

Euclidean geometry informs us that the projection of a straight line is again a straight line and thus that, as P describes l, P' describes a straight line upon the screen. Hence, equations (6), despite their strange form, are equations for a straight line, which (V,W) describes as h varies.

We must now distinguish two cases, the first being that in which $p = 0$, l therefore being within or parallel to the screen. Then $a > 0$ (by the first equation of (3) and our assumption that $u > 0$), and equations (6) reduce to

(7)
$$\begin{aligned} V &= X_0 b/a + (X_0 q/a)h \\ W &= X_0 c/a + (X_0 r/a)h. \end{aligned}$$

We recognize these as parametric equations of a straight line in the yz-plane (V giving the y-coordinate and W the z-coordinate), in which the parameter h occurs in the usual way. Direction numbers of this line, regarded as a line in space, are

$$0, \; X_0 q/a, \; X_0 r/a.$$

These are proportional to

$$0, \; q, \; r,$$

which are known from (2) to be direction numbers for l. Hence, the image of l in this case is parallel to l, a conclusion reached earlier by a Euclidean argument, which was simpler.

The second case to be distinguished is that in which $p \neq 0$, l therefore intersecting the screen in just one point. We shall treat separately the suppositions that l does, or does not, contain O. If l does contain O, we can take $(a,b,c) = (0,0,0)$ (Section 4), and then we have from (6) that $V = X_0 q/p$, $W = X_0 r/p$. This tells us that V and W are independent of h, P' thus also being independent of h, or, in other words, being the same for any position of P upon l. More precisely, $P' = B'$, where

$$B' = (X_0, X_0 q/p, X_0 r/p),$$

for every value of h and, thus, for any position of P upon l. For P the intersection of the screen with l, we have $B' = P' = P$. Hence, B' is this intersection. In summary: the line through the origin with direction numbers p, q, r, $p \neq 0$, intersects the screen in the point B', and this point is the image of every point P of l.

The last case to consider is that in which $p \neq 0$, and l does not pass through O. We shall find in this case that B' is the vanishing point for l: as P travels on l away from the screen and the observer, its image P' moves towards B', which it never actually reaches, but which it approaches more and more closely as P continues to recede. For convenience, we shall take (a,b,c), which is arbitrary (Section 4), as the intersection of l with the yz-plane; this means that we take $a = 0$, and, since l does not pass through O, that b and c are not both zero. We shall also take as the positive direction of l that which points into the screen from the observer's side. Then P is behind the screen for sufficiently large, positive values of h, and recedes further into the background as h grows larger yet. What does P' do, as P so recedes? Since $P' = (X_0, V, W)$, we are led to inquire how V and W behave when h grows very large and keeps on growing. Since $a = 0$, equations (6) can be rewritten as

(8)
$$V = X_0(b + qh)/(ph) = X_0 b/(ph) + X_0 q/p$$
$$W = X_0(c + rh)/(ph) = X_0 c/(ph) + X_0 r/p.$$

In these equations, X_0, b, c, p, q, r are all constants; as h varies, they remain the same. Hence, as h grows larger and larger, increasing beyond bound or limit, the ratios

$$X_0 b/(ph), \quad X_0 c/(ph)$$

eventually become exceedingly small. (For instance, the fraction $100/(.01 \cdot h)$ is 100 for $h = 100$, 1 for $h = 10{,}000$, .01 for $h = 10^6$, .0001 for $h = 10^8$, and will be as small as you like if h is sufficiently large.) Therefore, if h is sufficiently large, V will be almost indistinguishable from $X_0 q/p$, and W will be almost indistinguishable from $X_0 r/p$. On the other hand, V and W will never both attain these respective values, since not both b and c are zero. Thus, the distance between the moving point (X_0, V, W) and the fixed point $(X_0, X_0 q/p, X_0 r/p)$, i.e., the distance between P' and B', will become *almost* indistinguishable from zero for all sufficiently distant positions of P upon l, but will be zero for no such position of P. This is to say that B' is the vanishing point for l, as asserted. In the previous paragraph, we characterized B' as the intersection with the screen of the straight line through O with the same direction as l. This means that B' is the point that the artist, standing at O, sees when looking in the direction of l. Thus our contentions are proved.

EXERCISES

1. Prove that the vanishing points of horizontal lines all lie on a straight line (this is called the horizon) on a level with the eye.

2. Prove that parallel planes appear to approach one another as they recede from the eye, and that their images on the canvas meet in a straight line. (This is called the vanishing trace.) (See Figure 9-48.)

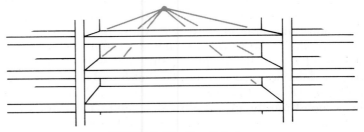

FIGURE 9-48   *Parallel planes.*

3. Let A denote the vanishing point for lines perpendicular to the screen, O again denoting the position of the observer's eye. Let B denote the vanishing point of a horizontal line through O making an angle of 45° with the line OA (Figure 9-49). (B is called a diagonal vanishing point.) Prove that $OA = AB$.

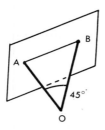

FIGURE 9-49   *A diagonal vanishing point.*

4. A building has a square facade (i.e., the front of the building is square). If a screen on which the building is projected is parallel to the front of the building, show that the image of the facade on the screen is square.

5. Let $EFGH$ be a square in a horizontal plane, the sides EF and GH being

perpendicular to the screen. Let A denote the vanishing point for lines perpendicular to the screen. Let B and C be the diagonal vanishing points, i.e., the
vanishing points for the two horizontal lines through O making angles of 45°
with OA (Figure 9-50). Let E', F', G', H' denote the images of E, F, G, H,
respectively. Prove that G' is on E'C and that F' is on H'B. Use these facts
and the result of Exercise 4 to draw in perspective a cube with the top face
visible and another face parallel to the screen.

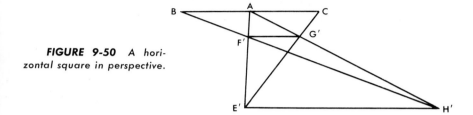

FIGURE 9-50 A hori-
zontal square in perspective.

6. Suppose a straight rail fence with its posts equally spaced occurs in a
scene to be depicted. Prove that if the face is in a plane parallel to the
canvas, the posts should be equally spaced in the picture (Figure 9-51).

FIGURE 9-51 Depiction of
a fence in the same plane as the
screen.

Prove that if the fence is in a vertical plane not parallel to the canvas, then the
posts in the picture can be correctly spaced by the procedure we shall now
describe. We need not consider in this procedure the actual posts or rails, which
are three-dimensional objects, but straight lines, such as their edges or medians.
Let l denote such a straight line (say the median) corresponding to the lowest
rail of the fence, m a parallel line representing the top rail, and n a line
midway between l and m. (If the fence has three evenly spaced, horizontal
rails, n might be the median of the middle rail.) Similarly, let $k_1, k_2, k_3, k_4, \ldots,$
denote equally spaced straight lines (again, say, medians) corresponding to
the successive vertical posts (Figure 9-52A). We assume l, m, and n to be

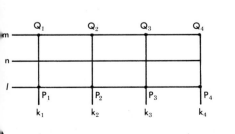

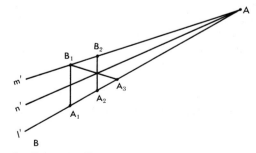

FIGURE 9-52 Equal spacing in perspective.

horizontal, k_1, k_2, k_3, k_4, ..., vertical, and all these lines to lie in the same (vertical) plane. Denote by P_1 and Q_1 the intersections of k_1 with l and m, respectively, by P_2 and Q_2 the respective intersections of k_2 with l and m, and so forth. Then, in particular, $P_1P_2 = P_2P_3 = P_3P_4 = \ldots$. On the screen (Figure 9-52B), let A denote the common vanishing point for l, m, and n; denote the images of l, m, and n by l', m', and n', respectively. Denote by A_1, A_2, A_3, ... the respective images of P_1, P_2, P_3, ... and by B_1, B_2, B_3, ... the respective images of Q_1, Q_2, Q_3, ... Once A_1 and A_2 are fixed, how are B_1 and B_2 determined? Then how is A_3 to be found, how B_3, and how A_4?

7. How might the grid image of Figure 9-42B have been constructed?

7.

Distances along a straight line represented in perspective

How are distances along a straight line faithfully represented in perspective? To answer this question in general, again suppose the observer's eye to be fixed at a point denoted by O, and consider an arbitrary line l and its projection l' through O upon a fixed vertical screen not containing O. Four cases present themselves: (a) l is parallel to the screen and passes through O, (b) l is not parallel to the screen and passes through O, (c) l is parallel to or within the screen and does not pass through O, (d) l is not parallel to and not within the screen and does not pass through O. The first three of these cases, which are extreme, are easily treated. Case (a): If l is parallel to the screen and passes through O, it has no projection upon the screen (in other words, l' is "void" or "empty") and thus does not appear in the picture at all. Case (b): If l passes through O and intersects the screen, the single point of intersection constitutes l' and thus is itself the image of every point of l. Case (c): If l does not pass through O and is parallel to or within the screen, then l' is parallel to l, and distances along l' are proportional to the corresponding distances along l.

Case (d), in which l is not parallel to and not within the screen and does not pass through O, alone offers difficulties. Special instances of this situation were presented in Exercises 5 and 6 in the preceding section but here we shall treat the general case. Let P denote an arbitrary point of l and P' its image, which is thus on l'. Let us measure distances along l from an arbitrary fixed point of l, which we shall denote by A. Correspondingly, we shall measure distances along l' from the point, denoted by A', which is the image of A. Let P denote an arbitrary point of l and P' its image (on l'). We want to know how the distance $P'A'$ is related to PA. The relationship obviously will depend partly on the direction of l, since, for instance, $P'A'$ is proportional to PA when l is parallel to the screen and otherwise is not proportional to PA. The direction of l is indicated on the canvas by the vanishing point of l'. Hence, we can expect this vanishing point, which we shall denote by D', to enter into the relationship between $P'A'$ and PA. Other factors, such as the locations of the canvas and the observer, also influence this relationship, the manner of their influence being indicated to some extent by the comparison between $B'A'$ and BA, where B is some *fixed* point of l other than A, and B' is its image on l'. For an *arbitrary* point P of l, we can thus anticipate that the relationship of $P'A'$ to PA may involve an arbitrarily chosen fixed point B of l and its image B', as well as the vanishing point D'. These qualitative considerations will be of importance in the following quantitative discussion.

To begin the quantitative discussion, we shall describe P by a parameter u equal to the signed distance of P from A (Section 4) and shall associate with an arbitrary point Q of l' a suitable parameter v *proportional* to the signed distance of Q from A'. By u' we shall denote the value of this parameter v for P' (Figure 9-53). Our first aim is to derive a concise expression of the relation between P' and P by expressing u' algebraically in terms of u.

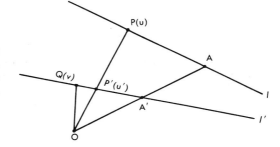

FIGURE 9-53 A line l with a fixed point A and a variable point P (corresponding to parameter u) and their images.

A line is characterized by its direction and any one of its points. Adopting the Cartesian frame of the previous section, denote direction numbers of l in this frame by

$$p, q, r,$$

and represent A as

$$A = (a,b,c).$$

For convenience, we require

$$p \geq 0, \ p^2 + q^2 + r^2 = 1$$

(Section 4), and we also take A such that $a \neq 0$. Since $p^2 + q^2 + r^2 = 1$,

$$P = (a + pu, \ b + qu, \ c + ru),$$

where u, as previously indicated, is the signed distance from P to A. We shall only consider points P that are on the other side of the screen from O. For these points, $a + pu \geq X_0$ and, therefore, in particular,

$$a + pu > 0.$$

Since l is not parallel to the screen, we have $p \neq 0$ (Section 6), and since we are not permitting p to be negative,

(1) $p > 0.$

Since l does not pass through O, p, q, r are not proportional to a, b, c, respectively, and, hence, we have

(2a) $aq - bp \neq 0,$

or

(2b) $ar - cp \neq 0,$

or

(2c) $br - cq \neq 0$

(see the remark at the end of Section 4). From our assumption that $p \neq 0$, we can actually conclude that either (2a) or (2b) must hold. If, to the contrary,

$$aq - bp = 0, \; ar - cp = 0,$$

we have, in the first place,

$$b = aq/p.$$

Substituting this expression for b, we have, secondly,

$$br - cq = (aq/p)r - cq = (q/p)(ar - cp)$$
$$= 0.$$

Hence, negating conditions (2a) and (2b) results in the negation of (2c) as well. This contradicts our previous finding that at least one of the three conditions is true, and we conclude therefore that, in fact, either (2a) or (2b) must hold, as asserted.

As suggested by the qualitative discussion at the beginning of the section, we now introduce a second fixed point B, different from A, located on l. If h is the value of the parameter for this point, we have $h \neq 0$ and

$$B = (a + ph, b + qh, c + rh).$$

We shall assume B not to lie on the plane $x = 0$. Under this assumption,

$a + ph \neq 0$. The two points A' and B' determine l', B' being the image of B. Hence, we can characterize l' algebraically from the coordinate representations of these points. By equations (6) of Section 6,

$$A' = (X_0, (b/a)X_0, (c/a)X_0), \ B' = (X_0, [(b+qh)/(a+ph)]X_0,$$
$$[(c+rh)/(a+ph)]X_0).$$

In the same way, we have

(3) $\qquad P' = (X_0, [(b+qu)/(a+pu)]X_0, [(c+ru)/(a+pu)]X_0).$

From A' and B' we easily obtain direction numbers for l'. In fact, the differences of corresponding coordinates of any two points of a line will serve as direction numbers, respectively, for the line (Section 4). Hence, direction numbers

$$p', q', r'$$

for l' can be determined as

$$p' = X_0 - X_0 = 0,$$
$$q' = [(b+qh)/(a+ph)]X_0 - (b/a)X_0$$
$$= [(b+qh)/(a+ph) - (b/a)]X_0$$
$$= [(aq-bp)h/(a(a+ph))]X_0,$$
$$r' = [(c+rh)/(a+ph)]X_0 - (c/a)X_0 = [(ar-pc)h/(a(a+ph))]X_0.$$

Since p', q', r', by definition, are the differences of corresponding coordinates of A' and B', we have

(4) $\qquad\qquad\qquad A'B' = \sqrt{p'^2 + q'^2 + r'^2}.$

Let Q be an arbitrary point of l'. Since l' has the direction numbers p', q', r' and passes through A', a value v exists such that

$$Q = (X_0, (b/a)X_0 + q'v, (c/a)X_0 + r'v);$$

by (4), v is equal to the signed distance of Q from A' divided by that from B' to A' (Section 4). Taking P' as Q, we thus have, in particular,

(3') $\qquad\qquad P' = (X_0, (b/a)X_0 + q'u', (c/a)X_0 + r'u'),$

u' denoting the value of the parameter v for P'. Comparing this result with (3) shows that:

(5) $\qquad$ $(b/a)X_0 + q'u' = [(b+qu)/(a+pu)]X_0,$
$\qquad\qquad$ $(c/a)X_0 + r'u' = [(c+ru)/(a+pu)]X_0.$

These equations enable us to express u' in terms of u, as we desire.

Confining ourselves for the moment to the first equation, let us substitute for q', obtaining

$$(b/a)X_0 + [(aq - bp)h/(a(a+ph))]X_0 u' = ((b+qu)/(a+pu))X_0.$$

We can cancel the factor X_0 common to all terms and move the first term in the left member to the right, to obtain:

(6a) $h(aq - bp)u'/(a(a+ph)) = (b+qu)/(a+pu) - (b/a)$
$$= (aq - bp)u/(a(a+pu)).$$

From the second equation in (5), we can derive in similar fashion

(6b) $h(ar - pc)u'/(a(a+ph)) = (ar - pc)u/(a(a+pu)).$

We have seen, however, that either $aq - bp \neq 0$ or $ar - pc \neq 0$; if the former, take equation (6a) and, if the latter, take equation (6b). In either case, divide by the factor concerned and multiply by a to arrive at the result

$$hu'/(a+ph) = u/(a+pu).$$

(If both the factors mentioned are not zero, both equations lead to this result.) This gives us:

(7) $u' = (a+ph)u/((a+pu)h).$

This algebraic relation between u and u' (h is regarded as fixed) was our first objective.

We shall now show how to interpret (7) as a relation among distances along l and l'. We shall do so by interpreting the individual parts of the relation in terms of such distances. (Another way is suggested in Exercise 5.) More accurately, we shall interpret in terms of distances the individual parts of

(7') $|u'| = |a+ph| \, |u|/(|a+pu| \, |h|),$

which is obtained from (7) by taking the absolute value of each side.

Since u is equal to the signed distance of P from A, either $u = PA$ or $u = -PA$, PA denoting the distance of P from A. In either case,

(8) $|u| = PA.$

For the same reason, h being the value of u corresponding to B,

(9) $|h| = BA.$

Since u' is equal to the signed distance from P' to A' divided by that from B' to A', we have, similarly,

$$(10) \qquad\qquad |u'| = P'A'/B'A';$$

this can be checked from (3') by means of the distance formula and (4).

So far, we have expressed (in (8), (9), and (10)) three of the component parts of (7') in terms of distances from A or A'. We shall not readily express the remaining parts of (7') similarly in terms of distances from A or A', but we recall from our qualitative discussion that D' must play a role. We shall identify this role and at the same time realize our present aim if we calculate the distances from D' of the other pertinent points $(A', B',$ and $P')$ on l'. Since

$$D' = (X_0, (q/p)X_0, (r/p)X_0)$$

(see Section 7; this also comes directly from (3)), and since P' is given by (3), we have from the distance formula

$$\begin{aligned}
(P'D')^2 &= ([(b+qu)/(a+pu) - q/p]X_0)^2 \\
&\quad + ([(c+ru)/(a+pu) - r/p]X_0)^2 \\
&= ([(bp-aq)/(p(a+pu))]X_0)^2 \\
&\quad + ([(pc-ar)/(p(a+pu))]X_0)^2 \\
&= [X_0/(p(a+pu))]^2\,[(bp-aq)^2 + (pc-ar)^2];
\end{aligned}$$

hence,

$$(11) \qquad\qquad P'D' = X_0 m/(|p|\,|a+pu|),$$

where

$$m = \sqrt{(bp-aq)^2 + (pc-ar)^2}.$$

Because either (1) or (2) is true in this case,

$$m > 0.$$

If B' takes the place of P' in the previous computation, then h takes the place of u; therefore,

$$(12) \qquad\qquad B'D' = X_0 m/(|p|\,|a+ph|).$$

From (11) and (12), by dividing, we have

$$|a+ph|/|a+pu| = P'D'/B'D',$$

from which and from (8), (9), (10), substituted into (7'), results

$$P'A'/B'A' = (P'D'/B'D')(PA/BA).$$

This is a relation among geometrically significant distances along l and l', such as we were seeking. It is illuminating to rewrite it as

(13)
$$\frac{P'A'/B'A'}{P'D'/B'D'} = PA/BA,$$

collecting in one member all the distances measured along l' and in the other both distances measured along l.

How do we interpret this rather complex relation? The ratio PA/BA, which appears on the right, measures the distance from P to A in units equal to the distance from B to A: if P is twice as far from A as is B, the ratio is 2; if P is three times as far from A as is B, the ratio is 3, and so forth. Two such ratios appear in the fraction on the left, the ratio in the numerator referring to distances (of P' and B') from A' and that in the denominator to distances from D'. This fraction,

$$\frac{P'A'/B'A'}{P'D'/B'D'},$$

is called a "cross ratio" and, more specifically, *the cross ratio for the four points P', A', B', D'*. Equation (13) tells us that we can find the value of this cross ratio — a relation holding among *image points* — from distances measured in the *actual scene*.

With the aid of relation (13), assuming the positions of P, A, and B (on l) and of A', B', D' (on l') to be known, we can now calculate $P'A'$. First, from P, A, and B we find the cross ratio for P', A', B', D', using (13) as explained in the previous paragraph. Let c denote the value of this cross ratio. Thus,

$$\frac{P'A'/B'A'}{P'D'/B'D'} = c,$$

where c now is known. This relation is equivalent to

(14)
$$P'A' = c\, B'A'(P'D'/B'D') = e\, P'D',$$

where

$$e = c(B'A'/B'D').$$

Since c, A', B', and D' are assumed to be known, e can be computed; hence, we shall regard e, too, as a known quantity. Our procedure now depends on the order of occurrence of A', P', and D' on l'. Suppose for illustration that P' is between A' and D', as in Figure 9-54.

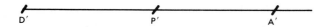

FIGURE 9-54 *Three points in a certain order along a straight line.*

Then

$$P'A' + P'D' = A'D',$$

$A'D'$ being assumed known. Therefore,

$$P'D' = A'D' - P'A',$$

and substitution for $P'D'$ in (14) gives

$$P'A' = e(A'D' - P'A')$$

and, thus,

$$(1 + e)P'A' = e\,A'D',$$

or

(15) $$P'A' = (e/(1 + e))\,A'D'.$$

This is one form of the desired result, $A'D'$ and e being known or computable from known quantities. Another form is obtained by substituting for e the expression it represents. We thus have

$$\frac{e}{1+e} = \frac{c(B'A'/B'D')}{1 + c(B'A'/B'D')} = \frac{c\,B'A'}{B'D' + c\,B'A'}$$

and, therefore,

(16) $$P'A' = c(B'A')\,(A'D')/(B'D' + c\,B'A').$$

A similar formula can be obtained in the case in which A' is between P' and D'.

EXERCISES

1. Find a formula analogous to (16) in the case in which A' is between P' and D' on l'.

2. Suppose five points are equally spaced along a straight line in a scene. How will their images be spaced?

3. Five points on l have equally spaced images on l'. How are the original five points spaced?

In the next examples, we denote the value of v at a specified point Q by the symbol v_Q and the value of u at a point R by u_R. (Thus, in particular, we use $v_{P'}$ in place of u'.)

4. Prove: $v_{A'} = 0$, $v_{B'} = 1$, $v_{D'} = (a + ph)/(ph)$.
5. Prove that (7) implies

$$\frac{(v_{P'} - v_{A'})/(v_{B'} - v_{A'})}{(v_{P'} - v_{D'})/(v_{B'} - v_{D'})} = (u_P - u_A)/(u_B - u_A).$$

Then deduce (13) from this.

8.

On the further significance of the cross ratio

As before, let l denote any straight line not within or parallel to a given plane screen, and let O be a point not on the screen or on l. Again let l' denote the projection of l through O upon the screen. Relation (13) of Section 7 states that

(1)
$$\frac{P'A'/B'A'}{P'D'/B'D'} = PA/BA,$$

where A, B, and P are points of l, A', B', and P' their respective images on l', and D' is the vanishing point of l'. (The formula assumes that $BA \neq 0$; since D' is the vanishing point, it is automatically true that $P'D' \neq 0$ and $B'D' \neq 0$.) We have shown how an artist can use this relation to calculate from distances measured in a scene the corresponding lengths in his perspective drawing. Here, we mention the opposite application. From a photograph of a straight road, for instance, relation (1) will enable us to determine the relative positions of doors, trees, hydrants, persons, the relative widths of buildings, driveways, street crossings, and so forth, disposed along the road. To make such determinations, we must first find the vanishing point for the image of the road in our picture. Denote this vanishing point by D'. Then select arbitrarily two reference points upon the road. Calling these A and B, let A' and B' denote their respective images in the picture. Now if P is any point of the road and P' its image, measure the distances $P'A'$, $P'D'$, $B'A'$, $B'D'$ in the picture and calculate the cross ratio for P', A', B', D'. Relation (1) then gives us PA/BA, the distance from P to A in units equal to the distance from B to A. Since the distances from A—in such units—of any pair of points of the road can thus be found, so can their distance—again in units equal to the distance from B to A—from one another. Moreover, if the distance from B to A happens to be known, say, in feet, then all the other distances can be found in feet. In this way, a good length of road could be surveyed from one photograph.

Let us now consider the cross ratio from a different point of view.

Since the right member of (1) is independent of the positions of the screen or the viewing point, the left member, too, is independent of the screen and the viewing point. In other words, pictures of the same scene projected upon different screens through different viewing points manifest the same cross ratios, the individual positions of P', A', B', D' possibly varying from one picture to another, but the cross ratio of the four points being in every case the same. This cross ratio, in short, characterizes the scene itself, rather than any picture of it. A computer, calculating cross ratios, could identify the same scene in different pictures. When we recognize a familiar scene from a new view of it, do our unconscious minds somehow, as if they were computers, also perceive, assess, and compare cross ratios?

Now suppose D' to be not the vanishing point of l', but the image of some fourth point of l, which we denote by D, distinct from A, B, and P. We shall see that the cross ratio for P', A', B', D' is equal to the cross ratio for P, A, B, D and, thus, again is the same in any picture. This added property of invariability of cross ratios is, in fact, an expression of a fundamental law of geometry we now give.

Let l' and l'' denote any two lines in the same plane. Let O be any point of this plane not on l' or l'', and associate to an arbitrary point P' of l' the point P'' of l'' that also lies on OP'. Consistently with our previous terminology, we call P'' the projection of P' upon l'' through O; O we denominate the *center* of projection. If A', B', C', D' are any four distinct (i.e., different) points of l', let A'', B'', C'', D'' denote their projections through O upon l''. The law we alluded to states that

$$\frac{C'A'/B'A'}{C'D'/B'D'} = \frac{C''A''/B''A''}{C''D''/B''D''}.$$

(2)

The term "central projection" is used to describe the process of associating with an arbitrary point of one line its projection upon a second line through a given center. The foregoing law states simply that the cross ratio for any four distinct collinear points (i.e., points on a straight line) is unaltered by central projection (Figure 9-55).

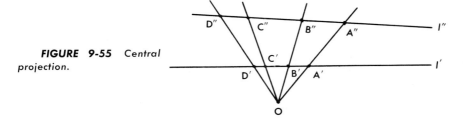

FIGURE 9-55 Central projection.

We shall prove this law from our previous results, first observing relation (1) to be more generally true than may have appeared. This relation holds, in fact, for all positions of A, B, and P upon l such that A and B are distinct and none of the three points lies on the plane through O parallel to the screen. This is the plane with the equation

$x = 0$; we shall denote it by Z. (The excluded position upon l being the intersection of l and Z has no image on the screen.) To verify the preceding observation, let us review the restrictions imposed upon P, A, and B in deriving (1). These are:

$p > 0$,
$u > 0$ when P is sufficiently far behind the screen,
$a + pu > 0$,
$a \neq 0$,
$h \neq 0$,
$a + ph \neq 0$.

The first inequality involves our assumption that l is not parallel to or within the screen (so that $p \neq 0$) and our freedom to employ as direction numbers for l either p, q, r or $-p$, $-q$, $-r$. The second inequality rests on our freedom to use either u or $-u$ as parameter along l. Thus, the first two inequalities pertain merely to our mode of representing l algebraically and do not restrict A, B, or P. The inequality $h \neq 0$ means that A and B are distinct. The inequality $a \neq 0$ means that A is required not to lie upon Z. The inequality $a + ph \neq 0$ means, similarly, that B may not lie upon Z. The inequality $a + pu > 0$, which is reasonable to require in a discussion limited to perspective drawing, is not necessary mathematically and can be replaced by the weaker condition

$$a + pu \neq 0.$$

This weaker condition, which we now adopt, means that P does not lie on Z. The only conditions ultimately required, in order that relation (1) shall be true, are that A and B be distinct and that none of the three points A, B, P, lie upon Z, as asserted. No restrictions, in particular, are placed on the order in which P, A, and B may occur along l.

We can now prove (2). Let l be a line not passing through O but parallel to OD' and in the plane of l' and l'' (Figure 9-56). Then OD'

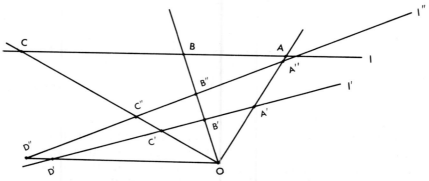

FIGURE 9-56   *Proof of cross ratio invariance.*

does not intersect l, while OA', OB', OC' do; denote the intersections by A, B, C, respectively. Imagining the plane of l' and l'' to be horizontal, erect a vertical screen containing l'. Obviously, l' is the image of l by projection through O upon this screen, A', B', C' are the images of A, B, C, respectively, and D' is the vanishing point for l'. We may, therefore, apply (1) with C in place of P to obtain

$$\frac{C'A'/B'A'}{C'D'/B'D'} = CA/BA.$$

Similarly, erecting a vertical screen containing l'' and projecting l through O upon this screen, we have

$$\frac{C''A''/B''A''}{C''D''/B''D''} = CA/BA.$$

Equality (2) follows at once.

EXERCISES

1. Suppose we have an aerial photograph of a certain region without distortion. How can we map the region accurately from the photograph? (This question can be regarded as the reverse of Exercise 7, Section 6.)

2. Let u denote the parameter for l', $u_{P'}$ its value at a point P' of l', v the parameter for l'', and $v_{P''}$ the value of v at a point P'' of l''. Prove that

$$\frac{(u_{C'} - u_{A'})/(u_{B'} - u_{A'})}{(u_{C'} - u_{D'})/(u_{B'} - u_{D'})} = \frac{(v_{C''} - v_{A''})/(v_{B''} - v_{A''})}{(v_{C''} - v_{D''})/(v_{B''} - v_{D''})}.$$

CHAPTER 10

MATHEMATICAL INDUCTION

Induction in its usual sense is the process of inferring the general from some knowledge of the particular. Induction is a fallible guide, its conclusions always tentative, always open to revision as new evidence may require. Mathematical induction is a different kind of thing, not a jumping to conclusions, but a logical procedure to justify conclusions of a certain kind already reached.† Induction in its ordinary sense led us to guess in Chapter 3, for example, that, if B is an integer greater than one, every number less than B^k has a k-place numeral in base B. Mathematical induction was used then to justify this guess.

We shall now give a simpler example, which depends on knowing even and odd numbers. An integer is *even* if divisible by 2 and *odd* if not divisible by 2. Any even integer, by definition, is twice some integer, i.e., is expressible as $2k$, where k is an integer. As k takes successively the values

$$0, 1, 2, 3, 4, \ldots,$$

$2k$ runs successively through the even numbers

$$0, 2, 4, 6, 8, \ldots.$$

---

†Induction as a guide to mathematical thinking is comprehensively discussed by Polya in *Mathematics and Plausible Reasoning*, Vols. I and II, Princeton University Press, Princeton, 1954. Mathematical induction is well described and illustrated by I. S. Sominskii in *The Method of Mathematical Induction*, D. C. Heath and Company, Boston, 1963 and, in geometrical contexts, by L. I. Golovina and I. M. Yaglom in *Induction in Geometry*, D. C. Heath and Company, Boston, 1963, from whose booklets we have borrowed several examples.

(These are the non-negative even numbers, the negative even numbers being −2,−4, ... In this section we restrict ourselves to non-negative integers.) For any value of k, $2k$ and $2(k+1) = 2k+2$ represent consecutive even integers. Between them is just one integer, $2k+1$. The odd integers are just those that occur between consecutive even integers. Hence, the odd positive integers, which are the numbers

$$1, 3, 5, 7, 9\ldots,$$

are representable as $2k+1$ for $k = 0, 1, 2, 3, \ldots$. The odd integers also are representable as

$$2l - 1 \text{ for } l = 1, 2, 3, \ldots.$$

This is because a number expressible as $2l - 1$ in terms of a positive integer l also is expressible as $2k+1$ in terms of a corresponding non-negative integer k, and conversely. Indeed, $2l - 1 = 2k+1$ with $k = l - 1$.

The example of induction we wish now to consider concerns the following relations, which are sometimes ascribed to Pythagoras in the 6th Century B.C.:

$$
\begin{aligned}
1 &= 1 \\
1 + 3 &= 4 \\
1 + 3 + 5 &= 9 \\
1 + 3 + 5 + 7 &= 16 \\
1 + 3 + 5 + 7 + 9 &= 25 \\
1 + 3 + 5 + 7 + 9 + 11 &= 36 \\
1 + 3 + 5 + 7 + 9 + 11 + 13 &= 49 \\
1 + 3 + 5 + 7 + 9 + 11 + 13 + 15 &= 64
\end{aligned}
$$

The left member of each relation is the sum of all the odd numbers up to a given number, which we may write symbolically as $2n - 1$. The left members thus are of the form

$$1 + 3 + \ldots + (2n - 1),$$

the sum being understood to consist of all odd numbers from 1 to $2n - 1$, inclusive ($n = 1$ in the first summation, $n = 2$ in the second summation, $n = 8$ in the eighth summation, and so on). The right members of these relations are squares: $1^2, 2^2, 3^2, 4^2$, and so forth. The eight relations written down thus state that

(1) $$1 + 3 + \ldots + (2n - 1) = n^2$$

for $n = 1, 2, 3, 4, 5, 6, 7, 8$. Is this statement true for $n = 9$? It is, in fact, easily verifiable for this value of n. Is it true for all values of n up to

1000? To assure oneself of this could take a lot of work. Is it true for *all* positive integers n? There being infinitely many integers, this question is not to be answered affirmatively from the mere checking of particular cases, no matter how many. To conjecture an answer is to use induction in the ordinary sense. Such a conjecture, when true, often can be proved by the method of mathematical induction, which we shall now describe.

1.

Formal mathematical induction

Mathematical induction usually is concerned with a sequence of statements, which we shall designate symbolically as

$$S_1, S_2, S_3, \ldots, S_n, \ldots$$

To each natural number n corresponds one of these statements, namely, S_n. In the preceding example, for instance, S_n is the statement that (1) holds, S_1 being the particular case in which $n = 1$, S_2 the case in which $n = 2$, and so on. The process of mathematical induction rests on two hypotheses concerning the statements S_n for $n = 1, 2, 3, \ldots$.

Hypotheses for mathematical induction:
(I) The statement S_1 is true.
(II) For all integers k greater than zero: if S_k is true, then S_{k+1} also is true. In brief, S_k implies S_{k+1} for $k = 1, 2, \ldots$.

Hypothesis (II), specialized to the case $k = 1$, says that, if S_1 is true, then, S_2 also is true. Since S_1 is assumed true (Hypothesis (I)), however, S_2 in fact is true. Hypothesis (II) says in the case $k = 2$ that if S_2 is true, S_3 also must be true. However, S_2 has been seen to be true: therefore, S_3 is true. Now applying Hypothesis (II) in the next case, $k = 3$, we establish the truth of S_4, and letting k take on successively the values $4, 5, \ldots$, we can similarly establish the truth of S_k for any integer k. We are thus led to formulate the following principle, a more formal proof of which will be given.

The Principle of Mathematical Induction. When both of the preceding hypotheses are satisfied, S_k is true for $k = 1, 2, 3, \ldots$ (i.e., all the S_k are true).

PROOF: If the principle of mathematical induction were not valid, a sequence of statements satisfying the two hypotheses would exist such that at least one of the statements was false. Denote such statements by the symbols $S_1, S_2, \ldots$ again, and let n be the least integer such that S_n is false (S_n, in other words, is the first false statement in the list). S_1 is not false; this is by the first hypothesis. Hence,

n exceeds 1, and S_{n-1} denotes a statement of the sequence. (The symbol S_{n-1} was not defined for $n=1$.) Since n was the *least* integer such that S_n is *not* true, S_{n-1} *is* true. By the second hypothesis, however, S_{n-1} implies S_n. Hence, S_n likewise is true, while (by definition) S_n was supposed to be false. This contradiction originated in our supposing that the sequence of statements S_1, S_2, ... satisfied the hypothesis of the principle of mathematical induction but not the conclusions. Such a sequence of statements, therefore, does not exist, and the principle of mathematical induction is correct as asserted.

To illustrate the principle of mathematical induction, let us justify the conjecture that relation (1) holds between the sum of the first n odd integers and n^2. S_n being the statement that (1) is true, we have to check that both of the hypotheses needed are satisfied. Hypothesis (I) requires that S_1 be true. Since S_1 here is the statement that $1=1$, Hypothesis (I) is satisfied. Hypothesis (II) demands for all k that, if

$$S_k: 1+3+\ldots+(2k-1)=k^2$$

is true, then

$$S_{k+1}: 1+3+\ldots+(2k-1)+(2k+1)=(k+1)^2$$

also is true. (With $n=k+1$, $2n-1=2(k+1)-1=2k+2-1=2k+1$.) If S_k is assumed, the left member of S_{k+1} can be written as

$$
\begin{aligned}
1+3+\ldots+(2k-1)+(2k+1) &= [1+3\ldots+(2k-1)]+(2k+1) \\
&= k^2+(2k+1) \\
&= (k+1)^2.
\end{aligned}
$$

After assuming S_k we can thus arrive at S_{k+1}, and Hypothesis (II) is verified. Since both hypotheses hold, the principle of mathematical induction permits us to conclude that all the S_k are true or, in other words, that the foregoing conjecture is a valid one.

Mathematical induction works just as well with a finite number of statements as with infinitely many. As an example, which also helps to reveal the mechanism of the process, suppose a number of dominoes are set on end in a row, all the dominoes facing the same way, so that when the first tips over towards the second, it pushes it down, the second then knocking down the third, and so on, until the dominoes in the row are all down. Let S_k denote the statement: "The kth domino will fall [in the appropriate direction]." S_1 may or may not be true; we can make it true by a little push. S_k implies S_{k+1} whether S_k itself is true or not. Hypothesis (II) thus is independent of Hypothesis (I) and may be satisfied even when all the S_k are false. When the two hypotheses jointly are true, however, the process of mathematical induction is depicted in the wave of falling dominoes.

Consider the following proposition: "I have an ancestor who

lived in the year 5000 B.C." Most of us would accept this proposition, believing it a logical conclusion from our present understanding of human life and human generation. But how compelling is it actually? What right do we have to declare that a person existed whose name, appearance, and geographical location we can never know — not to mention age, speech, customs, dress, capabilities, disposition, or attitudes? What knowledge and what logic allow us to come to this utterly unspecific and unverifiable conclusion?

We shall argue this question by mathematical induction from the following premises:

(a) Every human being for the past 10,000 years had a human mother, who was alive at the time of his birth.

(b) A human female bears no children until at least five years old.

(c) A person alive at two different times was also alive every moment of the interval between.

(d) I was born after 4000 B.C.

Let S_n denote the following statement: "At each moment, for at least $5n$ years before my birth, a female ancestor of mine was alive." To prove the original proposition, it suffices to prove S_n for all indices n from 1 to 1400. Since the first three premises imply the truth of S_1, Hypothesis (I) is satisfied in this problem. To justify Hypothesis (II), we must show that, for an arbitrary n (less than 1400), S_n implies S_{n+1}. Take *any* n less than 1400 and hold it fixed throughout the following discussion. S_n (for this fixed, particular n) is either true or false and, if false, certainly implies S_{n+1} (Chapter 1, Section 8). Thus, it suffices to prove that S_n, when true, implies S_{n+1}; i.e., that S_{n+1} is true if S_n is true. Let b denote the time of my birth, measured in years. If S_n is true, a female ancestor, whom we shall call A, was living at the time $b-5n$, $5n$ years before my birth. It is convenient to abbreviate this time ($5n$ years before my birth) by the letter t: thus, $t = b - 5n$. We now intend to prove that, at every moment during the five year interval prior to t, either A or her mother was alive. This will establish S_{n+1} and thus verify Hypothesis (II). Two cases are distinguished:

(i) A was less than five years old at time t. In this case, A's mother existed at least from the time $t-5$ until A's birth, and A lived from her birth until time t. Thus, either A or her mother was alive at every moment during the five-year interval prior to t.

(ii) A was at least five years old at time t. In this case, A herself existed during the five-year interval prior to t.

When S_n is true, we thus see that, at each moment for the five year period before t, a female ancestor of mine was alive. This was also so of the interval between t and my birth. Since $t = b - 5n$, statement S_{n+1} follows. In sum, S_{n+1} is true if S_n is true, n being any index between 1 and 1400. Hypothesis (II) is thus justified. Since Hypothesis (I) also is true, mathematical induction now shows all the S_n (for n between 1 and 1400) to be true, thereby vindicating our original proposition.

Medical advances may call Premises (a) and (c) into question, making it necessary to modify our proof. Premise (b) was stated in an extreme form simply to avoid irrelevant issues, but is obviously unsuitable for other purposes, such as estimating the number of generations elapsed since the ancestress of 5000 B.C.

EXERCISES

1. Let $S_1, S_2, \ldots, S_k$ denote k statements such that

$$S_n \text{ implies } S_{n+1} \text{ for } n = 1, \ldots, k-1.$$

In other words, each statement (but the last) implies its successor in the list. Prove that S_1 then implies S_k. This result is a consequence of transitivity (Chapter 1, Section 8), which it generalizes.

2. Justify the following formulas for all natural numbers n:
   (a) $1 + 2 + 3 + \ldots + n = n(1+n)/2$.
   (b) $1 + 2^2 + 3^2 + \ldots + n^2 = n(n+1)(2n+1)/6$.
   (c) $1/(1 \cdot 2) + 1/(2 \cdot 3) + 1/(3 \cdot 4) + \ldots + 1/(n(n+1)) = n/(n+1)$.

3. Prove that $2^n \geq n$ for $n = 1, 2, \ldots$.
4. Prove that if $a \geq 0$, then

$$(1+a)^n - 1 \geq na \text{ for } n = 1, 2, \ldots.$$

5. Prove that if $0 < a < 1$, then

$$(1-a)^n < 1 - na + (n(n-1)/2)a^2.$$

6. Prove that $x^n - y^n$ is divisible by $x - y$ for all values of n, where n is a positive integer. HINT: $x^{k+1} - y^{k+1} = x(x^k - y^k) + y^k(x - y)$.

7. If $a_1 < a_2, a_2 < a_3, a_3 < a_4, \ldots, a_{n-1} < a_n, \ldots$, prove that $a_1 < a_n$ for every n. HINT: If $a < b$ and $b < c$, then $a < c$.

8. Notice these equalities, which were given around 100 A.D. by Nicomachus:

$$1 = 1^3$$
$$3 + 5 = 2^3$$
$$7 + 9 + 11 = 3^3$$
$$13 + 15 + 17 + 19 = 4^3$$
$$21 + 23 + 25 + 27 + 29 = 5^3.$$

The odd numbers appear consecutively in their left members, the first equality containing the first odd number, the second quality the next two odd numbers, the third equality the succeeding three odd numbers, and the nth equality n consecutive odd numbers in their turn.

   (a) Prove that the right member of the nth equality must be n^3.

HINT: The left members of the equalities are arithmetic progressions, which begin with the numbers 1, 3, 7, 13, 21, and so on. Furthermore:

$$3 = 1 + 2$$
$$7 = 1 + 2 + 4$$
$$13 = 1 + 2 + 4 + 6$$
$$21 = 1 + 2 + 4 + 6 + 8.$$

(b) Prove from Nicomachus's equalities that

$$1^3 + 2^3 + 3^3 + \ldots + n^3 = (n(n + 1)/2)^2.$$

9. Prove by mathematical induction that every whole number greater than 1 either is a prime or is divisible by a prime. HINT: Let S_k denote: "Every number from 2 to k either is a prime or is divisible by a prime."

10. Prove that the sum of the cubes of any three consecutive natural numbers is divisible by 9.

11. Execute fully the mathematical induction hinted at in Section 4, Chapter 3.

12. "One good turn asketh another," wrote John Heywood.[†] Carry out the mathematical induction this statement suggests.

13. Find the fallacies in the following arguments:

   (a) All integers are the same because, if $k = k + 1$, it follows that $k + 1 = k + 2$.

   (b) All girls' eyes are the same color, a statement we prove by mathematical induction, as follows. Let S_k symbolize the statement that, in any set of k girls, all have eyes of the same color. Then Hypothesis (I) is satisfied, S_1 certainly being true. To prove Hypothesis (II), suppose S_k already established and, with the aim of justifying S_{k+1}, take any set of $k + 1$ girls. Temporarily moving one girl out of this set, we are left with k girls to whom the supposition S_k applies. All these k girls, therefore, have the same color eyes. Now let the girl removed from the original set return, and send one of the others away. Again we are left with a set of k girls, and again all must have the same color eyes. Therefore, the girl first removed, but a member of the present group of k, has eyes of the same color as the others. All $k + 1$ girls, in consequence, have the same color eyes, and S_{k+1} is seen to be true. Hypothesis (II) thus is verified, and we conclude that every S_k holds, which means that all girls' eyes have the same color, as asserted.

14. "The Tower of Hanoi"[‡] is a game played with perforated disks of different sizes that can be stacked on pegs (Figure 10-1). To begin the game,

---

[†]Bartlett, p. 93.

[‡]For more information and a very interesting discussion of this game, see Martin Gardner, MATHEMATICAL PUZZLES AND DIVERSIONS, Simon and Schuster, New York, 1959, pp. 57-62.

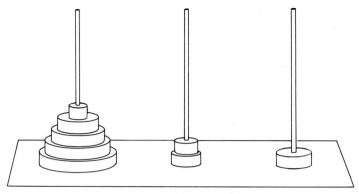

FIGURE 10-1   *The Tower of Hanoi.*

all the disks are arranged on one of three given pegs to make a tower, each disk in the tower being smaller than its neighbor underneath. The object of the game is to move the tower to one of the two other pegs, originally vacant, by moving the individual disks one at a time, never placing any disk on top of a smaller disk. A disk may be moved from the peg occupied to either of the other pegs.

  (a) Describe how a stack of three disks can thus be transferred in seven steps, and

  (b) A stack of four disks in fifteen steps.

  (c) Prove by mathematical induction that a stack of n disks can be transferred in $2^n - 1$ steps.

15. A puzzle we shall describe makes use of two kinds of geometrical shapes related to dominoes. The first is a square of side 1; it is called a monomino. The second shape is that which would result from assembling four monominoes in a square cluster and then removing one of the monominoes from the cluster; it is called a tromino. (See Figure 10-2.) The aim of the puzzle

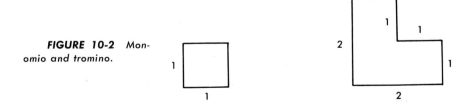

FIGURE 10-2   *Mon-omio and tromino.*

is to cover an arbitrary square of side 2^n, where n may be any positive integer, with figures of these two kinds and as few monominoes as possible. Prove that, for every value of $n = 0, 1, 2, 3, \ldots$, one monomino and $(2^{2n} - 1)/3$ trominoes suffice. The single monomino may occupy any place.[†] HINT: See Figure 10-3.

[†]Martin Gardner, *The Scientific American Book of Mathematical Puzzles,* New York, Simon and Schuster, 1959, p. 126.

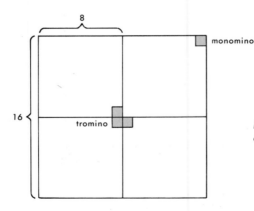

8

16

monomino

tromino

FIGURE 10-3 *A hint in a cover-ing problem. A square 16 × 16 is sub-divided into four 8 × 8 squares.*

2.

The need for mathematical induction

In the examples given, normal prudence might seem to permit the acceptance of the general rules proposed after a "reasonable" degree of verification but without the formalities of mathematical induction. How far, however, is normal prudence to be trusted? How reliable is the process of induction in the usual sense? We shall now give three examples† in which ordinary induction would be mis-leading.

The first example is a proposed formula for primes, a prime being an integer with no (integral) divisors other than itself and 1. (Examples of primes are $2, 3, 5, 7, 11, 13, 17, 19, 23, 29, 31$.) The proposed formula is

$$p = n^2 + n + 41,$$

where n is an integer. To see how plausible this formula is, let us calculate the value of p corresponding to several values of n. We obtain Table 10-1.

Table 10-1

n	0	1	2	3	4	5	6	7	8
p	41	43	47	53	61	71	83	97	113

All the numbers obtained in the table are primes, and so would they continue to be up to, and including, the value of p for $n = 39$. For $n = 40$, however,

---

†The first is well-known. The second has been taken from Golovina and Yaglom, *op. cit.*, p. 2. The third is based on a suggestion in B. M. Stewart, *Theory of Numbers*, Macmillan, 1952.

$$p = 40^2 + 40 + 41$$
$$= 40^2 + 2 \cdot 40 + 1$$
$$= (40 + 1)^2$$
$$= 41^2.$$

Thus the formula, working in 39 cases, fails in the fortieth! The formula is attributed to the 18th Century Swiss mathematician, Leonhard Euler.

The second example is concerned with the expression $991n^2 + 1$, in which n is any integer. Calculation shows this expression to be a perfect square for no value of n up to fantastically large numbers. Common sense therefore suggests that this expression should be a square for *no* value of n. This suggestion, however, is false: values of n exist for which the expression is a square, the least such value requiring 29 digits in the decimal system.

The third example is the misleading formula

$$1 + 3 + 5 + 7 + \ldots + (2n - 1) = n^2 + (n - 1)(n - 2)(n - 3)(n - 4),$$

which happens to be correct for $n = 1, 2, 3, 4$. Were we to have tested it for these values only, we might have been inclined to accept it, but it works for no other value of n.

We can conclude that ordinary induction, while indispensable, is as fallible in mathematics as in life, and that certainty, even in a practical sense, is not to be had in the absence of actual proof.

EXERCISES

1. Give a formula that is like the third example, but which is valid for the first thousand positive integers and no other.

2. Examine the expression $n^2 + n + 11$ as a prime generator. Try out other such expressions.

3.

Arithmetic progressions and the arithmetic mean

Given a finite set of numbers, consider their sum. The *arithmetic mean* of the numbers is the value each would have to have if all the numbers were equal and still possessed the same sum. (The terms *mean* and *average* frequently are used as synonyms for arithmetic mean.) Since, for instance,

$$1 + 2 = 3$$

and

$$1\,1/2 + 1\,1/2 = 3,$$

the arithmetic mean of 1 and 2 is 1 1/2. Since

$$4 + 5 + 9 = 18$$

and

$$6 + 6 + 6 = 18,$$

the arithmetic mean of the three numbers 4, 5, and 9 is 6. In general, let $a_1, a_2, \ldots, a_n$ denote the given numbers and let

$$s = a_1 + a_2 + \ldots + a_n$$

denote their sum. If the arithmetic mean of these n numbers is designated by y, we must have

$$s = y + y + \ldots + y,$$

the right side consisting of n summands, each equal to y. Therefore,

$$s = ny$$

and, as we find now by dividing by n,

$$y = s/n.$$

We have proved the following statement: *The arithmetic mean of n numbers is equal to the sum of the numbers divided by n.*

EXERCISES

1. Find the arithmetic mean of 0, 3, 5, 6, 7, 7, 8, 8, 9, 10, 12, 15, 19, 24.
2. Prove that the arithmetic mean of two numbers is the value midway between. HINT: If the two numbers are called a and b, their arithmetic mean is $(a + b)/2$. Suppose, say, that $a \leq b$ (i.e., is less than or equal to b—see Chapter 2, Section 8). We must then show that

$$(a + b)/2 - a = b - (a + b)/2.$$

See Figure 10-4.

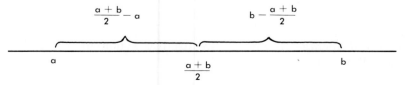

FIGURE 10-4   *The arithmetic mean of two numbers.*

3. If A denotes the arithmetic mean of n numbers $a_1, a_2, \ldots, a_n$, the differences

$$a_1 - A, a_2 - A, \ldots, a_n - A$$

are called the *deviations* of the numbers from the mean. Show that the sum of the deviations is zero.

4. If n numbers are not all equal, show that their arithmetic mean is less than the largest, and is greater than the smallest, of the numbers. HINT: Let the numbers be symbolized by $a_1, \ldots, a_n$ with a_1 denoting the largest. The arithmetic mean A is given by the expression

$$A = (1/n)(a_1 + \ldots + a_n).$$

Since not all the summands are equal and a_1 is the largest, at least one summand is less than a_1 so that the foregoing expression will increase if each summand by replaced by a_1. Thus,

$$A = (1/n)(a_1 + a_2 + \ldots + a_n)$$
$$< (1/n)(a_1 + a_1 + \ldots + a_1) = (1/n)(na_1) = a_1.$$

Hence, $A < a_1$, i.e., the arithmetic mean falls short of the maximum, as asserted. A similar argument applies to the minimum.

5. Let A denote the mean of n quantities, and B the mean of m other quantities. Show that the mean of all $m + n$ quantities combined is

$$(nA + mB)/(n + m).$$

6. A student has an overall grade average of 2.2 for the work of his first three terms. Assuming that he always takes the same number of credits each semester, what must his average for his fourth term be to bring his overall average for the first four terms up to 2.5?

7. Let c denote the mean weight (in ounces) of the candy packed by a certain firm, and let b denote the mean weight (in ounces) of the boxes and wrappings. Show that the mean weight of a complete package, consisting of candy, box, and wrappings, then is $b + c$ ounces.

8. If A denotes the arithmetic mean of n numbers $a_1, a_2, \ldots, a_n$, prove that

$$(1/n)[(a_1 - A)^2 + (a_2 - A)^2 + \ldots + (a_n - A)^2]$$
$$= (1/n)[(a_1)^2 + (a_2)^2 + \ldots + (a_n)^2] - A^2.$$

In words, *the mean squared deviation from the mean is equal to the mean square minus the squared mean.*

9. The *geometric mean* of two positive numbers is the (positive) value each would have to have if they were equal and still possessed the same *product.*

    (a) Find the geometric mean of 4 and 9.

    (b) Derive a general formula for the geometric mean of any two (positive) numbers a and b.

(c) Prove that, if two positive numbers a and b are different, their geometric mean is less than their arithmetic mean. HINT: What is to be proved is that, when $a \neq b$, $\sqrt{ab} < (1/2)(a + b)$. Square both sides and use the algebraic identities

$$(x + y)^2 = x^2 + 2xy + y^2, \quad (x - y)^2 = x^2 - 2xy + y^2.$$

An *arithmetic progression* is a sequence of numbers such that consecutive members (or terms) of the sequence differ by a constant amount. Examples are:

(a) 1, 3, 5, 7
(b) 4, 9, 14, 19, 24
(c) 29, 31, 33,

consecutive members differing in Example (a) by 2, in Example (b) by 5, and in Example (c) by 2 again. The sum of an arithmetic progression—i.e., the sum of the members of the progression—divided by the number of members is the (arithmetic) mean of these members. Hence, to know the mean of the constituent members of an arithmetic progression, and to know their number, is to know the sum of the progression. It is possible to find the mean with very little calculation.

To see how this is so, let us calculate the means of the numbers involved in the preceding progressions. The mean in Example (a) is $16/4 = 4$, the mean in Example (b) is $70/5 = 14$, and the mean in Example (c) is $93/3 = 31$. These are plotted in Figure 10-5, the positions of the means being indicated by vertical arrows. The figures show that, at least for the progressions considered, the *arithmetic mean of all the terms of a progression is equal to the arithmetic mean of the first and last terms only.* We shall see, when we express the matter in symbols, that this is always so.

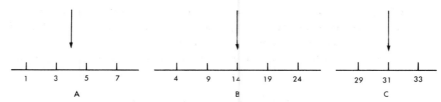

Figure 10-5 *Certain arithmetic progressions and the arithmetic means of their terms. (The vertical arrows indicate the arithmetic means.)*

Consider an arbitrary arithmetic progression. Let

$a =$ the first term of the progression
$d =$ the difference between consecutive terms
$l =$ the last term of the progression
$n =$ the number of terms in the progression.

The second term of the progression then will be $a + d$, the third term $a + 2d$, the fourth term $a + 3d$, and so forth. If k is any natural number not exceeding n, the kth term thus will be $a + (k - 1)d$, the last or nth term, in particular, being

$$(1) \qquad l = a + (n - 1)d.$$

EXERCISE

10. Prove by mathematical induction that $l = a + (n - 1)d$.

The sum of an arbitrary arithmetic progression, by the foregoing, is the sum of the n numbers

$$a, a + d, a + 2d, \ldots, a + (n - 1)d.$$

We shall denote the sum by the symbol s_n, the index referring explicity to the number of terms of the sequence being summed. Thus

$$(2) \qquad s_n = a + (a + d) + (a + 2d) + \ldots + (a + (n - 1)d).$$

In this notation, the arithmetic mean of the n numbers summed on the right side of (2) can be written as s_n/n. The arithmetic mean of the first and last terms is

$$(1/2)\,(a + l) = (1/2)\,[a + (a + (n - 1)d)] = (1/2)\,[2a + (n - 1)d]$$
$$= a + (1/2)\,(n - 1)d.$$

Hence, the proposition we are examining that the mean of all the terms is equal to the mean of the first and last is expressed by the equations

$$(3) \qquad s_n/n = (1/2)\,(a + l) = a + (1/2)\,(n - 1)d.$$

We shall justify these equations by mathematical induction on n.

The first step in the induction is to verify (3) for $n = 1$. For $n = 1$, the relation states, however, merely that $s_1 = a$, which is certainly true.

The second and final step in the induction is to prove that relation (3), if true for $n = k$, also is true for $n = k + 1$. For $n = k$, statement (3) reads:

$$s_k/k = a + (1/2)\,(k - 1)d.$$

Let us multiply both sides by k to obtain the equivalent (since $k \neq 0$) statement

$$(4) \qquad s_k = ka + (1/2)k(k - 1)d.$$

For $n = k + 1$, statement (3) reads:

$$s_{k+1}/(k+1) = a + (1/2)kd,$$

which, similarly, is equivalent to

(5) $$s_{k+1} = (k+1)a + (1/2)(k+1)kd.$$

Thus, we must prove that (4) implies (5). To do so, we note from (2) that, of the $k + 1$ terms involved in s_{k+1}, the first k are those of s_k, and the last is equal to $a + kd$. Hence,

$$s_{k+1} = s_k + a + kd.$$

Since we are supposing (4), we thus have

$$\begin{aligned} s_{k+1} &= ka + (1/2)k(k-1)d + a + kd \\ &= (k+1)a + (1/2)k(k+1)d. \end{aligned}$$

(This is because $(1/2)k(k-1) + k = (1/2)k^2 - (1/2)k + k = (1/2)k^2 + (1/2)k = (1/2)k(k+1)$.) This, however, is relation (5), the one we had desired to verify. Our mathematical induction thus is complete and formula (3) completely justified.

The first relation in (3), multiplied by n, reads

$$s_n = n(a + l)/2.$$

This is to say that

$$s_n = (a + l)/2 + (a + l)/2 + \ldots + (a + l)/2,$$

n summands, each equal to $(a + l)/2$, appearing on the right. Since the number of terms in the progression is n, we thus have the following rule: *The sum of an arithmetic progression is equal to the sum that is obtained when each term in the progression is replaced by the arithmetic mean of the first and last terms.* The value of the last term of course is known from formula (1) in terms of the first term and the difference between successive terms.

EXERCISES

11. Find the sum of all the integers from 1 to 100, inclusive.
12. Calculate the sum of:
   (a) The first fifteen multiples of 3 (3, 6, 9, . . .).
   (b) The first twenty terms of 1000, 995, 990, ...
   (c) 1, 3, 5, 7, 9, 11, . . . , 49.
13. Use the theory of this section to prove that

$$1 + 3 + 5 + \ldots + (2n - 1) = n^2.$$

14. A man takes a job starting at $4000 per year. At the end of each year he gets a raise of $100 per year. How much has he earned after thirty years?

4.

Geometric progressions

For an arbitrary number x, the succession

$$1, x, x^2, x^3, x^4, x^5, \ldots$$

is called a *geometric progression with ratio x; x* is the ratio of each new term to the previous. For instance,

$$1, 3, 9, 27, 81, 243, 729, \ldots$$

is a geometric progression with ratio 3, while

$$1, 1/3, 1/9, 1/27, 1/81, 1/243, 1/729, \ldots$$

is a geometric progression with ratio 1/3. Geometric and arithmetic progressions were of central importance in a famous argument of Malthus, first advanced in 1798, that population tends to outrun subsistence. The author summarized his view as follows:

> I said that population, when unchecked, increased in a geometrical ratio, and subsistence for man in an arithmetical ratio.
> Let us examine whether this position be just. . . .
> In the United States of America, where the means of subsistence have been more ample, the manners of the people more pure, and consequently the checks to early marriages fewer than in any of the modern states of Europe, the population has been found to double itself in twenty-five years.
> This ratio of increase, though short of the utmost power of population, yet as the result of actual experience, we will take as our rule, and say, that population, when unchecked, goes on doubling itself every twenty-five years or increases in a geometrical ratio.
> Let us now take any spot of earth, this island† for instance, and see in what ratio the subsistence it affords can be supposed to increase.
> If I allow that by the best possible policy . . . the produce of this Island may be doubled in the first twenty-five years, I think it will be allowing as much as any person can well demand.
> In the next twenty-five years, it is impossible to suppose that the produce could be quadrupled. It would be contrary to all our knowledge of the qualities of land. The very utmost that we can conceive, is, that the increase in the second twenty-five years might equal the present produce. Let us then take this for our rule, though certainly far beyond the truth, and allow that by great exertion, the whole produce of the Island might be increased every twenty-five years, by a quantity of subsistence equal to what it at present produces. The most enthusiastic speculator cannot suppose a greater increase than this. In a few centuries it would make every acre of land in the Island like a garden.
> Yet this ratio of increase is evidently arithmetical.
> It may be fairly said, therefore, that the means of subsistence increase in an arithmetical ratio. Let us now bring the effects of these two ratios together.
> The population of the Island is computed to be about seven millions, and we will suppose the present produce equal to the support of such a number. In the first twenty-five years, the population would be fourteen millions, and the food being also doubled, the means of subsistence would be equal to this increase. In the next twenty-five years the population would be twenty-eight millions, and the means of subsistence only

----

† "This Island" means England.

equal to the support of twenty-one millions. In the next period, the population would be fifty-six millions, and the means of subsistence just sufficient for half that number. And at the conclusion of the first century the population would be one hundred and twelve millions and the means of subsistence only equal to the support of thirty-five millions, which would leave a population of seventy-seven millions totally unprovided for. . . .

But to make the argument more general . . ., let us take the whole earth, instead of one spot, and suppose that the restraints to population were universally removed. If the subsistence for man that the earth affords was to be increased every twenty-five years by a quantity equal to what the whole world at present produces, this would allow the power of production in the earth to be absolutely unlimited, and its ratio of increase much greater than we can conceive that any possible exertions of mankind could make it.

Taking the population of the world at any number, a thousand millions, for instance, the human species would increase in the ratio of 1, 2, 4, 8, 16, 32, 64, 128, 256, 512, etc. and subsistence as 1, 2, 3, 4, 5, 6, 7, 8, 9, 10, etc. In two centuries and a quarter, the population would be to the means of subsistence as 512 to 10; in three centuries as 4096 to 13, and in two thousand years the difference would be almost incalculable, though the produce in that time would have increased to an immense extent.

No limits whatever are placed to the productions of the earth; they may increase for ever and be greater than any assignable quantity; yet still the power of population being a power of a superior order, the increase of the human species can only be kept commensurate to the increase of the means of subsistence, by the constant operation of the strong law of necessity acting as a check upon the greater power.†

Here is a different situation in which a geometric progression appears. A corporation attracts junior executives by promising a five per cent raise in pay yearly. A man earning a dollars his first year would receive, under this scheme, $a + (.05)a$, that is, $(1.05)a$, dollars his second year. The third year he would receive

$$(1.05) \cdot (\text{second year's salary}) = (1.05) \cdot [(1.05)a] = (1.05)^2a,$$

the fourth year,

$$(1.05) \cdot (\text{third year's salary}) = (1.05) \cdot [(1.05)^2a] = (1.05)^3a,$$

and so forth. The nth year, his salary would be

$$(1.05)^{n-1}a.$$

EXERCISE

1. Prove the last statement by mathematical induction.

The starting salary, which we denoted by a, was rather low, but the raises promised would bring compensation to an attractive level after a few years. However, total compensation received during these years would also be a consideration. During k years,

$$a + (1.05)a + (1.05)^2a + (1.05)^3a + \ldots + (1.05)^{k-1}a$$

†Thomas Robert Malthus, *On Population*, London, 1798 (reprinted by Modern Library, Random House, 1960), pp. 11-13.

dollars would have been received. This is equal to a multiplied by

$$1 + 1.05 + (1.05)^2 + (1.05)^3 + \ldots + (1.05)^{k-1}.$$

The last expression is of the form

$$1 + x + x^2 + x^3 + x^4 + \ldots + x^{k-1}$$

(with $x = 1.05$); it is called a *geometric series*.

Geometric series arise in innumerable connections, and it is thus fortunate that we can evaluate them by a simple formula. Anyone who notices what happens when we multiply the previous expression by $x - 1$ will be well on his way to the formula. To illustrate, let us work out

$$(x - 1)(1 + x + x^2 + x^3).$$

Distributing the multiplications by x and by -1 separately upon the terms of the right hand factor, we obtain:

$$\begin{aligned}(x - 1)(1 + x + x^2 + x^3) = \quad & x + x^2 + x^3 + x^4 \\ & -1 - x - x^2 - x^3 \\ = \; x^4 - 1 \end{aligned}$$

after several cancellations. Similar cancellations will occur with any value of k, and we should therefore expect:

(1) $$(x - 1)(1 + x + x^2 + \ldots + x^{k-1}) = x^k - 1.$$

From this, the desired formula for the sum of a geometric series is immediate:

(2) $$1 + x + x^2 + \ldots + x^{k-1} = (x^k - 1)/(x - 1) \text{ provided } x \neq 1.$$

EXERCISES

2. Prove formula (1) by mathematical induction.

3. This question refers to the junior executive with the assured annual raise. (a) How much will he earn in four years if his first year's salary is $5,000? (b) How much will he earn in eight years?

Here is a simple application of the geometric series in the theory of numbers.† We recall that a prime is a natural number that is divisible by no natural number other than itself or 1.

---

†See, for instance, Daniel Shanks, *Solved and Unsolved Problems in Number Theory*, Vol. 1, Chapter 1, Spartan Books, Washington, D.C., 1962.

Theorem (Cataldi-Fermat).   If 2^n-1 is a prime, then n is a prime.

PROOF: Suppose that 2^n-1 is a prime. If n is not a prime, then

$$n = rs,$$

where r and s are certain natural numbers greater than 1. Thus,

$$2^n - 1 = 2^{rs} - 1$$
$$= (2^r)^s - 1$$
$$= a^s - 1,$$

where $a = 2^r$. Since r is greater than 1, a is at least 4. But by (1) (with a substituted for x and s for k),

$$a^s - 1 = (a - 1)(1 + a + a^2 + \ldots + a^{s-1}).$$

This tells us that $a - 1$ (which is at least 3) divides $a^s - 1$, contrary to our supposition that $a^s - 1$ is a prime. This contradiction arose because we assumed that n was not prime. We therefore conclude that n is prime, as contended.

5.

Mathematical induction for polygons

Wherever whole numbers are important, mathematical induction may enter. In this and the next section are some examples from geometry.

By a *polygon* we shall mean a plane figure consisting of a finite number of straight line segments joined consecutively end to end in a chain (Figure 10-6A). The straight line segments are called the *sides*, the ends of these segments are called the *vertices*, of the polygon. A polygon is said to be *closed* if the chain is closed, i.e., if the first and last segments also join at their ends, two segments then issuing from every vertex (Figure 10-6B). A straight line segment between

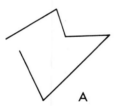 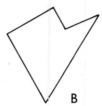

A   B   C

FIGURE 10-6.   A, a polygon; B, a closed polygon; C, a convex, closed polygon.

two nonadjacent vertices is called a *diagonal* of the polygon. A closed polygon is *convex* if no part of any of its diagonals is in the region of the plane exterior to the polygon (Figure 10-6*C*).

a. THE NUMBER OF VERTICES OF A POLYGON

A three-sided closed polygon (a triangle) has three vertices, a four-sided closed polygon (a quadrilateral) has four vertices, and a five-sided closed polygon has five vertices, and so forth (Figure 10-7).

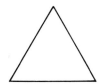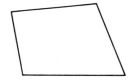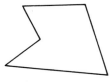

FIGURE 10-7   *Some closed polygons.*

EXERCISE

1. Prove that an *n*-sided closed polygon has *n* vertices. Assume for simplicity that the polygon is convex. HINT: Drawing a diagonal, cut the given figure into polygons with fewer sides.

b. THE EXTERIOR ANGLES OF A POLYGON

Consider any closed polygon, and assume for simplicity that it is convex. In this case, the smaller angle between the two sides intersecting at a given vertex *P* is called the *interior angle* at *P*, and its complement, i.e.,

$$180° \text{ minus the interior angle,}$$

is called the *exterior angle* at *P*. In Figure 10-8, for example, $\angle OPQ$ is the interior angle at *P* and $\angle RPQ$ is the exterior angle at *P*.

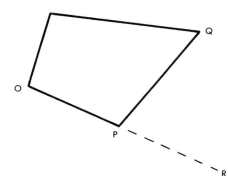

FIGURE 10-8   *Exterior angle of a polygon.*

It is a striking fact that the sum of the exterior angles of a closed polygon is 360° regardless of the number of sides. We can convince ourselves of this—yet without actually proving it—in the following way.†

Consider, for instance, a convex quadrilateral $ABCD$, as in Figure 10-9. We place an arrow with its tail at A pointing in the direction DA (i.e., oriented along the line DA and pointing in the opposite direction

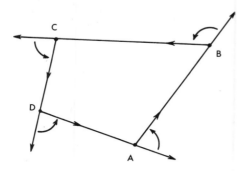

FIGURE 10-9 *The exterior angles of a quadrilateral.*

from D). Keeping the tail of the arrow fixed at A, turn the arrow counterclockwise until it lies along the line AB: the arrow thereby sweeps through the exterior angle at A. Without altering the arrow's newly acquired direction, move it now along AB until its tail is at the point B. Then, keeping the tail at B, swing the arrow counterclockwise until it has the same direction as BC: in this movement, the arrow sweeps through the exterior angle at B. The next two steps are like the previous two: move the arrow along BC until its tail is at C, turn it counterclockwise, move it along CD until its tail is at D, and turn it counterclockwise until its direction is that of DA. This is the original direction, and the arrow thus has turned a total of 360° simply by swinging successively in the same (counterclockwise) sense through all the exterior angles of the quadrilateral. Hence, the sum of the exterior angles is 360°, as asserted.

This type of reasoning, intuitively persuasive, but avoiding the explicit premises of geometry, is called "heuristic." Are these premises sufficient to prove the intuitively evident result, or do they fall short? This question can be settled affirmatively only by formal demonstration.

---

†This way is suggested by G. D. Birkhoff and R. Beatley in Fig. 26, p. 87 of their book, *Basic Geometry*, Third Edition. First published by Scott, Foresman, 1940, 1941. Reprinted by Chelsea.

EXERCISES

1. Prove by mathematical induction that the sum of the exterior angles of a closed polygon is 360°. For simplicity consider convex polygons.

2. For $n \geq 5$, form an "n-pointed star" as follows. Take an n-sided convex

polygon. Number its sides 1, 2, ..., n consecutively, agreeing to denote sides 1 and 2 by $n + 1$ and $n + 2$, respectively, upon occasion. For $k = 1, 2, ...,$ n, assume sides k and $k + 2$ to be nonparallel, and prolong these sides until they meet. The figure that results is called an *n-pointed star*. Figure 10-10 illustrates the cases $n = 5, 6$. By a heuristic argument analogous to the foregoing, find the sum of the interior angles at the n points of the star. (Hints are given in Figure 10-10.) Then justify your result from the previous result concerning the sum of the exterior angles of a polygon.

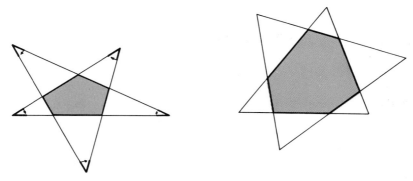

FIGURE 10-10

C. TRIANGULATION OF POLYGONS

If $A_1, A_2, ..., A_n$ denote the vertices of an n-sided polygon, in order, we shall designate the polygon itself as $A_1 A_2 ... A_n$.

EXERCISE

1. Prove by mathematical induction that any n-sided convex polygon can be divided into $n - 2$ triangles by nonintersecting diagonals. HINT: Consider any one of the divisions of a given n-sided polygon $A_1 A_2 ... A_n$. Let $A_1 A_k$ be one of the diagonals of the division considered. It divides the polygon into two smaller polygons.

6.

The areas of similar regions

Two regions are "similar" if, roughly, they are of the same shape, but possibly of different sizes. To give a definition suitable for our purposes, consider plane regions that are made up of a number of nonoverlapping triangular subregions. Suppose S and T to be such regions (Figure 10-11 illustrates) consisting of the same number of

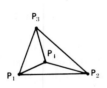
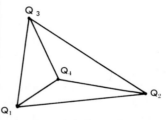

FIGURE 10-11   *Similar regions with appropriate labeling of corresponding vertices.*

triangular pieces, say S, of the triangles

$$U_1, U_2, \ldots, U_n$$

and T of the triangles

$$V_1, V_2, \ldots, V_n.$$

Two U's are permitted to share a side and two or more U's to have a vertex in common, but otherwise no two U's are supposed to intersect; similarly for the V's. (In other words, the U's constitute a dissection of S and the V's of T. See Section 3, Chapter 7.) We suppose that all the vertices of the U's are listed without repetitions as

$$P_1, P_2, \ldots, P_m$$

and that the vertices of the V's can be listed without repetitions as

$$Q_1, Q_2, \ldots, Q_m$$

in such a way that

$$P_r P_s = c \cdot Q_r Q_s$$

and

$$\angle P_r P_s P_t = \angle Q_r Q_s Q_t,$$

where r, s, t are any different indices from 1 to m, inclusive, and where c is a positive constant. These conditions say simply that corresponding distances are proportional, and corresponding angles equal, in the two regions S and T. When this is the case, we say that S and T are *similar* and that P_k and Q_k *correspond* for $k = 1, \ldots, m$.

Suppose S and T to be similar and to have dissections into triangles as indicated. Then each triangle U_k, in particular, is similar to the triangle in T with the corresponding vertices; we shall assume that this triangle is named V_k. By assumption, each side of U_k bears the same ratio to the corresponding side of V_k as c bears to 1. Hence

(Section 3, Chapter 7),

$$A(U_k)/A(V_k) = c^2,$$

where $A(U)$ denotes the area of U, and so on. As a consequence, we have the following theorem.

Theorem.   Under the previous hypotheses,

$$A(S)/A(T) = c^2.$$

In words: if two similar regions have linear measurements in the ratio $c:1$, then their areas are in the ratio $c^2:1$.

We shall prove a special case of this theorem, leaving the general cases to the reader. Consider two similar regions such as are diagrammed in Figure 10-12. We assume, in particular, that any

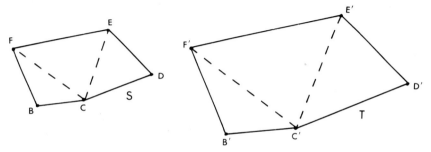

FIGURE 10-12   *Similar regions.*

distance in the first region bears the same ratio to the corresponding distance in the second as c bears to 1, where $c > 0$. The remarks preceding the statement of the theorem show that

$$A(BCF) = c^2 \, A(B'C'F'),$$
$$A(FCE) = c^2 \, A(F'C'E'),$$
$$A(CDE) = c^2 \, A(C'D'E').$$

Hence,

$$A(S) = A(BCF) + A(FCE) + A(CDE)$$
$$= c^2[A(B'C'F') + A(F'C'E') + A(C'D'E')]$$
$$= c^2 \, A(T).$$

This is the required result.

EXERCISE

1. Prove the theorem by mathematical induction.

7.

Maps and Euler's formula†

In the plane, consider segments of curves that may intersect only at certain points, $A_1, \ldots, A_v$ which also are their end points. These segments make up a network, which we assume to be *connected,* i.e., to be such that any one of the points $A_1, \ldots, A_v$ can be reached by traveling along the network from any other (Figure 10-13). The network is called a *map,* the given points $A_1, \ldots, A_v$ its *vertices,* the given segments of curves connecting vertices its *boundary segments,* and the pieces into which the network of segments divides the plane the *countries* of the map. The infinite part of the plane outside the network is considered one of the countries.

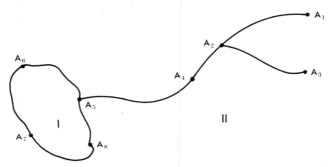

FIGURE 10-13   A map.

In Figure 10-13, the points A_1, A_2, A_3, A_4, A_5, A_6, A_7, A_8 are the vertices, the segments A_1A_2, A_2A_3, A_2A_4, A_4A_5, A_5A_6, A_7A_8, A_5A_8, A_6A_7 the boundary segments, and I and II the countries of the map.

A precise relation exists between the number of countries c, the number of vertices v, and the number of boundary segments b. We might arrive at the relation heuristically by the following reasoning, in which we begin with a map consisting of one boundary segment and its two end points as vertices. For this map, $b = 1, v = 2, c = 1$, and the relation

$$\text{(1)} \qquad\qquad v = b + 1$$

obtains. Joining a second segment to the first results in an increase of 1 in both b and v (Figure 10-14), so that equation (1) remains correct.

FIGURE 10-14 *Maps consisting of one or two boundary segments.*

†This and the following section are modeled after a treatment of Golovina and Yaglom, *op. cit.*, pp. 22-25.

Attaching a third boundary segment may have the same effect (Figure 10-15), raising both b and v by 1 and thereby preserving equality (1). If the third boundary segment (Figure 10-15), however,

FIGURE 10-15   *Maps with three segments.*

joins vertices already belonging to the first and second segments, then v is not changed, while for the first time a finite country is outlined in this map; c thus increases by 1 along with b. The equation

(2) $$v + c = b + 2$$

had held for the previous map (with two segments) because of (1) and the condition $c = 1$. Both sides of this equation increase by 1 when the third segment is attached (whether a country is closed off in the process or not), and their equality therefore is preserved. One can imagine continuing to attach boundary segments, one at a time, to this figure, at each step either increasing both b and v by 1 without changing c, or increasing both b and c by 1 without changing v. In either case, both sides of equation (2) would increase by 1, the equation thus being preserved. Thereby maintaining itself from step to step, equation (2) should be expected to be correct for every map.

Equation (2) was discovered by Leonhard Euler, the 18th Century Swiss mathematician, and bears his name.

The foregoing heuristic argument took for granted that we can arrive at any map by starting from a single segment and attaching further segments one at a time. We shall avoid this question, now demonstrating formula (2) by independent means. As the heuristic argument suggests, mathematical induction is used with respect to the number of boundary segments, b. The least possible value of b, the number of boundary segments, is zero, and the first of the two steps in the induction thus is to prove (2) in the case in which $b = 0$. (In our previous terminology, S_k here would represent the statement, "Euler's relation is true if $b = k - 1$." S_1 would be the statement that Euler's relation is true if $b = 0$.) A map without boundary segments, however, has just one vertex—with more than one vertex, the map would fail to be connected. The map also has just one country consisting of the entire plane outside the single vertex. When $b = 0$, therefore, $v = 1$ and $c = 1$, and relation (2) is seen to be true. This completes the first step in the process of mathematical induction.

For the second step in the mathematical induction, we assume relation (2) to be valid for an arbitrary map with n boundary segments and consider a map, which we denote by M_{n+1}, with $n + 1$ boundary segments. Let c and v denote the numbers of countries and of vertices, respectively, in the map M_{n+1}. To complete the mathematical induction, we must prove Euler's relation for this map.

By a simple closed network path we shall mean a figure consisting of boundary segments joined consecutively end to end, the first and last segments also being joined at their ends. ($A_5 A_6 A_7 A_8 A_5$ in Figure 10-13 is such a path.) Any simple closed network path is connected; moreover, the figure obtained from a simple closed network path by deleting one of its boundary segments is connected (Figure 10-16).

The nature of our argument depends on whether or not the map being considered contains a simple closed network path; we will show that the theorem can be proved in either case.

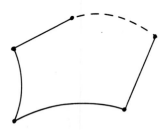

FIGURE 10-16 A simple closed network path with one segment deleted.

Case 1:   The map M_{n+1} contains a simple closed network path. In this case, we change M_{n+1} into a new map M_n by removing a boundary segment belonging to a simple closed network path but without removing the vertices that are the end points of the segment. The new map is still connected. It contains one fewer boundary segment and one fewer country than the old but has the same number of vertices. Thus

$$c - 1 = \text{number of countries in } M_n$$
$$n = \text{number of boundary segments in } M_n$$
$$v = \text{number of vertices in } M_n.$$

By assumption, however, Euler's relation applies to M_n. Hence,

$$c - 1 + v = n + 2,$$

from which equation we immediately see that

$$c + v = (n + 1) + 2,$$

the relation concerning M_{n+1} we were seeking.

Case 2:   The map M_{n+1} contains no simple closed network path (Figure 10-17). We shall see that in this case there is at least one vertex belonging (as an end point) to just one boundary segment. Such a vertex we shall call an *extremity* of the map.

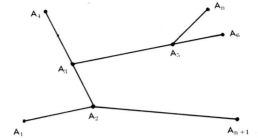

FIGURE 10-17 A map with no simple closed network path.

To find an extremity, pick an arbitrary vertex of the map. Starting from this vertex, travel along successive, arbitrarily selected boundary segments, never reversing direction. Because no simple closed network path exists, no vertex in this journey will be encountered twice. Thus the journey must eventually end, there being but a finite number of boundary segments, and the last vertex encountered is an extremity.

Knowing an extremity to exist, let us change M_{n+1} into a new map by removing both the extremity and the boundary segment on which it lies (but not the vertex that is the other end of the segment). In Figure 10-17, for example, we might remove A_5A_6. The new map N_n contains one fewer boundary segment and one fewer vertex than the old but has the same number of countries, namely, one. Thus,

$$c = 1 = \text{number of countries in } N_n$$
$$n = \text{number of boundary segments in } N_n$$
$$v - 1 = \text{number of vertices in } N_n.$$

By assumption, however, Euler's relation applies to N_n. Hence,

$$c + v - 1 = n + 2,$$

from which we see, as in the previous case, that

$$c + v = (n + 1) + 2,$$

the relations concerning M_{n+1} we wished to prove.

In Section 8 we shall give an example of how Euler's formula may be applied.

8.

An application of Euler's formula

Theorem.   If at least three boundaries meet at every vertex, then at least one country in the map has no more than five boundary segments around it.

PROOF: If we cut each boundary segment into two pieces, each vertex is a meeting place of at least three such pieces. The number of such pieces, therefore, is at least three times the number of vertices. The number of such pieces, however, is twice the number of boundary segments. Hence,

$$2b \geq 3v.$$

Now suppose that, contrary to the theorem, a map satisfying the vertex hypothesis exists, each country of which has more than five segments around it. Each country in this map would be surrounded by a simple closed network path consisting of at least six boundary segments. If the boundary segments are listed for each country and the lists combined, without eliminating duplications, at least $6c$ boundary segments would appear in the combined list. Each boundary segment, however, separates two countries and thus will appear exactly twice on the combined list. Hence, at least $6c/2 = 3c$ *different* boundary segments appear on this list, so that

$$b \geq 3c.$$

The inequalities of the previous two paragraphs are equivalent to

$$v \leq (2/3)b$$

and

$$c \leq (1/3)b,$$

respectively. Put so, they are seen clearly to imply

$$c + v \leq (1/3)b + (2/3)b$$

and thus

$$c + v \leq b.$$

Hence,

$$c + v < b + 1,$$

which contradicts Euler's relation (2) and thus is impossible. No map can satisfy the hypothesis in the foregoing theorem, therefore, and escape the conclusion. The theorem, in other words, is correct, as asserted.

9.

Well-ordering

The principle of mathematical induction at its purest is a law of positive integers. As such, it can be stated as follows:

Let A denote a set of positive integers with the two following properties:

(I) A contains 1.
(II) If A contains n, then A contains $n + 1$.

Then A is the set of all positive integers.

EXERCISES

1. Prove that this formulation and that given in terms of statements S_n (Section 1) are logically equivalent.
2. Replace Hypothesis (II) in this section by

(II′) If A contains all the integers from 1 up to and including n, then A contains $n + 1$.

Prove under Hypothesis (I) and (II′) that A is the set of all positive integers.

Attempts to study the logical origins of the natural numbers, i.e., to define them and to define addition and multiplication explicitly, and from their definitions to deduce their arithmetical properties, rely on mathematical induction heavily. Thus, mathematical induction must be regarded as one of the most fundamental of all the laws that govern the positive integers (and hence one of the most fundamental of all mathematical laws). Could so fundamental a law have been proved from anything less fundamental than itself? If the reader reexamines our proof of mathematical induction (Section 1), he will find that it depends upon the following property, which was assumed: any set of positive integers has a *least* member, i.e., a member that exceeds no other member of the set. This is called the property of being *well ordered*.

May this property be even more basic than that of mathematical induction? We shall show that the two properties are in fact equivalent: either entails the other. Therefore, they are equally fundamental.

As we already know, the well-ordering property implies the principle of mathematical induction. We shall now prove that, conversely, the principle of mathematical induction implies the well-ordering property.

Accordingly, assume the principle of mathematical induction. We must show that any nonvoid set S of positive integers contains a member N, a positive integer, not greater than any other member of S. Suppose, to the contrary, that S has no such least integer. Our aim is somehow to use mathematical induction to prove that this supposition is contradictory and, thus, untenable. If S has no least integer, then S certainly does not contain 1, this being the least positive integer of all.

Under the present supposition, therefore, the statement

$$S_1: \text{"S does not contain 1"}$$

is true. Consider the family of statements

$$S_n: \text{"S does not contain the integers from 1 to } n, \text{ inclusive"}$$

for $n = 1, 2, \ldots$. S_1 has been shown to be true. Thus, condition (I) of Section 1 has been verified, and condition (II) remains.

EXERCISES

3. Verify condition (II) and complete the argument to prove the equivalence of the principle of mathematical induction to the well-orderedness property.

4. Use the well-orderedness property in place of mathematical induction to argue the ancestor question already discussed in Section 1.

CHAPTER 11

THE THEORY OF NUMBERS

1.

The origins of number theory

The so-called theory of numbers refers to whole numbers only. It goes back to the Babylonians and their formulas:[†] algebraic identities such as

$$(a + b)^2 = a^2 + 2ab + b^2, \ (a + b)(a - b) = a^2 - b^2;$$

rules for summing arithmetic and other progressions, including

$$1 + 2 + 4 + 8 + \ldots + 2^n = 2^n + (2^n - 1),$$
$$1^2 + 2^2 + 3^2 + 4^2 + \ldots + n^2 = (1/3) + (2/3)n(1 + 2 + 3 + 4 + \ldots + n)$$

(see Chapter 10, Sections 1 to 4); formulas for numbers x, y, z that satisfy the condition $x^2 + y^2 = z^2$. (Such numbers were later called Pythagorean triples. See Chapter 4, Section 1.)

In the 6th Century B.C., Babylonian knowledge of numbers was transmitted to certain Greeks. Tradition has it that one of these, Pythagoras, had traveled in the Near East and there become imbued with number lore. Later, in Italy, Pythagoras founded and led a secret movement, known to history as the Pythagoreans, which was in part mathematical and scientific and in which the theory of numbers was a prime pursuit. The Pythagorean brotherhood was also musical,

---

[†]This summary of Babylonian achievement comes from B. L. Van der Waerden, *Science Awakening*, P. Noordhoff Ltd., Groningen, Holland, 1954, p. 80.

mystical, magical, political, and from first to last, religious. In their eyes, mathematics and science were religious occupations. They worshipped Apollo; Pythagoras — more than human, less than divine — was their prophet.†

"The history of Pythagoreanism is perhaps the most controversial subject in all Greek philosophy, and much about it must remain obscure."‡ Perhaps the main reason is the secrecy to which Pythagoreans were sworn. In any case, no Pythagorean writings exist at all before the end of the 5th Century B.C., extant allusions to their doctrines by other contemporaries are very few, and most of our information comes from writers of the 1st Century B.C. and later, when Pythagoreanism underwent a revival. These writers used earlier sources now lost but were often careless, uncritical, and otherwise unreliable. Thus, our knowledge is necessarily uncertain. Nevertheless, by close study of all the information available, painstaking checking and comparing, and some guessing from present knowledge of psychology and anthropology, modern scholars hope to have arrived at a picture of the Pythagoreans that is at least generally true. The following discussion follows Guthrie§ in almost all respects; in mathematical matters, it follows van der Waerden.††

In the background of Pythagoras's religious conceptions, which were at the core of his philosophy, was an apparently common Greek belief that the cosmos is surrounded by an eternal, invisible, inextinguishable fiery substance that is also living, intelligent, and divine. This substance was called *aither*. Changes it caused in itself brought about all other things. Remaining perfect and pure only outside or at the boundaries of the cosmos, aither penetrated everything to some extent. The souls of living creatures were actual fragments of aither, immortal, but contaminated. Because all things derived more or less remotely from aither, all things were related. All living things were close kin to one another.

In common with the worshippers of Orpheus, Pythagoras believed that the body of a mortal creature was the tomb of its soul. When the body died, the soul issued forth only to migrate into the body of another living creature, which became another tomb. But the soul could avoid an eternal succession of incarcerations in flesh and be re-united forever with its divine source by being purified. To purify and thereby deliver their souls, devotees of Orpheus relied on

---

†In this connection, George Sarton observed that the 6th Century B.C. was an era of great prophets: in China, Lao Tzu and Confucius; in India, Buddha and Mahavira; in Persia, perhaps Zoroaster (his dates are uncertain); in Israel, Ezekiel and the second Isaiah; and in Greece, Pythagoras. (*A History of Science — Ancient Science through the Golden Age of Greece*, Harvard University Press, 1959, p. 164.)

‡From W. K. C. Guthrie, *A History of Greek Philosophy*, Cambridge University Press, Vol. 1, p. 146.

§Ibid., principally pp. 146-340. Many of my expressions are paraphrases of Guthrie's. The unattributed quotations are from the pages of Guthrie's work referred to, except for the words, "All things are numbers," which are ascribed to Pythagoras.

††Ibid., pp. 108-116.

rites, mysteries, and daily rules. Pythagoras added to such practices an innovation in religion that was unique.

Pythagoras's new method of salvation seems to have stemmed from musical, or rather acoustical, discoveries. A taut string, when plucked, emits a note of a particular pitch. Pythagoras is said to have observed that if a string is shortened to half its original length, the tension upon it being unchanged, then the tone it produces is an octave higher than originally. In this sense, the ratio 2:1 (i.e., the ratio of 2 to 1) characterizes an octave. In what must have been the first truly scientific quantitative experiments ever performed, apparently Pythagoras then established that the ratios 3:2 and 4:3 similarly characterize the intervals of the fifth and the fourth, respectively, and that all these ratios apply to flutes as well as to strings. Apparently, he interpreted these discoveries to mean that sound possesses "an inherent order, a numerical organization," that can be described by means of the first four positive integers 1, 2, 3, 4. Then he seems to have leaped to the magnificent, prophetic conclusion that all form and structure in the universe are but the embodiments of numerical relations. At least, this is how we understand him. He lacked the words to express such an idea clearly, since even the distinctions between matter and form, or between the concrete and the abstract, were still undrawn. What he is supposed to have declared is that "all things are numbers." The perfection of the cosmos — the harmonious motions of the sun, moon, planets, and fixed stars — derived from the perfection of its numbers, perfection expressed by mathematical laws that somehow generalize the proportionalities determining harmonious sounds. The imperfections of a soul — disharmonies that require attunement — came from imperfections of their numbers. Harmony in one's soul — the attunement to the divine required for salvation — was to be achieved by contemplating the perfect harmony of the divine cosmos, knowing its numbers, appreciating their relationships. The mystical and the rational, magic as well as science and mathematics, were joined in this philosophy.

Pythagoras was apparently the first to call himself a philosopher and by philosophy to mean "using the powers of reason and observation in order to gain understanding." (Before Pythagoras, the word "philosophy" — literally, "love of learning" — had been used in a sense close to that of "curiosity.") By understanding something, Pythagoras doubtless would have meant knowing its numbers and the laws of mathematical proportions that they satisfy, and he would have had the the laws of acoustics or music at the back of his mind as models. Let us therefore glance further at these laws, which were based of course on the proportions 2:1, 3:2, and 4:3 already mentioned for a vibrating string. Pythagoras is said to have divided his string into 12 parts and then to have stretched it over a straight edge that could be moved, shortening or lengthening the vibrating section of the string as he liked. Shortening the string from 12 to 6, he achieved the ratio 2:1; shortening from 12 to 8 gave him the ratio 3:2, and shortening from 12 to 9, the ratio 4:3. (These different shortenings raise the pitch of the string by an octave, a fifth, and a fourth, respectively.) Just four lengths were involved:

$$6, 8, 9, 12.$$

To Pythagoras, it was highly significant, for instance, that the third length is the arithmetic mean of the least and greatest,

$$9 = (1/2)(6 + 12).$$

The second length, too, is a kind of mean of the two extremes. More precisely, the *reciprocal* of 8 is the arithmetic mean of the *reciprocals* of 6 and 12:

$$1/8 = (1/2)(1/6 + 1/12).$$

8 itself was called the *harmonic mean* of 6 and 12. In addition, all four lengths appear in the proportionality

$$\frac{12}{9} = \frac{8}{6},$$

a special case of the relation

$$\frac{\text{greater value}}{\text{arithmetic mean}} = \frac{\text{harmonic mean}}{\text{lesser value}},$$

which holds for any two quantities, here exemplified by 6 and 12, and their arithmetic and harmonic means. The mathematical harmoniousness of 6, 8, 9, 12 to which this and the previous relations attest were taken to be the true ground for the musical harmoniousness we can all hear.

The rationality of these researches and Pythagoras's staggeringly precocious commitment to mathematical science were closely related to beliefs very much of his day. Certain injunctions he is supposed to have laid on his followers are nothing but primitive taboos with an origin in sympathetic magic, for instance, the admonition to roll up one's bedclothes on rising and smooth out the imprint of the body. Sympathetic magic assumes that a man and, say, the imprint of his body in a bed, are so related that the one is affected by how the other is treated. Such doctrines perhaps underlie the conception of universal kinship at the center of Pythagorean ideas about the universe, aither, and the soul. Belief in universal kinship and sympathy may explain Pythagoras's audacious leap from the mathematical proportions he had found in music to the embracing mathematical order he claimed to prevail in the cosmos. If so, faith in sympathetic magic and faith in universal mathematical law must have been united in Pythagoras without qualms. The Pythagoreans, however, seem to have divided on these and related issues into two more or less distinct branches. One branch was responsible for the advances in mathematics and related thought for which they became famous. The other seems to have consisted of religious devotees who merely followed the rules and learned the precepts and held it wrong to say or do anything original.

Both the mystical and the rational qualities of the Pythagorean mind found expression in their interest in numbers. At one extreme is a tendency to identify pure abstractions with numbers. For instance, some Pythagoreans identified justice with 4 as the first square (apart from 1, which they did not count). (We can recognize this association in the English expression, "four-square without reproach," applying to an honest man.†) Other Pythagoreans said that justice was 9, the first odd square (again excluding 1), and all Pythagoreans seemed to agree that odd numbers are superior to even. Mysticism and mathematics blend in the following anecdote about Pythagoras. Asked what a friend is, he replied, "A second I," and then mentioned 284 and 220, which are called "amicable numbers" because each equals the sum of the proper divisors of the other:‡

$$1 + 2 + 4 + 5 + 10 + 11 + 20 + 22 + 44 + 55 + 110 = 284,$$
$$1 + 2 + 4 + 71 + 142 \qquad\qquad\qquad\qquad\quad = 220.$$

Small wonder that the Pythagoreans were susceptible to an oddity like perfect numbers (see Chapter 3, Section 8, and then Section 4 in this chapter). A formula for perfect numbers in Euclid's Elements is believed to have originated with the Pythagoreans and, if so, is certainly one of their highest achievements in number theory. We shall discuss it later.

About 1900 years after Euclid, perfect numbers were again to excite the interest of mathematicians and to be a guide to magnificent advances. One of the greatest who found inspiration in the old tradition of the Pythagoreans was Pierre de Fermat (1601–1665). Fermat was a lawyer by vocation but contributed mightily to every branch of mathematics known in his day and founded modern number theory. He was apparently too busy to write down proofs, but his statements of his results, scribbled in the margins of a book, provided challenging problems to generations of mathematicians to come. Not all the theorems he scribbled turned out to be true, and at least one has defied all subsequent attempts at proof or disproof until the present

---

†Cornford's remark, quoted in Guthrie, p. 304.
‡Van der Waerden, p. 98.

day. The theorem of Fermat's that we shall discuss (Section 9) is perhaps his best known and is altogether fundamental to later developments in the subject.

EXERCISES

1. A string 24 inches long under a certain tension produces a particular musical note. At the same tension, how should the string be shortened to give notes an octave, a fifth, and a fourth higher, respectively? Answer the same questions for a 22 inch string.

2. Let a and b be positive numbers and let A, G, and H be their arithmetic, geometric, and harmonic means, respectively. These are defined by the relations

$$A = (1/2)(a + b), \quad G = \sqrt{ab}, \quad 1/H = (1/2)(1/a + 1/b).$$

(a) Prove that

$$b/A = H/a.$$

(b) If $a \neq b$, prove that $H < G < A$. This is to prove:
(i) $H < G$, and
(ii) $G < A$.

3. The Pythagoreans are believed to have obtained the formula

$$1 + 3 + 5 + \ldots + (2n - 1) = n^2$$

from a figure like Figure 11-1, in which a square-shaped formation of evenly-spaced dots is divided into L-shaped arrays, each of which contains an odd number of dots. Prove the formula from this point of view, using mathematical induction.

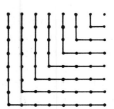

FIGURE 11-1 *A square-shaped formation of dots divided into L-shaped arrays.*

2.

Division and divisibility†

If m and n are any two integers with $m > 0$, the process of dividing n by m can be described in the following terms. Consider all multiples,

$$\ldots, -3m, -2m, -m, 0, m, 2m, 3m, \ldots,$$

of m by integers. Every number,‡ in particular n, either is such a multiple or else lies in an interval between consecutive multiples. This means that for some integer k

$$km \le n < (k+1)m$$

(see Figure 11-2). Since the length of the interval containing n is equal to m, it follows that the distance between n and the left end point of the interval is less than m. Algebraically,

$$n - km < (k+1)m - km = m.$$

FIGURE 11-2   Nearest approximation to n by multiples of m (m > 0).

Thus, setting $r = n - km$, we have

$$n = km + r$$

_____

†For the mathematics in this chapter, a good grasp of algebra and an ability to follow abstract algebraic reasoning are essential. In addition, a knowledge of mathematical induction is desirable. Thus, Chapters 2 (algebra), 4 (Babylonian mathematics), 6 (groups), and 10 (mathematical induction) are recommended as prerequisites.

Most of this chapter is essentially an adaptation of material in Daniel Shanks, *Solved and Unsolved Problems in Number Theory*, Spartan Books, Washington, D.C., 1962, Vol. 1, pp. 1-15, 19-24, 51-59. Many of our exercises are taken from Shanks. The interested reader is urged to continue in this book, which in an elementary way develops much number theory with considerable charm.

‡By "number" in this chapter we shall mean any positive or negative integer, or zero. The entire set of numbers in this sense is sometimes indicated as a doubly infinite array,

$$\ldots, -2, -1, 0, 1, 2, \ldots,$$

and sometimes as an array,

$$0, 1, -1, 2, -2, \ldots,$$

infinite in only one direction.

with k and r integers such that

$$0 \le r < m.$$

If we write this result as

$$n/m = k + r/m,$$

we can perhaps better see that what we have accomplished is to divide n by m, k being the *quotient* and r the *remainder*.

Generalizing this result, we easily see that if m and n are completely arbitrary integers with $m \ne 0$, then integers k and r exist such that

(1) $$n = km + r$$

with

$$0 \le r < |m|.$$

This is the previous result if $m > 0$, and if $m < 0$, set $u = -m$. Then $u > 0$, and the previous result tells us that, dividing n by u, we obtain numbers k_0 and r_0 such that $0 \le r_0 < u$ and

$$n = k_0 u + r_0.$$

Substituting for u gives us

$$n = -k_0 m + r_0,$$

which is of the form (1) desired with $k = -k_0$ and $r = r_0$. Therefore, (1) is justified for any two integers m and n for which $m \ne 0$, as asserted.

We shall now show that the remainder and quotient obtained by a division are unique. Suppose then that

$$n = km + r,$$

as in (1), and also that

$$n = k'm + r',$$

where

$$0 \le r < |m|, \; 0 \le r' < |m|.$$

Our aim is to prove that $k' = k$ and $r' = r$. Subtracting corresponding sides of the two expressions for n, we obtain

$$0 = n - n = km + r - (k'm + r')$$
$$= (k - k')m + r - r'.$$

Thus,

$$r - r' = (k' - k)m,$$

so that $r - r'$ is a multiple of m. Since r and r' are non-negative and less than $|m|$, it follows, however, that their difference is less than $|m|$, or, more precisely, that $|r - r'| < |m|$. Consequently, $r - r'$ is not a multiple of m, unless it is the zero multiple. Since we previously established that $r - r'$ is a multiple of m, we conclude that

$$r - r' = 0 \quad \text{and} \quad k' - k = 0.$$

Therefore, $r' = r$ and $k' = k$, as desired. Thus, the quotient and remainder in any division are unique, as asserted.

EXERCISES

1. Prove statement (1) for $m < 0$ by the means used for positive m.

2. If x is an arbitrary rational number, consider the problem of approximating x by a fraction m/n with given denominator n; this denominator n is a prescribed positive integer and the numerator m is an integer at our disposal. Use the idea of Figure 11-2 to prove that m can be chosen so that $|x - m/n| \le 1/(2n)$. HINT: Work the problem first for $n = 1$ and $n = 2$.

3. The division algorithm expressed by equation (1) is related to the problem of writing a number as a numeral in a given base. We formulated the solution of this problem in statement (1), Section 4, Chapter 3.

(a) Show that this statement implies the division algorithm.

(b) Conversely, show that the division algorithm implies this statement for $k = 2$ and $k = 3$.

(c) Prove by mathematical induction that the division algorithm implies the statement about numerals for every k.

Let m and n denote two numbers such that $m \ne 0$. If a third number k exists such that

$$n = mk,$$

we say that m *divides* n and is a *divisor* of n. (Of course, k also is a divisor of n.) If m divides n, we write

$$m \mid n;$$

if m does not divide n, we write†

$$m \dagger n.$$

Example: Let $n = ab + 1$, where a and b are arbitrary integers. If we divide n by a, then the quotient is b and the remainder is 1. Hence, $a \dagger n$, i.e.,

$$a \dagger (ab + 1).$$

---

† Do not confuse $\dagger$ with the plus sign $+$.

The attribute of dividing obeys the following rules: *for any integers a, b, c with a ≠ 0,*

> (1) $a \mid a$;
> (2) if $a \mid b$ and $b \mid a$, then $a = b$ or $a = -b$;
> (3) if $a \mid b$ and $b \mid c$, then $a \mid c$;
> (4) if $a \mid b$ and $a \mid c$, then $a \mid (b + c)$ and $a \mid (b - c)$;
> (5) if $a \mid b$ and $a \mid c$, then $a \mid (bs + ct)$ for any integers s and t;
> (6) $a \mid 0$;
> (7) $1 \mid b$ and $-1 \mid b$.

These rules are obvious from elementary algebra and the pertinent definitions.

EXERCISES

4-10. Prove rules 1 through 7 for divisibility.

11. Prove: if an integer is not divisible by 4, then it is not divisible by 8. HINT: this is the same as proving: if an integer is divisible by 8, then it is divisible by 4. (Why?)

12. Prove or disprove: if $a \mid bc$ then $a \mid b$ or $a \mid c$.

13. Prove: if $a \mid (b + c)$ and $a \mid (b - c)$ then $a \mid 2b$ and $a \mid 2c$.

14. Prove: if $a \mid b$ then $a \nmid (b + r)$, where $0 < r < \mid a \mid$.

3.

Primes

The concept of divisibility is the basis of the notion of prime.

Definition.   A number p that exceeds 1 but is divisible solely by $1, -1, p, -p$ is said to be a *prime*. A number exceeding 1 but not a prime is said to be *composite*.

Examples of primes are:

$$2, 3, 5, 7, 11, 13, 17, 19, 23, 29, 31, 37, 41, 43, 47, 53.$$

They are (as someone has said) the numbers with which we are *not* familiar from multiplication tables. A systematic way to find all primes less than, say, 1000 is to list the odd numbers from 3 to 999 in order and then to strike off the list every third number after 3, every fifth number after 5, every seventh number after 7, and so forth. All multiples of 3, of 5, of 7, and so forth, are thereby removed, and the numbers that remain are the primes. This method of filtering out primes is known as the "sieve" of Eratosthenes and must have been devised about the beginning of the 2nd Century B.C.

EXERCISES

1. What primes divide these numbers: 102, 105, 204, 266, 364, 379, 403, 592, 705, 1001?

2. Find the primes less than 300 by the sieve of Eratosthenes.

3. Are any even numbers prime?

Examples like those of Exercise 1 suggest that every number greater than 1 can be expressed as a product of primes. To prove this, we must first know that any number N greater than 1 has a prime divisor. In the first place, N has at least one divisor greater than 1, N itself being such a divisor. Let p be the *smallest* divisor of N that is greater than 1. Then p is a prime, for otherwise p itself would have a divisor q greater than 1; q would be less than p and still divide N in contradiction to the requirement that p shall be the *smallest* divisor of N greater than 1. We conclude that any number greater than 1 has a prime divisor, as asserted.

Now we can easily show how N, an arbitrary number greater than 1, is to be expressed as a product of primes. By the foregoing, N has a prime divisor p_1. Consider the number $N_1 = N/p_1$. If $N_1 = 1$, we have

$$N = p_1,$$

while if $N_1 > 1$, then N_1 in its turn has a prime divisor, say p_2. Then consider

$$N_2 = N_1/p_2$$
$$= N/(p_1 p_2),$$

which is an integer. If $N_2 = 1$, we have

$$N = p_1 p_2,$$

and if $N_2 > 1$, then N_2 has a prime divisor p_3, and we repeat the previous argument with the number N_2/p_3, which is $N/(p_1 p_2 p_3)$. Continuing this process, we obtain a succession of primes, $p_1, p_2, p_3, \ldots,$ for which the ratios

$$N_1 = N/p_1, \ N_2 = N/(p_1 p_2), \ N_3 = N/(p_1 p_2 p_3), \ \ldots$$

are integers. Since

$$N > N_1 > N_2 > N_3 > \ldots \geq 1,$$

we will find that $N_k = 1$ for some k less than N, and then the process will stop. We will have

$$N_k = N_{k-1}/p_k$$
$$= N/(p_1 p_2 \ldots p_k)$$

and thus

$$N = p_1 p_2 \ldots p_k.$$

In this way, any number greater than 1 can be had as a product of primes.

Possibly some of the primes $p_1, \ldots, p_k$ coincide. In this case, letting

$$P_1, P_2, \ldots, P_n$$

be the distinct primes among the p's, we can write the result in the form

(1) $$N = P_1^{a_1} P_2^{a_2} \ldots P_n^{a_n},$$

where the exponent a_j indicates the number of repetitions in the product of the prime $P_j (j = 1, 2, \ldots, n)$. It is usual to arrange the P's in order, thus conforming to the additional requirement:

$$P_1 < P_2 < \ldots < P_n.$$

Representing a number N in the form (1) is called *factoring N* into primes.

EXERCISES

4. The argument that leads to (1) ought strictly to be formulated as a mathematical induction. Do so.

5. Prove that any integer n may be written in the form $n = 2^m \cdot r$, where r is an odd number. HINT: Imitate the proof that any number greater than 1 can be expressed as a product of primes.

6. Prove that the representation in Exercise 5 is unique. (Explain.)

From (1), it is plain that the divisors of N include $1, P_1, P_2, \ldots, P_n$, $P_1 P_2, P_1 P_3, P_2 P_3, \ldots$ and, more generally, any expression of the form

$$P_1^{b_1} P_2^{b_2} \ldots P_n^{b_n},$$

where the exponents are integers such that

$$0 \le b_1 \le a_1, 0 \le b_2 \le a_2, \ldots, 0 \le b_n \le a_n.$$

Are these *all* the divisors of N? In the next section, this question will be asked again more urgently. It will be answered in the affirmative in Section 8.

EXERCISE

>   7. Factor and calculate all the divisors of these numbers: 12, 54, 72.

There are 168 primes less than 1000, 78,498 primes less than 1,000,000, and 50,847,534 primes less than 1,000,000,000. Identifying large primes requires an electronic computer, but the fact that more than 50,000,000 primes exist has been known with certainty since Euclid's day. In fact, Euclid showed that no matter how high we count, we shall continue to find more primes, or, in other words, that infinitely many primes exist.

Euclid's Theorem.   *Infinitely many primes exist.*

PROOF: If the theorem were false, then only a certain (finite) number of primes would exist. We could then list them all, say as

$$p_1, p_2, \ldots, p_n.$$

Set

$$N = p_1 p_2 \ldots p_n + 1.$$

None of the primes divides N, since none divides $N - p_1 \ldots p_n$. But N must have a prime divisor, a contradiction to the assumption that $p_1, p_2, \ldots, p_n$ are all the primes. The contradiction grew out of our supposing that there are just a finite number of primes. Hence, this supposition is untenable, and we conclude that infinitely many primes must exist, as asserted.

EXERCISES

>   In these exercises, we shall use the following definition: two integers a and b are *relatively prime*, either being *prime to* the other, if no number exceeding 1 divides them both.
>
>   8. Given n distinct primes, $p_1, p_2, \ldots, p_n$, let A be the product of r of them with $1 \leq r \leq n$, and let $B = p_1 p_2 \ldots p_n/A$. Prove that $A + B$ is prime to each of the n primes. (For instance, $2 \cdot 3 + 5 \cdot 7 \cdot 11$ is prime to 2, 3, 5, 7, 11.)
>   9. Let $A_1 = 2$, $A_2 = A_1^2 - A_1 + 1$,

$$A_3 = A_2^2 - A_2 + 1,$$

and for each index $k = 1, 2, 3, \ldots$,

$$A_{k+1} = A_k^2 - A_k + 1.$$

Prove that $A_1, A_2, \ldots$ are prime to each other. HINT: Show by mathematical induction that

$$A_{n+1} = A_1 A_2 \ldots A_n + 1.$$

10. Prove that the *Fermat Numbers*

$$F_m = 2^{2^m} + 1$$

for $m = 0, 1, 2, \ldots$ are prime to each other. HINT: Show that

$$F_{m+1} - 1 = (F_m - 1)^2$$

and from this (by mathematical induction) that

$$F_{m+1} = F_0 F_1 \ldots F_m + 2.$$

11. Accept the fact that (as proved in the previous exercises), infinitely many numbers exist that are relatively prime. From this fact, prove Euclid's theorem. HINT: Let $A_1, A_2, \ldots$ denote infinitely many numbers that are relatively prime. If only a finite number of primes, $p_1, p_2, \ldots, p_n$ exist, then at most a finite number of A's, in particular, are primes. If we drop these prime A's out, the A's that remain are all composite. Since there are infinitely many of these, we may as well assume to begin with that $A_1, A_2, \ldots$ is an infinite set of relatively prime, *composite* numbers. How many of these at most are divisible by p_1, how many by p_2, and so on?

12. Supply reasons for each step in the following proof.

Theorem.   To check that n is a prime number, it is sufficient to show that it is not divisible by any prime number $p \leq \sqrt{n}$.

PROOF: Suppose that n is not divisible by any prime number $p \leq \sqrt{n}$ and that n is composite.

(a) Then n has a prime divisor.
(b) A prime $p_0 > \sqrt{n}$ and an integer K exist such that $n = p_0 K$.
(c) $K < \sqrt{n}$ and $K \mid n$.
(d) Therefore n has a prime divisor $< \sqrt{n}$.
(e) Step (d) contradicts the hypothesis.
(f) Therefore the theorem is proved.

13. Give another proof of Euclid's theorem by assuming that there is a largest prime number p and considering the number

$$[p(p - 1)(p - 2) \ldots 3 \cdot 2 \cdot 1] + 1.$$

4.

Perfect numbers

Perhaps primes first arose in Euclid's perfect number studies.[†] We recall that a number is said to be perfect if equal to the sum of all its positive divisors other than itself. Earlier (Section 8, Chapter 3),

---

†Shanks's conjecture.

we proposed that the reader write the first four perfect numbers (6, 28, 496, 8128) in binary notation. He would have obtained the results shown in the first two columns of Table 11-1.

Table 11-1 *Formulas and binary expressions for some perfect numbers*

Decimal form	Binary form	Formula
6	110	$(2^2 - 1) \cdot 2$
28	11100	$(2^3 - 1) \cdot 2^2$
496	111110000	$(2^5 - 1) \cdot 2^4$
8128	1111111000000	$(2^7 - 1) \cdot 2^6$

To arrive at the formulas in the third column, we recall that a binary numeral consisting of n 1's represents a geometric series,

$$\overbrace{11 \ldots 1}^{n} = 1 + 2 + 4 + \ldots + 2^{n-1},$$

whose sum is $(2^n - 1)/(2 - 1) = 2^n - 1$ (see Section 4, Chapter 10). Therefore, in particular, the binary quantities 11, 111, 11111, and 1111111 have the values

$$2^2 - 1, \quad 2^3 - 1, \quad 2^5 - 1, \quad 2^7 - 1,$$

respectively, from which expressions the third column of Table 11-1 is obvious.

The formulas in Table 11-1 are all of the single type

$$(2^n - 1) \cdot 2^{n-1}$$

with appropriate choices of n. Do all perfect numbers arise in this way, and in any case with what kind of n? Answers to these questions were found about 2000 years apart. Around 300 B.C., Euclid proved the following theorem.

Theorem 1. The number $2^{n-1}(2^n - 1)$ is perfect if $2^n - 1$ is a prime.

PROOF: To tell whether a number is perfect, we must find all its (positive) divisors and add them up. The divisors of $2^{n-1}(2^n - 1)$ include:

$$
\begin{array}{ll}
1, & 2^n - 1, \\
2, & 2(2^n - 1), \\
2^2, & 2^2(2^n - 1), \\
\multicolumn{2}{c}{\cdots\cdots\cdots} \\
2^{n-1}, & 2^{n-1}(2^n - 1).
\end{array}
$$

We shall see later that, since $2^n - 1$ is a prime, no other positive divisors exist, and for the present we shall assume this fact. Then the sum S of all the divisors of $N = 2^{n-1}(2^n - 1)$, including the last divisor, which is N itself, is

$$S = (1 + 2 + 2^2 + \ldots + 2^{n-1})[1 + (2^n - 1)]$$
$$= (2^n - 1) \cdot 2^n.$$

The sum of the divisors of N *excluding* N itself thus is

$$S - N = 2^n(2^n - 1) - 2^{n-1}(2^n - 1)$$
$$= (2^n - 2^{n-1})(2^n - 1)$$
$$= 2^{n-1}(2^n - 1)$$
$$= N.$$

Therefore, N is perfect. The gap in this proof will be repaired in Section 8.

The previous theorem of Euclid answers one of the two questions we raised. A partial reply to the other question is given in this result of the 18th Century Swiss, Leonhard Euler.

Theorem 2. Every even perfect number is of the form $2^{n-1}(2^n - 1)$ with $2^n - 1$ a prime.

PROOF: If N is an even perfect number, then N is divisible at least by 2 and possibly by a higher power of 2, such as 4, 8, or 16. Suppose 2^{n-1} to be the highest power of 2 that divides N. Then

$$N = 2^{n-1}F,$$

where F is an odd number. Let S be the sum of the positive divisors of F, including F itself. The positive divisors of N include the positive divisors of F and also their multiples by 2^k for $k = 1, 2, \ldots, n-1$. We shall see later (Section 7) that N has no other positive divisors and for the present shall assume this fact. Then the sum of the positive divisors of N, including N itself, is

$$(1 + 2 + 2^2 + \ldots + 2^{n-1})S,$$

which is equal to

$$(2^n - 1)S.$$

Since N is perfect,

$$N = (2^n - 1)S - N,$$

and thus

$$2N = (2^n - 1)S.$$

But since $N = 2^{n-1}F$, we have $2N = 2^n F$. Comparing this with the formula for $2N$ gives

(1) $$S = 2^n F/(2^n - 1) = ((2^n - 1)F + F)/(2^n - 1)$$
        $$= F + F/(2^n - 1).$$

Since S and F are both integers, the number $F/(2^n - 1)$ also is an integer. Since

$$F = (F/(2^n - 1))(2^n - 1),$$

both $F/(2^n - 1)$ and $2^n - 1$ thus are divisors of F. In (1), S is expressed as the sum of these two divisors, while by definition S is the sum of *all* the positive divisors of F, one of which is 1 and another F. We conclude from (1) that $F/(2^n - 1) = 1$, i.e., that

$$F = 2^n - 1.$$

We also conclude that F has no divisors other than itself and unity and thus that $2^n - 1$ is a prime. Now the theorem is proved, except for the gap to be made good in Section 8.

No odd perfect numbers are known.

The perfect numbers in Table 11-1 all end in 6 or 8, and number enthusiasts in days of yore jumped to the conclusion that all perfect numbers do the same. Euler's theorem permits us to prove this conjecture at least for the even perfect numbers although without shedding light on whether a perfect number may be odd. The theorem of Cataldi (Section 4, Chapter 10) that n is a prime if $2^n - 1$ is a prime is also used.

Theorem 3.   Every even perfect number ends in either 6 or 8.

PROOF: By Euler's Theorem, every even perfect number is of the form

$$2^{p-1}(2^p - 1),$$

where $2^p - 1$ is a prime. By Cataldi's Theorem, p also is prime. Thus, it suffices to prove that every number N defined by the expression

$$N = 2^{p-1}(2^p - 1)$$

with p prime ends in either 6 or 8. If $p = 2$, then $N = 6$. Hence, the assertion is true for the single even prime, and from now on we suppose p to be odd.

As we already noted in Section 1 (see Figure 11-1), any positive number differs from an appropriate multiple of 4 by 0, 1, 2, or 3. Hence, a number k exists such that p, in particular, equals $4k, 4k+1, 4k+2$, or $4k+3$. Since p is odd, two possibilities only present themselves: (a) $p = 4k + 1$ and (b) $p = 4k + 3$. In case (a),

$$N = 2^{4k}(2^{4k+1} - 1)$$
$$= 16^k(2 \cdot 16^k - 1).$$

Any power of 16 ends in 6 (this is easily proved by mathematical induction). Hence, $2 \cdot 16^k - 1$ ends in 1, and N itself ends in 6. In case (b), we have

$$N = 4 \cdot 16^k(8 \cdot 16^k - 1),$$

while $8 \cdot 16^k - 1$ ends in 7; hence, N ends in 8. All even perfect numbers thus end in 6 or 8, as asserted.

EXERCISES

1. Can a prime number be perfect? Explain!

2. Prove that if m is a perfect number and p is relatively prime to m, then mp cannot be a perfect number.

3. A number is said to be "abundant" if the sum of its positive divisors other than itself exceeds the number. Prove that mp of Exercise 2 is an "abundant" number.

4. Prove more generally that the product of two relatively prime abundant numbers is again an abundant number.

5. A number is said to be "deficient" if the sum of its positive divisors other than itself is less than the number. Prove by a counterexample that the product of two relatively prime deficient numbers need not be deficient.

6. Prove that no power of a prime number can be a perfect number by proving that every power of a prime number is deficient.

7. Prove that the square of no perfect number is perfect.

5.

Greatest common divisors

Our proofs of the previous results on perfect numbers, which were incomplete, will be made good with the uniqueness theorem on prime factorization of Section 8. To prepare for this theorem, following Euclid we introduce the notion of greatest common divisor.

Definition. If g is the greatest integer that divides both of two integers a and b, we call g their *greatest common divisor* and write

$$g = (a,b).$$

If, in particular, $(a,b) = 1$, then we say that a is *prime to* b and also that a and b are *relatively prime* (see Section 3, Exercises 8 to 14).

For instance, $(6,9) = 3$, $(18,24) = 6$, $(6,35) = 1$; for any integer n, $(1,n) = 1$, $(n,n-1) = 1$; for any two primes, $(p,q) = 1$.

It is remarkable that the greatest common divisor of two numbers can be found without any factoring. Euclid gives the following routine for calculating (a,b), where a and b are any positive integers. Without loss of generality, we assume that $a \leq b$. Then dividing b by a, we obtain

$$b = q_0 a + a_1,$$

with positive quotient q_0 and a remainder a_1 such that $0 \leq a_1 < a$. If $a_1 \neq 0$, divide a by a_1 to obtain

$$a = q_1 a_1 + a_2,$$

where $q_1 > 0$ and $0 \leq a_2 < a_1$. If $a_2 \neq 0$, we next divide a_1 by a_2, and so on, the remainders diminishing at each step until one of them, say a_{n+1}, is zero. We then have

$$a_{n-3} = q_{n-2} a_{n-2} + a_{n-1}$$
$$a_{n-2} = q_{n-1} a_{n-1} + a_n$$
$$a_{n-1} = q_n a_n$$

with positive q's. The last nonzero remainder turns out to be the greatest common divisor we desire:

$$(a,b) = a_n.$$

In the first place, we shall see that $a_n | a$ and $a_n | b$. In fact, $a_n | a_{n-1}$ by the $(n+1)$st (the last) equation; since a_n thus divides both a_n and a_{n-1}, the nth (next to last) equation shows that $a_n | a_{n-2}$; since a_n thus divides both a_{n-1} and a_{n-2}, the $(n-1)$st (third from last) equation shows that $a_n | a_{n-3}$, and so forth. Working in this way from each equation to the preceding, we find eventually from the second equation that a_n, dividing both a_1 and a_2, also divides a, and then from the first equation that a_n, dividing both a and a_1, divides b. We thus find, in particular, that a_n is a common divisor of a and b. To identify a_n as the *greatest* common divisor of a and b, we shall now show that if d is any common divisor of these numbers, then $d \leq a_n$. We proceed as follows. Since d divides both a and b, from the first equation we deduce that $d | a_1$. Thus, d divides both a and a_1, and the second equation shows that $d | a_2$. Hence, d divides both a_1 and a_2, and the third equation shows that $d | a_3$, and so on. Working in this way from each equation to the following, we find ultimately from the nth (next to last) equation that, d dividing both a_{n-2} and a_{n-1}, d also divides

a_n. The last conclusion implies, in particular, that $d \le a_n$. Therefore,

$$a_n = (a,b),$$

as asserted.

The foregoing procedure is called *Euclid's algorithm*. Euclid himself described it as a procedure of successive subtractions: given any pair of numbers, replace the larger number by the difference between the two; repeating this procedure again and again, you will eventually reach a stage at which the two numbers are equal, their common value being the greatest common divisor of the original pair.

Since Euclid's algorithm is a general procedure, good for calculating any greatest common divisor (a,b), does it lead to a *formula* for (a,b) in terms of a and b? Consider, for instance, the case in which $n = 3$, there being 4 nonvanishing remainders and 5 equations:

$$b = q_0 a + a_1$$
$$a = q_1 a_1 + a_2$$
$$a_1 = q_2 a_2 + a_3$$
$$a_2 = q_3 a_3 + a_4$$
$$a_3 = q_4 a_4$$

To obtain a formula for a_4 in terms of a and b, we begin by solving the next to last equation for a_4 in terms of a_2 and a_3:

$$a_4 = -q_3 a_3 + a_2.$$

Then we solve the previous equation for a_3 in terms of a_1 and a_2, to obtain

$$a_3 = -q_2 a_2 + a_1.$$

Substituting this expression for a_3 into the equation for a_4 gives:

$$a_4 = -q_3(-q_2 a_2 + a_1) + a_2$$
$$= (q_3 q_2 + 1)a_2 - q_3 a_1$$
$$= s_2 a_2 + t_2 a_1,$$

where $s_2 = q_3 q_2 + 1$ and $t_2 = -q_3$. Thus, s_2 and t_2, in particular, are integers. Next (from the second equation), we solve for a_2 as

$$a_2 = -q_1 a_1 + a$$

and substitute in the last expression for a_4 to obtain

$$a_4 = s_2(-q_1 a_1 + a) + t_2 a_1$$
$$= s_1 a_1 + t_1 a,$$

where s_1 and t_1 are certain expressions that can be calculated from the

previous coefficients and are, in particular, integers. Finally, expressing a_1 in terms of a and b as

$$a_1 = -q_0 a + b,$$

we obtain by substitution

$$
\begin{aligned}
a_4 &= s_1 a_1 + t_1 a \\
&= s_1(-q_0 a + b) + t_1 a \\
&= sa + tb,
\end{aligned}
$$

where s and t again are quantities that can be calculated from the
previous coefficients and are, in particular, integers. An analogous
formula for a_n can be had by the same kind of procedure for any n.
(To carry the procedure out abstractly—i.e., with n general, not
specified—requires mathematical induction.) The formula states that
integers s and t exist such that

$$a_n = sa + tb.$$

in the case in which a and b are positive, we can thus state the
following theorem.

Euclid's Greatest Common Divisor Theorem.   For any two nonzero integers, a and b, integers s and t exist such that

(1) $$(a,b) = sa + tb.$$

The cases in which a or b is (or are) negative follow trivially from
this by considering their absolute values.

Condition (1) is not exactly a formula for (a,b), since the coefficients s and t—through their dependence upon $q_0, \ldots, q_{n-1}$—involve
a and b in a manner that the formula itself does not describe. But the
fact that s and t are *integers* is alone of great significance. Even if
condition (1) is just the shadow of Euclid's algorithm, it is all that is
needed for many purposes.

We remark that condition (1) holds with infinitely many choices
of s and t. For if

$$g = sa + tb,$$

where $g = (a,b)$, then clearly for every integer k

$$g = (s + kb/g)a + (t - ka/g)b.$$

Thus, the integer pair

$$s + kb/g, \quad t - ka/g$$

can be used in condition (1) in place of the original pair,

$$s, t,$$

and indeed for every k.

EXERCISE

1. Find the greatest common divisors of the pairs of numbers indicated:
   (a) (9,36)
   (b) (48,72)
   (c) (11,207392)
   (d) (26,486)
   (e) (77,1001)

The proof of (1) we have just given, which is essentially that of Euclid, is a *constructive* proof in the sense that we show how to calculate, or construct, all the quantities that enter. In mathematics today, a strong tendency exists towards *nonconstructive* proofs, or demonstrations by logic with little or no explicit calculation. Nonconstructive proofs can be very elegant, as we shall illustrate by giving a demonstration of Euclid's greatest common divisor theorem that completely by-passes Euclid's algorithm.

This nonconstructive proof is based on the following observation. If u and v are any integers, then

$$(a,b) \mid (ua + vb),$$

since, in fact, $(a,b) \mid a$ and $(a,b) \mid b$. It follows that

$$(a,b) \leq ua + vb$$

for all integers, u and v, such that $ua + vb > 0$. On the other hand, condition (1) — Euclid's greatest common divisor theorem — tells us that integers s and t exist such that

$$(a,b) = sa + tb.$$

Therefore, (a,b) is the smallest positive value taken by the expression $ua + vb$ for integer values of u and v.

Example: Taking $a = 4$ and $b = 6$, calculate the values of $4u + 6v$ for various integer values of u and v, as in Table 11-2. The smallest positive value of $4u + 6v$ occurring in the table is 2, which is equal to (4,6).

u	v	4u + 6v
0	1	6
1	0	4
−1	1	2
−1	2	8
2	−1	2

Table 11-2   *Some linear combinations of 4 and 6 with integer coefficients*

EXERCISE

2. For the values of a and b tabulated, look for integers u and v to make the expression ua + vb positive and as small as possible.

a	18	17	42	9	102
b	20	11	25	5	85

The nonconstructive proof of Euclid's greatest common divisor theorem we are going to give must have been devised by a man who already knew the theorem quite well. He certainly realized, in particular, that, as we have just remarked, (a,b) is the smallest positive value of the expression $ua + vb$ for integer values of u and v. This foreknowledge led him to the following argument. Consider all the values taken by the expression

$$(2) \qquad\qquad ua + vb$$

as u and v independently run through all the integers. (The values thus taken by the expression (2) include u, v, $-u$, $-v$, $u+v$, $u-v$, $-u+v$, $-u-v$, $u+2v$, $u-2v$, $-u+2v$, $-u-2v$, $2u+v$, $2u-v$.) Discarding all but the *positive* values taken by the expression $ua + vb$ as u and v vary, define g to be the smallest such positive value. Without knowing what this smallest value is, or how it can be found, we shall prove it to be the greatest common divisor (a, b). By its definition, g has two properties: (i) integers s and t exist such that

$$(3) \qquad\qquad g = sa + tb;$$

(ii) if u and v are arbitrary integers such that $ua + vb > 0$, then

$$(4) \qquad\qquad g \leq ua + vb.$$

Properties (3) and (4) imply that

$$(5) \qquad\qquad g \mid ua + vb$$

if u and v are any integers. In fact, divide $ua + vb$ by g to obtain

$$ua + vb = kg + r,$$

where k and r are integers such that

(6) $$0 \leq r < g.$$

From (3), we have

$$kg = k(sa - tb),$$

which we may subtract from the equality

$$kg + r = ua + vb$$

just proved. We obtain

$$r = ua + vb - k(sa + tb)$$
$$= (u - ks)a + (v - kt)b.$$

If $r > 0$, then inequality (4) shows that $g \leq r$, in contradiction to (6). Hence, $r = 0$, and consequently

$$ua + vb = kg,$$

proving (5).

According to (5), $g \mid (ua + vb)$ for any integers u and v. Choosing $u = 1$ and $v = 0$ thus proves that $g \mid a$; now choosing $u = 0$ and $v = 1$ proves that $g \mid b$. Hence, g is a common divisor of a and b. If d is any positive divisor of both a and b, we see from (3) that $d \mid g$. Therefore, g is the greatest of all the common divisors of a and b, i.e., $g = (a,b)$, as asserted.

EXERCISES

3. Prove that if m and n are relatively prime, then any integer K can be written in the form $K = rm + sn$, where r and s are integers. HINT: If m and n are relatively prime then $(m, n) = 1$ and there exist integers p and q such that

$$1 = pm + qn.$$

4. Give an example to show that if m and n are *not* relatively prime, then the result in Exercise 3 need not hold.

5. Prove that if integers p and q exist such that $1 = pm + qn$, then m and n are relatively prime.

6.

Euclid's algorithm and continued fractions

Euclid's algorithm is closely related to what are known as continued fractions. To illustrate a continued fraction, consider the following calculation:

$$\frac{47}{13} = 3 + \frac{8}{13} = 3 + \frac{1}{13/8}$$

$$= 3 + \frac{1}{1 + \frac{5}{8}} = 3 + \frac{1}{1 + \frac{1}{8/5}}$$

$$= 3 + \frac{1}{1 + \frac{1}{1 + \frac{3}{5}}} = 3 + \frac{1}{1 + \frac{1}{1 + \frac{1}{5/3}}}$$

$$= 3 + \frac{1}{1 + \frac{1}{1 + \frac{1}{1 + \frac{2}{3}}}} = 3 + \frac{1}{1 + \frac{1}{1 + \frac{1}{1 + \frac{1}{3/2}}}}$$

$$= 3 + \frac{1}{1 + \frac{1}{1 + \frac{1}{1 + \frac{1}{1 + \frac{1}{2}}}}}$$

The rather complicated structure that ultimately appears on the right is an example of a continued fraction.

The connection of continued fractions to Euclid's algorithm will become apparent if we consider, for instance, the case in which $a_5 = 0$ already used for illustration on page 434. This is the case of five equations:

$$b = q_0 a + a_1,$$
$$a = q_1 a_1 + a_2,$$
$$a_1 = q_2 a_2 + a_3,$$
$$a_2 = q_3 a_3 + a_4,$$
$$a_3 = q_4 a_4,$$

where $0 < a_4 < a_3 < a_2 < a_1 < |a|$. Let us rewrite these equations as

$$\frac{b}{a} = q_0 + \frac{a_1}{a}$$

$$\frac{a}{a_1} = q_1 + \frac{a_2}{a_1}$$

$$\frac{a_1}{a_2} = q_2 + \frac{a_3}{a_2}$$

$$\frac{a_2}{a_3} = q_3 + \frac{a_4}{a_3}$$

$$\frac{a_3}{a_4} = q_4.$$

Using these relations, we have the following succession of equalities:

$$\frac{b}{a} = q_0 + \frac{a_1}{a} = q_0 + \frac{1}{a/a_1}$$

$$= q_0 + \frac{1}{q_1 + \dfrac{a_2}{a_1}} = q_0 + \frac{1}{q_1 + \dfrac{1}{a_1/a_2}}$$

$$= q_0 + \frac{1}{q_1 + \dfrac{1}{q_2 + \dfrac{a_3}{a_2}}} = q_0 + \frac{1}{q_1 + \dfrac{1}{q_2 + \dfrac{1}{a_2/a_3}}}$$

$$= q_0 + \frac{1}{q_1 + \dfrac{1}{q_2 + \dfrac{1}{q_3 + \dfrac{a_4}{a_3}}}} = q_0 + \frac{1}{q_1 + \dfrac{1}{q_2 + \dfrac{1}{q_3 + \dfrac{1}{a_3/a_4}}}}$$

$$= q_0 + \frac{1}{q_1 + \dfrac{1}{q_2 + \dfrac{1}{q_3 + \dfrac{1}{q_4}}}}$$

Expressions like the term added to q_0 in the last member of these equalities are called continued fractions. We wish to point out simply that the procedure of converting a given fraction into a continued fraction, as illustrated earlier, suggests a very quick routine for getting greatest common divisors. In the case of Euclid's algorithm just discussed, for instance, the greatest common divisor of a and b is a_4, which turns up as the final denominator in the next to the last step of the routine. The greatest common divisor always occurs in this way. For instance, from the calculation

$$\frac{42}{24} = 1 + \frac{18}{24} = 1 + \frac{1}{24/18} = 1 + \frac{1}{1 + \dfrac{6}{18}} = 1 + \frac{1}{1 + \dfrac{1}{18/6}},$$

we read from the fact that the division $18/6$ has no remainder that $(42,24) = 6$.

EXERCISES

1. From the partial fraction for 47/13 obtained in this section, how do we conclude that $(47,13) = 1$?

2. Find continued fractions for each of the following fractions: 43/7, 52/5, 41/11, 16/107, 7/43, 49/52, 11/41.

3. Find the following greatest common divisors by use of continued fractions: (57,152), (49,154), (104,169), (117,1001), (127,257).

4. Must the continued fraction of every fraction terminate? Explain.

7.

Indeterminate equations

Consider the following problem: A bicycle store has exactly two models, one at \$29 and the other at \$43. At the end of a certain day, total sales were \$246. How many bicycles of the two kinds had been sold?

To formulate this problem algebraically, let

$$x = \text{number of bicycles sold at \$29 each,}$$
$$y = \text{number of bicycles sold at \$43 each.}$$

Then the information given can be summarized in the equation

$$29x + 43y = 246$$

and in the added stipulation that the unknown numbers x and y be non-negative integers. The equation alone is satisfied by any value of y and an appropriately corresponding value of x, which is given by

$$x = (246 - 43y)/29.$$

For instance, the equation is satisfied by the values $y = 0$ and $x = 246/29$, although these values, which are not integers, are of no use to us. How can we arrive at values of x and y that satisfy the equation and are both integers? How can we find integer values that are, in particular, non-negative?

The first to devise general methods to handle such problems were two Hindu mathematicians, Aryabhatas and Brahmagupta, of the 6th and 7th Centuries A.D., respectively. Their methods in principle seem to be the same as ours. Putting aside for the present the particular problem with which we started, consider an arbitrary equation of the form

(1) $$ax + by = c$$

with integer coefficients, a, b, c, such that

$$a \neq 0, \, b \neq 0.$$

By a *solution* of this equation we mean a pair of quantities x,y that satisfy it. This equation (like the previous special case) again has infinitely many solutions and, for this reason, is called an "indeterminate" equation. (The *solutions* of the equation are indeterminate, in the sense of not being wholly determined by the equation alone. Perhaps the equation itself ought to be called "undetermining.") We ask for all solutions of the equation, if any, that are pairs of integers.

Suppose for the moment that equation (1) is indeed satisfied by at least one pair of integer values of x and y. Let

$$g = (a,b).$$

Since $g \,|\, a$ and $g \,|\, b$, we see that $g \,|\, (ax + by)$ and therefore, equation (1) being satisfied, that

(2) $$g \,|\, c.$$

Thus, condition (2) is a *necessary* condition that equation (1) have integer solutions. If $g \nmid c$, equation (1) will have no integer solutions.

We shall now see that condition (2) is *sufficient* for the existence of integer solutions. Assuming that $g \,|\, c$ (condition (2)), we shall accordingly find a pair of integers x,y that satisfy equation (2). Since $g \,|\, c$, an integer k exists such that

$$c = kg.$$

By Euclid's greatest common divisor theorem, integers m and n exist such that

$$am + bn = g$$

and, hence, such that

$$k(am + bn) = kg$$
$$= c.$$

Thus, equation (1) is satisfied with

$$x = km, \, y = kn.$$

In sum: *equation (1) is satisfied by at least one pair of integers x, y if and only if $g \,|\, c$.*

EXERCISES

1. For what integers N does the equation $3x + 5y = N$ have integer solutions?

2. Prove that an equation of the form $ax + by = c$, where a, b, and c are integers, either has no integer solutions or has an infinite number of integer solutions. (Use the method suggested on p. 435.)

We have just seen that the indeterminate equation (1) may or may not have a pair of integers as a solution. May more than one solution exist? To face the matter squarely, suppose two pairs of values

$$x', y'$$

and

$$x'', y''$$

both satisfy equation (1). Then we have

$$ax' + by' = c$$

and

$$ax'' + by'' = c.$$

If we subtract corresponding members of the two equations, we obtain

$$a(x' - x'') + b(y' - y'') = 0.$$

Thus, the differences

$$u = x' - x'', \ v = y' - y''$$

satisfy the equation

$$(3) \qquad\qquad au + bv = 0.$$

This is called the *homogeneous equation* corresponding to equation (1). It is of the same form as (1), with the same coefficients — a and b — on the left, but with g replaced by 0. (The unknowns in equation (3) in general have different values from those in equation (1) and therefore are represented by different symbols. This contributes to the unlike appearance of the two equations.)

We have just seen that for both pairs x', y' and x'', y'' to be solutions of (1), it is necessary that the pair of differences

$$x' - x'', \ y' - y''$$

be a solution of (3), the homogeneous equation that corresponds to (1).

Now we shall prove that if

$$x, y$$

is a solution of (1) and

$$u, v$$

a solution of (3), then

$$x + u, y + v$$

again is a solution of (1). In fact,

$$ax + by = c$$

and

$$au + bv = 0.$$

Adding corresponding sides of these equations gives us

$$a(x + u) + b(y + v) = c,$$

verifying that $x + u, y + v$ is a solution of (1), as stated.

From the previous results, we draw the following conclusions: *to obtain all the pairs of integers x,y that satisfy equation (1), it suffices to find any particular pair, call it x_0, y_0, and, in addition, all the solutions u, v of the corresponding homogeneous equation (3). All pairs of integers x,y given by the formulas*

$$x = x_0 + u, y = y_0 + v$$

then satisfy equation (1), and every pair of integers x, y that satisfy (1) is so representable.

It thus devolves upon us to find all integer solutions of the homogeneous equation (3). We shall have to know Theorem 1.

Theorem 1 (Euclid). If a, b, and c are integers such that

$$c \mid ab \text{ and } (c,a) = 1,$$

then

$$c \mid b.$$

PROOF: Since $c \mid ab$, an integer q exists such that

$$ab = cq.$$

Since $(c,a) = 1$, by Euclid's greatest common divisor theorem integers m and n exist such that

$$mc + na = 1.$$

Multiplying by b gives us

$$bmc + bna = b,$$

and since $ab = cq$, we have

$$bmc + ncq = b.$$

Thus,

$$b = c(mb + nq),$$

from which we see that

$$c \mid b,$$

as asserted.

Now we return to the problem of finding all integer solutions of the homogeneous equation (3):

(3) $au + bv = 0.$

This equation is of course equivalent to

(4) $au = -bv.$

Let us substitute aw for v, w representing a new unknown, not necessarily an integer, that will take the place (in equation (4)) of v. We thus write

$$v = aw,$$

and, making this substitution in equation (4),

$$au = -bv$$
$$= -baw.$$

Cancelling a gives us

$$u = -bw.$$

Thus, any solution u, v of equation (4) can be represented in terms of w as

(5) $u = -bw, \; v = aw.$

What then are all the values of w for which u and v are integers? Since some such values may be fractions, set

$$w = p/q,$$

and for convenience require that the fraction be in lowest terms. (This means that no number divides both p and q, i.e., that $(p,q) = 1$.) By the theorem just proved,

$$bw = bp/q$$

is an integer if and only if $q \mid b$, and

$$aw = ap/q$$

is an integer if and only if $q \mid a$. Thus, bw and aw are both whole numbers if and only if

(6) $$q \mid a \text{ and } q \mid b.$$

But we easily see from Euclid's greatest common divisor theorem (equation (3), Section 5) that any common divisor of a and b also divides (a,b). Hence, condition (6) is equivalent to the condition that

$$q \mid (a,b).$$

In sum, therefore, the choice

$$w = p/q$$

in equations (5) leads to integer values of u and v if and only if $q \mid (a,b)$. It follows that all integer solutions of the homogeneous equation (3) are obtained by taking w in equations (5) to be of the form

$$w = m/(a,b)$$

and letting m run through all the integers. On the other hand, all solutions of (3) so obtained are pairs of integers.

Example 1: Find the integer solutions of the indeterminate equation

$$9x - 12y = 27.$$

SOLUTION: The equation is of the form (1) with $a = 9$, $b = -12$, $c = 27$. Since $(9,12) = 3$ and $3 \mid 27$, the condition $(a,b) \mid c$ is satisfied, and the problem has solutions. To obtain them, it is best first to divide both sides of the equation by 3 and thus reduce the equation to

$$3x - 4y = 9.$$

The next step is to obtain a particular solution of this equation, which we do by first finding integers m, n that satisfy the condition

$$3m - 4n = 1.$$

Trial and error show us quickly that we can take

$$m = -1, \; n = -1$$

and thus that the pair x_0, y_0 given by

$$x_0 = 9m \qquad y_0 = 9n$$
$$ = -9 \qquad = -9$$

is a solution of the given equation. To obtain the other solutions, we must now consider the homogeneous equation

$$3u - 4v = 0.$$

Since $(3,4) = 1$, the integer solutions of this equation are given by

$$u = 4p, \qquad v = 3p,$$

where p is permitted to be any integer. The integer solutions of the original equation are given then by

$$x = x_0 + u \qquad y = y_0 + v$$
$$ = -9 + 4p \qquad = -9 + 3p,$$

where p may be any integer. In Table 11-3, for instance, are a few of the solutions of the given problem for indicated values of p.

Table 11-3   *Several solutions of an indeterminate equation*

p	0	1	−1	2	−2	3	−3
x	−9	−5	−13	−1	−17	3	−21
y	−9	−6	−12	−3	−15	0	−18

In the second example, we return to the bicycle problem stated at the beginning.

Example 2:   Find all pairs of non-negative integers that are solutions of the indeterminate equation

$$29x + 43y = 246.$$

SOLUTION: In this problem $a = 29$, $b = 43$, $c = 246$, and $(a,b) =$ $(29, 43) = 1$. Hence, $(a,b)|c$, and the equation given has integer solutions. The first step in finding them is to obtain integers m, n satisfying the condition

$$29m + 43n = 1.$$

Trial and error give us, for instance,

$$m = 3, \ n = -2.$$

From these values, we see that the pair x_0, y_0 defined by

$$\begin{aligned} x_0 &= 246m & y_0 &= 246n \\ &= 738 & &= -492 \end{aligned}$$

is a solution of the given equation. To obtain the other integer solutions, we now consider the homogeneous equation

$$29u + 43v = 0.$$

Since $(29,43) = 1$, the integer solutions of this equation are

$$u = 43p, \ v = -29p,$$

where p may be any integer. Hence, the integer solutions of the given equation are

$$x = 738 + 43p, \ y = -492 - 29p.$$

It is easy to see that $y \geq 0$ only if $p \leq -17$ and that $x \geq 0$ only if $p \geq -17$. Hence, x and y will both be non-negative integers if and only if $p = -17$, and for this value of p

$$x = 7, \ y = 1.$$

EXERCISES

3. The Hindu Mahavira, who was apparently familiar with Brahmagupta's writings, gave indeterminate problems like the following in a treatise of about 850 A.D.:†

Into the bright and refreshing outskirts of a forest, which were full of numerous trees with the branches bent down with the weight of flowers and fruits, trees such as jambu trees, lime trees, plantains, areca palms, mack trees, date palms, hintala trees, palmyras, punnaga trees, and

†From D. E. Smith, *History of Mathematics*, Dover, New York, 1951, Vol. 1, p. 163.

mango trees, . . . a number of weary travelers entered with joy. [There were] sixty-three [numerically equal] heaps of plantain fruits put together and combined with seven of those same fruits, and these were equally distributed among twenty-three travelers so as to have no remainder. You tell me now the numerical measure of a heap of plantains.

The question is, of course, how many plantain fruits were piled in each heap.

4. The following problem was first proposed in the "Arithmetical Classic of Chang Ch'iuchien," of the 6th Century A.D., and is given again by later Chinese authors: † "A cock costs five pieces of money, a hen three pieces, and three chickens one piece. If then we buy with 100 pieces 100 of them, what will be their respective numbers?" HINT: We must find non-negative integers x, y, z that satisfy the two equations

$$5x + 3y + z/3 = 100, \quad x + y + z = 100.$$

Writing the first equation in the form

$$15x + 9y + z = 300,$$

we might subtract the second equation in order to eliminate z. We would obtain

$$14x + 8y = 200,$$

or

$$7x + 4y = 100.$$

The next step is to obtain all the pairs of integers that satisfy this equation. They will be expressed in terms of an arbitrary integer p. Substitute the expressions in p for x and y into the equation $x + y + z = 100$, thereby obtaining an indeterminate equation for p and z, which must be solved in its turn. Finally apply the conditions that x, y, and z are non-negative.

5. Suppose 100 bushels of grain are distributed among 100 persons so that each man receives three bushels, each woman two bushels, and each child half a bushel.

    (a) How many men, women, and children are there? (Give several solutions.)

    (b) Find a solution in which there are four more women than men.

6. A boy opens up a lemonade stand where he sells three different sizes of drinks for 2¢, 5¢, and 7¢ a glass. He has 18 customers and takes in 80 cents. If he sold one more 2¢ drink than 5¢ drink, how many drinks of each size did he sell?

7. Find all possible solutions to the following problem: A man buys stock in two different companies. If one stock costs $21 a share and the other stock costs $31 a share, how many of each can he buy for $1770?

8. Find values of x and y in the indeterminate equation

$$7x + 9y = 1921$$

for which the sum $x + y$ is the least possible. †

---

† From Florian Cajori, *A History of Mathematics*, Macmillan, New York, Second Edition, 1919, p. 73.

9. Find two fractions having 5 and 7 for denominators whose sum is equal to 26/35. †

---

†From Barlow, *An Elementary Investigation of the Theory of Numbers*, London, 1811.

Remark: Euclid's theorem (Theorem 1 of this section) states that if

$$(c,a) = 1 \text{ and } c + b,$$

then

$$c + ab.$$

(This is the contrapositive form of the theorem.) We call attention here to the following related fact.

Theorem 2.   If

$$(c,a) = 1 \text{ and } (c,b) = 1,$$

then

$$(c,ab) = 1.$$

To prove this, we take integers m_1, m_2, n_1, n_2 such that

$$m_1 a + n_1 c = 1, \ m_2 b + n_2 c = 1.$$

Such integers exist by Euclid's greatest common divisor theorem. Multiplying the equations gives us

$$(m_1 a + n_1 c)(m_2 b + n_2 c) = 1$$

and, thus,

(4) $$Mab + Nc = 1,$$

where $M = m_1 m_2$, $N = m_1 n_2 a + n_1 m_2 b + n_1 n_2 c$. Since M and N are, in particular, integers, equation (4) shows that no integer divides both ab and c. This means that ab and c are relatively prime, i.e., that

$$(ab,c) = 1,$$

as asserted.

8.

The uniqueness of factorizations into primes

In Section 1, we proved this fact:
(I) *Factorization into Primes.* Every number N greater than 1

can be represented as a product

(1) $$N = p_1^{a_1} p_2^{a_2} \dots p_n^{a_n}$$

of powers of primes

$$p_1, p_2, \dots, p_n.$$

The powers

$$a_1, a_2, \dots, a_n$$

are natural numbers. This representation of N is called its *factorization into primes*.

The main purpose of this section is to prove:

(II) *The Uniqueness of Factorization into Primes.* If we label the primes so that

(2) $$p_1 < p_2 < \dots < p_n,$$

then the product (1) is unique. This means that if $q_1, q_2, \dots, q_m$ are primes such that

$$q_1 < q_2 < \dots < q_m$$

and that

$$N = q_1^{b_1} q_2^{b_2} \dots q_m^{b_m},$$

where the exponents $b_1, b_2, \dots, b_n$ are natural numbers, then

$$m = n,$$
$$p_1 = q_1, \ p_2 = q_2, \dots, p_n = q_n,$$

and

$$a_1 = b_1, \ a_2 = b_2, \dots, a_n = b_n.$$

As a corollary of (II), we shall have the following principle, by means of which we can immediately fill the gaps in certain proofs in Section 3:

(III) Let N be an arbitrary number. If equation (1) expresses its factorization into primes, then its positive divisors are the numbers of the form

(3) $$p_1^{c_1} p_2^{c_2} \dots p_n^{c_n},$$

where $c_1, c_2, \dots, c_n$ are integers such that

$$0 \le c_1 \le a_1, \ 0 \le c_2 \le a_2, \dots, 0 \le c_n \le a_n.$$

The proof of (II) is based ultimately on Euclid's greatest common divisor theorem (Section 5) and more immediately on the following corollary, which we proved in Section 7.

Theorem 1. If a, b, and c are integers such that

$$c \mid ab \text{ and } (c,a) = 1,$$

then

$$c \mid b.$$

From this, we have the following theorem.

Theorem 2. If a prime p divides a product of n numbers,

$$p \mid (a_1 a_2 \ldots a_n),$$

then it must divide at least one of the numbers.

PROOF: If $p \nmid a_1$, then $(a_1, p) = 1$, and Theorem 1 tells us that

$$p \mid (a_2 \ldots a_n).$$

If $p \nmid a_2$, then $(a_2, p) = 1$, and Theorem 1 implies that

$$p \mid (a_3 \ldots a_n).$$

After n steps, p will be seen to divide a_n if no other.

EXERCISE

1. Formulate the proof of this theorem more properly as a mathematical induction.

Now we can prove that prime factorizations are unique.

PROOF OF (II): Suppose a positive number N has two factorizations into primes:

$$N = p_1^{a_1} p_2^{a_2} \ldots p_n^{a_n}, N = q_1^{b_1} q_2^{b_2} \ldots q_m^{b_m},$$

where $p_1, \ldots, p_n, q_1, \ldots, q_m$ are primes such that

$$p_1 < p_2 < \ldots < p_n; q_1 < q_2 < \ldots < q_m,$$

and $a_1, \ldots, a_n, b_1, \ldots, b_m$ are natural numbers. Then we see, in particular, that $q_1 \mid N$ and consequently, by Theorem 2, q_1 divides some p_k. Since q_1 and this p_k are both primes, we deduce that q_1 is equal to this p_k. Similarly, each q_i coincides with an appropriate p_j, which is to say that all the q's are to be found among the p's. Similarly, all the p's are to be bound among the q's. Hence, $m = n$, and since the p's and q's are numbered in order of size,

$$p_1 = q_1, \; p_2 = q_2, \; \ldots, \; p_n = q_n.$$

It remains to be seen that the powers to which the primes are raised are the same in the two expressions for N. Otherwise, for some k we would have, say,

$$a_k > b_k.$$

Then the quantity q defined as

$$q = N/p_k^{b_k}$$

is an integer that, from the first representation for N, still contains p_k as a factor. Hence,

$$p_k \mid q.$$

According to the second representation of N, p_k is not, however, a prime factor of q, Theorem 2 telling us then that

$$p_k \nmid q.$$

The last two results are contradictory, and we conclude that

$$a_k = b_k \text{ for } k = 1, 2, \ldots, n.$$

Statement (II) is thus proved.

PROOF OF (III):   If f is any divisor of N, write

$$N = fg$$

and then express both f and g as products of prime powers. If either f or g failed to be of the form (3), their product N would not be represented by (1). Statement (II) asserts, however, that N has no representation other than (1). Hence, f and g are of the form (3), and statement (III) is proved.

9.

Pythagorean triples

As another application of the uniqueness of factorization into primes, we shall show here that all Pythagorean triples without a common factor are given by the formulas of Chapter 4.

We shall need several simple facts we formulate now as propositions.

Proposition 1.   Let a be any number. If a^2 is even, then a is even, and if a^2 is odd, then a is odd.

PROOF: The statements made are equivalent to the following, which are their contrapositive forms: if a is odd, then a^2 is odd, and if a is even, then a^2 is even. These follow immediately from the fact that if a is odd, then $a = 2n + 1$ and if a is even, $a = 2m$, where m and n are suitable integers. In the first case, $a^2 = (2n + 1)^2 = 4n^2 + 4n + 1 = 4(n^2 + n) + 1$, which is an odd number. The second case is even more direct.

Proposition 2.   If f^2 is a divisor of a^2, then f is a divisor of a: i.e., if $f^2 \mid a^2$, then $f \mid a$.

PROOF: Let

$$a = p_1^{n_1} \ldots p_k^{n_k},$$

where $p_1, \ldots, p_k$ are primes and $n_1, \ldots, n_k$ positive integers. Then

$$a^2 = p_1^{2n_1} \ldots p_k^{2n_k},$$

and since f^2 is a divisor of a^2, assertion (III) of the last section tells us that

(1) $$f^2 = p_1^{m_1} \ldots p_k^{m_k},$$

where

(2) $$0 \le m_1 \le 2n_1, \ldots, 0 \le m_k \le 2n_k.$$

Furthermore, f is representable as

$$f = q_1^{s_1} \ldots q_h^{s_h},$$

where $q_1, \ldots, q_h$ are primes and $s_1, \ldots, s_h$ are positive integers. Squaring, we have

$$f^2 = q_1^{2s_1} \ldots q_h^{2s_h}.$$

This shows that every prime in the decomposition of f^2 is raised to an even power. Hence, applying the unique factorization theorem (assertion (II) of the last section) to (1) proves that $m_1, \ldots, m_k$ are even:

$$m_1 = 2t_1, \ldots, m_k = 2t_k.$$

(Each nonzero t_i is of course some s_j, and $p_i = q_j$.) Thus, (1) states that

$$f^2 = p_1^{2t_1} \ldots p_k^{2t_k},$$

and taking the square root of both sides we have

$$f = p_1^{t_1} \ldots p_k^{t_k}.$$

By (2),

$$0 \le t_1 \le n_1, \ldots, 0 \le t_k \le n_k.$$

In view of (III) of the last section, we see from this that $f \mid a$, as asserted.

Proposition 3. If a, b, c are numbers such that

$$a^2 = bc \text{ and } (b,c) = 1,$$

then b and c are squares.

PROOF: Again let

$$a = p_1^{n_1} \ldots p_k^{n_k}$$

be the prime decomposition of a. Then

$$a^2 = p_1^{2n_1} \ldots p_k^{2n_k}.$$

Hence,

$$p_1^{2n_1} \mid (bc).$$

Since $(b,c) = 1$, we have by Theorem 1, Section 8, that either

$$p_1^{2n_1} \mid b \text{ or } p_1^{2n_1} \mid c.$$

In the same way, every one of the factors

$$p_1^{2n_1}, \ldots, p_k^{2n_k}$$

divides either b or c: both b and c, therefore, are products of certain of these factors. Since each factor is a square itself, any product of such factors is a square. Consequently, b and c are both squares, as asserted.

We are now ready to consider our problem. Recall that positive integers a, b, c are said to constitute a Pythagorean triple if

$$a^2 + b^2 = c^2.$$

We assume a, b, and c to have no common factor (other than 1). It follows that a and b have no common factor, nor do a and c or, lastly, b and c. Indeed, if b and c, for instance, had a common factor f, thus being of the form

$$b = fB, \; c = fC$$

with suitable integers B and C, we would have

$$a^2 = c^2 - b^2 = f^2 C^2 - f^2 B^2 = f^2 (C^2 - B^2).$$

Thus, f^2 would be a divisor of a^2, and by Proposition 2, f would be a divisor of a. Then a, b, c would all have f as common divisor, contrary to our assumption, and we conclude that b and c indeed cannot have a common divisor. Similar reasoning proves the same thing for a and b and for a and c, as asserted.

Since a and b have no common factors, they are not both even. Furthermore, a and b are also not both odd. If both were odd, we would have

$$a = 2A + 1, \; b = 2B + 1$$

with suitable integers A and B. Then

$$
\begin{aligned}
c^2 = a^2 + b^2 &= (2A + 1)^2 + (2B + 1)^2 \\
&= 4A^2 + 4A + 1 + 4B^2 + 4B + 1 \\
&= 4(A^2 + A + B^2 + B) + 2 \\
&= 4C + 2,
\end{aligned}
$$

where $C = A^2 + A + B^2 + B$. The fact that $c^2 = 4C + 2$ implies that 4 is not a divisor of c^2. But by Proposition 1, since c^2 is even, we have that c is even and thus that c^2 is divisible by 4. This is a contradiction showing that a and b cannot both be odd, as asserted.

Since a and b are not both even and also not both odd, one must be even and the other odd, say a odd and b even. Since $c^2 = a^2 + b^2$, c^2 then is odd, and Proposition 1 says that c is odd. Now notice that

(3) $$b^2 = c^2 - a^2 = (c + a)(c - a).$$

Since a and c are both odd, their sum and difference, $c + a$ and $c - a$, must both be even:

(4) $$c + a = 2p, \; c - a = 2q,$$

where p and q are suitable positive integers. Equivalently to these we have

(5) $$c = p + q, \; a = p - q.$$

(Adding the previous two equations gives us $2c = 2p + 2q$ and thus $c = p + q$. Subtracting them gives $2a = 2p - 2q$ and thus $a = p - q$.)
Since b is even, we have

$$b = 2B$$

for a suitable integer B. Substituting from this and (4) into (3) gives

$$4B^2 = 2p2q = 4pq,$$

or

(6) $$B^2 = pq.$$

We see from (5) that p and q do not have a common factor: if they did, a and c would contain this factor, which is contrary to a previous finding. Thus, $(p,q) = 1$. In view of (6), Proposition 3 says that p and q are both squares:

$$p = P^2, \ q = Q^2,$$

where P and Q are appropriate integers. Consequently, $B^2 = pq = P^2Q^2$, and $B = PQ$, which implies

(6) $$b = 4PQ.$$

From (5) we have

$$c = P^2 + Q^2, \ a = P^2 - Q^2,$$

which, with (6), are the formulas desired.

10.

Fermat's theorem

In 1670, Fermat announced the following fact without proof.

Fermat's Theorem.   For every prime p and integer a,

$$p \mid (a^p - a).$$

The first known demonstration was given about 70 years later by the Swiss mathematician, Leonhard Euler.

Examples

$2 \mid (10^2 - 10), 3 \mid (2^3 - 2), 5 \mid (2^5 - 2), 3 \mid (4^3 - 4), 5 \mid (3^5 - 3).$

If $p \nmid a$, Fermat's Theorem is equivalent to the statement that

$$p \mid (a^{p-1} - 1).$$

This fact is less exotic than it may seem, and to relate it to more familiar things, take $a = 10$. For this choice, p may be any prime not 2 or 5. Fermat's theorem tells us with $p = 7$, for instance, that

$$7 \mid (10^6 - 1),$$

i.e., that

(1) $7 \mid 999,999.$

We know on the other hand that

$$1 = .999999999999999999999999 \ldots.$$

(The three dots indicate that the decimal never terminates, but approaches the value indicated—in this case, 1—more and more accurately as we fill in more and more of its places.) Hence,

$$1/7 = .999999 \ldots /7,$$

while by (1) the denominator 7 divides the first six nines evenly, without remainder. Hence, if we carry out the indicated division of 1 by 7, we shall find that the first six digits obtained are reproduced as the second six digits, again are reproduced as the third six digits, and so on. The decimal for 1/7 therefore must be made up of one string of six digits, endlessly repeated. Calculation shows that this string is 142857. Thus, we must have

$$1/7 = .142857142857142857 \ldots.$$

If p is an arbitrary prime other than 2 or 5, Fermat's Theorem without any calculation shows similarly that the decimal representing $1/p$ is made up of a string of $p - 1$ digits, endlessly repeated.

EXERCISE

1. Give a similar interpretation of Fermat's theorem for a value of a not equal to 10, using numerals in base a. (See Chapter 3.)

Fermat's Theorem is one of the most fundamental in number theory. Easy to state but hard to prove, it doubtless provided one of the reasons for a historic re-examination of method in number theory carried out around the beginning of the 19th Century by the German mathematician, Karl Friedrich Gauss. The heart of the matter was divisibility, or rather the best way to undertake problems in divisibility. Fermat's theorem is one of many examples of such problems, in which the issue is whether some number p divides or does not divide a certain other number. The quotients in the divisions contemplated are of no essential interest. The remainders alone are really relevant, a remainder of zero, in particular, signifying that p does divide the number in question. But there are only p possible remainders — $0, 1, 2, \ldots, p-1$ — after division by p. Hence, a method of calculation is desirable that somehow disregards all quotients, confining itself to the remainders alone. Such an arithmetic of remainders† was invented by Gauss, and its economy and simplicity have transformed the theory of numbers.

Gauss's arithmetic of remainders is based on the notion of "residue class."

Definition. If a, b, and c are integers, with $a > 0$, and if

$$a \mid (b - c), \qquad 8 \mid (19 - 3)$$

then we shall say equivalently that b is *congruent to c* with respect to the *modulus a*, or is congruent to c *modulo a*. In symbols:

$$b \equiv c \pmod{a}.$$

If b is not congruent to c modulo a, we write

$$b \not\equiv c \pmod{a}.$$

Let a and b be any integers, with $a > 0$. Dividing b by a (Section 1) gives us

$$b = qa + r,$$

where q is the quotient and r the remainder, satisfying the condition

$$0 \leq r < a.$$

We also call r the *residue* of b, mod a. ("Residue" is just another word for remainder.) By the previous definition,

$$b \equiv r \pmod{a}.$$

Thus, any number is congruent, modulo a, to its own residue, which is one of the a quantities

$$0, 1, \ldots, a - 1.$$

---

† Shanks's expression.

EXERCISE

2. If $(e_1, a) = 1$ and $e_1 \equiv e_2$ (mod a), prove that then $(e_2, a) = 1$, where e_1, e_2, a are any integers with $a > 0$.

Since remainders are unique (Section 2), each number has just one residue. For each r among the a quantities

$$0, 1, \ldots, a - 1,$$

consider the class of all numbers with residue r, mod a. This class of numbers is called the *residue class* with residue r, mod a. All numbers are divided into a residue classes (mod a), and we shall now verify that (1) two numbers in different residue classes are incongruent, mod a, while (2) all numbers in the same residue class are mutually congruent, mod a. To prove the first statement, suppose

$$b \equiv r \ (\text{mod } a), \ c \equiv s \ (\text{mod } a),$$

where $r > s$ and

$$0 \le r < a, \ 0 \le s < a.$$

Then integers m and n exist such that

$$b = ma + r, \ c = na + s.$$

Hence,

$$\begin{aligned} b - c &= ma + r - (na + s) \\ &= (m - n)a + r - s. \end{aligned}$$

The restrictions upon r and s imply that $r - s > 0$ and $r - s < a$. Hence, $a + (b - c)$, and

$$b \not\equiv c \ (\text{mod } a),$$

thus proving that two numbers in different residue classes are incongruent, mod a, as asserted.

To prove that two numbers in the same residue class are congruent, mod a, suppose

$$b \equiv r \ (\text{mod } a)$$

and

$$c \equiv r \ (\text{mod } a).$$

Then $b - r = ma$ and $c - r = na$, where m and n are suitable integers. Subtracting corresponding members of these equations gives us

$$\begin{aligned} b - c &= (b - r) - (c - r) \\ &= ma - na \\ &= (m - n)a. \end{aligned}$$

Thus, $a \mid (b - c)$, and

$$b \equiv c \pmod{a},$$

as asserted.

The previous proof also established the following property, called transitivity.

Transitivity. For any integers a, b, c, d with $a > 0$,

$$\left.\begin{array}{l} b \equiv c \pmod{a} \\ c \equiv d \pmod{a} \end{array}\right\} \Rightarrow b \equiv d \pmod{a}.$$

Let us also note these further properties of the congruence relation.

Reflexivity. For any integers a, b with $a > 0$,

$$b \equiv b \pmod{a}.$$

Symmetry. For any integers a, b, c with $a > 0$,

$$b \equiv c \pmod{a} \Rightarrow c \equiv b \pmod{a}.$$

Reflexivity, symmetry, and transitivity are the three attributes that characterize relations of equivalence. Congruence (mod a) having these attributes thus is regarded as an equivalence relation.

Congruences can be added, subtracted, and multiplied. More precisely, we have the following theorem.

Theorem 1. If b_1, b_2, c_1, c_2 are any numbers such that

$$b_1 \equiv b_2, c_1 \equiv c_2 \pmod{a},$$

then

$$\begin{array}{l} b_1 + c_1 \equiv b_2 + c_2 \pmod{a}, \\ b_1 - c_1 \equiv b_2 - c_2 \pmod{a}, \\ b_1 c_1 \equiv b_2 c_2 \quad \pmod{a}. \end{array}$$

The verifications are easy and are left to the reader.

Concerning the division of congruences, we state the following theorem.

Theorem 2. If a, b, c, e are integers with $a > 0$, and if

$$(e, a) = 1$$

and

$$eb \equiv ec \pmod{a},$$

then

$$b \equiv c \pmod{a}.$$

PROOF: Since $eb \equiv ec \pmod{a}$, a number n exists such that

$$eb - ec = na;$$

therefore,

$$e(b - c) = na.$$

Thus, $e \mid na$, while $(e,a) = 1$, and Theorem 1, Section 7, indicates that $e \mid n$. Hence,

$$n = ef$$

for an appropriate integer f, and by substitution we have

$$e(b - c) = na$$
$$= efa.$$

Cancelling e gives us

$$b - c = fa,$$

which implies that

$$b \equiv c \pmod{a},$$

as asserted.

EXERCISES

3. Prove that if $(e_1,a) = 1$, $e_1 \equiv e_2 \pmod{a}$, and

$$e_1 b \equiv e_2 c \pmod{a},$$

then

$$b \equiv c \pmod{a}.$$

4. Suppose $a \equiv b \pmod{c}$ and $(a,c) = 1$. Prove that $(b,c) = 1$.

5. Prove that if $a > b$, then $a \equiv b \bmod (a - b)$.

6. Prove that if $a \equiv b \pmod{d}$ and if $c \mid d$, then $a \equiv b \pmod{c}$.

7. Prove that if $(p,q) = 1$ and $a \equiv b \pmod{p}$ and $a \equiv b \pmod{q}$, then $a \equiv b \pmod{pq}$.

We are almost ready to prove Fermat's theorem. The following result is very useful.

Theorem 3.   If p and a are integers that are relatively prime, and $p > 0$, then each of the p numbers

$$0, a, 2a, \ldots, (p-1)a$$

is in a different residue class, mod p.

PROOF: If the theorem were false, then two numbers i and j would exist such that

$$0 \le i < p, \; 0 \le j < p$$

and

$$ia \equiv ja \;(\text{mod } p).$$

In this case,

$$(i - j)a \equiv 0 \;(\text{mod } p),$$

which means that

$$p \mid (i - j)a.$$

Since i and j are non-negative and less than p, their difference has absolute value less than p, i.e., $|i - j| < p$. Hence, $p + (i - j)$, and by hypothesis, $(p, a) = 1$. Theorem 1, Section 7, shows that, consequently,

$$p + (i - j)a,$$

in contradiction to a previous result. It follows that ia and ja are not congruent, mod a, and thus that the theorem stated is true.

Now, at last, we can prove Fermat's theorem. Since the contention of this theorem is obvious if $p \mid a$, let us assume that $p + a$, the theorem reducing then to the following statement.

If p is a prime and $p + a$, then $a^{p-1} \equiv 1 \;(\text{mod } p)$.

PROOF: The previous theorem implies that

$$a \equiv r_1 \;(\text{mod } p),$$
$$2a \equiv r_2 \;(\text{mod } p),$$
$$\cdots \cdots \cdots$$
$$(p - 1)a \equiv r_{p-1} \;(\text{mod } p),$$

where the set of numbers

$$r_1, r_2, \ldots, r_{p-1}$$

is just a rearrangement of the set

$$1, 2, \ldots, p - 1.$$

Thus, in particular,

$$r_1 r_2 \ldots r_{p-1} = 1 \cdot 2 \cdot \ldots \cdot (p - 1).$$

Hence, if we multiply the $p - 1$ congruences, as Theorem 1 permits, we obtain

$$a \cdot 2a \cdot \ldots \cdot (p-1)a \equiv r_1 r_2 \ldots r_{p-1} \pmod{p}$$
$$= 1 \cdot 2 \cdot \ldots \cdot (p-1),$$

or

$$1 \cdot 2 \cdot \ldots \cdot (p-1) a^{p-1} \equiv 1 \cdot 2 \cdot \ldots \cdot (p-1) \pmod{p}.$$

Theorem 2 allows us to cancel the common factors, to obtain

$$a^{p-1} \equiv 1 \pmod{p}.$$

Thus, Fermat's theorem is proved.

EXERCISES

8. Let a be a fixed number greater than 1. Denote the residue class of 0, mod a, by $\bar{0}$; denote the residue class of 1, mod a, by $\bar{1}$, and so forth. If b and c are any numbers, define the *product* of their *residue classes*, $\bar{b}$ and $\bar{c}$, as follows:

$$\bar{b} \, \bar{c} = \text{residue class of } bc = \overline{bc}.$$

(a) Why does this definition need justification?

(b) Prove that if $\bar{b}$ contains both b and b', and $\bar{c}$ contains both c and c', then the residue classes of bc and of $b'c'$ are the same. How does this fact justify the previous definition?

(c) If a is a prime, prove that the $a-1$ residue classes other than $\bar{0}$ constitute a group under the operation of multiplication just defined. HINT: For the existence of an inverse, apply Fermat's theorem.

9. If m is any integer, then define the number $\varphi(m)$ to be the number of integers less than m that are relatively prime to m. For example, since 1, 2, 4, 7, 8, 11, 13, 14 are the only integers less than 15 that are relatively prime to 15, and since there are 8 of them, $\varphi(15) = 8$.

(a) Find $\varphi(24)$, $\varphi(30)$, $\varphi(37)$ and $\varphi(60)$.

(b) Prove that if p is a prime number, then $\varphi(p) = p - 1$.

(c) If $\varphi(m) = 1$, describe m.

10. Let

$$r_1, r_2, \ldots, r_{\varphi(m)}$$

be the $\varphi(m)$ positive integers less than m that are prime to m. Prove that their residue classes, mod m, are also the residue classes of the $\varphi(m)$ numbers

$$r_1 a, r_2 a, \ldots, r_{\varphi(m)} a$$

if $(a, m) = 1$. HINT: Theorem 3 proves that the numbers of the second set are all in different residue classes, mod m. The numbers of this set are also prime to m, and there are $\varphi(m)$ of them.

    11. (a) Using the results of Exercises 9 and 10, alter the proof of Fermat's theorem to prove Euler's theorem:

$$\text{if } (a,m) = 1 \text{ then } a^{\varphi(m)} \equiv 1 \pmod{m}$$

    (b) Deduce Fermat's theorem from Euler's theorem using the result of part (b) in Exercise 9.

    12. Generalize Exercise 8, part (c), to composite a. HINT: The two previous exercises are useful.

CHAPTER 12

THE AXIOMATIC METHOD
AND APPLICATIONS
IN ALGEBRA

This chapter is devoted mainly to a new kind of algebra that has surprising ties to engineering, logic, statistics, and other fields and that serves also as a good example of "axiomatic" procedure. The axiomatic method, consisting essentially of close reasoning from abstract, idealized premises, is the method of systematic rational thought. It was well developed by 300 B.C. in the geometry of Euclid but was universally misunderstood in some respects until the advent of non-Euclidean geometry during the first third of the 19th Century. In our own day, studies by means of mathematical logic have led to further perceptions concerning axiomatic method — and the very nature of thought — that are truly astonishing. We shall mention some of these, but we are not prepared to face their technicalities. We shall also avoid the intricacies of Euclidean and non-Euclidean geometry, finding easier illustrations of the method in our new algebra. But geometry, the original model and inspiration of systematic thought, still provides us with the best background for a general discussion.

1.

The axiomatic method in geometry

Greek geometry is supposed to have begun with a collection of rules picked up by Thales on a visit to Egypt at the beginning of the

6th Century, B.C. The rules must have been of Babylonian origin, some right and some wrong, the reasons for them long forgotten.† Tradition has it that Thales added to the rules, applied them with originality (to measuring building heights, ship-to-shore distances, and so on), perceived that some follow logically from others, and thus invented the idea of proof. Thales and his immediate successors are largely legendary to us, but there is no doubt that Greek mathematicians by the 5th Century B.C. were committed to the rational method, by which they hoped to explore all the complex, varied phenomena of space and to reduce them to certain fundamental principles, indubitable, simple, and few. The effort thus to compress geometry into a small number of pregnant statements culminated about three centuries after Thales (around 300 B.C.) in the "Elements" of Euclid of Alexandria. Euclid began by enumerating certain "common notions" which, as Aristotle had said, anyone must hold if he is to learn anything at all: "Things which are equal to the same thing are also equal to one another. If equals be added to equals, the wholes are equal. If equals be subtracted from equals, the remainders are equal. Things which coincide with one another are equal to one another. The whole is greater than the part." Then he stated his specifically geometrical principles, also unproved, out of which all other propositions of geometry were to proceed by logical deduction. These first principles (somewhat paraphrased) were as follows:

(1) From any point a straight line may be drawn to any other point. Only one such straight line can thus be drawn.

(2) Any straight line segment can be produced in a straight line to any length.

(3) A circle can be described with any center and any radius.

(4) All right angles are equal.

(5) Suppose a straight line k to meet two straight lines, m and n, so as to make the two interior angles on the same side of k taken together less than two right angles. Then if m and n are produced, they will eventually meet on the same side of k as lie the aforementioned angles. (See Figure 12-1.)

---

†So speculates B. L. Van der Waerden in *Science Awakening*, P. Nordhoff Ltd., Groningen, Holland, 1954.

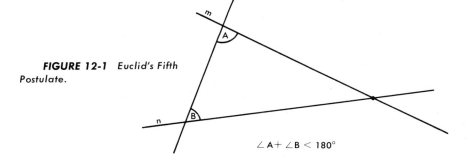

FIGURE 12-1 Euclid's Fifth Postulate.

$$\angle A + \angle B < 180°$$

The "common notions" traditionally are called "axioms" and the five geometrical principles "postulates," but in today's usage any assumed principle that is made the basis of systematic reasoning may be called either an axiom or a postulate without distinction. Any statement is also called a *proposition*. A statement deduced from the axioms or postulates is called a *theorem*. The body of doctrine arising from a set of axioms (or postulates) through deductive reasoning is called an *axiomatic system*, a *postulational system*, or, alternatively, a *deductive theory*.

The axioms underpinning a deductive theory are incomplete without statements of the rules of inference themselves and all other principles (such as Euclid's "common notions") employed in addition to the technical postulates specific to the theory. In deep matters, such as occur in the theory of proof (see Section 6), it is essential to be exhaustive, but ordinary mathematical needs are usually met well enough by listing the technical postulates alone, taking ordinary logic for granted. We shall confine our remarks on Euclidean geometry to the specifically geometrical principles, Euclid's "Postulates."

What processes had caused these Postulates to be selected? We can only guess. But we can easily raise questions that are pertinent to us, and here are some:

(1) Are the axioms and the propositions arising from them quite beyond doubt?

(2) Do they cover spatial phenomena?

(3) Is the reasoning impeccable?

(4) Are all terms defined, for are not undefined words meaningless, and are not statements couched in meaningless words nonsensical?

(5) Are the axioms mutually independent?

We shall take these questions up in order. The answers to some originally proved to be surprising.

(1) As the Greeks themselves well understood, the axioms of geometry are idealizations, for infinitely fine points, perfectly straight and narrow lines, precisely equal angles, and so forth exist only as abstractions in the mind. No real object exactly duplicates an ideal geometric one. No observation made on a real figure is wholly free of error. Therefore, the axioms and the propositions of geometry never can be tested absolutely. Their justification in practical affairs (surveying, mechanics, engineering, navigation, astronomy, and so forth) is that whenever a real object *almost* exactly duplicates an ideal one, the relations that are observed in the real object *almost* exactly agree with corresponding relations that can be demonstrated in the ideal one. In fact, the more nearly alike are the real object and the ideal, the more closely do the observed and the theoretical relations also agree. In this sense, Euclidean geometry correctly describes our experience of physical space in every-day affairs on an ordinary scale. Does it describe space equally well on the sub-atomic or on the cosmic scale? Can a straight line really be drawn to *any* point (First

Postulate), a segment produced to *any* length (Second Postulate), a circle described with *any* radius (Third Postulate)? Can the straight lines of the Fifth Postulate not meet for billions of miles and yet be sure to meet thereafter? Who can speak with authority on the remoter reaches of space? It is plain from such questions, which concern the nature of idealization itself, that the statements of geometry will always defy ultimate verification and can never be regarded as final. Thus, we can never know whether the Euclidean or any other system of axioms is true in an absolute sense. If a particular set of axioms were true, conclusions correctly drawn from them would be true, too. But since we do not and cannot know whether a given set of axioms be true or not, we do not and cannot know whether the propositions to which they lead are true, either. This is what Bertrand Russell meant in the second half of his celebrated definition of mathematics as "the subject in which we never know what we are talking about, nor whether what we are saying is true."

While we thus cannot expect an axiomatic system to be true, we can still demand that it be appropriate in the context in which we wish to use it. For instance, although the earth is neither a plane nor a sphere, plane geometry is perfectly suitable for drawing up the plans of a house, and spherical geometry is appropriate in mapping a continent. Euclidean geometry applies to the spatial phenomena of our planet as exactly as men can make measurements. On the other hand, astronomers have reason to prefer a non-Euclidean geometry in the vaster regions of space.

How can geometry be non-Euclidean in the universe at large, but Euclidean on earth? An analogous question is, How can plane geometry apply to blueprints of my house, but spherical geometry to a map of the United States? The answer to the second question is that the curvature of the earth is too slight to be noticed in the narrow confines of my house, and the answer to the first question is analogous.

(2) Question 2 asks whether Euclidean geometry covers all the phenomena of space. Up to a century or two ago, perhaps, most educated people would have answered yes, being unable to conceive of space at all in any other terms than Euclid's. They were also influenced by Plato's doctrine that the tidy idealizations of the mind are truer than wayward, impure, ineffable reality. Philosophers of nature make more modest claims today and expect no system of thought—man-made, artificial, and ideal—to be universal. Indeed, as we mentioned before, Euclidean geometry may not be the most suitable kind for cosmic studies.

However comprehensively Euclidean geometry may cover the empirical phenomena of space, additional axioms are needed for certain mathematical phenomena. Some of the matters at issue are discussed in Chapter 15, Section 1b.

(3) The question here is whether the logic of geometry is perfect. If so, a tight, compact foundation of almost self-evident principles safely supports a truly imposing edifice of thought. If not, the edifice

is unsound. Without anyone's realizing it for about 22 centuries, this edifice in fact was unsound, chiefly because Euclid, despite his great care, still had fallen into certain tacit assumptions unwarranted by his explicit postulates. For instance, in some proofs he uses the fact that if a straight line enters a triangle at a vertex, then it must, if sufficiently produced, intersect the opposite side. This use is certainly unconscious and indeed would require a new postulate for its justification. Perceptions such as this led to an intensive scrutiny of the foundations of geometry during the end of the 19th Century and the beginning of the 20th. Ultimately, several different sets of axioms were discovered, each of which meets present standards as a basis for Euclidean geometry.†

(4) The fourth question raises doubts concerning a system in which important technical words are undefined. Can the system make sense? Euclid seemingly thought not and offered such definitions of his terms as these: a point is that which has no part, a line is length without breadth, a straight line is that which lies evenly between its points, and so on. He never used these definitions, however, or even referred to them again. Hence, they were of no benefit. In fact, they were irrelevant to his design of a deductive theory, for as we have previously stressed (Chapter 1), logic is indifferent to substance, acting only upon form. Prof. R. L. Wilder‡ has brought out this point with exceptional force in a fragment of Euclidean geometry, as follows. Take "point" and "line" as *undefined* technical terms. We explicitly refuse to define them, but we shall define other technical terms from these and shall use ordinary language whenever necessary. We take the following as axioms and associated definitions.

Axiom 1.   Every line is a collection of points.

Definition 1.   Two lines are said to be *distinct* if their collections of points are not precisely the same. (This means that at least one point exists belonging to one of the two collections of points that constitute these lines but not belonging to the other.)

Axiom 2.   At least two points exist.

Definition 2.   If a point P is a member of the collection of points constituting a line m, then we say, variously, that m *contains* P, or that P *is on* m.

Axiom 3.   For two distinct points, one and only one line exists that contains them both.

Axiom 4.   For any line, a point exists that is not on the line.

---

†See H. Eves, Sections 5 and 6 and references in *An Introduction to the History of Mathematics,* second edition, Holt, Rinehart and Winston, New York, 1964.

‡*Introduction to the Foundations of Mathematics,* by R. L. Wilder, published by John Wiley and Sons, New York, 1952. Excerpted as "The Axiomatic Method" in *The World of Mathematics,* edited by James R. Newman, published by Simon and Schuster, New York, 1956, Vol. 3, pp. 1647-1667.

Definition 3.   Two lines are called *parallel* if no point is on them both.

Axiom 5.   If m is a line, and P is a point not on m, then one and only one line exists that contains P and is parallel to m.

The undefined terms in these axioms are capable of having various meanings. They might of course be the point and the straight line of Euclid, but other possibilities also exist. For instance, suppose we have exactly four different objects, each of which we call a "point." By a "line" we shall mean a collection consisting of exactly two of these objects. The objects, or "points," might, in particular, be persons and the "lines" clubs, each club having two members and each pair of persons possessing their own private club. The five axioms pertain to this situation just as well as to Euclidean geometry. The process of deduction from these axioms, however, manipulates the undefined terms by logical rules mechanically with no regard to their meanings or even to whether they have meanings. We illustrate this by proofs (from the five axioms) that every point is on at least two distinct lines, that every line contains at least two points, and that at least four distinct points exist. These proofs are good no matter what "point" and "line" are taken to mean and even if we do not know what they mean. We do not have to explain the axioms before setting in motion the formal, impartial machinery of logic.

Theorem 1.   Every point is on at least two distinct lines.

PROOF: Letting P denote any point, we shall show that P is on two distinct lines. Let Q denote a point other than P (Axiom 2). A line m exists containing P and Q (Axiom 3), a point R exists not on m (Axiom 4), and a line n exists containing P and R (Axiom 3). Since R is on n but not on m, we see that m and n are distinct lines (Definition 1). Both lines contain P. The proof is complete.

Corollary to Theorem 1.   Every line contains at least one point.

Remark: By "a collection of points" a mathematician means "a collection of *nothing but* points." The collection might be "empty," i.e., have no points. Hence, Axiom 1 by itself does not insure that each line has at least one point on it. The fact that it does do so, as the corollary states, is a consequence in part of the other axioms.

PROOF OF COROLLARY: Letting m denote any line, we shall show that m contains at least one point. Suppose that, to the contrary, m contains no point whatsoever. This supposition will lead us to a contradiction. Let P be any point (Axiom 2) and let k and n be two distinct lines containing P (Theorem 1). Then k and n are both parallel to m (Definition 3), while both contain P. This contradicts Axiom 5. Thus, our supposition that m contains no point is untenable, and the contrary must be true. The corollary is thus proved.

Theorem 2.   Every line contains at least two points.

PROOF: If k denotes any line, let P be one of its points (corollary to Theorem 1). We shall show that there is another point on k by supposing the contrary and progressing to a contradiction. Thus, assume that P is the only point on k. A line m distinct from k exists that also contains P (Theorem 1). Since m and k are distinct, m must contain at least one other point than P (Definition 1). Let Q then denote a point on m distinct from P. Also, let R denote a point not on m (Axiom 4), and let n be a line containing R parallel to m (Axiom 5). Then n does not contain P (Definition 3), and since P is assumed to be the sole point of k, n is parallel to k (Definition 3). Thus, k and m are distinct lines containing P that are parallel to n. This contradicts Axiom 5. Hence, our supposition that k consists solely of P is untenable, and we conclude that k also contains at least one other point, as contended.

Theorem 3.   At least four distinct points exist.

PROOF: Find two distinct points, P and Q (Axiom 2), a line k containing P and Q (Axiom 3), and a line m distinct from k but containing P (Theorem 1). Then m does not contain Q, since otherwise k and m would coincide (Axiom 3). Find a line n containing Q and parallel to m (Axiom 5). Since m contains at least two points (Theorem 2), n contains at least two points (Theorem 2), and m and n contain no common points (Definition 3), at least four distinct points exist, as contended.

EXERCISES

These exercises all pertain to Wilder's axiomatic system.

1. Prove that at least six distinct lines exist.

2. Can it be shown that (a) a line contains at least three points or (b) that at least five points exist?

3. Suppose that we have three distinct objects, each of which we agree to call a "point." Is it possible to satisfy Axioms 1 through 5 by appropriate definitions of "lines"? HINT: Axiom 5 is particularly important here.

4. Suppose that we have five distinct points and call each a "point." Is it possible to satisfy Axioms 1 through 5 by defining "lines" such that:

    (a) each line is a collection of just two points?

    (b) one line is a collection of three points and the others of two?

    (c) two lines are collections of three points?

    (d) one line is a collection of four points?

Prove from your answers that the five axioms cannot be satisfied by any definition of "lines."

The foregoing proofs illustrate our contention that logic, being a wholly formal process blind to substance, does not require us to declare meanings of terms used in axioms. Definitions of these terms indeed serve no *logical* function. But do they give the axioms *meaning*? Do Euclid's definitions, such as those of "point" and "straight line," for instance, stamp his system as geometry rather than something else? Conceivably they could if we knew the meanings of the terms *they* use ("part," "length," "breadth," "evenly," and so on), but Euclid is silent on the meanings of these terms.

Euclid in being silent was bowing to the inevitable, for he could not possibly have defined all his terms. This follows from the nature of definition. To define a word (or expression) is to tell its exact meaning in other words, among which the word being defined is not permitted to appear. If A denotes any word, its definition thus is not permitted to contain the word A. Let B denote any term that does occur in the definition of A. Then the definition of B likewise may not contain A, for otherwise A would be defined ultimately in terms of itself. For the same reason, the definition of any term that occurs in the definition of B is not permitted to contain A, and so on. This restriction is usually described by saying that definitions are not permitted to be circular. Any system of thought having just a finite number of terms, none of which are defined circularly, must contain some terms that are undefined. To prove this, we shall show that the contrary supposition involves a contradiction. Thus, suppose a system of thought exists having just a finite number of terms, all of which have definitions that are noncircular. Then let A denote any term of the system. If B denotes a term that occurs in the definition of A, then B is different from A, and if C denotes a term in the definition of B, then C is different from A and B both. This is because, by assumption, the definitions are noncircular. Similarly, any term D appearing in the definition of C differs from A, B, and C. We thus obtain a sequence of terms,

$$A, B, C, D, \ldots,$$

each of which after the first is a term that occurs in the definition of the one before. The terms are all different, because the definitions are not circular. The sequence is unending, because each term has a definition. The total number of terms, however, is finite, in contradiction to the previous two statements. We conclude that a system of thought such as we were considering is impossible and, thus, that any system of thought free from circularities has undefined terms.

The undefined terms in a deductive theory are the most basic, all other terms deriving from them. Therefore, we cannot *tell* what undefined terms mean in words alone. How otherwise can we and do we convey their meanings? By nonverbal means consisting at least partly in *showing* rather than in telling, as, for instance, in explaining the idea of "point" with a small dot on a blackboard or the idea of "straight line" with a stretched thread. In a similar way, we should explain "sweet" with a taste of sugar, "sparkle" with cut glass or a gem, and "pain" by recalling painful incidents such as wrenching a knee. Understanding arrived at through nonverbal processes is called *intuitive* understanding, meaning conveyed or received nonverbally, *intuitive* meaning. *Intuition* is the faculty of perceiving and understanding intuitively. The undefined terms in geometry are laden with intuitive meaning, and the axioms in geometry are intuitively plausible. Axioms thus can be meaningful notwithstanding the fact that their terms are undefined.

The answer to Question (4), which inspired these reflections, is now clear. Words can have meaning without being defined, and statements using undefined terms thus are not necessarily nonsense. But the meanings of the undefined terms are not an issue in proofs, and demonstrated theorems hold no matter what these meanings may be.

EXERCISES

5. Explain fully Bertrand Russell's statement quoted on page 469.

6. Not every statement in a logical system of thought can be demonstrated. Prove this for a system with a finite number of statements.

7. Comment on the view that every definition should be required to be of this form: "'x' means such-and-such," where x represents the word or expression being defined.

8. The way in which undefined terms are used in the axioms undoubtedly limits the possible meanings of these terms. Then is it reasonable to say that the set of axioms *defines* these terms *implicitly*?

9. How do you explain the apparent paradox that the most basic words in a deductive theory are just the ones that we choose not to define?

(5) Question (5) asks whether the axioms of geometry are *independent*, i.e., whether one or more of these axioms are deducible from the others. An axiom that is so deducible is said to be *redundant*. Redundancy is not a crime and often is tolerated for convenience to shorten an argument. For instance, had we added to Prof. Wilder's five axioms the additional supposition that each line contains at least one point, we should not have needed the tricky proof of the corollary to Theorem 1. On the other hand, if we wish to know clearly what must be assumed and what need not be assumed in this theory, we shall desire our axioms to be independent and be glad to have such a proof.

Euclid may have suspected his Fifth Postulate of redundancy and was in any case reluctant to invoke it. For instance, he took some trouble to show that the first four postulates alone imply that the sum of any two angles of a triangle is less than two right angles. Yet he never used this result, which was completely superseded by the more specific fact, proved independently later by use of the Fifth Postulate, that the sum of the three angles of a triangle is exactly two right angles.† Whatever Euclid's own doubts, multitudes of his successors during the next 2100 years tried to derive the Fifth Postulate from the preceding four. No one succeeded, but an interesting outcome of these labors was the discovery of several substitutes for the Fifth Postulate, statements logically equivalent to it that might be taken in its place. George Sarton‡ lists the following, as examples:

> If a straight line intersects one of two parallels, it will intersect the other. (Proclos)
>
> Given any figure, there exists a figure similar to it of any size. (John Wallis)
>
> Through a given point only one parallel can be drawn to a given straight line. (John Playfair)
>
> There exists a triangle in which the sum of the three angles is equal to two right angles. (Legendre)
>
> Given any three points not in a straight line, there exists a circle passing through them. (Legendre)
>
> If I could prove that a rectilinear triangle is possible the content of which is greater than any given area, I would be in a position to prove perfectly rigorously the whole of geometry. (Gauss, 1799)

None of these substitutes could be demonstrated either. During the 18th Century, particularly skillful, prolonged, determined efforts were made to prove the Fifth Postulate by assuming its negation to be true and trying to arrive at a contradiction. The consequence of thus supposing the Fifth Postulate to be false was a long chain of statements that grated against intuition and were impossible to represent convincingly in a diagram but that could not be proved to conflict with one another. No contradiction appearing, the enterprise against the Fifth Postulate again was stalled. Eventually, several people surmised that negating the Fifth Postulate simply does not lead to contradictions, and this proved to be the key to the riddle. When we take as an axiom the negation of Euclid's Fifth Postulate, and also take Euclid's other axioms, we now call the resulting deductive theory *non-Euclidean geometry*. The surmise was that Euclidean geometry and non-Euclidean geometry are *both* consistent, i.e., free of contradiction, and the judgment followed that therefore they are both good mathematical systems. Consistency—the lack of contradiction— was made the touchstone. Is this reasonable? Are we free to assume either the Fifth Postulate or its negation solely at our own pleasure? Have we the right to take words without regard for their accustomed meanings (if any), string them together into "sentences" in any way we like, pronounce these "sentences" axioms, and if the axioms are

---

† See the discussion, for instance, in Ettore Carruccio, *Mathematics and Logic in History and in Contemporary Thought*, Chicago, Aldine Publishing Co., 1964.

‡ George Sarton, *A History of Science—Hellenistic Science and Culture in the Last Three Centuries B.C.*, Harvard University Press, Cambridge, 1959, p. 40.

consistent, then draw logical deductions from them? This is almost like asking if we are free to play games. Any game can be played if its rules are consistent. Why not then play the game of logical deduction? If the strings of words or symbols that we choose as axioms are consistent — do not give rise to contradictions — can it be a crime to draw logical conclusions from them? No one who understands that axioms are merely formal arrangements of undefined terms will argue that it is. Every mathematician today will thus grant that mutual consistency is indeed the only requirement a set of axioms must satisfy to be acceptable as a basis for logical argument. This philosophical perception is one of the most significant outcomes of the rise of non-Euclidean geometry. It leads of course to this question:

(6) How can we decide whether given axioms are mutually consistent?

Consistency often can be made to hang upon the possibility of interpreting the undefined terms. In the case of plane non-Euclidean geometry, a certain kind of curved surface in three-dimensional Euclidean space was sought for this purpose and ultimately found. "Point" in non-Euclidean geometry then was interpreted as ordinary, Euclidean point upon this surface; "straight line" in non-Euclidean geometry was interpreted as a certain kind of curve upon this surface; distance, angle, and so forth, were given interpretations relating to the "straight line" curves of the surface. With the undefined terms so interpreted, the axioms of non-Euclidean geometry proved to be true statements about the surface *in the Euclidean sense*. Hence, these axioms contain no contradiction not already present in Euclidean geometry. In other words, non-Euclidean geometry is consistent if Euclidean geometry is.

Is Euclidean geometry consistent? It has survived the scrutiny of ages. Apart from its longevity, however, can a doctrine appeal so strongly to the intuition and be so fruitful of consequences, all faithfully reflecting the world of sense, and still be nonsense, as it would be if inconsistent? We cannot answer these questions absolutely, but every practical reason leads us to believe that the criteria for consistency they suggest — simplicity, plausibility, and unfailing respect for experience — are sound. On such grounds, the consistency of Euclidean geometry, in particular, has never been doubted practically. For elementary Euclidean geometry — including most results of Euclid, but not advanced types of curved surfaces such as those by which non-Euclidean geometry may be represented — consistency has been proved absolutely from the logical and mathematical structure of the axioms.

Absolute proofs of consistency are known only for theories of relatively simple logical and mathematical form. Relative proofs, such as the proof we referred to for non-Euclidean geometry, are more usual. The method of a relative proof of consistency is to find a set of objects, and relations among them, which the axioms considered will describe when their undefined terms are suitably interpreted. These objects and their relations provide what is called a *model* for the axioms. For instance, geometric objects and relations in a plane are a model for Euclid's axioms, and those on a suitable surface are a model for the axioms of non-Euclidean geometry. Prof. Wilder's axioms have Euclidean geometry as one model, while four points provided another. When a model is used to prove consistency, it is taken for granted that no relation in the model both holds and fails to hold. A set of axioms having this model then will have to be consistent. Professor Wilder's axioms, for instance, are consistent, since they are embodied in the four-point model. Another simple illustration will be given after a brief historical sketch.

The 18th Century preparation for non-Euclidean geometry was pre-eminently the work of Girolamo Saccheri (1733), Johann Heinrich Lambert (1766), and Adrien-Marie Legendre (1794). True non-Euclidean geometry was first developed by Karl Friedrich Gauss, apparently some time after 1799, but it remained in the author's notebooks unpublished, owing to his dislike of contention. Nicholaus Ivanovich Lobachevski was the second creator of non-Euclidean geometry. His original paper was in 1826, but was never printed and is lost; his work was first published in 1829 in an obscure journal in Russian. The third author credited with the independent invention of non-Euclidean geometry is Johann Bolyai (1833). Both Bolyai and Lobachevski had to wait thirty-four years more for any attention from the world at large. After knowledge of non-Euclidean geometry became general, proofs of its consistency through interpretation in suitable models were offered by several mathematicians, including Eugenio Beltrami, Arthur Cayley, Felix Klein, Henri Poincare, and others. Familiarity with non-Euclidean geometry led to interest in the foundations of Euclidean geometry. The critical study of axioms was first undertaken by Giuseppe Peano (1880), Moritz Pasch (1882), and Mario Pieri (1899), and then was taken up by many, in particular, by David Hilbert, Henri Poincare, and Oswald Veblen. Proof of the consistency of elementary geometry is due to Alfred Tarski.†

We conclude this section with another illustration. Consider three abstract mathematical objects, which we denote by A, B, and C. They are supposed to be distinct, i.e., $A \neq B$, $A \neq C$, $B \neq C$. An abstract relation between two such objects is given. If x and y denote two such objects (i.e., $x = A$, B, or C and $y = A$, B, or C), we write

$$R(x,y)$$

---

† See Tarski, "What is elementary geometry?" pp. 16-29 in *The Axiomatic Method*, edited by Henkin, Suppes, and Tarski, North-Holland Publishing Company, Amsterdam, 1959. For a readable nontechnical account of non-Euclidean geometry, see, for instance, Morris Kline, *Mathematics in Western Culture*, Oxford University Press, 1953, Chapter 26, or *Mathematics: A Cultural Approach*, Addison-Wesley, Reading, Mass., 1962, Chapter 26. A slightly more advanced treatment, but still within the scope of high school mathematics, is that of R. Courant and H. Robbins, *What Is Mathematics?* Oxford University Press, New York, 1941, pp. 214-227.

to mean that the relation holds between x and y, and

$$\sim R(x,y)$$

to mean that the relation does not hold between x and y. (For instance, if the objects were numbers, $R(x,y)$ might signify "$x < y$" and $\sim R(x,y)$, "$x \geq y$.") We adopt these axioms (the first repeats information already disclosed):

(i) The universe of discourse consists of three mathematical objects, A, B, and C. These are distinct.

(ii) For any object x (i.e., for $x = A$, B, or C),

$$\sim R(x,x).$$

(iii) For any objects x, y, z,

$$(R(y,x) \text{ and } R(z,x)) \Rightarrow y = z.$$

(iv) For any object x, an object y exists such that $R(x,y)$.

(v) $R(A,B)$.

These axioms are devoid of meaning, but we may still draw conclusions from them if they are consistent. Of course, the conclusions will mean no more than the axioms. First, however, we shall show that the axioms are consistent and to this end will describe a model embodying them. In fact, we shall give two models to stress that something has been accomplished by the abstraction. In the first model, A, B, and C represent three people sitting around a table, and $R(x,y)$ is interpreted as: "y is seated just to the right of x." The first four axioms are obviously fulfilled, and Axiom (v) specifies that B is seated to the right of A. Hence, the axioms are consistent. From the diagram (Figure 12-2), we notice, in particular, that

(1) $R(A,B)$, $R(B,C)$, $R(C,A)$, $\sim R(B,A)$, $\sim R(C,B)$, $\sim R(A,C)$.

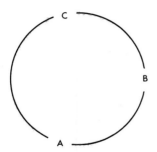

FIGURE 12-2   The "Three People" model.

Our second model of this system is given by a nursery game played by two people, as follows: the participants simultaneously make one of three signs, one sign meaning scissors, another sign meaning paper, and the third sign meaning stone. Scissors, paper, and stone are ranked according to this scheme:

> scissors cut paper,
> paper wraps stone,
> stone blunts scissors.

If one person makes the sign for stone and the other the sign for paper, the latter wins, and so forth. We interpret A as scissors, B as paper, C as stone, and $R(x,y)$ as: "x wins over y." Notice that relations (1) again are fulfilled. Will they hold in any model for these axioms?

EXERCISES

10. Prove relations (1) abstractly from the axioms themselves. HINT: We might start by deducing from (iv) and (i) that

$$R(C,A) \text{ or } R(C,B) \text{ or } R(C,C).$$

Since (ii) excludes $R(C,C)$, and (i), (iii), (v) exclude $R(C,B)$, we conclude that $R(C,A)$. Now consider $R(B,A)$, $R(B,B)$, and $R(B,C)$ in a similar way.

11. Can you now say whether relations (1) will hold in any model?

12. Prove that for any objects x, y, z (i.e., for x = A, B, or C, y = A, B, C, and z = A, B, or C),

$$(R(x,y) \text{ and } R(x,z)) \Rightarrow y = z.$$

HINT: All possibilities are enumerated in (1).

13. Prove that for two distinct objects x, y,

$$R(x,y) \text{ or } R(y,x),$$
$$\sim(R(x,y) \text{ and } R(y,x)).$$

14. Prove that for any object x, an object y exists such that $R(y,x)$.

15. How are these five axioms to be regarded as idealizations?

16. Consider the following four axioms:
   (1) Each aba belongs to at least one daba.
   (2) Each daba belongs to at least one aba.
   (3) There are more abas than dabas.
   (4) No two dabas belong to the same aba.
   (a) What are the undefined terms of this system?
   (b) Show how to interpret the axioms in terms of bees and their hives.
   (c) Devise another interpretation of these axioms.
   (d) Prove that some daba belongs to at least two abas.

17. Consider the following axiom system:
   (1) There are exactly three toves.
   (2) There are exactly three momes.
   (3) Each mome gyres exactly two toves.
   (4) Each tove gimbles exactly two momes.
   (a) What are the undefined terms of this axiom system?
   (b) Show that any triangle with its sides and vertices provides a model for this system.
   (c) How do we know that this system is consistent?

18. Let 0 and 1 denote undefined quantities, and let $+$ denote an operation, such that

$$0 + 0 = 0, \; 1 + 0 = 0 + 1 = 1, \; 1 + 1 = 0.$$

   (a) Prove that if x, y, and z represent either 0 or 1, then

$$(x + y) + z = x + (y + z).$$

   (b) Justify interpreting "0" as "an even number," "1" as "an odd number," and "$+$" as "plus (in the ordinary sense)."
   (c) Are the three given rules consistent?

19. This question is based on the notion of group (Chapter 6, Section 1):
   (a) What are the undefined terms in the definition of group?
   (b) Give a model for the abstract objects and relations contained in the definition of group.
   (c) Prove that the concept of group is consistent.

20. Let 0 and 1 represent undefined quantities and $+$ a binary operation satisfying the conditions:
   (1) $0 + 1 = 1$,
   (2) $1 + 1 = 1$,
   (3) $0 + 0 = 0$,
   (4) $1 + 0 = 0$.

We also assume that
   (5) $(x + y) + z = x + (y + z)$
   (6) $x + y = y + x$

when x, y, z are 0 or 1, and adopt these six statements as the axioms of a deductive system.
   (a) Show that this particular axiomatic system is *not* consistent.
   (b) Does this axiomatic system have a model?
   (c) Does trouble with this axiomatic system arise necessarily from the fact that we have not defined $0, 1, +$?

21. Consider the following axiomatic system:
   Axiom 1.   Every mome lives in a cravel.
   Axiom 2.   Exactly seven momes exist.
   Axiom 3.   Exactly two cravels exist.
   Axiom 4.   Not more than one mome lives in any single cravel.
   (a) What is meant by the consistency of this (or any) axiomatic system?
   (b) Show that this particular axiomatic system is *not* consistent.

(c) What is meant by a *model* for this (or any) axiomatic system?

(d) Does this axiomatic system have a model? Explain.

(e) Does trouble with this axiomatic system arise necessarily from the fact that we have not defined "mome" or "cravel"? Explain.

2.

An axiomatic system for electrical circuit analysis

The remainder of this chapter will be devoted to a very simple axiomatic system and its natural developments. Two abstract quantities enter this system. We bestow upon them the familiar names "zero" and "one" and also the corresponding symbols 0 and 1, respectively. We permit between them the relation of "equality" described by the conditions

(1) $$0 = 0,\ 1 = 1,\ 0 \neq 1,\ 1 \neq 0,$$

(by $0 \neq 1$ we mean $\sim (0 = 1)$, and so forth). If x and y are any quantities belonging to the system (i.e., $x = 0$ or 1 and $y = 0$ or 1), we allow two operations upon x and y that result again in a member of the system (i.e., result in either 0 or 1). These operations are called "multiplication" and "screening" and have the symbols · (which is often omitted altogether in imitation of usual practice) and $\vee$, respectively. The effects of these operations are detailed in Table 12-1.

	Multiplication	Screening
Table 12-1 The operations in circuit arithmetic.	$0 \cdot 0 = 0$ $1 \cdot 0 = 0 \cdot 1 = 0$ $1 \cdot 1 = 1$	$1 \vee 1 = 1$ $0 \vee 1 = 1 \vee 0 = 1$ $0 \vee 0 = 0$

In this axiomatic system, "zero," "one," "equality," "multiplication," and "screening" are the undefined terms. The axioms are the statement that the universe of discourse consists of 0 and 1, the conditions laid down in (1), and the six rules of Table 12-1, in addition to the ordinary laws of reasoning, which we shall assume without making explicit, and, lastly, the Principle of Substitution. This principle permits us to replace any quantity in any expression by an equal quantity.

We first ask whether this system is consistent. A simple arithmetical model answers this question affirmatively for all practical purposes. In this arithmetical model, 0 and 1 are interpreted as the ordinary numbers that are the namesakes of our abstract entities; the new multiplication is interpreted as ordinary multiplication; and screening two numbers is interpreted as the operation of taking the larger of them, i.e., screening them for size. All the axioms are easily seen to be true under these interpretations. Hence, the axioms are consistent if arithmetic is consistent. While arithmetic is not known with certainty to be consistent (of course, we are only using a tiny fragment of it), let the matter rest at that.

There are much more interesting models of our new axiomatic system than the one we just gave to argue its consistency. Claude Shannon used this system, in particular, to describe certain kinds of electrical connections. A current of electricity in a wire is a flow of electrical particles (electrons) which can be considered a little like the flow of water through a pipe. Such a flow of electricity occurs in a wire that, for instance, joins the two "poles" of a battery (Figure 12-3),

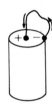

FIGURE 12-3   *Flow of electricity between two poles of a battery.*

the electrons moving through the wire from the negative pole (marked −) to the positive pole (marked +) as though being pumped. The current will stop if the connection between the two poles is interrupted. The whole path of the electricity is called the electric circuit. A portion of the path such as might−or might not−contain switches, appliances, and so forth, we shall call a *circuit assembly*, or, more briefly, an *assembly*. An electric light bulb, motor, or other appliance, wired into an electric circuit will operate while current is passing through, but will not operate in the absence of a current. We illustrate this in Figure 12-4A. Originating at the negative pole of the battery, a current of electrons is led through a wire to the base of an electric light bulb, passes through the bulb's filament, which glows as a result, and is conducted from there to the positive pole of the battery. In Figure 12-4B the same circuit is shown with the addition of a switch, or circuit breaker, by which the circuit may be

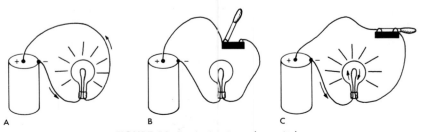

A   B   C

FIGURE 12-4   *A circuit and a switch.*

broken, or interrupted, at will. In the figure, the switch is "open," interrupting the circuit. The "closed" position of the switch, which permits current to flow, is shown in Figure 12-4C. A circuit, or circuit assembly, also will be said to be "open" when an interruption to the current exists somewhere within it and otherwise (when current can flow) to be "closed."

Details of construction and the actual appearance of circuits are of little interest to us. We are concerned only with their logical design. Hence, realistic pictures are less useful than simple schematic diagrams, in which wires are represented by lines, an open switch by the symbol in Figure 12-5A and a light bulb by the symbol in Figure

A

FIGURE 12-5   *Schematic diagrams: A, an open switch; B, a light bulb.*

B

12-5B. Thus, the circuit of Figure 12-4B might be diagrammed as in Figure 12-6A. In this figure, we have used dots labeled + and − to represent the poles of the battery. We find it convenient to omit the battery from our diagrams, however, and thus shall indicate the circuit rather as in Figure 12-6B, in which we may imagine the electricity to flow (when the switch is closed), say, from left to right.

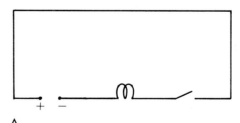

+ −

A

FIGURE 12-6   *Diagram of cir-cuit in Figure 12-4B.*

B

Now consider a portion of an electric circuit—an assembly— between two points, A and B. In Figure 12-7, the dashes indicate unspecified intermediate connections, which might be anything, such

A •———————— — — — — — ————————• B

FIGURE 12-7   *A portion of an electric circuit.*

as uninterrupted wire, a single switch, complexly wired switches and appliances, and so forth. We ask only whether the circuit is uninterrupted between A and B, i.e., whether a current can pass from A to B. If so, we shall say that the *transmitting capability* from A to B is 1; if not, that the transmitting capability from A to B is 0. Let us denote the transmitting capability from A to B by the symbol x_{AB}. Then

$$x_{AB} = \; 1 \text{ if current can flow from } A \text{ to } B,$$
$$= \; 0 \text{ if current cannot flow from } A \text{ to } B.$$

If, for instance, a single switch is all that intervenes in the circuit between A and B, then (Figure 12-8)

$$x_{AB} = 1 \text{ if the switch is closed,}$$
$$= 0 \text{ if the switch is open.}$$

FIGURE 12-8   *Transmitting capabilities: A, closed switch; B, open switch.*

Electrical connections of the most diverse capabilities can be built by combining two basic types of connection, which are diagrammed in Figure 12-9. These are known as *series* and *parallel* connections, respectively. It is clear that in each of them the transmitting capability from A to B depends solely on the transmitting capabilities from C to D and from E to F: i.e., x_{AB} depends solely upon x_{CD} and x_{EF}. Claude Shannon perceived that, in fact,

(2) $\qquad x_{AB} = x_{CD} \cdot x_{EF}$ for a series connection,

and

(3) $\qquad x_{AB} = x_{CD} \vee x_{EF}$ for a parallel connection.

FIGURE 12-9   *Two basic types of connections: A, series; B, parallel.*

(x_{CD} represents the transmitting capability from C to D and x_{EF} that from E to F.) These are simple and mathematically suggestive relationships. They are proved by considering individually the cases in which current *can* and *cannot* flow from A to B. Let us first consider a series connection (Figure 12-9A). If current *can* flow from A to B, in which case

$$x_{AB} = 1,$$

then the circuit assemblies from C to D and from E to F must both be capable of transmitting, and we thus also have

$$x_{CD} = 1, \ x_{EF} = 1;$$

hence, relation (2) is satisfied if current can flow from A to B. If current *cannot* flow from A to B, in which case

$$x_{AB} = 0,$$

then one or both of the two circuit assemblies must be incapable of transmitting, and we have:

$x_{CD} = 0, \ x_{EF} = 0$ (neither assembly able to transmit)
or $x_{CD} = 0, \ x_{EF} = 1$ (first assembly unable, second able, to transmit)
or $x_{CD} = 1, \ x_{EF} = 0$ (first assembly able, second unable, to transmit).

Hence, if current cannot flow from A to B, then the left side of equation (2) is zero and the right side is $0 \cdot 0$, $0 \cdot 1$, or $1 \cdot 0$, or again zero. Thus equation (2) holds in this case. Since the equation is already known to hold in the other case, it is completely general, as asserted.

The argument for equation (3) is similar, the cases in which current can or cannot be transmitted from A to B (Figure 12-9B) requiring separate consideration. If current can flow from A to B, in which case

$$x_{AB} = 1,$$

then one or both of the circuit assemblies from C to D and from E to F must be able to transmit, and we have:

$x_{CD} = 0, \ x_{EF} = 1$ (first assembly unable, second assembly able, to
                                                         transmit)
or $x_{CD} = 1, \ x_{EF} = 0$ (first assembly able, second unable, to transmit)
or $x_{CD} = 1, \ x_{EF} = 1$ (both assemblies able to transmit).

Hence, if current can flow from A to B, then the left side of equation (3) is 1, while the right side is $0 \lor 1$, $1 \lor 0$, or $1 \lor 1$, or again 1. Thus, equation (3) is satisfied in this case. If current *cannot* flow from

A to B, in which case

$$x_{AB} = 0,$$

both assemblies must be failing to transmit, i.e.,

$$x_{CD} = 0, \; x_{EF} = 0.$$

Again, condition (3) is verified. Thus, this condition holds in each case.

A slight change in notation will be helpful in the future. The transmitting capability between two points, A and B, we previously denoted by x_{AB}. We shall now represent it by a single letter without subscripts, for instance, by x. We shall also replace x_{CD}, x_{EF}, and so forth, by other letters, such as y and z, respectively. Furthermore, whenever possible we shall indicate the transmitting capabilities directly on the diagram and also omit labels for points A, B, C, and so forth. As an illustration, Figure 12-10B uses x, y, and z in place of x_{CD}, x_{EF}, and x_{GH}, respectively, which would pertain to the circuit as diagrammed in Figure 12-10A. If the same letter is attached to different circuit assemblies, we understand their transmitting capabilities to be the same. Of course, special electrical arrangements are needed to insure this.

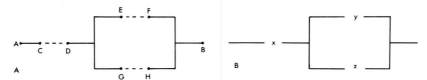

FIGURE 12-10 *A diagramming convention.*

Conditions (2) and (3) lead to what we shall call the "circuit" model or interpretation of our axiom system. In this model, 0 and 1 mean transmitting capabilities of circuit assemblies, $\cdot$ signifies a series connection, $\vee$ signifies a parallel connection, and $=$ symbolizes the relation (between two assemblies) of having exactly the same transmitting capability. More precisely, if x and y denote the transmitting capabilities of two circuit assemblies, respectively, then

$$x \cdot y$$

is the transmitting capability of a series connection of the two, and

$$x \vee y$$

is the transmitting capability of a parallel connection; the condition

$$x = y$$

means that the transmitting capabilities of the two assemblies are identical. Then the axiom $0 \lor 0 = 0$, for instance, can be interpreted as this statement: "The parallel connection of two open (nontransmitting) assemblies is again open." The other axioms have similar interpretations, and the consistency of the axiom system might just as well have been shown from this model.

The circuit interpretations for individual multiplications or screenings can be extended to all combinations of these operations upon a finite number of variables. Figure 12-11 presents a few examples.

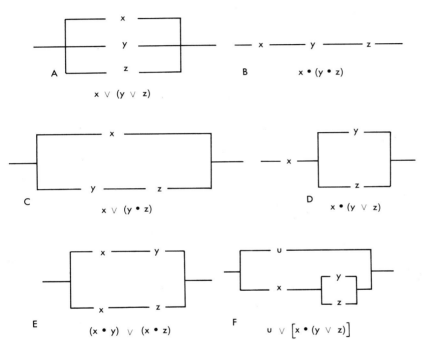

FIGURE 12-11 *Some circuit assemblies and their algebraic counterparts.*

EXERCISES

Sketch circuit assemblies corresponding to these algebraic expressions:

1. $x \lor (y \cdot (z \cdot w))$
2. $x \cdot (y \lor (z \lor w))$
3. $(x \lor y) \cdot (x \lor z)$
4. $(x \cdot y) \lor [(y \cdot z) \lor (z \cdot x)]$
5. $(u \lor v) \cdot \{[x \lor (y \cdot z)] \lor [y \lor (x \cdot z)]\}$
6. Give the algebraic expression for Figure 12-12.
7. Give the algebraic expression for Figure 12-13.
8. Does the network arithmetic have a model in which

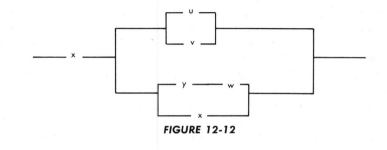

FIGURE 12-12

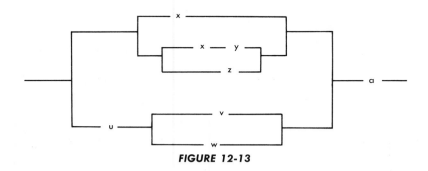

FIGURE 12-13

"0" is interpreted as "an even positive integer,"
"1" is interpreted as "an odd positive integer,"
"∨" is interpreted as ordinary addition,
"·" is interpreted as ordinary multiplication?

Explain.

9. Define S to be the set consisting of the two elements 0 and 1. Is $(S, \cdot)$ a group? Is $(S, \vee)$ a group? Here, $\cdot$ and $\vee$ denote multiplication and screening as defined in Table 12-1.

3.

Circuit algebra and design

If we know the general laws for the "arithmetic" of circuits, we can apply them to problems of design. These laws arise from Table 12-1, repeated here.

$0 \cdot 0 = 0$	$1 \vee 1 = 1$	
$1 \cdot 0 = 0 \cdot 1 = 0$	$0 \vee 1 = 1 \vee 0 = 1$	**Table 12-1** Circuit arithmetic
$1 \cdot 1 = 1$	$0 \vee 0 = 0$	

Let x,y,z be arbitrary quantities (each either 0 or 1). We then have:

(1a) $x \cdot 0 = 0$ (1b) $x \lor 1 = 1$

(2a) $x \cdot 1 = x$ (2b) $x \lor 0 = x$

(3a) $x \cdot x = x$ (3b) $x \lor x = x$

(4a) $x \cdot y = y \cdot x$ (4b) $x \lor y = y \lor x$

(5a) $(x \cdot y) \cdot z = x \cdot (y \cdot z)$ (5b) $(x \lor y) \lor z = x \lor (y \lor z)$

(6a) $x \cdot (y \lor z) = (x \cdot y) \lor (x \cdot z)$ (6b) $x \lor (y \cdot z) = (x \lor y) \cdot (x \lor z)$.

Each of these rules can be proved by verifying it for each possible combination of the variables involved. As an example, we shall prove (6a), a distributive law. Since x,y, and z each admit two possible values, eight cases occur. These are enumerated in Table 12-2.

Table 12-2 The eight possible combinations of values of three variables, each capable of taking the values 0 or 1.

x	y	z
0	0	0
0	0	1
0	1	0
0	1	1
1	0	0
1	0	1
1	1	0
1	1	1

We might now test relation (6a) for each of these eight combinations of values of x, y, z in turn. The first combination, in which the variables are all 0, certainly satisfies (6a), and having checked this we can go to the second combination, then on to the third, and so forth. But, as often happens, a less tedious argument exists. To prove (6a), it will actually suffice to consider two cases only, that in which $x = 0$ and that in which $x = 1$. In the first case ($x=0$), the left member is $0 \cdot (y \lor z)$, which is 0 because multiplication by 0 always gives 0 (this rule is stated in (1a)). The right member is $(0 \cdot y) \lor (0 \cdot z)$, which reduces to $0 \lor 0$ and thus to 0. Thus, (6a) holds in this first case. In the second case ($x = 1$), the left member of (6a) is $1 \cdot (y \lor z)$, which is $y \lor z$, because, according to Table 12-1, multiplication by 1 reproduces any factor (this is stated in (2a)). The right member is $(1 \cdot y) \lor (1 \cdot z)$, which reduces for the same reason to $y \lor z$. Hence, equation (6a) holds in the second case. We conclude that equation (6a) always holds.

The two associative laws ((5a) and (5b)) enable us to omit parentheses from such expressions as $x \cdot y \cdot z$ or $x \lor y \lor z$.

EXERCISES

1. Prove relations (1a) through (5b), and (6b).
2. Prove that $x \lor (x \cdot y) = x$ and $x \cdot (x \lor y) = x$.

3. Prove that $(x \cdot u) \vee (x \cdot v) \vee (y \cdot u) \vee (y \cdot v) = (x \vee y) \cdot (u \vee v)$.
4. Prove that $(x \cdot y) \vee (u \cdot v) = (x \vee u) \cdot (x \vee v) \cdot (y \vee u) \cdot (y \vee v)$.

Two circuit assemblies are said to be *equivalent* if their transmitting capabilities are equal, i.e., if one can conduct current when
the other can and cannot when the other cannot. Any identity such as
(1a) through (6b) can be interpreted as the equivalence of different
circuit assemblies. For instance, the identity

$$1 \cdot x = x$$

corresponds to the equivalence of the two circuit assemblies in
Figure 12-14. The identity

$$x \vee y = y \vee x$$

——— 1 ——————— x ———   ——————— x ———

A 1 · x   B   x

FIGURE 12-14   *Circuit interpretation of* $1 \cdot x = x$.

can be interpreted as expressing the equivalence of these two circuit
assemblies (Figure 12-15). The identity

$$x \cdot (y \vee z) = (x \cdot y) \vee (x \cdot z)$$

A   x ∨ y   B   y ∨ x
FIGURE 12-15   *Circuit interpretation of* $x \vee y = y \vee x$.

is interpreted as the equivalence of the two assemblies of Figure 12-16.

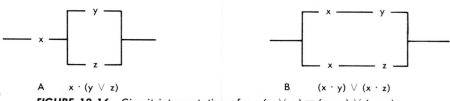

A   x · (y ∨ z)   B   (x · y) ∨ (x · z)
FIGURE 12-16   *Circuit interpretation of* $x \cdot (y \vee z) = (x \cdot y) \vee (x \cdot z)$.

EXERCISES

Give analogous circuit interpretations of these identities:

5. $x \lor x = x$

6. $(x \lor y) \cdot (x \lor z) = x \lor (y \cdot z)$

7. $x \lor (x \cdot y) = x$

8. $x \cdot (x \lor y) = x$

9. $(x \cdot y) \lor (u \cdot v) = (x \lor u) \cdot (x \lor v) \cdot (y \lor u) \cdot (y \lor v)$

10. $(x \cdot u) \lor (x \cdot v) \lor (y \cdot u) \lor (y \cdot v) = (x \lor y) \cdot (u \lor v)$

Many circuits require a dual switch, such as is shown in Figure 12-17, that can feed current into either of two alternative wires. Its blade (B) is not permitted to stand free, as it is shown in Figure

FIGURE 12-17   A dual switch.

12-17A, but is required to touch one of the two stationary contacts, P or Q, as in Figure 12-17B. Figure 12-18 shows how we might indicate such a switch in a wiring diagram; the arrow represents the blade and is understood to be touching either P or Q at all times. Dual

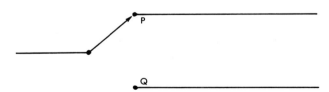

FIGURE 12-18   Diagrammatic representation of a dual switch.

switches are required, for instance, in the common household circuit in which two switches exercise equal control over a light. Such a circuit is diagrammed in Figure 12-19. Either switch may open this circuit (turning off the light) if the circuit is closed and may close it (turning the light on) if it is open.

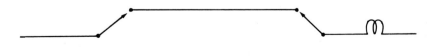

FIGURE 12-19   Two switches controlling the same light.

In order to represent dual switches algebraically, we introduce the following idea of algebraic *duality*.

Definition.   The *dual* of 0 is 1; the *dual* of 1 is 0. To *dualize* a quantity is to write its dual.

We indicate the dual of a quantity by a prime. Thus:

$$0' = 1, \ 1' = 0.$$

Similarly, x' denotes the dual of x, i.e.,

(7) $$x' = 0 \text{ if } x = 1,$$
$$= 1 \text{ if } x = 0.$$

With this new notation, it is easy to represent the assembly of Figure 12-19 algebraically. First we redraw the figure with symbols for the transmitting capabilities (see Figure 12-20). From this, the transmitting capability is immediately seen to be

$$(x \cdot y) \ \vee \ (x' \cdot y').$$

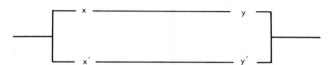

FIGURE 12-20   *Previous circuit assembly with transmitting capabilities indicated.*

The most basic algebraic properties of duals are these:

(8) $$(x')' = x,$$

(9a) $$x \cdot x' = 0,$$

(9b) $$x \vee x' = 1.$$

Relation (8) states that any quantity is the dual of its dual. All three relations are immediately verifiable from (7) by considering, first, the case in which $x = 0$ and $x' = 1$ and, secondly, the alternative case in which $x = 1$ and $x' = 0$.

Circuit algebra has remarkable duality properties, which depend upon certain rules for finding the duals of sums and products. To obtain these rules, first let us draw up a table of values of $(x \vee y)'$ for all possible combinations of values of x and y (Table 12-3). The first rule we shall seek associates $(x \vee y)'$ with x' and y' and is easily read off from a table in which we list the values of $(x \vee y)'$, which we have just computed, next to those of x' and y' (see Table 12-4).

x	y	x ∨ y	(x ∨ y)'
0	0	0	1
0	1	1	0
1	0	1	0
1	1	1	0

Table 12-3   *The dual of a screening*

x'	y'	(x ∨ y)'
1	1	1
1	0	0
0	1	0
0	0	0

Table 12-4   *The dual of a screening, and the duals of the quantities screened*

From this table, it is apparent that

(10a) $$(x \vee y)' = x' \cdot y'.$$

In the same way, we might also prove

(10b) $$(x \cdot y)' = x' \vee y',$$

but the last rule is also obtainable from (10a) deductively, as follows. Since (10a) is true no matter what quantities x and y represent, it is true for x' in place of x and y' in place of y. After these replacements, it states:

$$(x' \vee y')' = (x')' \cdot (y')'.$$

But $(x')' = x$ and $(y')' = y$. Hence,

$$(x' \vee y')' = x \cdot y.$$

If we dualize both sides of this relation and again invoke (8), we have

$$(x' \vee y') = (x \cdot y)',$$

which is (10b). Thus, (10a) implies (10b). In a similar way, it can be shown that (10b) implies (10a). These two relations therefore are logically equivalent. They are known as *de Morgan's laws*.

De Morgan's laws (10a,b) are easily generalized to a rule for obtaining the dual of any expression consisting of products and screenings of quantities in circuit algebra. This rule is simply to replace every product by a screening of duals and to replace every screening by a product of duals. For instance, to dualize $x \cdot (y \vee z)$, we have:

$$[x \cdot (y \lor z)]' = x' \lor (y \lor z)' \qquad \text{(by (10b))}$$
$$= x' \lor (y' \cdot z') \qquad \text{(by (10a))}.$$

Also, to dualize $(x \cdot y) \lor (x \cdot z)$, we have

$$[(x \cdot y) \lor (x \cdot z)]' = (x \cdot y)' \cdot (x \cdot z)' \qquad \text{(by (10a))}$$
$$= (x' \lor y') \cdot (x' \lor z') \qquad \text{(by (10b))}.$$

We recall that $x \cdot (y \lor z) = (x \cdot y) \lor (x \cdot z)$ (Equation (6a)). Since the duals of equal quantities are equal, dualizing the two members of this equation and using the results just obtained show, in particular, that

$$x' \lor (y' \cdot z') = (x' \lor y') \cdot (x' \lor z').$$

This identity can be somewhat simplified from the fact of its being true for *all* x, y, z. It is true, in particular, for x' in place of x, y' in place of y, and z' in place of z and reads after these replacements

$$x \lor (y \cdot z) = (x \lor y) \cdot (x \lor z),$$

since $(x')' = x$, and so forth. This is (6b).

From the rule for dualizing and the trivial remark that if two expressions are equal, then their duals are equal, we have just shown that (6a) implies (6b). In the same way, any equality implies a dual equality. We thus have this remarkable law: if two expressions in circuit algebra are equal, then the expressions derived from these by replacing each quantity by its dual, each multiplication by a screening, and each screening by a multiplication, also are equal. This is the *duality principle*.

For each axiom in Table 12-1, the dual of the axiom also occurs. This is of course the source of the duality principle. The duals of the equalities (1a) through (6a) are the equalities (1b) through (6b), respectively; the duals of (9a) and (10a) are (9b) and (10b), respectively.

EXERCISES

11. Prove that Identity (10b) implies (10a).

For convenience in the following identities, dots to indicate multiplication have been omitted. Prove the identities and give their duals:[†]

12. $x' \lor xy = x' \lor y$

13. $(x \lor y)(x' \lor z) = xz \lor x'y$

[†] Most of these have been selected out of Chapters 2 and 3 of R. K. Richards, *Arithmetic Operations in Digital Computers*, Van Nostrand, New York, 1955.

14. $(xy \lor yz \lor zx)' = x'y' \lor y'z' \lor z'x'$
15. $(xy' \lor yz' \lor zx')(x'y \lor y'z' \lor z'x') = (x \lor y \lor z)(x'y' \lor y'z' \lor z'x')$
16. $xy' \lor x'y = (x \lor y)(x' \lor y')$
17. $(xy \lor z) \lor (xy \lor z)'(x \lor zu) = x \lor z$
18. $xy \lor y'z' \lor xz' = xy \lor y'z'$
19. $xy' \lor yz \lor xz = xy' \lor yz$
20. $x'y' \lor yz' \lor x'z' = x'y' \lor yz'$
21. $x'y \lor y'z \lor x'z = x'y \lor y'z$
22. $xyz \lor x'yz \lor xy'z \lor xyz' \lor xy'z' \lor x'yz' \lor x'y'z \lor x'y'z' = 1$
23. Prove that $xy \lor x'y' = 1$ if and only if $x = y$.
24. Prove that $xy' \lor x'y = 0$ if and only if $x = y$.
25. Let x, y, z denote transmitting capabilities. Prove or disprove:

$$xy \lor yz \lor xz = xy \lor yz.$$

26. Let a_1, a_2, a_3, $\ldots$, a_n, $\ldots$ denote infinitely many quantities from the "network" arithmetic. (Thus, each a_n is 0 or 1 in this arithmetic.) Prove by mathematical induction that the quantities

$$a_1 \lor a_1 a_2, \ a_1 \lor a_1 a_2 \lor a_1 a_2 a_3, \ a_1 \lor a_1 a_2 \lor a_1 a_2 a_3 \lor a_1 a_2 a_3 a_4, \ldots,$$
$$a_1 \lor a_1 a_2 \lor \ldots \lor a_1 a_2 \ldots a_n, \ldots,$$

all equal a_1.

27. Prove by mathematical induction:

$$(a_0 \lor a_1)(a_0 \lor a_2) = a_0 \lor a_1 a_2$$
$$(a_0 \lor a_1)(a_0 \lor a_2)(a_0 \lor a_3) = a_0 \lor a_1 a_2 a_3$$
$$\cdots$$
$$(a_0 \lor a_1)(a_0 \lor a_2) \ldots (a_0 \lor a_k) = a_0 \lor a_1 a_2 \ldots a_k$$

28. In the circuit arithmetic, define a new operation (denoted by "$\circ$") by:

$$x \circ y = xy' \lor x'y.$$

Prove:

    (a) $x \circ y = y \circ x$.
    (b) $x \circ 0 = x$.
    (c) $x \circ y = 0 \Rightarrow x = y$.

29. Let A be the transmitting capability of the circuit assembly in Figure 12-21A. Let B be the transmitting capability of the assembly in Figure 12-21B.
    (a) Write the algebraic expressions for A and B.
    (b) Prove $A = B$.

30. Simplify the circuit in Figure 12-22 as far as possible, using Exercise 19.

31. Consider the electric circuit assembly in Figure 12-23.
    (a) Write its algebraic expression.
    (b) Simplify this expression as far as possible.

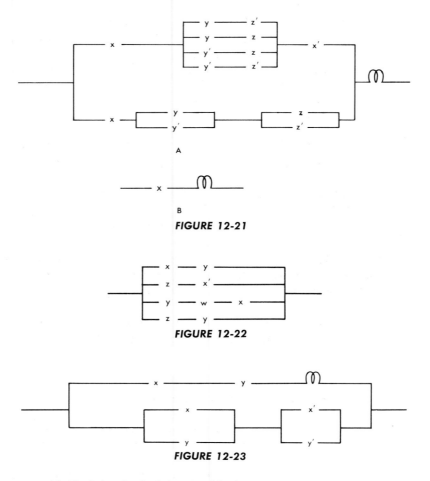

FIGURE 12-21

FIGURE 12-22

FIGURE 12-23

(c) Find the dual of the simplified expression.
(d) Design another circuit with a light bulb that is on only when the bulb in the circuit above is off and is off only when the bulb in the circuit above is on.

32. You are given the circuit assembly in Figure 12-24.
    (a) What is its algebraic expression?
    (b) Simplify this expression.
    (c) Draw a diagram for the simplified expression.

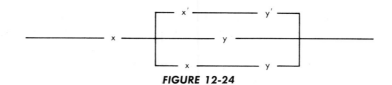

FIGURE 12-24

33. Write a formula for the transmitting capability between A and B in the wiring diagram in Figure 12-25. Simplify the formula algebraically as far as possible, and draw a diagram for the simplified formula.

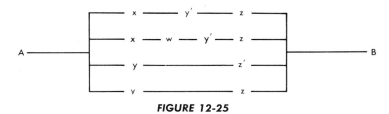

FIGURE 12-25

34. Note the circuit assembly of Figure 12-26, which is called a "star," in which a, b, c represent transmitting capabilities of switches. We shall compare

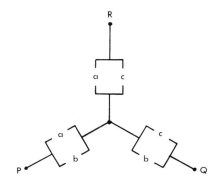

FIGURE 12-26   A "star" circuit assembly.

this with the assembly in Figure 12-27, called a "delta." In either assembly, P, Q, and R are called the *vertices* of the assembly. The transmitting capability between any two vertices in the star equals the transmitting capability between the corresponding vertices in the delta. Prove, in particular, that the transmitting capability between P and Q in the star is equal to the transmitting capability between P and Q in the delta.

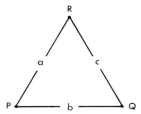

FIGURE 12-27   A "delta" circuit assembly.

35. Give the transmitting capabilities of the six circuit assemblies in Figure 12-28, which are grouped in pairs (A and B, C and D, E and F). Then prove algebraically that the two circuit assemblies of each pair are equivalent.

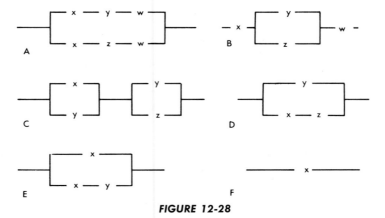

FIGURE 12-28

It is worth remarking that all the preceding identities can be proved algebraically, i.e., from relations (1a) through (9b) without otherwise using the fact that each variable takes only the values 0 and 1. To illustrate the methods in more difficult cases, let us first prove:

$$x' \lor xy = x' \lor y.$$

This follows from the ensuing sequence of equalities:

$$
\begin{aligned}
x' \lor y &= (x \lor x')(x' \lor y) \\
&= x(x' \lor y) \lor x'(x' \lor y) \\
&= 0 \lor xy \lor x' \lor x'y \\
&= xy \lor x'(1 \lor y) \\
&= xy \lor x'1 \\
&= xy \lor x'.
\end{aligned}
$$

Using this result, we shall now prove:

$$xy \lor x'z \lor yz = xy \lor x'z.$$

First,

$$x'z = x'z(1 \lor y) = x'z \lor x'yz.$$

Consequently,

$$
\begin{aligned}
xy \lor x'z &= xy \lor x'z \lor x'yz \\
&= y(x \lor x'z) \lor x'z \\
&= y(x \lor z) \lor x'z \qquad \text{(by the previous result)} \\
&= yx \lor yz \lor x'z,
\end{aligned}
$$

this proving the identity desired.

Now we are ready to design some circuits.

Problem 1:   The girls permitted to appear in a certain beauty contest had to win the unanimous consent of the three judges in a preliminary viewing. A judge was to indicate his dissatisfaction by sounding a buzzer, which he worked by pressing a button attached to his chair. The buttons (one for each judge) are circuit breakers that are normally open (not transmitting), but are closed when pressed. How were the buttons and the buzzer to be wired?

To explain the solution, let us suppose for simplicity that there are only two judges, and let x and y denote the transmitting capabilities of their respective buttons. In other words, let

$x = 0$ when the first judge's button is not being pressed,
$= 1$ when the first judge's button is being pressed,
$y = 0$ when the second judge's button is not being pressed,
$= 1$ when the second judge's button is being pressed.

The buttons are supposed to be wired so that current will flow through the assembly, activating the buzzer, when *either* button is pressed. It may now be obvious that the buttons should be connected in parallel. If it is not obvious, consider Table 12-5, in which B stands for the transmitting capability of the entire circuit assembly. The

Table 12-5   *Transmitting capabilities in Problem 1*

x	y	B
0	0	0
0	1	1
1	0	1
1	1	1

table simply expresses the condition that the current should fail only when neither button is being pressed. From the table, it is clear that

$$B = x \lor y.$$

Hence, the connection is indeed parallel, as we had surmised, and looks like that of Figure 12-29. Here, the symbol for the buzzer is

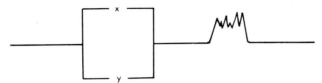

FIGURE 12-29   *The circuit assembly in Problem 1.*

that given in Figure 12-30. This result in the two-judge problem suggests the proper circuit in the three-judge problem, which, however, we leave to the reader.

FIGURE 12-30

Problem 2: A subsequent beauty contest was held under the same rules as before, each contestant having to win the unanimous approval of three judges in a preliminary viewing. But the buzzers had been criticized as noisy, negative, and vulgar, and a different means of registering opinion was demanded. Accordingly, each judge was provided with a light switch, and a bulb was wired to light up just when all three switches were "on," i.e., closed. The light switches were simple circuit breakers. How were they and the light bulb to be wired?

Again for simplicity consider the case of two judges only, and let x and y denote the respective transmitting capabilities of their switches. Thus,

$$x = 0 \quad \text{when the first judge's switch is off,}$$
$$= 1 \quad \text{when the first judge's switch is on,}$$
$$y = 0 \quad \text{when the second judge's switch is off,}$$
$$= 1 \quad \text{when the second judge's switch is on.}$$

The switches are supposed to be wired so that current will flow, lighting the bulb, only when both switches are on. It may now be obvious that the switches should be connected in series. If it is not obvious, consider Table 12-6, in which L stands for the transmitting capability of the entire circuit assembly. This table simply expresses the condi-

x	y	L
0	0	0
0	1	0
1	0	0
1	1	1

Table 12-6   Transmitting capabilities in Problem 2

tion that the current should flow only when both switches are on. From this table, it is clear that

$$L = x \cdot y.$$

This expression shows that the connection is indeed in series, as surmised, and that the circuit assembly is as depicted in Figure 12-31. We leave the three-judge problem to the reader.

FIGURE 12-31   The circuit assembly in Problem 2.

EXERCISES

36. Do the three-judge problems, as stated.

37. (a) A locomotive engineer may not start his train until a certain light on his instrument panel goes on. The light is to turn on when each of the three train conductors has signalled that his section is ready. What circuit is called for?

    (b) Each of the three conductors has a button by which he can sound an alarm bell in the locomotive cab. What wiring will accomplish this?

38. A quiz machine is desired that will present two alternative answers to each question asked and will light a bulb when all questions are answered correctly. How is it to be wired?

Problem 3:   A home owner wishes to be able to switch his living room lights on or off at will from the east side of the room, from the west side, and also from the head of the stairs. What connections are necessary to permit this?

This is a generalization of the two-switch problem (pp. 491-492) but more difficult. A sketch of the circuit in the two-switch problem (Figure 12-19) is not very helpful here, but its algebraic expression turns out to be most suggestive. This expression was

$$(x \cdot y) \vee (x' \cdot y').$$

Often calculation is aided by omitting dots signifying multiplication. Doing so here, we write this expression as

(11) $xy \vee x'y'.$

It has several noteworthy attributes, the first two of which are these:

(1) The terms that are screened are products of the transmitting capabilities (of the two switches) or their duals.

(2) The expression is symmetrical with respect to the two transmitting capabilities.

We must explain the meaning of *symmetry*. An algebraic expression in x and y is *symmetric*, or *symmetrical*, if the value of the expression is the same after changing x to y and y to x. For instance, the expression

$$xy$$

is symmetric, since it becomes

$$yx$$

when x and y are interchanged, and thus its value is not changed. Similarly,

$$x'y',$$

which becomes

$$y'x'$$

upon the interchange of x and y, also is symmetric. The same is true of

$$x \lor y$$

and of

$$x' \lor y'.$$

But

$$x \lor y'$$

is not symmetric, for changing x to y and y to x transforms this expression into

$$y \lor x'.$$

An expression in three variables, x, y, z, is defined to be symmetric if the value of the expression is the same after *any* interchange of the three variables. Thus, xyz or $x'y'z'$ is symmetric in the three variables, but

$$xy$$

is not symmetric in the *three* variables. In fact, interchanging x and z transforms this expression into

$$zy$$

and interchanging y and z transforms it into

$$xz.$$

The expression

$$xy \lor yz \lor zx,$$

however, is symmetric. Similarly,

$$x \lor y$$

is not symmetric in x, y, z, but

$$x \lor y \lor z$$

is symmetric in the three variables.

Symmetry is a very far-reaching concept by no means confined to algebraic expressions, or even to the field of mathematics. For instance, justice is supposed to be administered symmetrically to rich and poor alike; the questions involved in civil rights are questions of symmetry. In our lighting problems, all the switches enter symmetrically—they all do the same job. Thus, the mathematical symmetry of (11) merely expresses the physical symmetry in the two-switch problem itself. We can expect to see three-switch symmetry manifested similarly.

The most fundamental attribute of the circuit assembly expression in the two-switch problem is yet to be mentioned. It is the algebraic counterpart of the physical condition that, regardless of the position of one switch, the other can still control the light. It is this:

(3) If the value of x is specified, the value of the algebraic expression for the circuit assembly, namely

(11) $$xy \vee x'y',$$

can still be made 0 or 1 at will by suitable choice of y. (For instance, if $x = 1$, the expression (11) reduces to y.) Symmetrically, if the value of y is specified, then the value of this expression can be made either 0 or 1 by suitable choice of x.

These three properties are clues to an algebraic expression for the three-switch problem. Let x, y, z denote the transmitting capabilities of the first, second, and third switches, respectively. Attribute (1) pertaining to (11) suggests that the algebraic expression we desire should result from screening such terms as xyz, $x'y'z'$, $x'yz$, and so on, which are products of the three transmitting capabilities or their duals. Considerations of symmetry—attribute (2)—lead us to guess that individually unsymmetric terms will occur only as parts of symmetric formations. For instance, the term $x'yz$ should occur, if at all, as part of the symmetric formation

$$x'yz \vee xy'z \vee xyz'.$$

Attributes (1) and (2) pertaining to (11) thus lead us to conjecture that the algebraic expression we seek is to be obtained by screening one or more of these four symmetric formations:

$$xyz, \qquad\qquad x'y'z \vee xy'z' \vee x'yz',$$
$$x'yz \vee xy'z \vee xyz', \qquad x'y'z'.$$

Such an expression would necessarily be of the form

$$axyz \vee b(x'yz \vee xy'z \vee xyz') \vee c(x'y'z \vee xy'z' \vee x'yz') \vee dx'y'z',$$

where a, b, c, d are constants equal either to 0 or to 1. A constant is 1 if the expression that it prefixes appears in the desired circuit expression and is 0 if the expression does not appear. Our aim is to determine which of these constants are 0 and which 1.

We shall determine the constants by generalizaing the third condition we stated concerning (11). For convenience, let L denote the expression:

$$L = axyz \lor b(x'yz \lor xy'z \lor xyz') \lor c(x'y'z \lor xy'z' \lor x'yz') \lor dx'y'z'.$$

Then we shall try to determine a, b, c, d in such a way that if the values of y and z are specified, the value of L can still be made 0 or 1 at will by suitable selection of x. Symmetrically, if the values of any two of the variables x, y, z are specified, we wish to be able to control the value of L through appropriate choice of the third variable. In Table 12-7, we have listed the values of L (in terms of a, b, c, d, x, x') for all possible combinations of values of y and z. Our aim is to find values of a, b, c, d such that each entry appearing under L in this table can be made 0 or 1 at will through appropriate choice of x.

y	z	L
0	0	$cx \lor dx'$
0	1	$bx \lor cx'$
1	0	$bx \lor cx'$
1	1	$ax \lor bx'$

Table 12-7 Values of a circuit expression in x, y, z when y and z are determined

Consider the first entry:

$$cx \lor dx'.$$

It is clear from its form that, first, c and d cannot both be 0: for if $c = 0$ and $d = 0$, then this quantity $cx \lor dx'$ would be zero unalterably. Similarly, c and d are not both 1: for if $c = 1$ and $d = 1$, then $cx \lor dx' = x \lor x' = 1$, unalterably. On the other hand, for

$$c = 1, d = 0,$$

$cx \lor dx'$ is made equal to x, an expression that certainly is responsive to changes in x, as required. Let us then make these choices of c and d (i.e., $c = 1$ and $d = 0$) and next try their effects upon the second entry in the column under L in Table 12-7. We have

$$bx \lor cx' = bx \lor x'.$$

If b were 1, this would reduce to $x \lor x' = 1$, again an unalterable result insensitive to changes in x. But if $b = 0$, we have

$$bx \lor cx' = bx \lor x'$$
$$= x'.$$

Thus, choosing

$$b = 0$$

makes the second entry, like the first, responsive to changes in x. (In fact, $bx \lor cx' = 1$ for $x = 0$ and $= 0$ for $x = 1$.) The third entry in the column under L happens to coincide with the second. The fourth becomes

$$ax \lor bx' = ax$$

with the choice we have made of b, and this will respond appropriately to changes in x if we take

$$a = 1.$$

Thus, in summary, if we take

$$a = 1, \ b = 0, \ c = 1, \ d = 0,$$

then no matter how y and z may be specified, the value of L can be made 0 or 1 at will by suitable selection of x. When the values of *any* two of the variables x, y, z are specified, will we similarly be able to control the value of L by appropriate choice of the third? Because of the symmetry built into L from the start, whatever is true of one variable is true of another. Hence, we can be assured that the answer to the last question is yes. But it is worthwhile, as a check upon our calculations, to verify this fact directly.

With the indicated choices of a, b, c, d, we have

$$L = xyz \lor x'y'z \lor xy'z' \lor x'yz'.$$

Figure 12-32 is a schematic diagram for the corresponding circuit assembly. This assembly can be realized electrically with two dual

FIGURE 12-32   *Schematic diagram for circuit assembly in Problem 3.*

switches and a "double-decker" switch (Figure 12-33). The second switch in Figure 12-33 is the "double-decker," consisting of two dual switches that work together. The two arrows representing the two movable contacts (or blades) of the double-decker switch are sup-

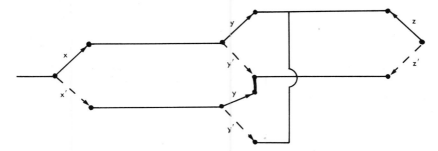

FIGURE 12-33   *Wiring circuit in Problem 3.*

posed to be parallel, both pointing upwards $(y=1)$ or both pointing downwards $(y=0)$. The loop (Figure 12-34) is to indicate that the two wires represented do not actually touch.

FIGURE 12-34   *Two wires not touching.*

EXERCISE

39. A man wishes to be able to control his garage light from any one of its four walls. Design a suitable circuit.

4.

Computer circuits

Electronic computers are among the crowning achievements of technology. We cannot enter into their engineering principles, but we can give an idea of their logic. Arithmetic in a computer is simplest in base two, in which just two digits, 0 and 1, are used, any numeral in this base being an arrangement of 0's and 1's along a string in a particular order. Within the computer, a suitable circuit assembly is provided for each position on the string for each number that may take part in a calculation, and the *transmitting capability* of the assembly for a particular position indicates the *digit* in that position. For instance, the *transmitting capability* 0 might indicate the *digit* 0 and the *transmitting capability* 1 the *digit* 1. In this case, we shall say that the digit 0 is *realized by,* or is *translated into,* the transmitting capability 0 and, similarly, that the digit 1 is realized by, or translated into, the transmitting capability 1. Numbers to be entered into calculation are registered, and numbers calculated are read off digit by digit as transmitting capabilities of suitable circuit assemblies. To indicate how this may be done, we shall discuss addition. To add a column of numbers, an electronic computer will first add the first two numbers, to their sum will add the third number, to the resulting sum will add the fourth number, and so on. Keeping cumulative sums, the computer thus totals a column by adding just two numbers at a time, an operation that may require no more than several millionths of a second. To add two numbers, a modern computer is unlikely to use the particular procedure to which we are accustomed. Nevertheless, we shall explain the logic of this procedure, as typical. Consider, for instance, this sum:

$$
\begin{array}{r}
101101 \\
+111001 \\
\hline
1100110
\end{array}
$$

The numerals are in base two, which means that the first place on the right in each numeral tells how many ones, the second place from the right how many twos, the third place from the right how many fours, and the fourth, fifth, sixth, and seventh places from the right how many eights, sixteens, thirty-twos, and sixty-fours, respectively, combine to make the number. To be quite explicit, let us rewrite this problem, heading each column with the amount the digit 1 counts for in that column. We obtain Table 12-8. The two numbers to be added occupy Rows (A) and (B). The first step in our addition procedure is to add the digits in the column of units (Column I). The sum of these digits being two, we put 0 in Row (D) of Column I and "carry" 1 to Row (C) of the column of twos (Column II). (The carried digit, standing for two, which we have just obtained, is put in parentheses to distinguish it from the numbers that were given in advance.) Now we

Table 12-8 *Addition in the binary system*

Place of column from right:	VII	VI	V	IV	III	II	I
Value represented by digit 1:	SIXTY-FOUR	THIRTY-TWO	SIXTEEN	EIGHT	FOUR	TWO	ONE
(A) First summand	0	1	0	1	1	0	1
(B) Second summand	0	1	1	1	0	0	1
(C) Carried digits	(1)	(1)	(1)			(1)	
(D) Total	1	1	0	0	1	1	0

add Column II, its two 0's and single 1 having 1 as total. Being in Column II, this 1 represents a single two; it is entered in Row (D) of its column. Next we total the digits in Column III, obtaining unity. The digit 1, representing a single four, is therefore entered in Row (D) of Column III. Now we add the digits in Column IV. They make two, which in this column stands for two eights, or sixteen. Hence, we record 0 in Row (D) of Column IV and carry 1 into Column V, the column of sixteens. Adding the digits now in Column V gives two, which represents two sixteens, or thirty-two. We thus place 0 at the foot of Column V and carry 1 to Column VI, the column of thirty-twos. With the two 1's already in this column, we have a sum of three, meaning three thirty-twos. To enter these, we place 1 in Row (D) of Column VI and carry 1 into Column VII, the carried digit standing for sixty-four (the remaining two thirty-twos). Column VII being otherwise blank, its sum is one, which stands for sixty-four. Therefore, we enter 1 in Row (D) of Column VII and are done.

This example illustrates the general procedure by which we propose to add two numbers in base two, which is as follows. First, add the two digits in the column for units (Column I in Table 12-8), and record 0 at the foot of the column if the column adds to zero, record 1 if the column adds to unity, and record 0 and carry 1 if the column adds to two. If nothing is carried, add the column of twos (Column II) in the same way, recording 0 at its foot if the column adds to zero, recording 1 if the column adds to unity, and recording 0 and carrying 1 if the column adds to two. But if 1 is carried from the units column, then add this 1 to the two digits originally standing in the column of twos, recording 1 at the foot of the column if the resulting sum (of the three digits) is unity, recording 0 and carrying 1 if the sum is two, and recording 1 and also carrying 1 if the sum is three. The column of fours (Column III), thus receiving a carryover of either 0 or 1, is treated in just the same way as the column of twos and contributes in its turn a carryover of either 0 or 1 to the column of eights. In fact, the procedure given for the column of twos applies to every column after the first, each such column receiving a carryover of 0 or 1 from the previous and communicating a carryover of 0 or 1 to the next.

We shall now show how to incorporate this column-by-column procedure in a suitable electrical adder (i.e., machine that will add). Although an electronic adder would consist of different engineering devices and would use a modification of this numerical scheme as more economical, the logical side to its design would be very similar. First, consider the right hand column (Column I in Table 12-8). It contains two digits, which we denote by x and y, and no carryover. Its sum may be a two-digit number, according to the scheme:

$$\begin{array}{r} x \\ +y \\ \hline cs. \end{array}$$

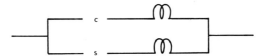

FIGURE 12-35 *Schematic circuit assembly for the addition of single digit numbers.*

Our aim is to devise such a circuit that when x and y have been translated into the transmitting capabilities of suitably wired switches, c and s will emerge as the transmitting capabilities of certain circuit assemblies, respectively. The translation of the *digit* 0 is to be the *transmitting capability* 0, and the translation of the *digit* 1 the *transmitting capability* 1. If we desire to read c and s, we shall be able to do so, for instance, from light bulbs wired into the appropriate assemblies, as in Figure 12-35. To devise this circuit, we first tabulate the binary numeral cs for all possible values of x and y (Table 12-9).

Table 12-9 *The sum of two binary digits*

x	y	c	s
0	0	0	0
0	1	0	1
1	0	0	1
1	1	1	0

(The fourth line, for instance, tells us that the sum of one and one is 10, which is two in the binary representation.) Since $c = 0$, except when $x = 1$ and $y = 1$, we have clearly

$$c = xy.$$

We can easily arrive at an algebraic expression for s if, for instance, we notice from Table 12-9 that $s = 0$ wherever $x = y$. Taking this fact as a hint, let us look for the combinations of x, y, x', y' that are 0 whenever $x = y$. As we see at once, xy' is such a combination, and $x'y$ is another; hence, $xy' \lor x'y$ also is an expression that is 0 whenever $x = y$. Of the three expressions

$$xy', x'y, xy' \lor x'y,$$

does one represent s? If we try them all, we will find that the last one does:

$$s = xy' \lor x'y.$$

(Another way of arriving at this formula follows from the considerations of Section 5.) These formulas enable us to fill in the details in Figure 12-35, to obtain Figure 12-36. The upper bulb (Figure 12-36)

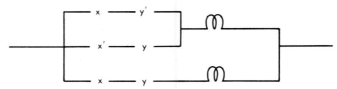

FIGURE 12-36 *Details of schematic circuit assembly for the addition of single-digit numbers.*

indicates the value of s (1 when the bulb is lighted, 0 when dark) and the lower bulb the value of c. A double-decker switch (but differently wired from the previous) would be used in actually building this assembly.

In adding up any column after the first (for instance, Columns II through VII in Table 12-8), the carryover from the preceding column must be taken into account. Hence, we must find a scheme to add three digits, which we shall denote by x, y, and c; we shall think of c as the digit that was carried. The sum of the three digits, which may be zero, one, two, or three, is of course to be represented as a binary numeral ks. In Table 12-10, we indicate k and s for each of the eight possible combinations of values of x, y, and c. From this table, we

Table 12-10   The sum of three binary digits

x	y	c	k	s
0	0	0	0	0
0	1	0	0	1
1	0	0	0	1
1	1	0	1	0
0	0	1	0	1
0	1	1	1	0
1	0	1	1	0
1	1	1	1	1

$c = 0$, $k = xy$, $s = xy' \lor x'y$

$c = 1$, $k = x \lor y$, $s = xy \lor x'y'$

must express s and k algebraically in terms of x, y, c. In trying to do this, it is well to consider first the special cases in which $c = 0$ and $c = 1$. The first is the case ($c = 0$) we have just treated. We found that

(1) $\qquad\qquad k = xy, \quad s = xy' \lor x'y \quad$ when $c = 0$.

In the second case ($c = 1$), k is 0 only when $x = y = 0$. Hence, $k = x \lor y$ in this case. In addition, s is zero only when x and y are unequal. Hence, $s = xy \lor x'y'$ in this case. To summarize:

(2) $\qquad\qquad k = x \lor y, \quad s = xy \lor x'y' \quad$ when $c = 1$.

We can combine the information in (1) and (2) by means of this simple principle: if z is a quantity with the value u when $c = 0$ and the value v when $c = 1$, then

$$z = c'u \lor cv.$$

Applying this principle, from (1) and (2) we have, in general,

$$k = c'xy \lor c(x \lor y), \quad s = c'(xy' \lor x'y) \lor c(xy \lor x'y').$$

The reader may verify that

$$k = c(x \lor y) \lor c'xy$$
$$= c(x \lor y) \lor xy$$
$$= cx \lor cy \lor xy.$$

Also slightly rewriting the expression for s, we thus have

(3)
$$k = cx \lor cy \lor xy$$
$$s = cxy \lor cx'y' \lor c'xy' \lor c'x'y$$

for the digit recorded and the digit carried when the column is added.

EXERCISES

1. Let x_2x_1 and y_2y_1 denote any two two-digit binary numbers. We wish to be able to do the sum

$$x_2\ x_1$$
$$+ y_2\ y_1$$
$$s_3\ s_2\ s_1$$

electrically. Design an appropriate circuit, and draw a schematic figure.

2. Let x and y be binary digits (i.e., $x = 0$ or 1, $y = 0$ or 1). Design a circuit assembly in which a bulb will light to indicate that $x < y$.

3. Do the same for the inequality $x \le y$.

4. Let x_2x_1 and y_2y_1 denote any two-digit binary numbers. Design a circuit assembly in which a bulb will light to indicate that the first number is less than the second.

5. Do the same for the relation $\le$.

6. Design an electrical instrument for the subtraction of two binary two-digit numbers.

7. A circuit assembly is diagrammed in Figure 12-37. Not all the connections in this assembly are of series or parallel type.

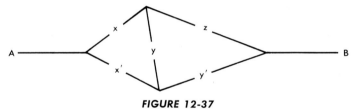

FIGURE 12-37

(a) Write in the transmitting capability from A to B, denoted by x_{AB}, in the last column of the following table.

x	y	z	x_{AB}
0	0	0	
0	0	1	
0	1	0	
0	1	1	
1	0	0	
1	0	1	
1	1	0	
1	1	1	

(b) Give a formula for x_{AB} in terms of y and z in the case x = 0. Then give a formula for x_{AB} in the case x = 1.
(c) Give a formula for x_{AB} in terms of x, y, z. (This formula should fit every case.)
(d) Diagram the circuit assembly corresponding to the formula obtained in (c).
(e) Is the circuit assembly diagrammed equivalent to the given one?

5.

Functions of transmitting capabilities

Suppose several circuit assemblies, whose individual transmitting capabilities are represented by x, y, x', or y', are connected together to make up a total assembly with the transmitting capability L. This L will have a particular value (always either 0 or 1) for each combination of values of x and y. Accordingly, we say that L is a *function of x and y* and often write such a relation symbolically as

$$L = f(x,y).$$

The symbol $f(x,y)$ is read, "f of x and y," and denotes the value of L associated with the combination of values (x,y) displayed. For instance, $f(0,1)$ means the value of L resulting when x = 0 and y = 1. A function of x and y can always be described by a four-row table (Table 12-11) setting forth the value of L corresponding to each of the

x	y	L
0	0	0
0	1	1
1	0	1
1	1	0

Table 12-11   An example of a function of x and y

four possible combinations of values of x and y. This instance is one of several that arose before (see Table 12-9, in which s takes the place of the present symbol L). In this instance, we saw that $L = xy' \lor x'y$. Thus, in this instance, a function originally described by a table turned out to have an algebraic expression. Is this true of all functions of x and y?

The analogous question can be raised when L depends on three or more variables. Suppose that L, for instance, is the transmitting capability of a total assembly built by connecting individual circuit assemblies whose transmitting capabilities are represented by x, y, z, x', y', or z'. In this case, L has a particular value for each combination of values of x, y, z. We say that L is a *function* of the three variables x, y, z, and we write

$$L = f(x,y,z).$$

Analogously to the two-variable case, $f(0,1,1)$, for instance, means the value of L that results when $x = 0$, $y = 1$, $z = 1$; $f(0,b,c)$ means the value of L when $x = 0$, $y = b$, $z = c$; and so on. A function of three variables can always be described by an eight-row table, in which the value of L that corresponds to each of the eight possible combinations of values of x, y, z is specified. Similarly, a function of four variables can be described by a sixteen-row table, a function of five variables by a thirty-two-row table, and so forth. Our question is: does every function of several variables have an algebraic expression?

We shall show that the answer is yes. This fact has an interesting consequence: *any* circuit assembly, *regardless of its actual construction*, is equivalent to an assembly in which all connections are of either the series or the parallel type. In fact, we can certainly record whether the total assembly is open or closed for each possible combination of transmitting capabilities of the individual parts. We will then have a table giving us the transmitting capability of the original total assembly as a function of the transmitting capabilities of its parts. As we intend to show, such a function has an algebraic expression, while any algebraic expression corresponds to an assembly in which all connections are of either the series or the parallel type. It follows that the original assembly is equivalent to such an assembly, as asserted.

Let us now prove our contention that any function of circuit algebra variables has an algebraic expression. To learn how to proceed, we begin with a function of a single variable, which we shall denote by $f(x)$. We know this function completely when we know it for the two possible values of x, or, in other words, when we know $f(0)$ and $f(1)$. But it is easy to write an algebraic expression for this function in terms of these values. The expression is:

$$f(x) = xf(1) \lor x' f(0).$$

To verify this, we need merely consider separately the two possible values of x. For $x = 0$, the left member of this purported equality is $f(0)$, and the right member is $0 \cdot f(1) \vee 0' \cdot f(0) = 0 \vee 1 \cdot f(0) = f(0)$. For $x = 1$, the left member is $f(1)$, and the right member is $1 \cdot f(1) \vee 0 \cdot f(0) = f(1)$. Thus, the equality does hold in both cases.

Next, consider a function of two variables, denoted by $f(x,y)$. This function is determined from the four values

$$f(0,0), \quad f(0,1), \quad f(1,0), \quad f(0,0).$$

To arrive at an algebraic expression, notice that when one of the two variables is fixed, this function of two variables is reduced to a function of one — the other — variable. For instance, if y is fixed as either 0 or 1, $f(x,y)$ becomes either $f(x,0)$ or $f(x,1)$, respectively. These are functions of x, and the preceding result applies, giving:

$$f(x,0) = x f(1,0) \vee x' f(0,0)$$

and

$$f(x,1) = x f(1,1) \vee x' f(0,1).$$

On the other hand, if x is held fixed, then $f(x,y)$ is to be regarded as a function of the single variable y, and we have:

$$f(x,y) = y f(x,1) \vee y' f(x,0).$$

Substituting for $f(x,1)$ and $f(x,0)$ gives us

$$f(x,y) = y (xf(1,1) \vee x'f(0,1)) \\ \vee y'(xf(1,0) \vee x'f(0,0))$$

and thus, finally,

(1) $f(x,y) = xy f(1,1) \vee x'y f(0,1) \vee xy' f(1,0) \vee x'y' f(0,0).$

This formula can, of course, be checked directly in each of the four cases arising.

EXERCISES

1. If $f(x,y,z)$ is a function of three circuit algebra variables, prove that

(2) $f(x,y,z) = xyz\, f(1,1,1) \vee x'yz\, f(0,1,1) \vee xy'z\, f(1,0,1)$
        $\vee\ xyz'\, f(1,1,0) \vee xy'z'\, f(1,0,0) \vee x'yz'\, f(0,1,0)$
        $\vee\ x'y'z\, f(0,0,1) \vee x'y'z'\, f(0,0,0).$

2. State and prove an analogous result for a function of n circuit variables. HINT: Use mathematical induction.

3. Prove: $f(x,y) = (x \vee y \vee f(0,0))(x \vee y' \vee f(0,1))$
$\cdot (x' \vee y \vee f(1,0))(x' \vee y' \vee f(1,1))$.

HINT: Dualize (1).

4. Table 12-12 defines u, v, w as functions of x, y. Find algebraic expressions for them.

Table 12-12 *Certain functions of two variables*

x	y	u	v	w
0	0	0	1	0
0	1	1	0	0
1	0	0	0	1
1	1	0	1	1

5. Prove:
   (a) $x\, f(x,y) = x\, f(1,y)$
   (b) $x \vee f(x,y) = x \vee f(0,y)$
   (c) $x'\, f(x,y) = x'\, f(0,y)$
   (d) $x' \vee f(x,y) = x' \vee f(1,y)$.

6. In the circuit assembly in Figure 12-38, the two lights can be turned on either separately (by the upper switches) or together (by the lowest switch). Give an equivalent circuit assembly having only series and parallel connections. HINT: Examine the transmitting capabilities from A to B and from A to C in the two cases $z = 0$ and $z = 1$.

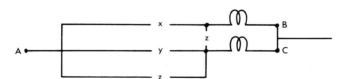

FIGURE 12-38 *An assembly for lighting control.*

7. Find an algebraic expression and a corresponding series-parallel arrangement for this circuit assembly (Figure 12-39): HINT: Consider individually the two cases $z = 0$ and $z = 1$. In the first case, the assembly is represented by the expression $xu \vee yv$ and, in the second case, by $(x \vee y)(u \vee v)$. Justify these expressions and combine them.

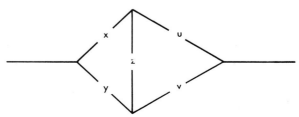

FIGURE 12-39 *A bridge assembly.*

For each of the following† find an equivalent assembly having only series and parallel connections.

8. The circuit in Figure 12-40.

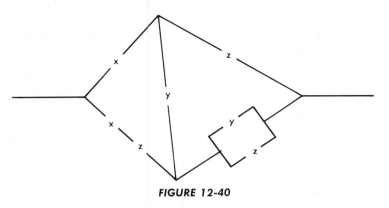

FIGURE 12-40

9. The circuit in Figure 12-41.

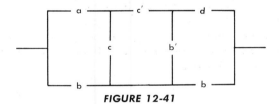

FIGURE 12-41

10. The circuit in Figure 12-42. In this example, find the transmitting capabilities:

      (a) from A to B   (c) from A to D

      (b) from A to C   (d) from A to E.

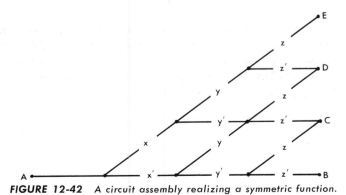

FIGURE 12-42   *A circuit assembly realizing a symmetric function.*

†These are taken from J. E. Whitesitt, *Boolean Algebra*, Addison-Wesley, Reading, Mass., 1961, pp. 89, 100.

6.

The theory of proof

Anyone who has ever struggled for inspiration in a difficult proof, say in Euclidean geometry, must have longed for an unfailing routine that would grind out proofs mechanically for all true propositions. He may have wondered whether his proposition, if true, could be proved at all. All deductive theories arouse such thoughts, and the responses these thoughts have evoked are among the wonders of philosophy.

The axioms of a deductive theory involve a certain stock of concepts, and any sentence relating solely to these concepts is certainly either true or false. Some sentences that relate solely to these concepts can be *proved* true or *proved* false — i.e., can be proved or disproved — by deductive inference from the axioms. Can all? In other words, can we be certain that any such sentence has a proof or a disproof, even though no one may have worked it out?

Asking this question indiscriminately concerning "any" sentence is idle, since we care only for sentences of mathematical interest. Fortunately, in some theories, all the sentences of mathematical interest have relatively simple internal structure and composition, and as a result we can discuss their provability successfully. Circuit algebra is an example. To make ourselves aware of the kinds of sentences that are of interest in this theory, let us examine a few instances:

(I) $1 \vee 1 = 1$.

(II) For all x,

$$((x = 1) \text{ or } (x = 0)).$$

(III) For all x, y, z,

$$xy \vee x'z = xy \vee x'z \vee yz.$$

(IV) For all x, y,

$$\sim (x = y) \equiv (xy' \vee x'y = 1).$$

(V) For all a, b,

$$\{[\text{For all } x \ ((a \vee x = b \vee x) \text{ and } (a \vee x' = b \vee x'))] \Rightarrow a = b\}.$$

(VI) For each value of x, there is a value of y such that

$$x \vee y = 1 \text{ and } xy = 0.$$

These sentences are all stated by means of, first, the mathematical symbols of circuit algebra and, secondly, certain words and expressions (and symbols previously introduced for words and expressions) belonging to logic or to ordinary language. We list these ingredients as follows:

1. Mathematical symbols
   (a) 0 and 1, symbols representing the two constants in circuit algebra.
   (b) Such symbols as x, y, z, and so forth, representing variable or unspecified quantities. Any variable can take only the values 0 or 1, i.e., $x = 0$ or 1, $y = 0$ or 1, and so forth.
   (c) The symbols $\vee$, $\cdot$ (usually omitted), $'$, $=$, for the operations of screening, multiplying, and dualizing and for the relation of equality, respectively. Also, parentheses.
2. Words or symbols for logical operations or relations
   (a) Those discussed in Chapter 1. These are called *sentential connectives:*

"or"	(disjunction)
"and"	(conjunction)
$\sim$	(negation)
$\Rightarrow$	(implication)
$\equiv$	(equivalence)

To these we add parentheses, brackets, and so forth.
   (b) Expressions of the form,
      (1) "For all x,"
      and
      (2) "There exists x such that."
      Expressions of form (1) are called *universal quantifiers;* expressions of form (2) are called *existential quantifiers.* Each symbol denoting a variable quantity in a sentence is accompanied by a quantifier, which may be of either kind. The quantifier is said to *bind* the variable it accompanies in the sentence.

The sentences (I) through (VI) are of three kinds:
   (i) Equalities containing symbols for the constants and the mathematical operations (1(a), (c)) only.
   (ii) Sentences concerning equalities that include symbols for variables as well as, possibly, the constants and the mathematical operations. Each variable is accompanied by an existential or a universal quantifier that binds it.
   (iii) Composite sentences, the constituents of which are sentences of the previous two kinds joined by sentential connectives (2(a)).

EXERCISES

1. Classify the sentences (I) through (VI).
2. Express this statement in the words (including the symbols) of the previous list: At most one value y exists such that

$$x \vee y = 1, \quad xy = 0$$

for every value of x.

The reader glancing over the previous sections may agree that few, if any, statements of interest in circuit algebra are of other forms than those described. Hence, circuit theory limited to statements of these three kinds would be quite comprehensive. We shall so limit it and shall find that all statements admitted then can be proved or disproved easily.

Any sentence of the first type, and any composite of sentences of this type, can be judged true or false from Table 12-1. Hence, in particular, if 0 or 1 is substituted for each variable occurring in a sentence of the second or third type, the resulting sentence can be judged to be true or to be false. Any sentence of type (ii) beginning: "For all x, . . ." actually amounts to two sentences that result from the original by substituting 0 or 1 for x. (For instance, the sentence, "For all x, $x \vee x' = 1$," consists actually of the two statements: "$0 \vee 0' = 1$," and "$1 \vee 1' = 1$.") Similarly, a sentence beginning: "For all x and y, . . ." actually consists logically of the four sentences that result from the original by substituting 0 or 1 for x and y in all four possible combinations. More generally, any statement containing variables that are bound by universal quantifiers reduces to a finite number of statements derived by replacing each such variable by 0 or 1. The statements so derived still contain all the variables bound by existential quantifiers. If no such variable was originally present—i.e., if all the variables in the original statement were universally quantified— then the derived statements resulting after the substitutions contain no variables, but only constants, and can be tested by use of Table 12-1; the original statement is true if the tests are all affirmative and otherwise false. But if some variables in the original statement were bound by existential quantifiers, these variables remain so bound in the statements derived by substitution. We must then see whether the existentially quantified variables have values for which all the derived statements are true. Since each variable can have only the two values 0 and 1, there is but a finite number of possibilities, each of which for each derived statement can be tested. If these tests reveal a set of values of the existentially quantified variables for which each of the statements derived from the original by substitutions is satisfied, then the original statement is true; otherwise, it is false. Any statement of the kinds described thus can be proved or disproved, as asserted. This can be done, moreover, by means of a definite and routine procedure.

For the more complex axiomatic systems, much more formal procedures are necessary in order to study the provability of statements. Symbols are used not only for mathematical constants, variables, operations, and relations but also for all logical words and expressions. For instance, it is customary to represent

"and"	by $\wedge$
"or"	by $\vee$
"For all x"	by $\forall x$
"There exists x such that"	by $\exists x$

as well as to use the symbols already introduced. Formal rules are promulgated on how admissible sentences may be constructed out of the symbols. (These rules, for instance, would exclude "$(\exists x) \wedge$" as meaningless.) Rules of inference are formulated telling us that if we have accepted certain statements, then we must also accept others. These originate from such logical propositions as:

$$(A \wedge B) \Rightarrow A$$
$$A \Rightarrow A \vee B$$
$$(A \wedge (A \Rightarrow B)) \Rightarrow B$$
$$[(A \Rightarrow B) \wedge (B \Rightarrow C)] \Rightarrow (A \Rightarrow C).$$

(The third, for instance, tells us that if we accept A, and if A implies B, then we must accept B.) Rules of inference pertaining to the universal quantifier would tell us, for example, that

$$(\forall x (x^2 \geq 0)) \Rightarrow 2^2 \geq 0,$$

or, in other words, that if a certain relationship is satisfied for all numbers x, then it is satisfied in particular by the value 2. The rules of sentence formation and the rules of inference are used quite mechanically. If through a string of applications of these rules we can proceed from a given set of sentences to a new sentence, we say that the new sentence is *deducible* from the given set. A sentence deducible from a set of *true* sentences (e.g., axioms) is also true and is known as a *theorem*. The string of applications of rules of logic by which a theorem is deduced is called the *proof* of the theorem. Proof of a negation is called a *disproof*. It is by no means certain that any sentence permitted by the rules has a proof or a disproof, i.e., that the sentence or its negation can be deduced from the axioms. If every sentence permitted by the rules can be proved or disproved, the theory and its underlying axioms are said to be *complete* and, otherwise, to be *incomplete*.

Prof. Alfred Tarski† proved in 1951 that elementary Euclidean geometry, with its axioms suitably revised and augmented, is complete. He did so by actually inventing a universal routine procedure by means of which any statement permitted by the rules can, in principle, be proved or disproved. The routine is doubtless rarely practical. Its mere existence, however, is enough to demonstrate completeness.

The situation for arithmetic is quite otherwise: any system of axioms strong enough to imply all the basic facts of elementary arithmetic will necessarily give rise to an incomplete theory. Since most fields in mathematics depend upon arithmetic in one way or another, they, too, are incomplete. Such a limitation upon systematic thought

---

† "What is elementary algebra?" pp. 16-29 in *The Axiomatic Method*, edited by Henken, Suppes, and Tarski. North Holland Publishing Company, Amsterdam, 1959.

was unsuspected during almost two and a half millennia of experience with axiomatic procedure until discovered by Kurt Gödel in
1931.†

7.

The Propositional Calculus

Circuit algebra has a variety of models besides that provided by
circuits. The so-called Calculus of Propositions is another model. Let
capital letters, such as A, B, C, denote sentences, i.e., declarative
sentences, which we may also call statements, propositions, or
assertions (see Chapter 1). We shall adhere to the logician's convention that a sentence is either true or false and is not both true and also
false. As before, we shall say that the truth or falsity of a sentence is its
state, but instead of labeling these states by T and F, respectively, we
shall now use 1 and 0 as even more appropriate. Accordingly, we
define the *algebraic state* of an arbitrary sentence A to be the
"number" x such that

$$x = 1 \quad \text{if } A \text{ is true}$$
$$= 0 \quad \text{if } A \text{ is false,}$$

where 1 and 0 are the two quantities in circuit arithmetic (Section 2).

If A and B are any two sentences, we have already explained
what are meant by the composite sentences, "A and B" and "A or B."
The explanation consisted in giving the states of the composites for
each combination of states of the constituents, or, in other words, in
drawing up truth tables. It is enlightening to draw up similar truth
tables here with 0 and 1 in place of F and T, respectively. Let x, y, u, v
denote the algebraic states of A, B, (A or B), (A and B), respectively.
Tables 1-2 and 1-4 with the agreed substitution of 0 for F and of 1 for
T give us the third and fourth columns, respectively, of Table 12-13.

Table 12-13 *Truth table for "and" and "or"
with algebraic states*

A (x)	B (y)	(A or B) (u)	(A and B) (v)
1	1	1	1
1	0	1	0
0	1	1	0
0	0	0	0

†For a layman's account of Gödel's discovery, see E. Nagel and J. R. Newman,
Gödel's Proof, New York University Press, New York, 1958. A general account of logic
and axiomatics for laymen is given by Alfred Tarski, *Introduction to Logic*, 3rd Edition,
Oxford University Press, New York.

(The first line indicates that the algebraic states of (A or B) and of (A and B) are 1 when the algebraic states of A and of B are 1, the second line that (A or B) has the algebraic state 1 and (A and B) the algebraic state 0 when A has the algebraic state 1 and B the algebraic state 0, and so on. From this table, it is clear that

$$u = x \vee y, \quad v = xy.$$

In words: if x and y denote the algebraic states of two sentences, A and B, respectively, then xy is the algebraic state of (A and B), and $x \vee y$ is the algebraic state of (A or B).

This result makes it convenient to represent disjunction and conjunction by the symbols for screening and multiplication, respectively. Then

$$A \vee B \qquad \text{means: "Either } A \text{ or } B\text{,"}$$
$$A \cdot B, \text{ or } AB, \text{ means: "Both } A \text{ and } B\text{."}$$

Consistently with this, we have, for instance,

$$ABC \qquad \text{means: "} A \text{ and } B \text{ and also } C\text{,"}$$
$$A(B \vee C) \quad \text{means: "Both } A \text{ and also either } B \text{ or } C\text{,"}$$
$$A \vee BC \qquad \text{means: "Either } A, \text{ or both } B \text{ and } C\text{,"}$$
$$AB \vee CD \quad \text{means: "Either } A \text{ and } B, \text{ or } C \text{ and } D\text{."}$$

The advantage of this notation is that it indicates very clearly how the algebraic state of a composite statement depends upon the algebraic states of its constituents. To obtain the algebraic state of the composite, you replace each constituent by the algebraic state of the constituent and then interpret the symbols for multiplication and screening in their original senses in circuit arithmetic. For instance, if w, x, y, z are the algebraic states of A, B, C, D, respectively, then the algebraic states of the four composites are wxy, $w(x \vee y)$, $w \vee xy$, $wx \vee yz$, respectively.

If the algebraic state of A is denoted by x, then the algebraic state of $\sim A$ is x' (the dual of x). Indeed, $\sim A$ is the statement that is true if A is false and is false if A is true. Hence, the algebraic state of $\sim A$ is 1 if $x = 0$ and is 0 if $x = 1$. Therefore, the algebraic state of $\sim A$ is x', as asserted.

We shall now work out algebraic counterparts to the logical rules touched upon in Chapter 1.

(1) *The convention of having two states.* The convention that any statement is either true or else false is equivalent to the assertion that, for any sentence A,

$$A \vee \sim A$$

is true. If x denotes the algebraic state of A, then the algebraic state of $A \lor \sim A$ is $x \lor x'$. Hence, the convention that a statement is either true or false is expressed algebraically by the identity

$$x \lor x' = 1.$$

(2) *The law against contradictions.* The condition that no sentence be both true and also false amounts to the condition that

$$A \cdot \sim A$$

be false if A represents any sentence whatsoever. Let x denote the algebraic state of A. Then the algebraic state of $A \cdot \sim A$ is xx'. Hence, the counterpart to the logical requirement that $A \cdot \sim A$ be false is the algebraic identity

$$xx' = 0.$$

(3) *Logical equivalence.* If two sentences are logically equivalent, then their states are the same, and their algebraic states also coincide. Conversely, if their algebraic states coincide, then they are equivalent. Hence, the statement, "$A \equiv B$" is logically equivalent to the algebraic relation,

$$x = y,$$

between the algebraic states, x and y, respectively, of A and B. The equivalence of statements thus corresponds to the equality of their algebraic states. What is the algebraic state of the sentence: "$A \equiv B$"? To find out, we examine the truth table defining the statement under consideration. This is given in Table 12-14, which is a copy of Table 1-5 except that T and F are replaced by 1 and 0, respectively, and that

Table 12-14 Truth table for equivalence, with algebraic states

A (x)	B (y)	(A ≡ B) (u)
1	1	1
1	0	0
0	1	0
0	0	1

x, y, u are introduced as symbols for the algebraic states of A, B, $(A \equiv B)$, respectively. We can read from this that

$$u = xy \lor x'y'$$

(see Section 5 for a different way to obtain the formula). Thus, if x and

y are the algebraic states of A and B, the algebraic state of $(A \equiv B)$ is

$$xy \lor x'y'.$$

This is also the algebraic state of

$$AB \lor \sim A \sim B.$$

Hence,

$$(A \equiv B) \equiv (AB \lor \sim A \sim B).$$

(4) *Rules for negating.* Consider de Morgan's relations (relations (10a) and (10b), Section 3):

$$(x \lor y)' = x'y',$$
$$(xy)' = (x' \lor y').$$

If x and y are interpreted as algebraic states of sentences A and B, respectively, these equalities express the equivalences:

$$\sim (A \lor B) \equiv \sim A \sim B$$
$$\sim (AB) \equiv \sim A \lor \sim B.$$

These equivalences, which are also known under de Morgan's name, are already familiar to us from Section 7, Chapter 1.

(4) *Implication.* The statement, "$A \Rightarrow B$," was defined as $\sim (A \cdot \sim B)$. But if x and y are the algebraic states of A and B, respectively, the algebraic state of $\sim (A \cdot \sim B)$ is $(xy')'$. Hence, the algebraic state of $(A \Rightarrow B)$ also is $(xy')'$. The reader can check this from Table 12-15, which is a copy of Table 1-14 except that 0 and 1 are substituted for F and T, respectively. (In the first row, for instance, $x = 1$, $y = 1$;

A (x)	B (y)	(A ⇒ B)
1	1	1
1	0	0
0	1	1
0	0	1

Table 12-15 Truth table for implication, with algebraic states

hence, $(xy')' = (1 \cdot 1')' = (1 \cdot 0)' = 0' = 1$, which is just the value that was recorded in the third column of the first row as the algebraic state of $(A \Rightarrow B)$.) Now we shall re-examine the laws for implication from the point of view of the Propositional Calculus.

a. THE CONTRAPOSITIVE FORM

We have just found that the algebraic state of the statement

$$(A \Rightarrow B)$$

is

(1) $(xy')'$,

x and y denoting the algebraic states of A and B, respectively. To calculate the algebraic state of the contrapositive form,

$$(\sim B \Rightarrow \sim A),$$

we must, in (1), replace the algebraic state of A by that of $\sim B$ and the algebraic state of B by that of $\sim A$. This means replacing x by y' and y by x', whereby expression (1) is changed to

$$[y'(x')']'$$

Since $(x')' = x$, this result, which is the algebraic state of the contrapositive form, is equal to (1), the algebraic state of the original form. Hence, the contrapositive and the original forms of the implication are equivalent, as asserted.

b.   EQUIVALENCE RESULTING FROM IMPLICATIONS

We shall now show how it can be proved in the Propositional Calculus that the two statements,

(2) $(A \Rightarrow B) \cdot (B \Rightarrow A)$ ("A implies B, and B implies A")

and

(3) $(A \equiv B)$ ("A and B are logically equivalent"),

are logically equivalent. It suffices to prove that their algebraic states are the same. If x and y denote the algebraic states of A and B, respectively, the algebraic state of statement (3) is already known to be:

(4) $xy \lor x'y'$.

Hence, we must show this to be the algebraic state of statement (2). The algebraic state of $(A \Rightarrow B)$ is $(xy')'$, or, by de Morgan's rule, $x' \lor y$; the algebraic state of $(B \Rightarrow A)$ similarly is equal to $y' \lor x$. Hence, the algebraic state of the product (2) is the product

$$(x' \lor y)(y' \lor x).$$

Expanding this product gives us

$$x'y' \lor x'x \lor yy' \lor yx,$$

which reduces to

$$x'y' \lor yx,$$

since $x'x = 0$, $yy' = 0$. The last expression is equal to (4), which thus is revealed as the algebraic state of statement (2), as desired.

c. THE TRANSITIVE LAW FOR IMPLICATIONS

Using the Propositional Calculus, we shall justify the transitive law for implications in this form:

(5) $$[(A \Rightarrow B) \cdot (B \Rightarrow C)] \Rightarrow (A \Rightarrow C).$$

Let X and Y denote the algebraic states of the left and right members, respectively, of statement (5). Then the algebraic state of this statement is $(XY')'$, and to prove the statement to be true we must thus show that $(XY')' = 1$. This is equivalent to proving:

(6) $$XY' = 0$$

Let x, y, z denote the algebraic states of A, B, C, respectively. Then

(7) $$Y = (xz')'.$$

To obtain the algebraic state of X, we note that the algebraic state of $(A \Rightarrow B)$ is $(xy')'$, which, by de Morgan's rule, equals $x' \lor y$, and that the algebraic state of $(B \Rightarrow C)$ similarly is equal to $y' \lor z$. Hence, the algebraic state of $[(A \Rightarrow B) \cdot (B \Rightarrow C)]$ is

$$X = (x' \lor y)(y' \lor z).$$

Since, by (7), $Y' = xz'$, we thus have

$$\begin{aligned}
XY' &= (x' \lor y)(y' \lor z)xz' \\
&= [x(x' \lor y)][(y' \lor z)z'] \\
&= (xx' \lor xy)(y'z' \lor zz') \\
&= (xy)(y'z') \\
&= x(yy')z' \\
&= 0,
\end{aligned}$$

since $xx' = yy' = zz' = 0$. Thus, condition (6) is verified, as required.

EXERCISES

In these exercises, let A, B, C denote any statements and let x, y, z denote their algebraic states.

1. Find the algebraic states of these composite sentences. Reduce them to as simple forms as possible:

(a) $(A \Rightarrow B) \lor (B \Rightarrow A)$

(b) $(A \equiv B) \lor (B \Rightarrow C)$

(c) $\sim(A \equiv B)$

(d) $AB \lor (A \lor B)$

(e) $\sim(AB) \cdot (A \Rightarrow B)$

2. Prove from the Propositional Calculus:

(a) If A is false, then $A \Rightarrow B$.

(b) If B is true, then $A \Rightarrow B$.

3. The assertion that A implies B means that the sentence "A implies B" is true. Why is the assertion that A implies B equivalent to the equality:

$$xy' = 0?$$

4. We may give an alternative proof of the transitive law (5), as follows. If the left side of the implication (5) is false, then this implication is true without further argument. Let us therefore consider only the case in which the left side of (5) is true. Then it is also true that A implies B and that B implies C, or that

$$xy' = 0, \; yz' = 0$$

(see the previous exercise). It is to be proved that A implies C, or that

$$xz' = 0.$$

Complete this proof. HINT: $xz' = x(y \lor y')z'$.

5. Prove that

$$[(A \Rightarrow B) \cdot (B \Rightarrow A)] \Rightarrow (A \equiv B),$$

as follows. (This proof is an alternative to that of Subsection b.) If the left member is false, the statement is true by definition. Hence, consider only the case in which the left member is true. In this case, A implies B, and B implies A, or

$$xy' = 0, \; yx' = 0.$$

We need to show that $A \equiv B$, and, thus, that $x = y$. Do so from the identities:

$$x = x(y \lor y'), \; y = y(x \lor x').$$

6. Prove from the Propositional Calculus that if

$$(A \Rightarrow B) \cdot (B \Rightarrow C) \cdot (C \Rightarrow A),$$

then

$$A \equiv B \equiv C.$$

7. Let A, B, C, D denote sentences and a, b, c, d their respective algebraic states. What are the algebraic states of the following composite sentences:

   (a) $(A$ and $\sim B)$,

   (b) $(C \Rightarrow D)$,

   (c) $[(A \Rightarrow B)$ and $(B \Rightarrow C)]$.

Prove by using the propositional calculus:

   (d) For any sentences A and B, $[A$ or $(B$ and $A)] \equiv A$.

   (e) For any sentences A and B, $[\sim(A$ or $\sim B)$ or $(A$ and $B)] \equiv B$.

   (f) For any sentences A and B, $[(A \Rightarrow B)$ and $(B \Rightarrow \sim A)] \equiv \sim A$.

8. We quote from Gilbert and Sullivan:

   (1) "If you're lying awake with a dismal headache
       and repose is tabooed by anxiety,
       I conceive you may use any language you choose
       to indulge in without impropriety."

   (a) On the face of it, this quotation is of the form
       (2) "If A and B, then C."
       What sentences play the roles in (1) of A, B, and C? Draw up a truth table for sentences of the form (2).

   (b) Letting x, y, z denote the algebraic states of A, B, C, respectively, write the algebraic state of statement (2). Making use of de Morgan's rules, find the algebraic state of the negation of statement (2). Express the negation of (2) in words and symbols A, B, C, using the "If . . ., then . . ." construction.

   (c) The quotation no doubt is to be understood as a generalization and, so regarded, is logically of the form: "In all instances, A and B imply C." Interpreting the quotation this way, put its negation into good English.

9. We quote from Gilbert and Sullivan:

   (1) "If a man would woo a fair maid
       He must 'prentice himself to the trade
       And study all day in methodical way
       How to flatter, cajole, and persuade."

   (a) On the face of it, the statement quoted (1) is of the form:
       (2) "If A, then B and C."
       What sentences play the roles in (1) of A, B, and C? Draw up a truth table for sentences of the form (2).

   (b) Letting x, y, z denote the algebraic states of A, B, C, respectively, write the algebraic state of statement (2). Making use of de Morgan's rules, find the algebraic state of the negation of statement (2). Express the negation of (2) in words and the symbols A, B, C, using the "If . . ., then . . ." construction.

   (c) Quotation (1) no doubt is to be understood as a generalization and, so regarded, is logically of the form:

       "In all instances, A implies B and C."

       Interpreting the quotation this way, put its negation into good English.

10. Let x represent the algebraic state of the statement "You can study."
Let y represent the algebraic state of the statement "You watch T.V."

Consider the following statements:

    (a) You can study and not watch T.V., or watch T.V. and not study, or do neither.

    (b) Either you study and don't watch T.V., or you can't study.

    (c) It's impossible both to study and to watch T.V.

    (d) Either you can watch T.V. and can't study, or you don't watch T.V.

    (e) Either you can't study or you don't watch T.V.

        (i) Write an expression for the algebraic state of each of the foregoing statements.

        (ii) Prove that all of the previous statements are logically equivalent.

11. Let a represent the algebraic state of the statement "The function is continuous." Let b represent the algebraic state of the statement "The function is differentiable." The statement $X \equiv$ "If the function is differentiable, then the function is continuous," is a true statement, but the statement $Y \equiv$ "If the function is continuous, then the function is differentiable," is a false statement.

    (a) Write equations in propositional calculus to express the facts that X is a true statement and that Y is a false statement.

    (b) Write expressions for the algebraic states of each of the following statements, and decide whether each is true or false.

        (i) Either the function is differentiable, or the function is not continuous.

        (ii) Either the function is not continuous, or the function is differentiable.

        (iii) It is impossible for the function to be continuous and not differentiable.

        (iv) It is impossible for the function to be differentiable and not continuous.

        (v) Either the function is continuous and not differentiable, or the function is differentiable and not continuous.

12. Heckel and Jeckel are friends. One of them always lies and the other always tells the truth. A stranger asks them how to get to Rockville. Heckel says, "Jeckel is a liar, and Rockville is straight ahead." Jeckel says, "Heckel is a liar, and Rockville is not straight ahead." We have the additional facts that:

    (1) Either Rockville is not straight ahead or Heckel is not a liar.

    (2) Either Rockville is not straight ahead or Jeckel is not a liar.

Who is telling the truth and which way is Rockville?

HINT: Let a represent the algebraic state of the statement

"Jeckel is a liar."

Let b represent the algebraic state of the statement

"Heckel is a liar."

Let c represent the algebraic state of the statement

"Rockville is straight ahead."

Write expressions for the statements made by Heckel and Jeckel and write equations for the two additional facts. Notice that $b = a'$. Why?

Use identities of propositional calculus (including, in particular, those on p. 495) to prove statements (a) and (b) in each pair of the following exercises to be equivalent.

13. (a) If he is nominated, he will serve; but he either will not be nominated or will not serve.
    (b) He will not be nominated.

14. (a) If he doesn't know the answer, he looks it up.
    (b) Either he doesn't know the answer, or he looks it up.

15. (a) Our team either took the first prize, or else took both the first and the second prizes.
    (b) Our team took the first prize.

16. (a) Either I'll go to Hamlet and skip Macbeth, or I'll skip Hamlet and take in Macbeth.
    (b) I'll see either Hamlet or Macbeth, not both Hamlet and Macbeth.

17. (a) Either I'll be late for dinner, or else I'll be on time for dinner and stay for bridge.
    (b) Either I'll be late for dinner, or I will stay for bridge.

18. (a) He is either shaving or is in the shower; if shaving, he will have breakfast next.
    (b) Either he is shaving and will have breakfast next, or he is not shaving but is in the shower.

19. (a) She wears a necklace without sequins, or sequins and a silver pin, or a necklace and a silver pin.
    (b) She wears a silver pin and sequins, or a necklace without sequins.

20. (a) She likes antiques and coin collections, or antiques but not cultured pearls, or neither coin collections nor cultured pearls.
    (b) She likes antiques and coin collections, or not coin collections and not cultured pearls.

21. (a) He violated our rule to wear a blue shirt and a yellow tie, or a yellow tie and black shoes, or black shoes and a blue shirt.
    (b) He wore neither a blue shirt nor a yellow tie, or neither a yellow tie nor black shoes, or neither black shoes nor a blue shirt.

Logic is revealed by our mathematical analysis to be the logic of circuits. This relationship is often turned to practical account, as we shall here illustrate.

Problem 1: A committee desires to expedite its work by voting electrically, with a green light to signify that the ayes have it. How can they do this?

Solution: We shall discuss the problem for a committee of three. Let

$$A \equiv \text{``The first member votes `aye.'''}$$
$$B \equiv \text{``The second member votes `aye.'''}$$
$$C \equiv \text{``The third member votes `aye.'''}$$

Also, let

$$M \equiv \text{``The ayes have it.''}$$

Since M is true if and only if any two members vote 'aye,' we have:

$$M \equiv AB \vee BC \vee CA.$$

Consequently, if a, b, c, m denote the algebraic states of A, B, C, M, respectively, we have

$$m = ab \vee bc \vee ca.$$

Install a switch at each member's place, and tell the members to close their switches to vote 'aye,' to open them for 'nay.' If they follow these instructions,

$a =$ transmitting capability of first member's switch,
$b =$ transmitting capability of second member's switch,
$c =$ transmitting capability of third member's switch.

Connect the switches into an assembly with the algebraic expression

$$ab \vee bc \vee ca.$$

Finally, wire the green light in series with this assembly, its transmitting capability thus being m, where

$$m = ab \vee bc \vee ca.$$

Figure 12-43 represents the diagram of the resulting installation.

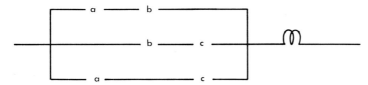

FIGURE 12-43   *A light to signify a majority vote.*

EXERCISES

22. Solve the analogous problem for a committee of five.

23. A committee of three, voting electrically, asks for a green light when the ayes have it and a red light when the nays have the majority. Design an appropriate assembly.

24. A committee consists of two ordinary members and a chairman. They wish to vote electrically.

   (a) Design an instrument that will put on a green light if a majority (including the chairman) vote 'aye.'

   (b) Modify the design so that a red light will go on if a majority vote 'nay.'

   (c) Design an instrument with red and green lights as before and also with a buzzer, which is to sound off if the chairman and his committee disagree.

25. A committee of four, desiring to vote electrically, demand a green light to signify that the ayes have it, a red light to indicate that the nays have it, and a white light if there is a draw, every member always being understood to be voting. Design the installation.

26. A committee has four ordinary members and a chairman, who may vote only to resolve a tie. An electrical voting mechanism to serve all five members is desired that will turn on a green light under either of the following circumstances:

   (i) a majority of the ordinary members vote 'aye,' or

   (ii) half the ordinary members and the chairman vote 'aye.' Design an appropriate circuit assembly.

27. A quiz machine is desired that will present two alternative answers to each of seven questions and will light a bulb when five are answered correctly. Devise the circuit.

Problem 2: Three couples, vacationing at a lake, must share the use of a single canoe, which is available from the boat boy upon request. The three wives make common cause. They ask an electrician to install in the boathouse one switch for each of the six persons at the lake, each switch with an "in the canoe" position and a "not in the canoe" position. The boat boy is to flick the appropriate switches upon checking out the canoe. When a man and woman venture forth in the canoe unaccompanied and unmarried to each other, red lights are to turn on in all three cabins. How might the electrician design the circuit?†

Solution: Let

$$A \equiv \text{"The first wife is in the canoe,"}$$
$$B \equiv \text{"The second wife is in the canoe,"}$$
$$C \equiv \text{"The third wife is in the canoe,"}$$
$$E \equiv \text{"The first husband is in the canoe,"}$$
$$F \equiv \text{"The second husband is in the canoe,"}$$
$$G \equiv \text{"The third husband is in the canoe,"}$$

and let

$$R \equiv \text{"The red lights go on."}$$

---

†This problem is adapted from one given in the manual for GENIAC, a kit for building switching machines. The manual is entitled: *GENIACS: Simple Electronic Brain Machines and How to Make Them*, copyright 1955 by Oliver Garfield, New York.

For convenience, also let

$I \equiv$ "The first husband and a wife not his own are alone in the canoe,"
$J \equiv$ "The second husband and a wife not his own are alone in the canoe,"
$K \equiv$ "The third husband and a wife not his own are alone in the canoe."

Since the alarm is to be raised if I or J or K materializes,

$$R \equiv I \vee J \vee K.$$

We must find expressions for I, J, and K. Since I is true if and only if the first husband and the second wife are alone in the canoe *or* the first husband and the third wife are alone in the canoe,

$$I \equiv EB \sim A \sim C \sim F \sim G \vee EC \sim A \sim B \sim F \sim G$$
$$\equiv E(B \sim C \vee C \sim B) \sim A \sim F \sim G.$$

Similarly,

$$J \equiv F(C \sim A \vee A \sim C) \sim B \sim E \sim G$$

and

$$K \equiv G(A \sim B \vee B \sim A) \sim C \sim E \sim F.$$

Let small letters a, b, c, e, f, g, i, j, k, r denote the algebraic states of A, B, C, E, F, G, I, J, K, R, respectively. Then we have, in particular,

$$i = e(bc' \vee cb')a'f'g'$$

with similar expressions for j and k; from all of these we obtain

$$r = i \vee j \vee k$$
$$= e(bc' \vee cb')a'f'g' \vee f(ca' \vee ac')b'e'g' \vee g(ab' \vee a'b)c'e'f'.$$

This algebraic expression for r gives the desired circuit, in which, if the boat boy follows his instructions, the relevant algebraic states are all realized as transmitting capabilities. A schematic diagram is given in Figure 12-44.

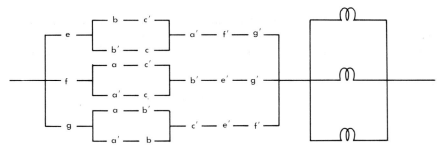

FIGURE 12-44 Circuit assembly for canoe problem.

EXERCISES

28. A young woman who has just been divorced occupies a fourth cabin by the lake, and the three wives of course wish to include her in their alarm system. Adding a switch to the boathouse installation, how is the electrician now to do the wiring?

29. The electrician warns the three wives that the battery supplying the current for the alarm lights may run down without warning. He advises as a check on the battery that a white light be installed, which is always to be on, except when the red light is flashing. Design an assembly to meet this requirement.

30. (a) Design a circuit that will turn a light bulb on when $A \Rightarrow B$ and otherwise will turn it off.

   (b) Design a circuit such that a green light will be on when (and only when) A implies B and a red light will be on when (and only when) A does not imply B.

31. Traffic across a short, narrow bridge is regulated by automatic signals. If cars approach the bridge from one direction only, a signal stating "All clear—Proceed" is flashed on. But if cars approach the bridge from both directions, a warning sign is turned on instructing the car from the south to "Proceed with caution" and the car from the north to "Withdraw from the bridge." Let $\mathscr{N}$ denote the statement that traffic is approaching the bridge from the north; let $\mathscr{S}$ denote the statement that traffic is approaching the bridge from the south. Let N and S denote the states of these respective statements, i.e., let

$$N = 1 \text{ when } \mathscr{N} \text{ is true,} \qquad S = 1 \text{ when } \mathscr{S} \text{ is true,}$$
$$= 0 \text{ when } \mathscr{N} \text{ is false,} \qquad = 0 \text{ when } \mathscr{S} \text{ is false.}$$

Using these symbols:

   (a) Write symbolically the statement that traffic is approaching the bridge from one direction only. Then diagram a circuit in which a sign lights up when traffic approaches the bridge from one direction only.

   (b) Write symbolically the statement that traffic is approaching the bridge from both directions. Then diagram a circuit in which a sign lights up when traffic approaches the bridge from both directions.

   (c) Diagram a circuit for which the bridge signs would flash on as described.

32. Dick Tracy and Little Orphan Annie play the following game: Dick Tracy has three switches marked R_1, P_1, S_1 which stand for rock, paper, and scissors, respectively. Little Orphan Annie has three similar switches marked R_2, P_2, S_2. Each presses one (and only one) switch (without the other seeing which).

The following combinations are winning combinations.

Rock beats scissors.
Scissors beat paper.
Paper beats rock.

Any other combination results in a tie. The game is played until one of the two loses. Design a circuit that will electrocute the loser.

33. Consider a panel of three judges, each of whom is to decide "yes," "no," or "I abstain." Design a circuit assembly in which the judges may register their decisions electrically such that:

    (a) a neon sign saying "passed" will light up if at least two judges vote yes,

    (b) a neon sign saying "failed" will light up if at least two judges vote no,

    (c) a neon sign saying "judges are confused" will light up for all other outcomes.

HINT: Each judge requires two (not three) dual switches. Considering the first judge, for instance, let

$$A_1 \equiv \text{the first judge abstains,}$$

and

$$Y_1 \equiv \text{the first judge votes yes.}$$

Since a judge who votes no does not abstain, the statement "the first judge votes no" is representable symbolically as $\sim Y_1 \sim A_1$. Identity 14, p. 495, is helpful with algebraic details.

34. A committee has five members, including the chairman. Their rules require all members to vote on any measure and accord the chairman a veto. This means that a measure carries if and only if the chairman and at least two additional members vote for it. Design a circuit so that each member votes for a measure by pressing a button, and a light goes on if and only if the measure is carried.

8.

Boolean algebras

Statements are equivalent if their algebraic states are equal. Hence, any statements A, B, C satisfy the following relations:

$$A \vee B \equiv B \vee A \qquad\qquad AB \equiv BA$$
$$A \vee (B \vee C) \equiv (A \vee B) \vee C \qquad A(BC) \equiv (AB)C$$
$$A \vee BC \equiv (A \vee B)(A \vee C) \qquad A(B \vee C) \equiv AB \vee AC$$
$$A \vee A \equiv A \qquad\qquad AA \equiv A.$$

Consider, for instance, the distributive law in the second column. The composite sentences $A(B \vee C)$ and $AB \vee AC$ in the left and right members, respectively, have equal algebraic states; therefore, they are equivalent. A similar argument will apply to any of these asserted equivalences and, of course, to many more.

These equivalences are evidence that statements are subject to algebraic law directly. Are there statements that play the roles of zero and one? This means, do statements, which we might denote by $\emptyset$ and I, respectively, exist such that

$$A \vee \emptyset \equiv A \qquad A\emptyset \equiv \emptyset$$
$$A \vee I \equiv I \qquad AI \equiv A\,?$$

We can easily see that there are such statements. Choose a sentence C arbitrarily and define $\emptyset$ by the equivalence

$$\emptyset \equiv C \sim C.$$

Then $\emptyset$ is false, and its algebraic state, in particular, is 0. Therefore,

$$A \vee \emptyset \equiv A, \qquad A\emptyset \equiv \emptyset,$$

the left members and the right members of the two equivalences having the same algebraic states, respectively. These equivalences mean that $\emptyset$ plays the role of zero among propositions. Now define I as

$$I \equiv \, \sim\!\emptyset.$$

The algebraic state of I is $0'$, i.e., is 1, and therefore

$$A \vee I \equiv I, \qquad AI \equiv A.$$

Hence, among propositions I plays the role of 1.

The negations of statements play the role of duals. We see this very clearly if just for the time being we agree to write A' instead of $\sim\!A$ to denote the negation of A. We then have for any statement A

$$(A')' = A, \qquad A \vee A' \equiv I, \qquad AA' \equiv \emptyset,$$

and for any A and B

$$(A \vee B)' \equiv A'B' \qquad (AB)' \equiv A' \vee B'.$$

EXERCISE

1. Prove these rules for the duals of statements.

George Boole[†] first perceived that "the laws of thought" are algebraic and noticed that the same laws also apply to some other

---

[†] *An Investigation of the Laws of Thought*, London (reprinted by Dover Publications), 1854.

domains. Today, we call any set of abstract mathematical objects subject to such laws a Boolean algebra. A Boolean algebra, in the first place, contains at least two members, which we may denote by 0 and 1, and it may also have others. Upon any pair of members, two operations can be performed that are analogous to what, in circuit algebra, we conveniently called "multiplication" and "screening." In other Boolean algebras, the term "screening" does not seem to serve any purpose and we shall replace it by "addition," which is a conventional word for the same operation; but we shall continue to use the symbol $\vee$ for this operation and also the dot $\cdot$ for "multiplication." (As before, we shall generally omit the dot, however, indicating multiplication by juxtaposition alone.) This addition and this multiplication are subject to the following laws, in which x, y, z denote arbitrary members of the Boolean algebra:

$$x \vee y = y \vee x \qquad\qquad xy = yx$$
$$x \vee (y \vee z) = (x \vee y) \vee z \qquad\qquad x(yz) = (xy)z$$
$$x \vee yz = (x \vee y)(x \vee z) \qquad\qquad x(y \vee z) = xy \vee xz$$
$$x \vee x = x \qquad\qquad xx = x$$
$$x \vee 0 = x \qquad\qquad x1 = x$$
$$x \vee 1 = 1 \qquad\qquad x0 = 0.$$

Each member x of the algebra has an associate x', called its dual, such that

$$x \vee x' = 1 \qquad\qquad xx' = 0.$$

Only one dual of x exists. (This means that if z belongs to the algebra and satisfies the two conditions, $x \vee z = 1$ and $xz = 0$, then $z = x'$.) The dual of a dual is given by

$$(x')' = x,$$

and the duals of sums and products are given by the formulas

$$(x \vee y)' = x'y' \qquad\qquad (xy)' = x' \vee y'.$$

This algebra, like the Propositional Calculus, is one of the primary tools of mathematical logic. While we shall not develop it far in that direction, we can pause to glance at a pretty application that the algebra both suggests and justifies.[†] This is a way to diagram a composite sentence for the purpose of finding out whether the sentence is true for suitable choices of its constituents or is false for every choice. Any systematic way so to establish inconsistencies would be of use, in particular, in proving or disproving general implications. In fact, let

(1) $$P \Rightarrow Q$$

[†] I am indebted to Prof. Carol Karp for suggesting and describing this application to me.

represent an implication with composite antecedent P and consequent Q. (For example, take $P \equiv A(A \Rightarrow B)$ and $Q \equiv AB$.) The implication (1) was defined as the sentence

$$(2) \qquad\qquad\qquad \sim (P \sim Q).$$

We ask whether this implication is general, i.e., true for all choices of its constituents. This is to ask whether the negation of sentence (2), namely

$$(3) \qquad\qquad\qquad P \sim Q,$$

is false for all choices of the constituents. How to work the answer out by diagramming is what we shall now describe.

Let S denote an arbitrary composite sentence (for instance, sentence (3)). The form of S determines the shape of its diagram. Six basic forms occur, of which the first two are:

(a) a product of some of the constituent sentences or negations of constituent sentences

and

(b) a product of sentences including both some particular sentence and also its negation.

The four remaining forms are products of sentences of these respective types:

(c) $T(U \vee V)$,
(d) $T \sim (UV)$,
(e) $T \sim (U \vee V)$,
(f) $T \sim (\sim U)$;

here, T, U, and V may represent composite sentences themselves. We permit T to be the identity I, so that these forms include, in particular, $U \vee V$, $\sim (UV)$, $\sim (U \vee V)$, and $\sim (\sim U)$.

The diagram for S is obtained through a succession of steps, beginning by writing down the full expression (in terms of its constituents) for S upon a sheet of paper. This expression must be of at least one of the six forms (a) to (f). If it is of form (a) or (b), no additional step is taken. If S is of one of the four other possible forms, one or two branches are drawn downward from S to terminate appropriately in certain new sentences as indicated in the following key (Figure 12-45). The new sentences with which the branches terminate

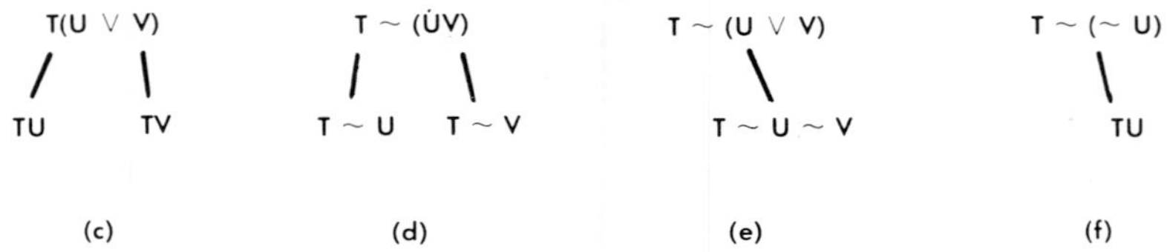

FIGURE 12-45   Key for diagramming composite sentences.

are then treated similarly according to the key, and so on, until the forms occurring are of types (a) or (b) only.

We illustrate the procedure with the diagram (Figure 12-46) for the sentence $(\sim A \lor \sim B) \sim (A \sim B \lor \sim A)$.

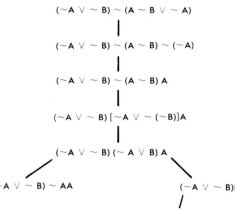

FIGURE 12-46 An example of a sentence diagram.

EXERCISES

2. Justify the expressions that occur in Figure 12-46 by referring to the appropriate directions in the key (Figure 12-45).

3. The final expressions in Figure 12-46 are all self-contradictory, i.e., contain both some particular sentence and its negation. Why does this mean that the original composite sentence — the sentence that is diagrammed — is false for every choice of A and B?

4. Explain how the diagram in Figure 12-46 proves this implication,

$$(\sim A \lor \sim B) \Rightarrow (A \sim B \lor \sim A),$$

for every A and B.

The laws on p. 537 occur both in circuit algebra (or Propositional Calculus), which is a Boolean algebra with only two members, and in the algebra of statements just discussed. We shall now give a different kind of model of a Boolean algebra. In this new model, we interpret the members of the algebra as sets, or collections, of points in the plane. The set of all points in the plane we shall call "the universe of discourse" and shall denote by I. The members of this algebra thus are sets of points selected from this particular universe of discourse. If x and y denote two members of the algebra, then by the equality

$$x = y,$$

we shall mean that the points in these sets are the same, i.e., that each point of x is a point of y and each point of y a point also of x. By

$$x \lor y$$

we shall mean the *union* of x and y, which is the set of all points that occur in x *or* in y (see Figure 12-47A). By

$$xy$$

we shall mean the *intersection* of the sets, which is the set of all points that occur in x *and* in y (see Figure 12-47B). If x and y do not intersect, this definition of xy does not seem to apply, and we have here a "multiplication" that is defined for some pairs of quantities but not for all. This would be monumentally inconvenient, but there is a simple remedy. The remedy is the artifice of introducing a set without members, which we call "the empty set," and of agreeing to say, when x and y have no points in common, that their intersection is this empty set. Under this convention, any two point sets have an intersection (which may be the empty set) and, hence, have a product, as defined. The symbol we shall use for the empty set is $\emptyset$.

A
B

FIGURE 12-47   The union (A) and the intersection (B) of two sets.

By the dual x' of a point set x, we shall mean its *complement*, i.e., the set of all points in the universe of discourse that are *not* contained in x.

Under these definitions, the algebra of point sets is a Boolean algebra in which $\emptyset$ takes the place of 0 and I of 1. This is to say that the conditions for a Boolean algebra (with $\emptyset$ and I replacing 0 and 1, respectively) are all satisfied. They are, in fact, quite simple to verify, and most will be left to the reader. To prove that $xx = x$, for instance, recall that xx signifies the intersection of x with itself, i.e., the set of points in x and also in x. This is simply the set of points in x, or x itself, which is what the equality states. As a second illustration, let us prove that

$$x(x \lor z) = xy \lor xz.$$

We must show that (1) every point in the set represented on the left side of this equality also belongs to the set represented on the right and that (2) each point of the set on the right also occurs in the set on the left.

(1) Consider an arbitrary point P of the left-hand set $x(y \lor z)$. This belongs both to x and also to $y \lor z$, i.e., either to y or to z. Hence, P belongs either to xy (both x and y) or to xz (both x and z), i.e., to $xy \lor xz$. We have proved that any point in the set on the left side of the equality considered also occurs in the set on the right.

(2) Now consider an arbitrary point Q of $xy \lor xz$. This point is either in xy or in xz. In either case, Q occurs in x and also occurs either in y or in z. Hence, Q belongs to $x(y \lor z)$. This shows that any point in the set on the right side of the equality considered also occurs in the set on the left.

These two steps together prove the equality desired. They are illustrated in Figure 12-48, in which the shaded region corresponds to $x(y \lor z)$ or, equivalently, to $xy \lor xz$.

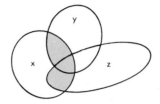

FIGURE 12-48   Diagram for the equality: $x(y \lor z) = xy \lor xz$.

As further instances, the equality $x \lor x' = I$ states that any set and its complement unite into the universe of discourse, and the equality $xx' = \emptyset$ states that a set and its complement do not intersect.

EXERCISE

5. Justify for point sets:

$$(x \lor y) \lor z = x \lor (y \lor z)$$
$$x \lor yz = (x \lor y)(x \lor z)$$
$$x \lor \emptyset = x$$
$$(x')' = x$$
$$(x \lor y)' = x'y'.$$

Boolean algebra is applicable in many analogous situations. Any set, or collection, of objects may be agreed upon as universe of discourse, and assemblages of these objects as the members of the algebra. Then I is defined as the universe of discourse, $\emptyset$ as the empty set, an assemblage's complement as its dual, addition as union, and multiplication as intersection. The result is a Boolean algebra in the same way as before.

EXERCISES

6. If the universe of discourse consists of exactly two objects, describe the corresponding Boolean algebra: the number of members of the algebra, the dual of each member, the tables for addition and multiplication.

7. Describe in the same particulars the Boolean algebra for a universe of discourse with just three members.

8. Show that a Boolean algebra cannot consist of exactly three members. HINT: Use the conditions $x \vee x' = 1$ and $xx' = 0$ particularly.

9. Boole himself excluded sums of overlapping classes and saw that his system could then be interpreted as an algebra in which the symbols for quantities are restricted to 0 and 1 in the ordinary sense, $\cdot$ is interpreted as ordinary multiplication, and $\vee$ (for which his symbol was $+$) as ordinary addition. Verify this interpretation of Boolean algebra.

The operations and relations — union, intersection, complementation, equality — of Boolean algebras for sets or classes all involve the concept of *inclusion*. If x and y denote any two sets of objects in the universe of discourse, we write

$$x \subseteq y$$

to symbolize: "Every object belonging to x also belongs to y," or, more succinctly, "x *is included in* y," or "x *is contained in* y." (We understand this statement, "x is contained in y," to include the possibility that x coincides with y. If we wish to exclude this possibility, we say x is *properly* contained, or included, in y, and we write $x \subset y$. Note the analogy of $\subset$ to $<$ and of $\subseteq$ to $\leq$.) The relation of inclusion has a purely algebraic formulation, which we may arrive at by noticing that if x is contained in y (see Figure 12-49), then x is the intersection of itself with y; conversely, if the intersection of x and y is x, then x is contained in y. These facts suggest this definition.

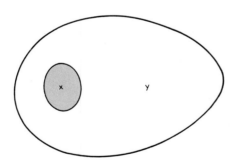

FIGURE 12-49 *Inclusion.*

Definition.   In any Boolean algebra, we define

$$x \subseteq y$$

to mean that the condition

$$xy = x$$

is satisfied.

The geometrical relation of inclusion is characterized by such properties as these, which the reader will easily verify for himself:

(1) $x \subseteq y$ if and only if $x \lor y = y$;
(2) $x \subseteq x$;
(3) if $x \subseteq y$ and $y \subseteq x$, then $x = y$;
(4) if $x \subseteq y$ and $y \subseteq z$, then $x \subseteq z$;
(5) if $x \subseteq y$, then for any a we have: $xa \subseteq ya$;
(6) if $x \subseteq y$, then $xy' = 0$.

The algebraic definition of inclusion is a true counterpart of the geometrical definition only to the extent that it shares such attributes. We shall see that it does. As an example, let us prove that (1) is true under the algebraic definition. First, assume $x \subseteq y$, i.e., $xy = x$. We must deduce that $x \lor y = y$. Since $x = xy$, we have

$$
\begin{aligned}
x \lor y &= xy \lor y \\
&= y(x \lor 1) \\
&= y1 \\
&= y,
\end{aligned}
$$

the last equality giving us the desired result. Secondly, assume that $x \lor y = y$. We must then prove that $xy = x$. Since $y = x \lor y$, we have

$$
\begin{aligned}
xy &= x(x \lor y) \\
&= x \lor xy \\
&= x(1 \lor y) \\
&= x1 \\
&= x.
\end{aligned}
$$

Thus, $xy = x$, as desired, and the second part of (1) is proved. The other relations can all be demonstrated in a similar way.

EXERCISE

10. Justify the conditions (2) through (6). HINT: In proving (4), start from the relation $xz = (xy)z$.

9.

The analysis of class frequencies

Boolean algebra brings system to the study of complexly overlapping classes, aiding us to trace out intricate relationships with a minimum of effort. For this reason, Boolean algebra is of help, in particular, in testing reported data for consistency or in computing or estimating unreported quantities. For instance, if we know the total number of students at a certain school, the number who are men, the number who play an instrument, and the number of men who play an instrument, Boolean algebra will assist us in calculating the number of women who do not play an instrument. Whenever we know how many of a given set of objects belong to certain specified classes, we may similarly be able to calculate how many occur in other classes. If our information is too incomplete for exact calculations, estimates may be possible. If our data are faked, we may be able to find that out.

Any problem of the kind envisaged is concerned with a given set of objects, which we shall call *the universe of discourse* and denote by I. By a "set," hereinafter we shall mean a subset of I, i.e., a collection of members of I; by a "subset" of a set x, we shall mean a collection of members of x. We shall use the words "class" and "subclass" synonymously with set and subset, respectively. We shall assume that the universe of discourse is finite, or in other words consists of just a finite number of objects, and for any set x we define:

$$N(x) = \text{the number of objects belonging to the set } x.$$

(Thus, in particular, $N(I) = $ the number of objects in the universe of discourse I.) We call $N(x)$ the *frequency* of the class, or set, x. Our analysis of class frequencies will be based on these simple properties:

(i) $N(x)$ is either 0 or a positive integer. In symbols,

$$N(x) \geq 0 \text{ for any subset } x \text{ of } I.$$

(ii) If two sets are disjoint,† then the number of objects contained in their union is the sum of their individual frequencies. In symbols,

$$xy = \varnothing \Rightarrow N(x \vee y) = N(x) + N(y).$$

Hence, in particular,

$$N(x) + N(x') = N(I) \text{ for any subset } x \text{ of } I,$$

and for any two subsets x and y,

$$N(xy) + N(xy') = N(x).$$

(iii) The empty set contains no objects:

$$N(\varnothing) = 0.$$

———————
†Two sets are "disjoint" if they have no common members.

EXERCISES

1. Show that property (iii) is a mathematical consequence of properties (i) and (ii).

2. Prove this property:

(iv) If x, y, z are disjoint sets (i.e., $xy = xz = yz = \emptyset$), then

$$N(x \vee y \vee z) = N(x) + N(y) + N(z).$$

Conscious use of these properties and of the relations of Boolean algebra greatly increases our power to extract information from data. As a first illustration, consider this example:

In a class of 20 students, 13 are boys, 12 have long hair, and 8 are boys with long hair. How many girls in the class do not have long hair?

Let I denote the entire class, b the set of boys in the class, and h the set of students in the class with long hair. Using this notation, we can compress the information given into the following equalities:

$$N(I) = 20$$
$$N(b) = 13$$
$$N(h) = 12$$
$$N(bh) = 8.$$

It is worthwhile to organize this information in the form of a table (Table 12-16).

Table 12-16 *Certain frequency distributions*

	h	h′	
b	8		13
b′			
	12		20

The entries in the bottom row and in the extreme right-hand column are sums. The quantity we wish to calculate (the number of girls who do not have long hair) is represented by $N(b'h')$ and should appear in the space common to the second row and second column of the table. It can easily be found without algebra, but we wish to describe the process mathematically.

First, we have

$$N(b') = N(I) - N(b) = 20 - 13 = 7$$

(since $N(b) + N(b') = N(I)$, by property (ii)). Secondly,

$$N(b'h) = N(h) - N(bh) = 12 - 8 = 4$$

(since $N(h) = N(bh) + N(b'h)$, again by property (ii)). Finally,

$$N(b'h') = N(b') - N(b'h) = 7 - 4 = 3$$

(since $N(b') = N(b'h) + N(b'h')$, once more by property (ii)). Thus, exactly three students are girls who do not have long hair.

If we are now asked how many students either are boys or have long hair, we can easily answer from the last result. The set of students who either are boys or have long hair is represented symbolically by

$$b \vee h.$$

By de Morgan's law,

$$(b \vee h)' = b'h',$$

so that

$$N((b \vee h)') = N(b'h') = 3.$$

Hence,

$$N(b \vee h) = N(I) - N((b \vee h)')$$
$$= 20 - 3$$
$$= 17.$$

It is often desirable to be able to calculate $N(x \vee y)$ from $N(I)$, $N(x)$, $N(y)$, and $N(xy)$, where x and y denote two subclasses of a finite universe I. In the preceding example, we saw how to do this by obtaining, in succession, $N(x')$, $N(x'y)$, $N(x'y')$, and, finally, $N(x \vee y)$. Another method — or, rather, the same method rearranged — will be described later.

EXERCISES

3. Using the method of the preceding example, prove that

$$N(x \vee y) = N(x) + N(y) - N(xy),$$

where x and y denote any two subsets of I.

4. Of 100 spiders caught on Simmering Marsh, 43 were red, 77 were hairy, and 25 were both red and hairy. How many spiders were: (a) not red, (b) red, but not hairy, (c) not red and not hairy, (d) either red or hairy?

5. A restaurant proprietor estimates that 60 per cent of his customers will have eggs (with or without ham) for breakfast, 40 per cent will have ham (with or without eggs), and 25 per cent will have ham and eggs. From these figures, what percentage of his customers eat:

(a) no ham,
(b) ham without eggs,
(c) eggs without ham,

(d) neither ham nor eggs,
(e) either ham or eggs?

In Exercise 3, we called the reader's attention to this property:
(v) For any two classes, x and y, disjoint or not,

$$N(x \lor y) = N(x) + N(y) - N(xy).$$

This property is important, and we pause to consider it further. Its intuitive basis is that when you add the individual frequencies of x and y, you count *once* any member of $x \lor y$ not belonging to xy, and you count *twice* any member that does belong to xy. Subtracting the number of members of xy corrects this double counting to give the actual total frequency of $x \lor y$. This is illustrated in Figure 12-50.

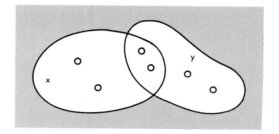

FIGURE 12-50 Frequencies of overlapping sets.

$$N(x) = 4$$
$$N(y) = 4$$
$$N(xy) = 2$$
$$N(x \lor y) = 6$$
$$4 + 4 - 2 = 6$$

One way of proving this property from the previously accepted attributes of N was suggested in Exercise 3. We now give another method, based on rule (ii) for *disjoint* sets. This method requires that we divide $x \lor y$ appropriately into nonoverlapping sets. In the first place,

(1a)
$$x = x(y \lor y')$$
$$= xy \lor xy'$$

and

(1b)
$$y = y(x \lor x')$$
$$= yx \lor yx'.$$

Hence,

$$x \lor y = xy \lor xy' \lor yx \lor yx'$$
$$= xy \lor xy' \lor yx',$$

since repetition of any set in a sum can be suppressed. The three sets xy, xy', and yx' are mutually disjoint. (For instance, $(xy)(xy') =$

$(xy)(y'x) = x(yy')x = x\varnothing x = x\varnothing = \varnothing$.) Therefore, property (iv) is applicable and gives

$$(2) \qquad N(x \vee y) = N(xy) + N(xy') + N(yx').$$

By (1a) and (ii),

$$N(x) = N(xy) + N(xy'),$$

and by (1b) and (ii),

$$N(y) = N(xy) + N(yx'):$$

hence,

$$N(xy') = N(x) - N(xy), \ N(yx') = N(y) - N(xy).$$

Substituting the last results into (2) now gives us

$$N(x \vee y) = N(xy) + N(x) - N(xy) + N(y) - N(xy)$$
$$= N(x) + N(y) - N(xy),$$

verifying property (v).

As we have stressed, property (v) is of great importance. One simple application is in estimating how much *at least* $N(xy)$ must be if $N(I)$, $N(x)$, and $N(y)$ are known (but $N(xy)$ is not known). Suppose, for instance, that a class of 20 contains 12 boys and 10 students with long hair, and that we wish to estimate at least how many boys in the class have long hair. Since 8 students are girls and 10 students have long hair, it is obvious that at least 2 students with long hair must be boys. Let us work this out more formally, however, as a guide in more complicated cases. As before, let I denote the set of all students in the class, b the set of boys in the class, and h the set of students with long hair. Then

$$N(I) = 20, \ N(b) = 12, \ N(h) = 10.$$

By property (v) (with b and h in place of x and y), we have that

$$N(b \vee h) = N(b) + N(h) - N(bh)$$

and thus that

$$N(bh) = N(b) + N(h) - N(b \vee h)$$
$$= 12 + 10 - N(b \vee h).$$
$$= 22 - N(b \vee h).$$

We do not know $N(b \vee h)$ exactly, but we do know that it does not exceed the number in the entire class:

$$N(b \vee h) \le N(I) = 20.$$

From this we can conclude that

$$22 - N(b \lor h) \geq 22 - 20 = 2$$

and, thus, that

$$N(bh) \geq 2.$$

In other words, at least two boys in that class have long hair.

The new principle involved in the last estimation may be stated as follows:

(vi) A set contains at least as many elements as any subset of itself. Hence, for each subset x of I,

$$N(x) \leq N(I),$$

and for any subsets x and y,

$$N(xy) \leq N(x), \; N(xy) \leq N(y).$$

This principle will continue to be helpful.

EXERCISES

6. Justify property (vi) mathematically from the properties previously indicated.

7. In Exercise 4 suppose the number of red, hairy spiders had not been given. Then estimate it from the other information, if possible.

8. In Exercise 5, suppose the proportion of ham and egg orders had not been given. Estimate it from the other information, if possible.

9. Prove that for any sets x and y we have:

$$N(xy) \geq N(x) + N(y) - N(I).$$

HINT: Imitate the procedure used in the example in the text.

10. Prove that for any sets x and y we have:

$$N(xy') \geq N(x) - N(y).$$

HINT: Use the formula in the previous exercise.

11. At a certain party of 100 people in all, 56 are rich and 62 are Democrats.

(a) At least how many rich people at the party are also Democrats?

(b) At most how many rich people at the party are also Democrats?

(c) From the information given, what can be said concerning the number at the party who are not rich and not Democrats?

The previous methods can be extended without real difficulty to the consideration of more than two classes in I. We shall confine ourselves to three such classes, which we denote by x, y, and z, and first shall prove the following analogue to property (v):

(vii) If x, y, and z are arbitrary sets, then

$$N(x \lor y \lor z) = N(x) + N(y) + N(z)$$
$$- N(xy) - N(xz) - N(yz) + N(xyz).$$

To demonstrate property (vii), we regard $x \lor y \lor z$ as the union of *two* sets, $x \lor y$ and z, and apply (v). We obtain:

(3) $$N(x \lor y \lor z) = N((x \lor y) \lor z)$$
$$= N(x \lor y) + N(z) - N((x \lor y)z).$$

Again by (v), however,

$$N(x \lor y) = N(x) - N(y) - N(xy),$$

and

$$N((x \lor y)z) = N(xz \lor yz)$$
$$= N(xz) + N(yz) - N(xyz).$$

Substituting these results into (3) gives us

$$N(x \lor y \lor z) = N(x) + N(y) - N(xy) + N(z)$$
$$- [N(xz) + N(yz) - N(xyz)],$$

and this reduces to the formula in (vii) after a little rearrangement.

Using property (vii), we can give a good idea of how some data can be tested for consistency. Consider this hypothetical example. The Striking Charms Academy, a young ladies' finishing school, claims for all its graduates unusual proficiency in conversation, glamor, and dancing. Its latest class is held to have beaten all records with this remarkable showing:

Number of girls in entire class	55
Number who are *scintillating* conversationalists	37
Number who are *incitingly* glamorous	41
Number who dance *divinely*	40
Number who are scintillating conversationalists and also incitingly glamorous	23
Number who are scintillating conversationalists and also dance divinely	25
Number who are incitingly glamorous and also dance divinely	33
Number who are scintillating conversationalists and incitingly glamorous and also dance divinely	20

These figures are challenged by the Mona Lisa School, a sister institution, which ascribes them to a publicity agent's imagination. You would, too, says Mona Lisa, if you knew the girls of Striking Charms, and besides, there are not enough of them in the class to account for all the paragons that are being claimed. Are more girls in fact being represented as scintillating conversationalists, incitingly glamorous, or dancers divine than are present in the entire class? This is a point that we can settle. Let

I = set of girls in latest class to graduate,
C = set of girls in this class who are scintillating conversationalists,
D = set of girls in this class who dance divinely,
G = set of girls in this class who are incitingly glamorous.

In this notation, the preceding information is presented as:

$$N(I) = 55$$
$$N(C) = 37$$
$$N(G) = 41$$
$$N(D) = 40$$
$$N(CG) = 23$$
$$N(CD) = 25$$
$$N(GD) = 33$$
$$N(CGD) = 20$$

By property (vii),

$$N(C \vee G \vee D) = N(C) + N(G) + N(D) - N(CG)$$
$$- N(CD) - N(GD) + N(CGD)$$
$$= 37 + 41 + 40 - 23 - 25 - 33 + 20$$
$$= 57,$$

while $N(I) = 55$. Thus, Mona Lisa has reason to smile, too like a lady to guffaw.

EXERCISES

12. Of 400 students, 150 studied French, 100 studied German, 120 studied Russian, 40 studied French and German, 50 studied French and Russian, 30 studied German and Russian, and 10 studied all three languages.
  (a) How many studied neither French nor German?
  (b) How many studied German and Russian but not French?
  (c) How many studied none of the three languages?
13. Of 50 Hippies interviewed,
  20 said they use marijuana,
  16 said they use LSD,

19 said they use cocaine,

5 said they use marijuana and LSD,

6 said they use marijuana and cocaine,

2 said they use LSD and cocaine,

2 said they use all three drugs.

How many of the Hippies claimed to use none of these drugs?

14. Of 100 persons asked,

40 favored the Vietnam war,

60 supported federal aid to education,

70 thought the United Nations should be made stronger,

25 favored both the Vietnam war and federal aid to education,

20 favored the Vietnam war and also believed the UN should be strengthened,

55 advocated federal aid to education and also a stronger UN.

(a) How many at most supported the Vietnam war, federal aid to education, and also a stronger UN?

(b) If the class described in (a) actually contained 25, then how many did *not* support the Vietnam war while favoring federal aid to education and believing that the UN should be made stronger?

15. Find a formula analogous to that of (vii) for $N(x \vee y \vee x'z)$.

16. Find a formula analogous to that of (vii) for $N(x \vee y \vee z \vee w)$, where x, y, z, w denote any sets.

We shall devote the remainder of the section to showing how, when the frequencies of three classes, x, y, and z, and also of the intersections, xy, xz, and yz, are known, we can find upper and lower bounds for $N(xyz)$. All but one of these new bounds may be derived rather mechanically from the inequalities,

$$(4) \qquad\qquad N(xy) \leq N(x), N(xy) \leq N(y),$$

$$(4') \qquad\qquad N(xy) \geq N(x) + N(y) - N(I),$$

which were indicated in (vii) and in Exercise 9. First, we have

$$N(xyz) \leq N(yz), N(xyz) \leq N(xz), N(xyz) \leq N(xy).$$

These arise from (4), which shows, for instance, that

$$N(xyz) = N(x(yz) \leq N(yz)$$

(replace y by yz in the second inequality of (4)). If we apply (4') with z as universe (in place of I) and with xz and yz as the two subsets of z (in place of x and y), we obtain the first of these three relations:

$$N(xyz) \geq N(xz) + N(yz) - N(z),$$
$$N(xyz) \geq N(xz) + N(xy) - N(x),$$
$$N(xyz) \geq N(xy) + N(yz) - N(y).$$

The other two relations follow from the first by interchanging z and x and interchanging z and y, as we may do since x, y, z are quite arbitrary sets. A final relationship satisfied by $N(xyz)$, but not strictly analogous to any of the inequalities for $N(xy)$, is obtainable from (vii), which can be written in the form

$$N(xyz) = N(x \lor y \lor z) - N(x) - N(y) - N(z)$$
$$+ N(xy) + N(xz) + N(yz).$$

This and the inequality

$$N(x \lor y \lor z) \leq N(I)$$

lead to

$$N(xyz) \leq N(I) - N(x) - N(y) - N(z) + N(xy) + N(xz) + N(yz),$$

the relationship to which we referred. This relationship gives another upper bound to $N(xyz)$, supplementing those stated earlier. For convenience, we list all the upper and lower bounds we have found for $N(xyz)$ in terms of $N(x)$, $N(y)$, $N(z)$, $N(xy)$, $N(xz)$, $N(yz)$, and $N(I)$:

$$N(xyz) \leq N(xy)$$
$$N(xyz) \leq N(yz)$$
$$N(xyz) \leq N(xz)$$
$$N(xyz) \geq N(xz) + N(yz) - N(z)$$
$$N(xyz) \geq N(xz) + N(xy) - N(x)$$
$$N(xyz) \geq N(xy) + N(yz) - N(y)$$
$$N(xyz) \leq N(xy) + N(xz) + N(yz) - N(x) - N(y) - N(z) + N(I).$$

EXERCISES

17. A survey showed that of 100 gardens in a suburb of Washington,

65 contained roses,

55 contained azaleas,

40 contained marigolds,

30 contained roses and azaleas,

25 contained roses and marigolds,

20 contained azaleas and marigolds.

Find an upper estimate for the number of gardens growing roses, azaleas, and marigolds.

18. Prove these inequalities:

$$N(x'yz) \leq N(x) + N(yz) - N(xy) - N(xz),$$
$$N(xy'z) \leq N(y) + N(xz) - N(yx) - N(yz),$$
$$N(xyz') \leq N(z) + N(xy) - N(zx) - N(zy).$$

19. Show that, for any three classes, denoted by x, y, and z, we have:

$$N(x) + N(yz) - N(xy) - N(xz) \geq 0,$$
$$N(y) + N(xz) - N(yx) - N(yz) \geq 0,$$
$$N(z) + N(xy) - N(zx) - N(zy) \geq 0.$$

Data must satisfy these inequalities to be consistent. HINT: Refer to the previous exercise.

20. Can you deduce additional consistency conditions by calculating $N(x'y'z)$, and so forth? Explain.

21. Prove that $N(x'y'z') \leq N(I) - N(x) - N(y) - N(z) + N(xy) + N(xz) + N(yz)$.

10.

On redundancy

In a deductive theory, an axiom that is itself a consequence of the other axioms is said to be redundant (Section 1). A redundant axiom thus is an assumption that need not have been made, a statement that could have been proved but instead was assumed. Perhaps its redundancy was never guessed, or was guessed but could not be established. Fortunately, the presence of redundant axioms cannot make a consistent theory inconsistent and thus does no irreparable harm. It may, however, be a cause of inconvenience. Consider as an illustration the seventeen conditions by which we defined Boolean algebras in Section 8. A mathematical system to be a Boolean algebra must satisfy all these conditions, and indeed we felt obliged to check them all when investigating the algebra of sets. To check the many redundant conditions in the list was superfluous, however, and we would have saved considerable effort had we not done so. A similar economy will result in any deductive theory whenever axioms that are redundant are uncovered and struck out.

In this section, we shall show that a certain eight of the seventeen relations by which Boolean algebras were defined imply the remaining nine, which thus are redundant. For seven of the nine, this result is easily proved and also perhaps easily guessed in advance, but the last two redundancies are likely to be a surprise. Thus, our intuitive expectations again are a valuable guide. Again, however, they are not infallible.

We start with a list (in a new order) of the seventeen relations by which we originally defined Boolean algebras, as follows:

(1a) $x \vee y = y \vee x$ (1b) $xy = yx$

(2a) $x \vee 0 = x$ (2b) $x1 = x$

(3a) $x \vee yz = (x \vee y)(x \vee z)$ (3b) $x(y \vee z) = xy \vee xz$

(4a) $x \lor x' = 1$ (4b) $xx' = 0$

$$(5) \ (x')' = x$$

(6a) $x \lor x = x$ (6b) $xx = x$

(7a) $x \lor 1 = 1$ (7b) $x0 = 0$

(8a) $x \lor (y \lor z) = (x \lor y) \lor z$ (8b) $x(yz) = (xy)z$

(9a) $(x \lor y)' = x'y'$ (9b) $(xy)' = x' \lor y'.$

Here, x, y, and z denote arbitrary members of the algebra; for each such member x, the primed symbol x' denotes an associated member (which we do not *assume* to be unique) called the dual of x. We intend to show that the first eight relations ((1a) through (4a) and (1b) through (4b)—more briefly, (1) through (4)) imply all the rest.† This is most surprising perhaps for the two associativity laws (8) (i.e., (8a) and (8b)).

    We do not assume that each member has more than one dual and shall now prove this fact as a consequence of relations (1) through (4). Equations (4) state that if x is given, the two conditions

$$x \lor y = 1, \quad xy = 0,$$

are satisfied for $y = x'$. Our aim is to prove that if these two conditions are also satisfied for $y = z$, then $x' = z$. This result means that x has but one dual and thus, in other words, that duals are unique. Suppose then that

(4a) $x \lor x' = 1$ (4b) $xx' = 0$

(4c) $x \lor z = 1$ (4d) $xz = 0;$

we are to show that $x' = z$. First,

$$
\begin{aligned}
z(x \lor x') &= zx \lor zx' && \text{by (3b)}\\
&= xz \lor zx' && \text{by (1b)}\\
&= 0 \lor zx' && \text{by (4d)}\\
&= zx' \lor 0 && \text{by (1a)}\\
&= zx' && \text{by (2a).}
\end{aligned}
$$

However,

$$
\begin{aligned}
z(x \lor x') &= z1 && \text{by (4a)}\\
&= z && \text{by (2b).}
\end{aligned}
$$

Hence,

$$zx' = z.$$

By considering $x'(x \lor z)$ (in other words, by interchanging the roles of x' and z), we can prove in the same way that

$$x'z = x'.$$

---

†We have followed Whitesitt, *op. cit.*, in many details.

Since $x'z = zx'$ by (1b), we conclude that $x' = z$, as contended. Thus, each member of the algebra has just one associate satisfying (4), or, in other words, has just one dual.

Now we shall prove (5). Denote the dual of x' by y:

$$y = (x')'.$$

Conditions (4) and the uniqueness of duals show that y is the one and only member of the algebra to satisfy the two conditions

$$x' \lor y = 1$$

and

$$x'y = 0.$$

By the commutation rules (1), these equations are equivalent to

$$y \lor x' = 1, \; yx' = 0;$$

hence, they are satisfied for $y = x$. It follows that y is necessarily equal to x and thus that $(x')' = x$, as is stated in (5).

Before going to further proofs, we note a feature of the four pairs of assumptions (1) through (4) that will be very helpful technically. This is the fact that the first assumption of each pair changes into the second, and the second into the first, when we change addition into multiplication, multiplication into addition, 0 into 1, and 1 into 0. This is duality (see Section 3). The two assumptions of each pair are called duals to one another. More generally, any two formulas (for instance, (6a) and (6b)) each of which is transformed into the other under the changes described are said to be duals to one another. If a formula can be proved from some of the assumptions (1) through (4), then its dual can be proved by a dual argument from the dual assumptions. (We shall illustrate this.) Hence, when we have proved a formula, we can immediately affirm the dual of the formula, too.

Let us now prove

(6b) $\qquad\qquad\qquad\qquad xx = x.$

First,

$$x(x \lor x') = x1 \qquad\qquad \text{by (4a)}$$
$$= x \qquad\qquad \text{by (2b).}$$

Secondly,

$$x(x \lor x') = xx \lor xx' \qquad\qquad \text{by (3b)}$$
$$= xx \lor 0 \qquad\qquad \text{by (4b)}$$
$$= xx \qquad\qquad \text{by (2a).}$$

Consequently, $xx = x$, as contended.

The formula

(6a) $$x \lor x = x$$

is dual to (6b) and, from what we have written before, can now be asserted automatically. This is because a proof of (6b), when dualized, becomes a proof of (6a). To illustrate dualization, let us see how this is so. Since the proof of (6b) began by considering $x(x \lor x')$, we start the corresponding proof of (6a) by considering $x \lor xx'$, the dual expression. From (4b) and (2a)—the duals to (4a) and (2b), to which we appealed in the original proof—we demonstrate that $x \lor xx' = x$. Then we apply (3a), (4a), (2b) to show that $x \lor xx' = x \lor x$. These two equalities of course imply that $x \lor x = x$, the identity desired.

EXERCISES

1. Prove (7b). HINT: Consider $x(0 \lor x')$.
2. Prove (7a) by dualizing your argument for (7b) in the preceding exercise.
3. Prove:

$$(10a)\ x \lor xy = x \qquad (10b)\ x(x \lor y) = x.$$

4. Show that de Morgan's identities (9) follow from formulas (1) through (8). (Formulas (8) will be justified later.) HINT: A dual is unique. Hence, it suffices to prove that

$$(xy) \lor (x' \lor y') = 1,\ (xy)(x' \lor y') = 0.$$

Use both (3a) and (3b).
5. Prove from identities (1) through (4) that if x, y, and z satisfy the two conditions,

$$x \lor y = x \lor z,\ x' \lor y = x' \lor z,$$

then $y = z$. HINT: Multiply the first condition by x', and the second by x, and then add.

We shall now show that conditions (1) through (7), together with (10), imply conditions (8). Since (5), (6), (7), and (10) are consequences of (1) through (4), we thus shall have the remarkable fact that conditions (1) through (4) alone imply additive and multiplicative associativity. We need only demonstrate, say, condition (8b), condition (8a) then following by duality. Letting

$$L = x(yz),\ R = (xy)z,$$

we thus must prove that $L = R$. According to the criterion given in

Exercise 5, it suffices to justify for an arbitrary x the two conditions,

(11) $$x \vee L = x \vee R,$$

(12) $$x' \vee L = x' \vee R.$$

First, we have

$$x \vee L = x \vee x(yz)$$
$$= x \qquad\qquad\qquad \text{by (10a),}$$

while

$$x \vee R = x \vee (xy)z$$
$$= (x \vee xy)(x \vee z) \qquad\qquad \text{by (3a)}$$
$$= x(x \vee z) \qquad\qquad \text{by (10a)}$$
$$= x \qquad\qquad \text{by (10b).}$$

Thus, $x \vee L = x \vee R = x$, and condition (11) is verified. Secondly,

$$x' \vee L = x' \vee x(yz)$$
$$= (x' \vee x)(x' \vee yz) \qquad\qquad \text{by (3a)}$$
$$= 1(x' \vee yz) \qquad\qquad \text{by (4a) and (1a)}$$
$$= x' \vee yz \qquad\qquad \text{by (2b) and (1b),}$$

while

$$x' \vee R = x' \vee (xy)z$$
$$= (x' \vee xy)(x' \vee z) \qquad\qquad \text{by (3a)}$$
$$= [(x' \vee x)(x' \vee y)](x' \vee z) \qquad\qquad \text{by (3a)}$$
$$= [1(x' \vee y)](x' \vee z) \qquad \text{by (4a) and (1a)}$$
$$= (x' \vee y)(x' \vee z) \qquad \text{by (2b) and (1b)}$$
$$= x' \vee yz \qquad\qquad \text{by (3a).}$$

Thus, $x' \vee L = x' \vee R$, and condition (12) is verified. We conclude that $L = R$, as condition (8b) contends.

EXERCISE

6. Give a complete proof of (8a) not invoking the duality principle or the result just obtained.

CHAPTER 13

PROBABILITY AND STATISTICS

1.

Probabilities of simple and compound events

The theory of probability might be called the logic of chance. If we are not sure whether a specified event will take place or not, we may expect it with greater or lesser confidence and may even venture —for instance, if we intend to bet on the event—to estimate the exact chance we feel it has to occur. Such an estimate in part is subjective and depends on our knowledge and judgment. The theory of probability enters when we consider the chances of occurrence of two or more related events. For instance, we may declare the chance of rain before noon to be 40 per cent, or 2/5 (which are the same), or any other number we like from 0 to 1. But once we do so, we leave ourselves no latitude at all in our opinion on the chance of no rain before noon. If the chance of rain is 2/5, then the chance of no rain is 3/5, for the chance that a specified event will occur and the chance that the contrary event will occur must add to 1. We proceed with these ideas in the light of an example.

Any game of chance provides a good example of a set of related events to which probability theory applies. Consider, for instance, the experiment of tossing a coin 4 times, with the outcome each time either *H* (heads) or *T* (tails). We can record the result of the experiment as a chain of 4 letters, each either *H* or *T*, the first letter referring to the first toss, the second letter to the second toss, and so forth. Sixteen results are possible (Table 13-1).

Table 13-1 The possible results of tossing a coin 4 times

1. HHHH	5. HTHH	9. THHH	13. TTHH
2. HHHT	6. HTHT	10. THHT	14. TTHT
3. HHTH	7. HTTH	11. THTH	15. TTTH
4. HHTT	8. HTTT	12. THTT	16. TTTT

By an *event* we mean any outcome of the experiment, such as *THTH*, or obtaining more heads than tails, or obtaining three of the same kind consecutively. The sixteen events in the table are called *simple*, or *indecomposable*, events. All other events are disjunctions of simple events (Chapter 1, Section 5) and are said to be *compound*, or *decomposable*. For instance, the event of obtaining 3 heads and 1 tail is compound, the disjunction of events 2, 3, 5, 9 in Table 13-1. If we denote this event by E, we have

$$E \equiv HHHT \text{ or } HHTH \text{ or } HTHH \text{ or } THHH.$$

In the notation of Boolean algebra (Chapter 12, Section 8),

$$E \equiv HHHT \lor HHTH \lor HTHH \lor THHH.$$

Imagine the experiment to be carried out a great many times and the proportions calculated in which the sixteen simple events occur. Rarely indeed would these proportions all be exactly the same. Some would be greater and some less due to chance alone. Furthermore, we may have reasons for *expecting* certain events to occur more frequently, or less frequently, than others. No coin is absolutely uniform, every coin is biased at least a little towards heads or towards tails. If we know our coin, we may know what to expect, although again chance alone will mar the exact fulfillment of any expectation. If we do not know how our coin is biased and indeed have no reason to expect any particular indecomposable events to be preferred to any others, we shall say that the sixteen indecomposable events are *equally likely*, or *equally probable*, and that the *probability*, or *chance*, of each is 1/16. The probability of any other event, which must be the disjunction, say, of k indecomposable events, then is $k/16$. For instance, the probability of event E (that the experiment result in three heads and one tail) is $4/16 = 1/4$. The probability that the contrary of E occur is 3/4, this contrary event being the disjunction of the 12 simple events not included in E.

EXERCISES

Assume that the events in Table 13-1 are equally likely.
1. What is the probability that event 7, Table 13-1, will not occur?
2. What is the probability that neither event 1 nor event 2 will occur?

   3. What is the probability of obtaining more heads than tails?
   4. What is the probability of having three heads consecutively?
   5. What is the probability of not having three heads consecutively?
   6. What is the probability of obtaining the same number of heads and tails?
   7. What is the probability of obtaining at least one head after the first toss?
   8. What is the probability of obtaining a head on the first toss and a tail on the last toss?

Any experiment in probability is definable mathematically by specifying all the *simple*, or *indecomposable*, events possible as outcomes and also giving their probabilities. We shall only consider experiments with a finite number of simple events, which we denote by

$$e_1, e_2, \ldots, e_s.$$

(An exception is made in Section 5.)

The occurrence of an event corresponds to the truth of the sentence describing the event. (For instance, to say that the event *HHHH* occurs is to say that the following sentence is true: "Heads appeared on the first, second, third, and fourth tosses.") We shall use the same symbols for events and for the sentences that describe them, to which the terminology and rules of Boolean algebra (Chapter 12, Section 8) apply. The occurrence or nonoccurrence of an event defines its *state*. If two events necessarily have the same state, they are *equivalent;* the symbol $\equiv$ indicates equivalence as before. We define the *contrary*, or *complementary*, event to an arbitrary event E to be the event described by the negation of the sentence that describes E, and we denote this complementary event by E'. The occurrence of E is equivalent to the nonoccurrence of E'. The symbol I refers to an event that must occur; thus,

$$I \equiv E \lor E'$$

for any event E. The symbol $\varnothing$ denotes an event that cannot occur; for any event E,

$$\varnothing \equiv EE'$$

Two events E and F such that $EF \equiv \varnothing$ are said to be *mutually exclusive.*

We assume the set of s simple events to satisfy the following condition:

   (a) When an experiment is performed, one and just one of the s simple events will be the outcome. Thus,

$$e_1 \lor e_2 \lor \ldots \lor e_s \equiv I$$

and

$$e_i e_j \equiv \varnothing \text{ for } \begin{cases} i = 1, 2, \ldots, s \\ j = 1, 2, \ldots, s. \end{cases}$$

We wish the simple events to be indecomposable, as they are also
called, so that any thinkable outcome of the experiment can be
expressed by means of the simple events in a Boolean way. Thus
we make this agreement:

  (b) The only events we shall consider are the simple events and
      their Boolean sums. An event that is the Boolean sum of two
      or more distinct simple events is said to be *compound* and to
      be *decomposable* into the events of which it is the sum.
      Under this definition, to any compound event E correspond
      simple events, which we shall denote by

$$\hat{e}_1, \hat{e}_2, \ldots, \hat{e}_i$$

such that

$$E \equiv \hat{e}_1 \vee \ldots \vee \hat{e}_i.$$

Any decomposition can be changed in appearance by repeating one
or more of the simple events in it. For instance,

$$e_1 \vee e_2 \equiv e_1 \vee e_2 \vee e_1.$$

If no such repetitions occur, we shall say that the decomposition is
standard.

EXERCISES

  9. Express e_1' in terms of simple events.
  10. Prove that any compound event has just one standard decomposition.
HINT: Suppose

$$\hat{e}_1, \ldots, \hat{e}_i$$

and

$$\bar{e}_1, \ldots, \bar{e}_j$$

to be two sets of simple events such that

$$\hat{e}_1 \vee \ldots \vee \hat{e}_i \equiv \bar{e}_1 \vee \ldots \vee \bar{e}_j.$$

What happens when both sides of this equivalence are multiplied (in the
Boolean sense) by e_1?
  11. Show that $(e_1 \vee e_2 \vee e_3 \vee e_4)(e_1 \vee e_3 \vee e_4 \vee e_6)$ can be expressed

as a Boolean sum and thus represents a compound event. This is an instance of the fact that any Boolean combination of simple events can be expressed as a Boolean sum.

   12. Give standard decompositions of the compound events mentioned in Exercises 2 to 8 on coin tossing.

   13. Consider two compound events and their standard decompositions. Prove that the events are mutually exclusive if and only if no simple event appears in both decompositions.

As we saw in our example, an experiment in probability is not fully described mathematically until probabilities have been assigned to the simple events. Suppose the probability p_i to be attached to event e_i, $i = 1, 2, \ldots, s$. The only mathematical requirements upon the p_i are that they be positive (or zero) and add to 1:

(1)
$$p_i \geq 0 \text{ for } i = 1, 2, \ldots, s,$$
$$p_1 + p_2 + \ldots + p_s = 1.$$

Their exact values are supposed to reflect the nature of the experiment. Imagine trying the experiment N times. Let N_i = the number of times in the N trials that event e_i occurs, and define

$$f_i = N_i/N \text{ for } i = 1, 2, \ldots, s.$$

We call N_i the *frequency* and f_i the *relative frequency* (of occurrence) of event e_i in the N trials. Since

$$N_1 + N_2 + \ldots + N_s = N,$$

we have

$$\begin{aligned} f_1 + f_2 + \ldots + f_s &= N_1/N + N_2/N + \ldots + N_s/N \\ &= (1/N)(N_1 + N_2 + \ldots + N_s) \\ &= (1/N)N \\ &= 1. \end{aligned}$$

Thus,

$$f_i \geq 0 \text{ for } i = 1, 2, \ldots, s$$

and

$$f_1 + f_2 + \ldots + f_s = 1,$$

conditions of just the form we required in (1).

   Frequency and relative frequency of arbitrary events are defined similarly to those of simple events: the *frequency* of any event is the number of its occurrences in the N trials of the experiment and the *relative frequency* the ratio of this number to N.

   As an illustration, suppose that during 1000 repetitions of our coin tossing experiment, the 16 simple events of Table 13-1 occurred the numbers of times indicated by Table 13-2.

1. 66	5. 59	9. 65	13. 52
2. 56	6. 69	10. 67	14. 69
3. 65	7. 52	11. 63	15. 64
4. 69	8. 61	12. 61	16. 62

Table 13-2 *Frequencies of occurrence, in 1000 trials, of the simple events of Table 13-1*

(By e_1 and e_2 we mean event 1 and event 2 in Table 13-1, and so forth. According to this table, e_1 occurred 66 times, e_2 occurred 56 times, and so forth, in 1000 repetitions of the coin tossing experiment described.) Here, $N = 1000$, and hence, for instance, $f_1 = 66/1000 = .066$, $f_2 = 56/1000 = .056$. The relative frequency of the compound event $e_1 \lor e_2$ is $(66 + 56)/1000 = .122$.

EXERCISES

What are the relative frequencies of the following compound events?

14. $e_1 \lor e_3$.
15. e_1'. (Recall that e_1' is the event that is contrary to e_1.)
16. $e_1' \lor e_2$.
17. $(e_1 \lor e_2)'$.
18. Equal numbers of heads and tails.
19. Just three heads.
20. Just one head or just one tail.

As N grows, the relative frequencies f_i, $i = 1, 2, \ldots, s$, continually change. Often they may seem to become rather stable, fluctuating slightly within narrow precincts, but in experiments such as games of chance, relative frequencies do not promise sincerely to be stable forever. Chance is purposeless, moving now this way and now that with complete impartiality. Nevertheless, as in our experiment in tossing coins, we may be able to state an "ideal" relative frequency for each event e_i such that no more reason exists to expect f_i to exceed this ideal than to fall short of it. We then select p_i to be this ideal relative frequency of e_i.

Let E denote an arbitrary compound event with the standard decomposition

$$E \equiv \hat{e}_1 \lor \ldots \lor \hat{e}_1,$$

$\hat{e}_1, \ldots, \hat{e}_i$ denoting appropriate simple events. Let $N(E)$ denote the frequency (i.e., number of occurrences) of E in N trials of the experiment, and $f(E)$ its relative frequency. Thus, $f(E) = N(E)/N$. Since E occurs whenever one of the simple events in its decomposition occurs, we have

$$N(E) = \hat{N}_1 + \ldots + \hat{N}_1,$$

$\hat{N}_k$ denoting the frequency of occurrence of $\hat{e}_k$. Hence, representing the relative frequency of $\hat{e}_k$ by $\hat{f}_k = \hat{N}_k/N$, we have

$$
\begin{aligned}
f(E) = N(E)/N &= (1/N)(\hat{N}_1 + \ldots + \hat{N}_i.) \\
&= \hat{N}_1/N + \ldots + \hat{N}_i/N \\
&= \hat{f}_1 + \ldots + \hat{f}_i.
\end{aligned}
$$

This says that the relative frequency of a compound event E is the sum of the relative frequencies of its component simple events. Analogously, we define the *probability*, or *chance*, $p(E)$ of event E to be the sum of the probabilities of the component simple events:

$$
p(E) = \hat{p}_1 + \ldots + p_i,
$$

where $\hat{p}_k$ is the probability of $\hat{e}_k$. We can regard $p(E)$ as the ideal relative frequency of E. Correspondingly, $p(E)N$ represents the ideal frequency of E in N trials of the experiment.

Now that the probability of an arbitrary event is defined, we can prove one of its most fundamental properties, known as *additivity*.

Additivity Theorem. If E and F are any mutually exclusive events, then

$$
p(E \lor F) \equiv p(E) + p(F).
$$

PROOF: If

$$
\hat{e}_1 \lor \ldots \lor \hat{e}_i
$$

is the standard decomposition of E and

$$
\bar{e}_1 \lor \ldots \lor \bar{e}_j
$$

the standard decomposition of F, then

$$
(\hat{e}_1 \lor \ldots \lor \hat{e}_i) \lor (\bar{e}_1 \lor \ldots \lor \bar{e}_j)
$$

is (apart from the parentheses, which are irrelevant) the standard decomposition of $E \lor F$. In fact, E and F being mutually exclusive, no simple event in the last string of disjunctions is repeated. Therefore,

$$
\begin{aligned}
p(E \lor F) &= (\hat{p}_1 + \ldots + \hat{p}_i) + (\bar{p}_1 + \ldots + \bar{p}_j) \\
&= p(E) + p(F),
\end{aligned}
$$

accents marking appropriately the probabilities pertaining to the simple events considered.

The two conditions

(2) $p(E) \geq 0$ for any event E

and

(3) $EF \equiv \varnothing \Rightarrow p(E \vee F) = p(E) + p(F)$

are the same in form as those stated in (i) and (ii), Chapter 12, Section 9, on which we based our treatment of class frequencies. They have analogous consequences, among which we mention in particular the following result on the probability of contrary events.

Theorem on Complements.   For any event E,

(4) $p(E) + p(E') = 1.$

EXERCISES

From (2), (3), (4), prove the following relations, in which E, F, G denote arbitrary events.

21. $p(\varnothing) = 0$,
22. $p(EF) + p(EF') = p(E)$,
23. $p(E \vee F) = p(E) + p(F) - p(EF)$,
24. If $EF \equiv EG \equiv FG \equiv \varnothing$, then $p(E \vee F \vee G) = p(E) + p(F) + p(G)$;
25. $p(E \vee F \vee G) = p(E) + p(F) + p(G) - p(EF) - p(EG) - p(FG)$
$+ p(EFG).$

2.

Calculation of probabilities by counting†

We have seen that to describe an experiment in probability mathematically, we must give the simple events and their probabilities, satisfying conditions (a) and (b) and relations (1) of the previous section. In many situations, the simple events can be considered equally probable, and we have merely to count them up to know their common probability. Counting may be tedious and often can be lightened by a little numerical reasoning, as we now illustrate in a series of examples and propositions.

Example 1.   A book club permits its members to choose one out of 8 plays of the absurd and one out of 15 novels of debauchery. John Doe makes his selections at random,‡ having heard of none of them before. What is the probability of any particular pair of selections?

---

†The classic textbook on this subject is W. A. Whitworth, *Choice and Chance*, Fifth Edition, 1901. Reprinted by Hafner, 1965. A companion book by Whitworth with worked exercises is *DCC Exercises in Choice and Chance*, 1897, reprinted by Hafner, 1965.

‡Selection is said to be at random when all possibilities are equally probable. As an adjective, "random" is essentially a synonym for "chance."

SOLUTION: He can pick a play in 8 ways and, for each choice of play, then has 15 choices of a novel. Hence, the total number of pairs of selections available to him is $8 \times 15 = 120$. By assumption, all pairs of selections are equally probable, while the sum of their probabilities is 1. Hence, the probability of any particular pair is 1/120.

In this example, counting the pairs of selections is like counting objects in a rectangular arrangement. Let us draw up a table (Table 13-3) with 8 (horizontal) rows and 15 (vertical) columns. Each row will correspond to a play and each column to a novel. We can indicate the selection of a play and a novel by marking the space in the table

Table 13-3   *A rectangular table*

	1	2	3	4	5	6	7	8	9	10	11	12	13	14	15
1															
2															
3															
4															
5															
6															
7															
8															

belonging to the corresponding row and column. The number of pairs available for selection is equal to the number of such spaces, which is obviously 8×15.

Were there m plays and n novels to be selected, the total number of possible pairs would be mn. If all pairs were equally probable, the probability of each would be $1/mn$. More generally, we have the following principle.

Proposition 1.   If m ways exist to make one selection and n ways to make another, then there are mn ways to make both selections. If the mn ways are equally probable, the probability of each is $1/mn$.

Example 2.   How many ways are there to select one out of 8 plays, one out of 15 novels, and one out of 10 biographies?

SOLUTION: Since there are 8×15 ways to select a play and a novel, the number of ways to do this and also to select a biography is $(8 \times 15) \times 10 = 1200$.

As this example illustrates, Proposition 1 can be extended as follows.

Proposition 2.   Suppose we are to select r objects successively and have m_1 possibilities for the first object, m_2 possibilities for the second, ..., m_r possibilities for the rth. Then the total number of possible selections of the r objects is the product

$$m_1 m_2 \cdots m_r.$$

Example 3.   What is the probability of obtaining 10 heads in 10 tosses of a coin believed to be unbiased?

SOLUTION: On each toss, the coin selects one of two objects, namely either heads or tails. Hence, the total number of possibilities in 2 tosses is $2 \cdot 2 = 2^2$; in three tosses, it is $2 \cdot 2 \cdot 2 = 2^3$; and in 10 tosses, it is $2 \cdot 2 \cdot 2 \cdot 2 \cdot 2 \cdot 2 \cdot 2 \cdot 2 \cdot 2 \cdot 2 = 2^{10} = 1024$ (Proposition 2 with $r = 10$). Assuming all these outcomes to be equally probable, their individual probability is $1/1024$, which thus is, in particular, the probability of obtaining all heads.

Example 4.   We can regard a die as a cube whose six faces are numbered from 1 to 6. It is rolled, say on a table, and after it has come to rest the number facing up is read off. If two dice are rolled, what is the probability that their numbers will have sum at most 5?

SOLUTION: The first die selects one out of 6 numbers; so does the second die. Hence, there are $6 \times 6 = 36$ possible results. If they are equally probable, which we assume to be the case, the probability of each is $1/36$. Of all these possible results, the ones with sum at most 5 are

$$1 + 1, 1 + 2, 1 + 3, 1 + 4,$$
$$2 + 1, 2 + 2, 2 + 3,$$
$$3 + 1, 3 + 2,$$
$$4 + 1,$$

ten in all. The probability of the compound event that one of these ten events will occur is $10/36$.

EXERCISES

1. If you order a sundae in a certain ice cream parlor, you may pick one of 28 kinds of ice cream and one of 9 kinds of syrup. Then how many kinds of sundae may you order?

2. A high school student writing a story is considering for use in a certain context one of the adjectives in the first column and one of the nouns in the next:

mysterious	fanatic
mealy-mouthed	official
grumpy	outcast
funny	wife
cadaverous	

How many possibilities in all is he considering?

3. A restaurant serves eggs boiled, fried, scrambled, poached, and shirred; they offer white, whole wheat, and rye bread, rolls, raisin bread, cornbread; they pour orange juice, tomato juice, and grapefruit juice; and

they serve coffee, tea, milk, and buttermilk. How many ways are there to order breakfast with one kind of eggs, one kind of bread, one kind of juice, and one kind of beverage?

4. Out of nine different pairs of gloves, in how many ways could I choose a right-hand glove and a left-hand glove, *which should not form a pair?*† HINT: A right-hand glove and a left-hand glove *do* form a pair in exactly 9 ways. How many ways to choose a right-hand glove and a left-hand glove are there in all?

5. If two dice are rolled, what is the probability that their numbers will add to 7?

6. If three dice are rolled, what is the probability that the total will be 5?

---

†From Whitworth, *Choice and Chance*, p. 11.

Example 5: A chess club is arranging a tournament in which every member will play every other, once with red pieces and once with white. If the club has 14 members, how many games will be played?

SOLUTION: There are 14 ways to pick a member to play white. After that, 13 ways exist to select his opponent. There are thus $14 \times 13 = 182$ ways in all to arrange games.

Example 6: In how many ways may 5 people seat themselves in 5 chairs?

SOLUTION: Number the people for convenience. The first person might be in any of the 5 chairs. After he is seated, the second person might be in any of the remaining 4 chairs. The third person has 3 choices, and so forth. By Proposition 2, the total number of seating arrangements is thus $5 \cdot 4 \cdot 3 \cdot 2 \cdot 1 = 120$.

The arrangement of certain objects in a particular order is called a *permutation*, or simply an *arrangement*, of those objects. For instance,

$$abc, \ acb, \ bac, \ bca, \ cab, \ cba$$

are permutations of the letters a, b, c. Example 6 suggests the following rule.

Proposition 3. The number of permutations of n objects is

$$n(n-1)(n-2) \ \cdots \ 1.$$

This number, the product of the integers from 1 to n, inclusively, is so common in mathematics as to merit a special symbol. We shall use the conventional notation:

$$n! = 1 \cdot 2 \cdot 3 \cdots n.$$

PROOF OF PROPOSITION 3: The number of objects eligible for the first position is n. When the first position has been filled, $n - 1$

objects remain to compete for the second position. After it too is occupied, there are $n-2$ objects available for the third position, and so forth. By Proposition 2, the total number of arrangements therefore is $n(n-1)(n-2)\cdots 1 = n!$, as asserted.

EXERCISES

7. There are 8 boys and 8 girls at a folk dance. If every boy must dance once with every girl, how many couples will be formed?

8. In how many ways can eight children form themselves into a ring to dance around a maypole?† HINT: Label places in the ring from 1 to 8, and find the number of ways of arranging the children on the labeled places. Then take account of the fact that what counts in a ring is the order of the children, not the particular places they happen to occupy.

9. In how many ways can 8 beads be strung on a wire to form a bracelet?‡ HINT: Such a bracelet is the same if the order of the beads is reversed.

10. Five men, A, B, C, D, E, are going to speak at a meeting. In how many ways can they take their turns without B speaking before A?§ HINT: B will speak before A in as many orderings as A before B.

11. In how many ways so that A speaks *immediately* before B?§ HINT: Only 4 objects are to be arranged: AB, C, D, E.

---

†From Whitworth, *Choice and Chance*, p. 20.
‡From Whitworth, *Choice and Chance*, p. 20.
§From Whitworth, *DCC Exercises*, p. 5.

Example 7:   A table is set for 10, but 2 are missing. In how many ways may the 8 present seat themselves?

SOLUTION: The first person might be in any one of 10 places. When he is settled, the second person has his choice of 9 places. The third person has 8 possibilities, and so forth. By Proposition 2, the total number of seating arrangements is thus

$$10 \cdot 9 \cdot 8 \cdot 7 \cdot 6 \cdot 5 \cdot 4 \cdot 3 = 1,814,400.$$

From a given "population," or set, of n objects, suppose r objects to be removed successively. Arranged in the order in which they are removed, they constitute a *sample* of r objects from the original population of n. (In the previous example, we counted the samples of 8 objects from a population of 10.) Frequently, we shall be able to assume that all samples of r objects from a population of n are equally probable, and then it will be important to be able to count them. Therefore, we state the following proposition.

Proposition 4.   The number of samples of r objects from a population of n objects is

$$n(n-1) \cdots (n-r+1).$$

PROOF: The number of objects eligible to fill the first position in the sample is n. When this position has been occupied, $n-1$ objects are available for the second position. When this too has been allotted, $n-2$ objects remain for the third position, and so forth. By Proposition 2, the total number of samples therefore is the product of r consecutive integers of which n is the highest.

Example 8:   Of r people chosen at random, what is the probability that no two have the same birthday?

SOLUTION: We shall make certain simplifying assumptions, the first of which is that a year consists of exactly 365 days. For convenience, we set $n = 365$. Since any one of these n days might have been the birthday of any one of the r persons chosen, the total number of possibilities for their birthdays is n^r (Proposition 2). Our second assumption is that these possibilities are equally probable, the probability of each thus being $1/n^r$. In how many of these possibilities are no two birthdays the same? Considering the people in any established order, we note n possible days for the birthday of the first. Whatever this may be, $n-1$ alternatives are left for the birthday of the second person, and so forth, just as in the proof of Proposition 4. We conclude that the number of possibilities in which no two birthdays are alike is $n(n-1) \cdots (n-r+1)$. In view of the probability previously found for each possibility, the probability we seek that no two persons have the same birthday is

$$n(n-1)(n-2) \cdots (n-r+1)/n^r.$$

If, for instance, $r = 23$, this probability is

$$365 \cdot 364 \cdot 363 \cdots 341/365 \cdot 365 \cdot 365 \cdots 365,$$

which turns out to be less than 1/2.† Hence, *the probability that at least two among 23 people chosen at random have the same birthday is greater than 1/2.*

---

†See the discussion in William Feller, *An Introduction to Probability Theory and Its Applications*, Vol. 1, Third Edition, Wiley, pp. 31-33.

EXERCISES

12. A couple wish to give their baby a first name and a second name selected from their own list of ten names. In all, how many names for the baby are they considering?

13. First, second, and third prizes will be awarded in a chess tournament in which 20 masters take part. What is the number of possible outcomes? In how many ways is it possible to make the awards?

14. In how many ways may a club with 20 members select president, vice president, secretary, and treasurer?

Example 9:   How many ways are there to select 4 kinds of ice cream out of 9?

SOLUTION: Suppose we have to write our choices on separate lines of an order slip. Proposition 4 tells us that $9 \cdot 8 \cdot 7 \cdot 6$ different order slips are possible. But in this counting, two order slips for the same items are considered different if the items are differently arranged. By Proposition 3, the same 4 items will appear (in different arrangements) on exactly 4! order slips. Hence, the total number of different orders is

$$9 \cdot 8 \cdot 7 \cdot 6/4! = 126.$$

Often, as in the previous example, we are interested only in the composition of a sample, not in its arrangement. A subset of a given population, considered without regard for the order of its members, is also called a *combination*, a *selection*, or a *parcel* of members of the given population. (Recall that the terms *permutation* and *arrangement* refer to subsets the members of which have a specified order. Propositions 3 and 4 refer only to permutations.) The foregoing example is a good hint at the connection between permutations and combinations.

Proposition 5.   The number of combinations of r objects out of a population of n objects is

$$n(n - 1)(n - 2) \cdots (n-r+1)/r(r-1)(r-2) \cdots 1.$$

PROOF: Given a population of n objects, let C denote the number of combinations of r objects of the population, and let P denote the number of permutations of r different objects. Since each combination can be arranged in $r!$ ways (Proposition 3), each combination corresponds to $r!$ different permutations. Hence,

$$C \cdot r! = P,$$

while $P = n(n-1)(n-2) \cdots (n-r+1)$ (Proposition 4). It follows that $C = p/r! = n(n - 1) \cdots (n - r + 1)/r!$, which is what the proposition asserts.

Example 10:   In a tennis club, every member is to play at least one game of singles with every other. If the club has 20 members, at least how many games will be played?

SOLUTION: The question we are asking amounts to this: how many combinations of 2 things can be selected from a population of 20 things? The answer is

$$20 \cdot 19/2 \cdot 1 = 190.$$

Example 11:   Two sisters and 19 other girls apply for 6 jobs in a chorus. They are all so spry and lovely that chance is the only element in their selection. What is the probability that both sisters will be accepted?

SOLUTION: We are told that all combinations of 6 are equally probable. The number of such combinations out of a population of 21 is

$$21 \cdot 20 \cdot 19 \cdot 18 \cdot 17 \cdot 16/6 \cdot 5 \cdot 4 \cdot 3 \cdot 2 \cdot 1;$$

hence, the probability of any single selection is the reciprocal of this number. Now we have to calculate how many combinations contain both sisters. The 4 other members of such combinations are selected from the 19 other girls; hence, the number of such combinations is

$$19 \cdot 18 \cdot 17 \cdot 16/4 \cdot 3 \cdot 2 \cdot 1.$$

The probability we seek is this number multiplied by the probability of occurrence of an individual combination, or

$$(19 \cdot 18 \cdot 17 \cdot 16/4 \cdot 3 \cdot 2 \cdot 1) \cdot (6 \cdot 5 \cdot 4 \cdot 3 \cdot 2 \cdot 1/21 \cdot 20 \cdot 19 \cdot 18 \cdot 17 \cdot 16)$$
$$= 6 \cdot 5/21 \cdot 20 = 1/14.$$

EXERCISES

15. From a class of 30 students, in how many ways can a committee of 4 be selected?

16. A has 7 different books, and B has 9 different books. In how many ways can 2 of A's books be exchanged for 2 of B's books? †

17. A committee in the Senate has 9 Democrats and 8 Republicans. In how many ways can a subcommittee be selected consisting of 3 Democrats and 2 Republicans?

18. In how many ways can 4 scarves be selected from a heap of 50, all of which are different?

19. How many four-digit numbers can be formed from the integers 1, 2, 3, 4, 5, 6, 7 if no integer can be used more than once? How many of these numbers will be even? How many numbers will be divisible by 4? (HINT: See Chapter 3, Section 7) How many will be odd?

20. In how many ways can 3 secretaries be assigned to 6 offices if each secretary must go to a different office? In how many ways if the secretaries do not necessarily go to different offices?

21. A school has 9 classrooms. In how many ways can 6 teachers be assigned to classrooms if each teacher is to have his own classroom?

22. Ten girls and five boys try out for parts in a play. There are 7 female

---

†From DCC Exercises, p. 5.

roles and 3 male roles in the play. In how many ways can a complete cast be selected if each person selected is assigned a specific role?

23. There are 12 girls at a beauty contest, six red heads and six blonds. How many ways can they be seated on the stage in a row of chairs so that blonds and redheads alternate?

24. A set of encyclopedias contains 30 volumes. In how many ways can a user pull out one or more? Indicate what calculations are necessary, but do not work them out. HINT: For each volume, two possibilities exist.

25. This same set of encyclopedias containing 30 volumes is to be arranged on a shelf. In how many ways can it be arranged so that at least one volume is out of numerical order?

26. All Maryland license plates for noncommercial cars have two letters of the alphabet followed by a 4-digit number. How many possible Maryland license plates for noncommercial cars are there?

27. In how many ways can 6 students be seated in a classroom with 30 desks?

28. In how many ways can 12 students — 10 right-handed students and 2 left-handed students — be seated in a classroom with 25 right-handed desks and 5 left-handed desks so that a right-handed student sits in a right-handed desk and a left-handed student sits in a left-handed desk?

29. A student has five different final exams to take, and there are 12 different examination periods. How many possible examination programs for the student are there?

30. A hostess has a tray of hors d'oeuvres containing 20 cocktail hot dogs, 12 Swedish meatballs, and 16 pieces of cheese. How many ways can a guest make a selection if he chooses at least one (but possibly more) hors d'oeuvres?

31. An airline serves 40 airports. If the names of the point of departure and the destination are printed on each ticket, how many different kinds of single, one way tickets can be printed?

32. A certain community is served by the 434 telephone exchange. (Each telephone no. is 434 followed by a four digit number.) What is the largest possible number of telephones in this community?

33. A sandwich shop has white bread, rye bread, rolls, pumpernickel, lettuce, tomatoes, mayonnaise, mustard, butter, salt, pepper, ketchup, American cheese, swiss cheese, provolone, ham, baloney, salami, and liverwurst. If a customer can choose any number of ingredients in a sandwich, how many possible sandwiches are there?

34. An ordinary bridge deck of 52 cards is thoroughly shuffled. The cards are then dealt face up, one at a time, until an ace appears. What is the probability that the first ace appears at the fifth card?

35. A symphony is recorded on 4 discs, both sides of each disc being used. In how many ways can the 8 sides be played on a phonograph so that some part of the symphony is played out of its correct order?

36. Find the probability of the occurrence of each of the following events:

(a) picking a black card from a bridge deck
(b) tossing five consecutive heads on five tosses of a coin
(c) picking an honor card (J, Q, K, A) from a bridge deck.

3.

Statistical tests of significance

The propositions of Section 2 open many paths, among them a modest access to the ideas behind statistical tests. Is a coin biased if we obtain 57 heads out of 100 tosses? If 570 heads appear in 1000 tosses? If the average height of senior boys in a certain high school exceeds that of their fathers, can the difference have been the consequence of chance alone? Suppose the effectiveness of a drug in curing a viral disease to be tested by infecting 200 mice with the virus, treating just 100 with the drug, and otherwise caring for all the animals identically. If 60 treated mice and 70 untreated mice die, has the drug been effective, or does chance alone suffice for explanation? Questions like these, in which chance is a major consideration, arise whenever measurements are made and abound particularly in medicine, biology, and the social sciences. The instances we shall discuss are elementary but represent problems of great significance and are in themselves good illustrations of statisticians' logic.

a. ON DESIGNING STATISTICAL EXPERIMENTS

By a statistical experiment, we mean one in which pure chance may conceivably account wholly or partly for the result. For instance, if several fertilizers are being compared, the differences in yields among the plots to which the respective fertilizers were applied may at least in part be attributable to chance. What the experimenter wants to know is whether all the differences in yields can reasonably be ascribed to chance, or whether some of these differences are assignable to the fertilizers themselves. Ordinarily in such an experiment, he will have to use probability theory to interpret his results and indeed would have been well advised to design the experiment originally with the requirements imposed by theory in mind.

A rational approach to the design of statistical experiments is a development of our century and owes most perhaps to the British mathematician R. A. Fisher, an inventive thinker and a persuasive advocate. Fisher was also a teacher who could strip away technical details to explain ideas in their barest form. Our discussion is based on his famous essay, "The Mathematics of a Lady Tasting Tea."†

"A lady declares that by tasting a cup of tea made with milk she can discriminate whether the milk or the tea infusion was first added to the cup." To test her claim, an experiment is designed calling for 8 cups of tea, 4 made one way and 4 the other, to be given the lady for

†From *Design of Experiments*, published by Oliver and Boyd Ltd. Excerpted by James R. Newman, *The World of Mathematics*, Vol. 3, Simon and Schuster, pp. 1512-1521. The passages quoted are from Newman's excerpt.

her consideration. The 8 cups of tea are to be as much alike as possible apart from the single difference being tested, although "in practice it is probable that the cups will differ perceptibly in the thickness or smoothness of their material, that the quantities of milk added to the different cups will not be exactly equal, that the strength of the infusion of tea may change between pouring the first and the last cup, and that the temperature also at which the tea is tested will change during the course of the experiment," and so forth. To avoid systematic effects owing to such elements, the cups are to be served in an unpredictable order determined by dice, cards, or similarly random means. The lady is to state her opinion as to which 4 cups were made one way and which 4 the other, and we are to attempt to judge whether she can really tell.

Our method is to ask whether the lady's performance is so good as to be quite improbable if attributed solely to chance. Indeed, suppose her to lack utterly the delicate sensory discrimination that she claims and to base her judgments on irrelevant things having only chance connections with the point at issue. If on this supposition her performance is startlingly improbable, then we are willing to grant that the supposition is unreasonable and to concede her claim.

First, suppose she determines all the cups correctly. Even in this most favorable case, she will not have proved her point if our experiment was on too small a scale. Her task is to pick out the 4 cups into which, say, the milk was poured first, the other 4 cups then being determined. The number of ways to select 4 objects out of a population of 8 objects is

$$8 \cdot 7 \cdot 6 \cdot 5/4 \cdot 3 \cdot 2 \cdot 1 = 70$$

and if all these ways are equally probable, the probability of each is 1/70. Therefore, the probability that the lady will classify the cups correctly by chance is 1/70. Is this probability so low that we cannot believe chance to be the only factor? We should be foolish to affirm any such thing, and the lady may justly complain that we provided her but a poor opportunity to prove her extraordinary sensibility. Had 6 cups of each kind been presented to her instead of 4, the probability of her judging them all correctly by pure chance would have been 1/924; our reservations in that case would have been much less.

If the lady is not invariably right, perhaps she is more often right than wrong, but an experiment with just 4 cups of either kind would be useless to decide that. Suppose, for instance, that of one kind the lady classifies 3 cups correctly and 1 cup incorrectly. There are 4 ways to choose 3 right cups (out of 4 in all) and also 4 ways to choose 1 wrong cup (again out of 4). Thus, there are 16 ways to classify 3 cups of one kind correctly and 1 cup incorrectly. Hence, the probability of arriving at such a classification by chance is 16/70, and the probability of classifying *at least* 3 cups of one kind correctly by chance is 17/70. Occurrence by chance of an event with so high a probability cannot be deemed remarkable. In fact, statisticians have a rule of thumb under which no event with a probability of 1/20 or greater is considered exceptional or worth discussing if it should occur. Thus, our experiment with 4 cups of either kind is of very limited value.

These considerations illustrate how carefully a statistical experiment must be planned to prove that a phenomenon is nonrandom. First, extraneous elements—in this example, "the strength of the infusion, the quantity of milk, the temperature at which it is tasted, etc."—must be reduced to a minimum and, beyond that, kept from producing even small systematic effects. This was the purpose in our experiment of randomizing the order in which the several cups were presented to the lady. Secondly, since no statistical experiment is absolutely decisive, we must agree on a desirable level of sensitivity of the experiment and are then wise to make the experiment large enough to achieve that sensitivity. To do so successfully, we must plan. Detailed logical analysis is necessary, in which we calculate the probabilities of the contemplated outcomes assuming provisionally that they are due solely to chance. A result with low probability under this provisional assumption casts doubt on the assumption, supporting the conclusion that the phenomenon in question is not due to chance.

R. A. Fisher calls the provisional assumption that chance alone is at work the "null hypothesis." As he notes, "the null hypothesis is never proved or established, but is possibly disproved, in the course of experimentation. Every experiment may be said to exist only in order to give the facts a chance of disproving the null hypothesis."

EXERCISES

1. Assuming the lady's selections to be governed by chance, find the probabilities of the following determinations:
   (a) Of each kind, 2 cups right and 2 cups wrong.
   (b) Of each kind, 1 cup right and 3 cups wrong.
   (c) All cups wrong.

2. In a new experiment, 6 cups are to be made one way and 6 the other. Again assuming the lady's selections to be governed by chance, find the probabilities of the following events:
   (a) All 12 cups correctly named.
   (b) Of each kind, 5 judged correctly and 1 incorrectly.
   (c) Of each kind, 4 judged correctly and 2 incorrectly.
   (d) Of each kind, 3 judged correctly and 3 incorrectly.
   (e) Of each kind, at least 4 judged correctly.

3. In another experiment, suppose 8 cups to be used, but the way in which the milk and tea are mixed to be determined for each cup by tossing a coin. Still assuming the lady's selections to be governed by chance, find the probabilities of the following events:
   (a) Judging all 8 cups correctly.
   (b) Judging 7 cups correctly and 1 incorrectly.
   (c) Judging 6 cups correctly and 2 incorrectly.
   (d) Judging at least 6 cups correctly.

b.   THE DETECTION OF RELATIVE BIAS†

Subjective and random elements occur in all kinds of exact measurement. For instance, anyone can read a rule accurately to the nearest millimeter, but readings to tenths of millimeters are uncertain. An observer who requires precision will for this reason make not one but several independent measurements. If these are no more likely to be too high than too low, their average will be more reliable than they individually and thus a better determination of the quality in question.

If measurements are consistently too high or consistently too low, they are said to be *biased*. An almost certain source of bias, in the absence of special measures against it, is the natural tendency of any person to let his knowledge of earlier observations influence new findings. Even without this, bias is a constant possibility, which an observer must be alert to notice, trace, and remedy.

We consider here a very simple text of relative bias. Suppose two persons, A and B, each to make 4 measurements of a certain quantity, and suppose all of A's measurements to exceed all of B's. Can we conclude that A's measurements will be consistently higher than B's, or might the difference on this one occasion be reasonably ascribed to chance? To test the matter, we make the "null hypothesis" (Subsection a) that A's and B's results differ solely because of chance. Since we are not concerned with the 8 actual measurements but only with the inequalities between them, let us list them in order of size. We shall refer to each measurement just by indicating its place in the list, for instance, first, second, or eighth. Under the null hypothesis, A has an equal chance to get any 4 places. Since the number of ways to select 4 places out of 8 is

$$8 \cdot 7 \cdot 6 \cdot 5 / 1 \cdot 2 \cdot 3 \cdot 4 = 70,$$

the probability that A will receive any particular combination of 4 places is (under the null hypothesis) 1/70. Therefore, the probability that A (under the null hypothesis) will have made the 4 highest measurements is 1/70. In the same way, the probability that B will have made the 4 highest measurements is 1/70. Hence, the probability that all the measurements of either observer will by pure chance exceed all those of the other is 2/70 = 1/35. This probability is low enough to cast doubt on the null hypothesis but not so low as to rule it out. Bias must be suspected, and further tests should be made.

Bias for inexperienced observers is very common, as usually is apparent when the members of a class make a precise measurement. W. J. Youden ‡ proposes measuring the average thickness of the pages

---

†I am indebted to Prof. T. A. Willke for suggesting this topic and its treatment.
‡*Experimentation and Measurement*, by W. J. Youden. Produced by the National Science Teachers Association in cooperation with the National Bureau of Standards. Published by Scholastic Book Services, 1962, New York. See in particular pp. 26-28, Table 2 on p. 31, p. 39.

in a book and gives the following directions: open the book *near* the beginning and *near* the end; pinch together the intervening pages and by means of a rule measure their total thickness to the nearest tenth of a millimeter; find how many pages you have pinched together; divide their total thickness by their number. This procedure has the advantage that no one's later observations are likely to be biased by his earlier. The reason is that readings are always made on an unknown number of pages and therefore cannot be compared directly with previous readings.

CLASS EXERCISE

Let everyone in the class make 4 measurements (on the same book) by Youden's procedure. Tabulate the results, and compare for bias.

EXERCISES

1. If each observer makes 5 measurements, what is the probability under the null hypothesis that all measurements of one observer will exceed those of the other? What is the probability that at least 4 measurements of one observer will exceed those of the other?

2. How many measurements must each observer make to have the probability less than 1/1000 that all measurements of one observer will exceed those of the other by chance alone?

3. A man caught 4 fish in Lake X Monday and 5 fish in Lake Y Tuesday. If the 3 largest of the 9 fish were caught in Lake X, is it reasonable to claim that this lake has the larger fish? State the pertinent null hypothesis explicitly. What conceivable conditions — such, for instance, that the man had his wife along one day and not the other — might invalidate the null hypothesis whether or not the fish in the first lake are larger?†

---

† This example is developed by W. J. Youden in a nontechnical abstract of a paper on Experimentation and Measurement presented at the Philadelphia meeting of the AAAS, Dec. 28, 1962.

4.

Statistical independence

In the previous examples, an unspoken presumption has often been our guide. For instance, we took it for granted in the coin tossing experiment of Table 13-1 that the outcome of one toss will not influence that of another; otherwise, we should hardly have supposed all 16 elementary events to be equally likely. We presumed, in other words, that events pertaining to different tosses of the coin are mutually independent. The concept of independence, which hitherto has been implicit, must now be developed explicitly.

Let E and F be any two possible events in a probability experiment. Imagine N trials of the experiment, and consider specially those in which F occurs. The number of occurrences of F being $N(F)$, the proportion of such occurrences in which E also takes place is

(1) $$N(EF)/N(F).$$

This ratio is the relative frequency of E *among the trials in which F has occurred.* The relative frequency of E *among all trials* is

(2) $$N(E)/N$$

We deem E and F to be mutually dependent if the relative frequency of E among the trials in which F has occurred is appreciably different from the relative frequency of E among all trials. For instance, we should consider a connection proved between overweight and running ability if the relative frequency of track winners among *overweight* high school students was appreciably different from the relative frequency of track winners among *all* high school students. On the other hand, two arbitrary events E and F may be considered independent to the extent that no appreciable difference exists between the relative frequency of E among the trials in which F has occurred and the relative frequency of E among all trials.

Let
$$f(E) = N(E)/N, \ f(F) = N(F)/N, \ f(EF) = N(EF)/N.$$
Since (for $f(F) > 0$)
$$\frac{N(EF)}{N(F)} = \frac{N(EF)/N}{N(F)/N} = \frac{f(EF)}{f(F)},$$

the criterion for independence we have just suggested is that

$$f(EF)/f(F)$$

and

$$f(E)$$

be approximately equal or, equivalently, that $f(EF)$ and $f(E)f(F)$ be approximately equal. Adapting this idea to ideal relative frequencies, or probabilities, we lay down the following definition.

Definition: Two events E and F are said to be *statistically independent* if

$$p(EF) = p(E)p(F).$$

Example 1: In the experiment of tossing a coin twice, let

H_1, T_1, H_2, T_2 indicate heads on the first toss, tails on the first toss, heads on the second toss, and tails on the second toss, respectively. There are 4 indecomposable events:

$$H_1H_2, \; H_1T_2, \; T_1H_2, \; T_1T_2.$$

If we assume them to be equally probable, the probability of each is 1/4. Furthermore, $p(T_1) = p(T_2) = p(H_1) = p(H_2) = 1/2$, since, for instance,

$$p(T_1) = p(T_1H_2) + p(T_1T_2) = 1/4 + 1/4 = 1/2.$$

Thus, $p(T_1H_2) = p(T_1)p(H_2)$ (this says simply that $1/4 = (1/2)(1/2)$), so that T_1 and H_2, in particular, are independent. Similarly, T_1 and T_2 are independent, and also H_1 and H_2, and H_1 and T_2.

Example 2:   Let two urns be given, the first containing three white balls and one black ball, the second containing one white ball and four black balls. Suppose the balls to be indistinguishable except in color, and consider an experiment in which a blindfolded observer selects one ball at random from each urn. For $i = 1, 2$, let

$B_i \equiv$ the observer has taken a black ball from the ith urn,
$W_i \equiv$ the observer has taken a white ball from the ith urn.

Since a ball can be drawn from the first urn in 4 ways, and a ball can be drawn from the second urn in 5 ways, there are $4 \times 5 = 20$ ways to draw both balls. Assuming these 20 ways to be equally likely, we shall show, for instance, that B_1 and B_2 are statistically independent. Each way of drawing the balls has probability 1/20, and the number of ways of drawing two black is $1 \times 4 = 4$. Hence, the probability $p(B_1B_2)$ that both balls drawn will be black is $4/20 = 1/5$. On the other hand, $p(B_1) = 1/4$ and $p(B_2) = 4/5$. Consequently, $p(B_1B_2) = p(B_1)p(B_2)$, the condition that B_1 and B_2 be independent, as claimed.

EXERCISES

1. A research engineer estimates that the chance that he can solve a certain problem is 1/2. He engages a consultant whose chance to solve the problem he estimates as 2/3. If they both work on the problem, independently, what is the chance that either will do it? HINT: What is the chance that neither will do it?

2. The chance that Henry left his bedroom window open when he went out Friday night was 1/3, and the chance that there would be a thunderstorm before he returned, 2/5. What is the chance that his room remained dry while he was out?

3. Prove that if E and F are independent events, then E' and F are independent and, consequently, that E and F' are independent, and also E' and F'.

4. If E, F, G are events such that E is independent both of F and of G, prove that

$$p(EF \lor E'G) = p(E)p(F) + (1 - p(E))p(G).$$

5. Bob is a confirmed bachelor, happy if his friends invite him out a lot or if he has plenty of money and the restaurants are good. Otherwise, he tends to mope. For next year, he thinks his chance to have sufficient income is 2/3, but, his favorite chefs having retired, he is only 50 per cent certain that the restaurants will please him. The chance is 1/5 that his friends will be out of the city. What is Bob's chance to be happy next year?

5.

Gambler's ruin†

We conclude this chapter with a problem of considerable scientific and mathematical interest, but we shall first describe it in terms of a game of chance. Two gamblers bet against each other on the toss of a coin. If heads are uppermost, the first gambler wins a dollar from the second, while if tails, the first gambler pays a dollar to the second. The first gambler starts with z dollars, his initial "capital," and the second with a − z dollars; their combined capital is a dollars. The game lasts until one of the two gamblers has all the money—a dollars —and the other none. What is the probability that the first gambler, in particular, will be the one who is ruined?

This problem of gambling is equivalent to one concerning "random walk." Think of an alley a units long and a drunk staggering one unit at a time up the alley or down the alley with equal likelihood. He keeps on until he reaches one end of the alley or the other, the bottom or the top. When he is z units from the bottom of the alley (and a − z units from the top) what is the probability of his ultimately arriving at the bottom of the alley?

Both these problems are related mathematically to the physical process of diffusion in gases. Gas molecules are in continual motion. "In a gas at low pressure, ... the forces between molecules are of short range,"‡ and an individual molecule therefore tends to move in a straight line between rebounds from haphazard collisions with other molecules. Thus, "the motion of a molecule is an exceedingly irregular track consisting of short steps of varying length at sharp angles

---

†I am grateful to Paul Rosenbloom for suggesting this discussion.
‡This and the later quotations are from Section 3 of Diffusion, Encyclopaedia Britannica, 1957 edition.

with each other," each corner resulting from a collision with another molecule. Each molecule performs in effect a kind of random walk in three dimensions. The mathematics of its motion is not available on short notice. It must be fermented, distilled, and aged. We can get a whiff of it, however, in our problem of the drunk tottering back and forth in his alley.

It is more convenient to use the terminology of the gambling problem, in which one dollar changes hands at each toss. Since the number of tosses in a game has no upper limit, the number of simple events to be considered also has no upper limit and indeed is potentially infinite. What are the probabilities of the simple events,[†] and how do we define the probabilities of compound events, in such a situation? Our previous theory does not apply, and to adapt it properly is technical business. Nevertheless, in the problem we are considering, we shall feel our way to a solution through existing concepts.

Assume the first gambler to start with a capital of z dollars, where z is an integer such that $0 < z < a$.

Let R_z denote the event that this gambler is eventually ruined. Here we meet the difficulty mentioned, for our present theory, being confined to finite situations, is unable to assign a probability to such an event. Only with reference to an expanded theory may we properly speak of the probability of R_z. But in a pragmatic spirit, hoping that someone will make good our logical deficiencies (someone has), we assume R_z to have a probability and now proceed to the task of finding it. The probability of R_z of course will depend upon z: denote it by q_z. We shall obtain q_z not by counting but by a new method in which we first establish a mathematical law it obeys and then determine it by applying that law.

For simplicity, let us suppose that the coin is unbiased. At each toss, the first gambler thus wins or loses a dollar with the same probability, 1/2. To deduce the law alluded to,[‡] consider a toss made when the first gambler has capital z with $1 < z < a - 1$. Let W denote the event that the first gambler wins this toss, W' standing for the contrary event that he loses. Since the coin is unbiased,

$$p(W) = p(W') = 1/2.$$

If the first gambler wins the toss, his capital increases to $z + 1$; if he loses, it decreases to $z - 1$. Hence

$$R_z \equiv WR_{z+1} \vee W'R_{z-1} \quad \text{for } 1 < z < a - 1.$$

The events WR_{z+1} and $W'R_{z-1}$ being mutually exclusive, we have

$$q_z = p(R_z) = p(WR_{z+1}) + p(W'R_{z-1}) \quad \text{for } 1 < z < a - 1.$$

[†] This question is more complex than might appear. See Feller, op. cit., p. 74.
[‡] Our discussion is based on that of Feller, op. cit., Chap. 14, Sec. 2.

Since W and R_{z+1} are events that pertain to different sets of tosses, they must be independent, and we have

$$p(WR_{z+1}) = p(W)p(R_{z+1}) = q_{z+1}/2.$$

Similarly, W' and R_{z-1} must be independent events, so that

$$p(W'R_{z-1}) = q_{z-1}/2.$$

Substituting these two results in the preceding gives us

(1) $\qquad q_z = (1/2)\,(q_{z+1} + q_{z-1}) \quad$ for $1 < z < a - 1$,

essentially the law referred to, except that the cases $z = 1$ and $z = a - 1$ so far are excluded.

   If $z = 1$ and the first gambler loses the toss, he will be ruined. Thus, $R_1 \equiv WR_2 \vee W'$, which implies

(1)₀ $\qquad\qquad\qquad\qquad q_1 = q_2/2 + 1/2.$

If $z = a - 1$ and the first gambler wins the toss, then he wins the game, and we have $R_{a-1} \equiv W'R_{a-2}$. Therefore,

(1)$_{a-1}$ $\qquad\qquad\qquad\qquad q_{a-1} = q_{a-2}/2.$

We can combine equations (1), (1)₀, and (1)$_{a-1}$ into a single formula by setting

(2) $\qquad\qquad\qquad\qquad q_o = 1, \; q_a = 0,$

and then requiring

(3) $\qquad q_z = (1/2)\,(q_{z+1} + q_{z-1}) \quad$ for $0 < z < a.$

Condition (3) is classified as a *difference equation*, because it can be written in terms of "differences" $q_{z+1} - q_z$ and $q_{z-1} - q_z$. It is so formulated as

$$(q_{z+1} - q_z) + (q_{z-1} - q_z) = 0.$$

A difference equation is a local relationship, condition (3), in particular, holding for any 3 consecutive values of the variable z. By contrast, conditions (2) pertain only to the extreme values of z; we can call them *end conditions*.

   Our point of view now changes. We put gambling and probability into the background and focus on the purely technical problem of finding $a + 1$ quantities

(4) $\qquad\qquad\qquad\qquad q_0, q_1, \ldots, q_a$

to satisfy the difference equations (3) and the end conditions (2). It will turn out that one, and only one, set of quantities (4) exist that satisfy conditions (2) and (3), and these must be the probabilities we desire.

Any $a+1$ quantities (4) that satisfy the difference equations (3) (whether they also satisfy the end conditions or not) will be called a solution of (3). Two different kinds of solutions of (3) are apparent and will prove to be important. The first solution is

$$q_z = c \qquad \text{for } z = 0, 1, \ldots, a,$$

where c is an arbitrary constant (i.e., number independent of z). The second solution is

$$q_z = kz \qquad \text{for } z = 0, 1, \ldots, a,$$

where k is an arbitrary constant. Furthermore, we can build new solutions of (3) out of old.

Proposition 1. If

$$u_z = (1/2)\,(u_{z+1} + u_{z-1}) \text{ and } v_z = (1/2)\,(v_{z+1} + v_{z-1})$$

for $z = 0, 1, \ldots, a$, then the sum

$$w_z = u_z + v_z$$

satisfies the equations

$$w_z = (1/2)\,(w_{z+1} + w_{z-1})$$

for $z = 0, 1, \ldots, a$. The same is true if $w_z = u_z - v_z$. In words: given two solutions of (3), their sum and difference are again solutions.

To prove this proposition for the sum, add the equations satisfied by the u's and by the v's and replace $u_z + v_z$, $u_{z+1} + v_{z+1}$, $u_{z-1} + v_{z-1}$ by w_z, w_{z+1}, w_{z-1}, respectively. To prove the proposition for differences, subtract the equations and proceed similarly.

Applying the proposition to the two solutions previously noted, we see that

(5) $$q_z = c + kz \quad \text{for } z = 0, 1, \cdots, a,$$

is a solution of the difference equations (3) for any constants c and k. We can pick the constants in such a way that this solution of (3) satisfies the end conditions (2). Indeed,

$$q_0 = c + k0 = c;$$

thus, the condtion $q_0 = 1$ is satisfied if we choose

$$c = 1.$$

Making this choice, we next have

$$q_a = c + ka = 1 + ka.$$

Hence, $q_a = 0$ if $ka + 1 = 0$, i.e.,

$$k = -1/a.$$

With $c = 1$ and $k = -1/a$, the solution (5) becomes

(6) $$q_z = 1 - z/a \quad \text{for } z = 0, 1, \cdots, a.$$

It satisfies both the difference equations (3) and the end condition (2), in these respects imitating the probability we are seeking.

Finally, we shall show that the solution (6) is in fact the probability desired. This ensues from the following result that not more than one solution (4) of the difference equations (3) also satisfies the end condition (2).

Proposition 2.   Suppose

$$u_0 = 1, u_a = 0, v_0 = 1, v_a = 0$$

and

$$u_z = (1/2)(u_{z+1} + u_{z-1}), v_z = (1/2)(v_{z+1} + v_{z-1}) \text{ for } z = 1, \cdots, a-1.$$

Then

$$u_z = v_z \quad \text{for } z = 0, 1, \cdots, a.$$

PROOF: Set $w_z = u_z - v_z$. By Proposition 1,

(7) $$w_z = (1/2)(w_{z+1} + w_{z-1}) \text{ for } z = 1, \ldots, a-1,$$

and, in addition,

$$w_0 = 0, w_a = 0.$$

It suffices to show that

$$w_z = 0 \quad \text{for } z = 0, 1, \ldots, a.$$

If this is not the case, then values of z exist for which w_z is positive or negative. Supposing the former, let M be the largest positive value taken by w_z. Then an integer $z*$ exists such that $0 < z* < a$ and

$$w_{z*} = M;$$

furthermore,

$$w_z \leq M \quad \text{for } z = 0, 1, \ldots, a.$$

If the value M is assumed for more than one value of z, we require z_0 to be the least such value: then

$$w_{z_0 - 1} < M.$$

But by (7), we have

$$w_{z_0} = (1/2) (w_{z_0+1} + w_{z_0-1}),$$

which leads to a contradiction. Indeed, the left side equals M, while the right side is less than $(1/2)(M + M) = M$. The contradiction arose from assuming w_z to be capable of positive values, so we see that it is not. We can prove similarly that w_z does not take negative values and conclude that w_z is zero for every z, as asserted.

EXERCISES

1. Give the proof referred to that w_z does not take negative values.

2. Consider an arbitrary solution (4) of the difference equations (3). If the largest value among the $a + 1$ quantities (4) is taken for a value of z such that $0 < z < a$, prove that all $a + 1$ quantities are the same. Then prove the same thing for the smallest value.

3. Use the previous exercise to prove that $0 < q_z < 1$ for $0 < z < a$ if q_z satisfies conditions (2) and (3).

4. If the first gambler in the problem starts with capital z, what is the probability that he will ultimately win the game?

5. What is the probability that neither will win but that the game continue endlessly?

6. Why is it advantageous to a gambler against a very rich opponent to set an upper limit to his own winnings, making up his mind to stop playing when he has either achieved this upper limit or been ruined?

7. Find difference equations analogous to (3) in the case of a biased coin.

8. Suppose a random walk starts at the origin. If $a > 0$ and $b > 0$, find the probability that the point $-b$ will be reached before the point a. †

9. Prove that in a random walk starting at the origin, the probability of reaching the point a $(a > 0)$ before returning to the origin is $(1 - q_1)/2$. †

---

†Adapted from Feller, op. cit., p. 367.

CHAPTER 14

INFINITY AND
INFINITE PROCESSES

The concept of infinity perhaps owes its origins to the poetical exaggeration of such negatives as "countless," "bottomless," "endless," and "infinite" itself. At least, so we may guess. Religious beliefs in immortality and the idea of eternity — temporal infinity — reach back before recorded history. Leucippus and Democritus were apparently the first,[†] in the 5th Century B.C., to argue persuasively that empty space is infinite. They conceived on metaphysical grounds of infinitely many atoms of different shapes drifting aimlessly in this infinite space and forming transient combinations through accidents of collision and attachment. They also believed that there are innumerable worlds, but both their metaphysics and their beliefs went out of fashion in ancient times. Not until Copernicus proposed that the earth revolves around the sun did the suspicion of an infinite universe revive. Copernicus's great work, "De Revolutionibus," was first published in 1543. In 1576, Thomas Digges, explaining and advocating Copernicus's system, became "the first modern astronomer of note to portray an infinite, heliocentric universe, with the stars scattered at varying distances throughout infinite space."[‡] Perhaps

---

[†] That they were the first to so argue is a surmise of W. K. C. Guthrie, *A History of Greek Philosophy*, Vol. 1, p. 114. I have borrowed Guthrie's words to describe their views.

[‡] Quoted from Francis R. Johnson, "Thomas Digges and the Infinity of the Universe," in *Theories of the Universe*, ed. Milton K. Munitz, Free Press, Glencoe, Ill., 1957, p. 186. This article is a reproduction of pp. 161-169 in Johnson, *Astronomical Thought in Renaissance England*, Johns Hopkins Press, Baltimore, 1937.

influenced by Digges, Giordano Bruno later wrote: "The universe is of infinite size and the worlds therein without number.... There are innumerable suns, and an infinite number of earths revolve around those suns." † Bruno was a metaphysician, believing in worlds without number "because infinite perfection is far better presented in innumerable individuals than in those which are numbered and finite." ‡ Such reasons were not to everyone's taste, especially when Bruno was burned as a heretic in 1600. But his majestic, haunting vision lived on, and many came to share it, incited by discoveries after 1609, the year in which Galileo first used a telescope to make celestial observations. The seemingly countless new stars that then came into view suggested vastnesses that had been totally unknown, and imagination leaped to think of what must lie beyond, unseen. A generation after Galileo, John Milton conceived in these words of interstellar space:

> ... the hoary Deep—a dark
> Illimitable ocean, without bound,
> Without dimension; where length, breadth, and highth
> And time, and place, are lost. §

Thus a poet's intuitions.

To arrive at a mathematical concept of infinity, we might well begin by asking what Democritus or Bruno might have meant by "an infinite number of earths." More generally, considering any kind of set, or collection, of objects, what shall we mean by the statement that the set is infinite? We shall mean that no matter how many objects we count, others remain uncounted. A more precise way to say this is as follows. If we select at pleasure any number, no matter how great, then more than this number of objects belong to the set.

This definition, however, is only a beginning. The concept of infinity in mathematics has many aspects, including the infinitely many, the infinitely large, the infinitely small, infinite divisibility, infinite repetition, infinite summation, and other infinite processes of the greatest variety. Perhaps no concept in mathematics has been more fruitful or more versatile. At the same time, few if any ideas have been so full of surprises.

---

† From Dorothea Waley Singer, *Giordano Bruno, His Life and Thought with Annotated Translation of His Work*, "On the Infinite Universe and Worlds," Abelard-Schuman, Inc., New York, 1950. Excerpted in *Theories of the Universe*, ed. by Milton K. Munitz, Free Press, Glencoe, Ill., 1957, pp. 179, 183.

‡ Munitz, p. 179.

§ "Paradise Lost," II, 891 ff. Quoted in Marjorie Hope Nicolson, *Science and Imagination*, Cornell University Press, Ithaca, 1956, p. 100. Professor Nicolson writes: "Milton's description of Chaos, both in its vocabulary and its conception, is the first great attempt of English poetry to picture the indefinite the telescope had shown. Many of its details are classical, some are medieval, but fundamentally it is a modern Chaos which no mind had conceived before Galileo." (*Ibid.*, p. 100.)

1.

The infinitely many

Mathematical collections, or sets, containing infinitely many members abound: for instance, the set of all natural numbers,

$$\{1, 2, 3, \ldots\},$$

the set of positive even numbers,

$$\{2, 4, 6, \ldots\},$$

the set of positive multiplies of 3,

$$\{3, 6, 9, \ldots\},$$

the set of all squares,

$$\{1, 4, 9, 16, 25, \ldots\},$$

the set of all primes,

$$\{2, 3, 5, 7, 11, \ldots\}$$

(see Chapter 11, Section 3). (We have followed the usual convention of representing a set by enclosing symbols for the members of the set in braces.) A set with infinitely many members is called an *infinite set*, a set with just a finite number of members, a *finite set*.

Some other infinite sets are the set of points on a straight line, the set of triangles in a plane, the set of tangents to a given circle, the set of translations in a plane (Chapter 7, Section 6).

Do degrees of infinitude exist? Are some sets in some sense more highly infinite than others, and, on the other hand, is it ever appropriate to call two sets "equally infinite"? For instance, what of two equal line segments (each segment, say, including its end points), regarded as sets of points? Labeling the two segments AB and CD, as in Figure 14-1, we see that every point P of the segment AB is duplicated on CD by a point Q such that $AP = CQ$. Ought we not, therefore, regard the two segments as, in some sense, equally infinite point sets?

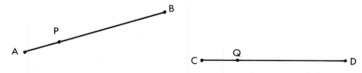

FIGURE 14-1   *A correspondence between two equal line segments.*

As a second example, take the set of positive numbers and the set of negative numbers. Each number of one set has, in its negative, a companion in the other, the positive and the negative numbers in this way being uniquely paired. Is it not then reasonable to regard the sets of positive and negative numbers as being equally infinite? Thirdly, consider the set of translations and the set of vectors in the plane (see Chapter 7, Section 6). Each translation determines one, and just one, vector, and each vector thereby is determined by one, and just one, translation. Does this mutual correspondence not justify our considering the two sets to be equally infinite?

The criteria for equal infinitude suggested in these examples can be made general by means of the notion of one-to-one correspondence. Let two sets, X and Y, be given. If to each member of X we assign one and only one member of Y in such a way that each member of Y thereby is assigned to one, and only one, member of X, then the assignment is called a *one-to-one correspondence between X and Y*. Some instances of one-to-one correspondences have already come to our notice: the correspondence diagrammed in Figure 14-1 between two equal line segments, the correspondence between the positive and the negative numbers obtained by assigning to each positive number x its negative $-x$, the correspondence between translations and vectors that results from assigning to each translation the vector it determines, the correspondence established in coordinate geometry between the set of points in the plane and the set of ordered pairs of numbers (x, y) (see Chapter 8, Section 2).

Guided by the previous examples, we now define two infinite sets to be *equally infinite* if a one-to-one correspondence between them exists. More generally, we define any two sets — infinite or not — to be *cardinally equivalent* if a one-to-one correspondence between them exists. If two sets X and Y are cardinally equivalent, we write

$$X \sim Y.†$$

As noted earlier (Chapter 11, Section 9), a relation is deemed to be an equivalence relation only if it has three properties known as reflexivity, symmetry, and transitivity. It is easy to see that cardinal equivalence, in particular, has these properties and thus is a true equivalence relation. We must show:

(a) reflexivity: $X \sim X$,
(b) symmetry: $(X \sim Y) \Rightarrow (Y \sim X)$,
(c) transitivity: $[X \sim Y \text{ and } Y \sim Z] \Rightarrow X \sim Z$,

where X, Y, and Z denote any sets. The first two properties are trivial and are left to the reader, but let us prove the third. Since $X \sim Y$, a one-to-one correspondence exists between X and Y. If x denotes an arbitrary member of X, let $f(x)$ denote the member of Y that is assigned to x under this correspondence. Since $Y \sim Z$, a one-

†The symbol for cardinal equivalence thus introduced is similar to that for negation, the context indicating which is meant.

to-one correspondence exists between Y and Z, and if y is an arbitrary member of Y, let $g(y)$ denote the member of Z assigned to y under this correspondence. We shall refer to the assignment from X to Y by the single letter f and to the assignment from Y to Z by g. Our aim is to justify the statement that $X \sim Z$ by finding a one-to-one correspondence between X and Z. Figure 14-2 suggests that we assign $g(f(x))$, which is a member of Z, to x. Is this assignment one-to-one? One and only one member of Z—namely, $g(f(x))$—is

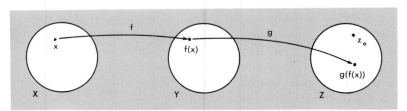

FIGURE 14-2   *Successive correspondences.*

thereby allotted to an arbitrary member x of X. But consider an arbitrary member z_0 of Z. Did we in this assignment allot z_0 to a member of X and, if so, to only one? Since g is one-to-one, one and only one member y_0 of Y exists such that $g(y_0) = z_0$; and since f is one-to-one, one and only one member x_0 of X exists such that $f(x_0) = y_0$. Hence, in particular,

$$z_0 = g(y_0) = g(f(x_0)),$$

which shows that we did indeed allot z_0 to a member of X, namely to x_0. But in this assignment did we happen by mischance to allot z_0 also to some other member, say x_1, of X with $x_1 \neq x_0$? No, for $f(x_1) \neq f(x_0)$, f being one-to-one. Hence, $f(x_1) \neq y_0$, and since g is one-to-one, $g(f(x_1)) \neq g(y_0)$. Therefore, $g(f(x_1)) \neq z_0$, a result showing that we did not allot z_0 to x_1. We conclude that the correspondence between X and Z that we set up through our assignment is one-to-one, as desired. Property (c) (transitivity) is thus proved.

EXERCISES

1. Prove properties (a) and (b).
2. Use properties (a), (b), and (c) of an equivalence relation to prove that if

$$(X \sim Y) \text{ and } (Z \sim Y) \text{ then } (X \sim Z)$$

3. A football stadium holds 40,000 people. During a game an attendant noticed only 100 seats vacant. He concluded that 39,900 seats were filled. How does one-to-one correspondence play a rule in verifying the attendant's conclusion? (HINT: Read the following discussion.)

4. The following sets are all equally infinite. Find rules that establish one-to-one correspondences between *a* and *b*, *a* and *c*, and *a* and *d*, where *a*, *b*, *c*, *d* are four sets defined as follows:

$$a = \{1, 2, 4, 6, 8, 10, \ldots\}$$
$$b = \{1, 1/2, 1/4, 1/6, 1/8, 1/10, \ldots\}$$
$$c = \{3, 6, 12, 18, 24, 30, \ldots\}$$
$$d = \{0, 1, 3, 5, 7, 9, \ldots\}$$

Is it odd that we permit ourselves to call two sets equally infinite before defining different degrees of infinitude? Consider the analogous question with respect to finite sets. Without knowing how to count, could we still say that two sets are equally numerous? We could indeed. A mathematician observed to me in this connection that his granddaughter at the age of three used to set the table for the correct number, not by counting, but by associating each place with the member of the family who occupied it. She thereby achieved a one-to-one correspondence between the two sets

{Mommy, Daddy, Grandpa, Grandma, Aunt Mabel, Uncle Henry, Jimmie, Bill, Sue}

and

{the places at the table}

as well as if she had been able to count to nine. Even after we grow up, we often find such matching procedures to our advantage. For instance, at the theatre we can tell whether the seats and the customers are equally numerous without actually counting either. At an embassy ball, one may not know how many men and women are dancing and yet be assured that the numbers are the same. Such examples make it quite clear that the concept of two sets being equally numerous is acceptable psychologically as well as logically, even without the concept of actual numbers.† In this light, the question at the beginning of the paragraph has a negative answer: it is not odd to permit ourselves to call two sets equally infinite before defining different degrees of infinitude.

The property of cardinal equivalence is very different among infinite sets from what our experience with finite sets suggests. For instance, as we shall show, a part of a line segment is cardinally equivalent to the whole segment. Take any straight line segment *AB*, and let *C* denote a point between *A* and *B*, *AC* thus being a line segment that is a portion only of *AB* (Figure 14-3). Now take a straight

---

†Bertrand Russell and A. N. Whitehead made cardinal equivalence the fundamental idea from which their logical development of numbers begins. This was in their celebrated work, *Principia Mathematica*, Cambridge University Press, Cambridge. Vol. 1, 1925; Vol. 2, 1927; Vol. 3, 1927.

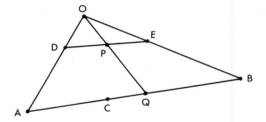

line segment DE equal in length to AC, such that the straight lines AD and BE are different and thus intersect in one point O. We assume each of the segments AB, AC, DE to include its end points. Since AC and DE are equal, we have already noted a one-to-one correspondence between them showing them to be equally infinite. By transitivity, it therefore suffices to prove that DE and AB are cardinally equivalent and, thus, to establish a one-to-one correspondence between them. To D we assign A, to E we assign B, and to any point P of DE we assign the point Q at which the straight line OP intersects the segment AB. This assignment obviously is one-to-one and shows, by its existence, that DE and AB are equally infinite, as asserted.

If we try to put this result into intuitive terms, we seem to run into a paradox. Cardinal equivalence generalizes the idea of two sets having the same number of members. Hence, wishing to express the previous result as well as we can in every day terms, we might say that a small segment has as many points as a large one. This does seem a paradox, especially if the small segment belongs to the large. But the every day words, "has as many points as," simply do not convey the exactly defined meaning of the technical expression, "is cardinally equivalent to." Intuitive language in this case is misleading, and this is the cause of the paradox. Perhaps a deeper cause was an unfortunate expectation that infinite sets will resemble finite sets, for, in striking ways, they do not.

The result we have just proved may seem at first sight to conceal another paradox, for it does appear to imply — and Figure 14-3 confirms — that the points of shorter line segments are more closely packed than those of longer segments. But points are not physical entities, like beads or atoms. They are ideal objects conceived to occupy no space, between any two points infinitely many other points occurring. No two points are contiguous; no two points are consecutive. It is misleading to think of the points on a line as being somehow packed together like peas in a pod, and this is the explanation of the paradox.

EXERCISES

5. Prove that any line segment not containing its end points is cardinally equivalent to a half-line that does not contain its end point. HINT: Refer to Figure 14-4.

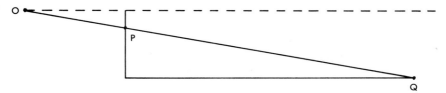

FIGURE 14-4   *One-to-one correspondence between segment and half-line.*

6. Prove that any line segment of finite length that does not include its end points is cardinally equivalent to a whole straight line. HINT: Refer to Figure 14-5.

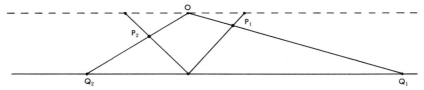

FIGURE 14-5   *One-to-one correspondence between a bent segment and a straight line.*

7. Prove that a half-line that does not include its end point is cardinally equivalent to a whole straight line.

8. Prove that any circle with a single point deleted is cardinally equivalent to a whole straight line. HINT: See Figure 14-6.

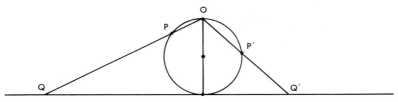

FIGURE 14-6   *One-to-one correspondence between a circle with one point deleted and a straight line.*

9. Prove that any square is cardinally equivalent to any circle by proving:

(a) a square is cardinally equivalent to its circumscribed circle;

(b) all circles are cardinally equivalent (HINT: translate circles so that their centers coincide);

(c) all squares are cardinally equivalent;

(d) use the transitive law of equivalence to arrive at the conclusion.

10. Let T be the set of points *inside* a square, for instance, the set

$$T = \text{set of all points } (x, y) \text{ such that } \begin{cases} 0 < x < 1 \\ 0 < y < 1 \end{cases}.$$

Prove that T is cardinally equivalent to the whole plane. HINT: Use the result of Exercise 6.

2.

Denumerable infinity

A set that is cardinally equivalent to the set of natural numbers

$$1, 2, 3, 4, \ldots$$

is said to be *denumerable*.

Example 1: Positive even numbers. A one-to-one correspondence is easily set up between the set of natural numbers and the set of positive even numbers, proving the latter to be denumerable. In fact, to each natural number k assign the even number $2k$. Under this correspondence, one and just one even number is assigned to each natural number, and, on the other hand, each even number is assigned to one and just one natural number. In other words, the correspondence is one-to-one, and the denumerability of the positive even numbers follows.

Example 2: The set $\{1, 3, 2, 4, 6, \ldots\}$ consisting of 1, 3, and all the positive even numbers. This set also is denumerable, as we show by setting up a one-to-one correspondence with the set of natural numbers (Table 14-1), n here being restricted to natural numbers greater than 2.

Natural Number	Associated Member of the Given Set	
1	1	
2	3	
3	2	Table 14-1
4	4	
5	6	
n	2(n − 2)	

Example 3: The set of primes. We know that infinitely many primes exist (Chapter 11, Section 3). We shall prove that the set of primes is denumerable by setting up a one-to-one correspondence with the set of natural numbers, as follows. To the natural number 1, assign the smallest prime. To the natural number 2, assign the second smallest prime. To the natural number 3, assign the third smallest prime. In general, to the natural number k, assign the kth smallest prime.

Example 4: The set of all integers. We can prove this set to be denumerable by constructing a one-to-one correspondence with the natural numbers, as suggested by Table 14-2. We can describe the assignment in general terms as follows. To the natural number 1, we assign the integer 0; to the natural numbers 2 and 3, we assign the integers 1 and -1, respectively. Then for $n = 1, 2, 3, 4, \ldots$, if we assigned the integer $-n$ to the natural number k, we next assign the integers $n + 1$ and $-(n + 1)$ to the natural numbers $k + 1$ and $k + 2$, respectively. Each integer thereby is assigned to one and just one natural number, and every natural number has one and just one integer assigned to it. In other words, the assignment defines a one-to-one correspondence such as was desired.

	Natural Number	Assigned Integer
	1	0
	2	1
	3	-1
Table 14-2	4	2
	5	-2
	6	3
	7	-3
	8	4
	9	-4

Example 5: The set of rational numbers between 0 and 1. Each rational number is represented by one, and but one, irreducible fraction. (This is a fraction of the form p/q, where $q \neq 0$ and p and q are integers with no common divisors.) Let us arrange all fractions between 0 and 1 by their denominators and eliminate all those not in lowest terms. The first few assignments made this way are shown in Table 14-3. All irreducible fractions (including 0 and 1) between 0 and 1 are thus listed, first those with denominator 1, then those with denominator 2, then those with denominator 3, and so forth, fractions with the same denominator being placed in order of size. Each fraction is assigned to the natural number that indicates its place on the list. This assignment is obviously one-to-one.

Table 14-3

Natural Number	1	2	3	4	5	6	7	8	9	10	11	12	13	14	15	16	17
Assigned Fraction	$\frac{0}{1}$	$\frac{1}{1}$	$\frac{1}{2}$	$\frac{1}{3}$	$\frac{2}{3}$	$\frac{1}{4}$	$\frac{3}{4}$	$\frac{1}{5}$	$\frac{2}{5}$	$\frac{3}{5}$	$\frac{4}{5}$	$\frac{1}{6}$	$\frac{5}{6}$	$\frac{1}{7}$	$\frac{2}{7}$	$\frac{3}{7}$	$\frac{4}{7}$

Example 6: The set of all positive rationals. The preceding example gives us no reason to expect the set of all positive rationals to be denumerable. Yet it is, as we shall see by arranging all positive irreducible fractions successively in one list and then associating each fraction with the natural number that indicates its order in the list. The association obviously will be one-to-one. We shall arrange the

positive fractions according to the *sum* of numerator and denominator. First comes

$$1/1 \quad \text{(numerator plus denominator} = 2),$$

then come

$$1/2, \ 2/1 \quad \text{(numerator plus denominator} = 3),$$

then

$$1/3, \ 3/1 \quad \text{(numerator plus denominator} = 4),$$

next

$$1/4, \ 2/3, \ 3/2, \ 4/1 \quad \text{(numerator plus denominator} = 5),$$

and so on. The list thus begins as follows:

$$1, \ 1/2, \ 2, \ 1/3, \ 3, \ 1/4, \ 2/3, \ 3/2, \ 4, \ 1/5, \ 5, \ 1/6, \ 2/5, \ 3/4, \ 4/3, \ 5/2, \ 6, \ \ldots.$$

EXERCISES

1. Suppose the set $\{b_1, b_2, \ldots, b_n\}$ to have n members and the set $S = \{a_1, a_2, a_3, \ldots\}$ to be denumerable. Prove that the set $\{b_1, b_2, \ldots, b_n, a_1, a_2, a_3, \ldots\}$ is denumerable.

2. Suppose that the set $S = \{a_1, a_2, a_3, \ldots\}$ and the set $T = \{b_1, b_2, b_3, \ldots\}$ are both denumerable. Prove that the set $S \cup T$ containing all the members of S and all the members of T is denumerable.

3. Consider the denumerable sets $A_1, A_2, \ldots, A_k$, where

$$A_1 = \{a_{11}, a_{12}, a_{13}, \ldots\}$$
$$A_2 = \{a_{21}, a_{22}, a_{23}, \ldots\}$$
$$A_k = \{a_{k1}, a_{k2}, a_{k3}, \ldots\}.$$

Prove that $A_1 \cup A_2 \cup \ldots \cup A_k$ (that is, the set found by combining all members of the sets $A_1, \ldots, A_k$) is again denumerable. This proves that the union of a finite number of denumerable sets is again denumerable.

4. If n and k are, say, positive integers, by the positive kth root of n we mean the positive number x such that $x^k = n$; we denote this kth root by $n^{1/k}$. (Here we pass over the fact that $n^{1/k}$ in general is "irrational." See Chapter 15.) Show that the set $\{n^{1/k}\}$ for all pairs of positive integers n and k is denumerable. HINT: Adapt the method of Example 6.

In a denumerable set, the member assigned to the natural number 1 under a particular one-to-one correspondence is commonly denoted by such a symbol as a_1, the member assigned to the natural number 2 under this correspondence by a_2, and so on. The member of the set assigned to the natural number n under the given correspondence is denoted by a_n and the set itself by

$$\{a_1, a_2, \ldots\}.$$

(Of course, a different one-to-one correspondence will lead to a different system of labeling.) A denumerable set so presented as a list, in which all the members appear successively, is called a *sequence*.

Example 7: A denumerable set from which one member has been removed. From a denumerable set, remove one member. We shall show that the set of remaining elements is again denumerable. Call the removed member a_1, and represent S as

$$S = \{a_1, a_2, a_3, \ldots\}.$$

We have to find a one-to-one correspondence between S and

$$A = \{a_2, a_3, \ldots\}.$$

We assign a member of A to each member of S as in Table 14-4,

Member of S	Assigned Member of A
a_1	a_2
a_2	a_3
a_3	a_4
a_4	a_5
a_n	a_{n+1}

Table 14-4

where, in general, $n = 1, 2, 3, \ldots$. This is evidently a one-to-one correspondence as required, and the assertion is proved.

Example 8: Any infinite subset of a denumerable set. Recall that a subset of a set S is a set all of whose members belong to S. If S is denumerable, and A is an arbitrary subset, we shall show that A also is denumerable. Arranging S as a sequence, we can write

$$S = \{a_1, a_2, \ldots\}.$$

Beginning with a_1, we now examine each a_j in turn to see whether it belongs to A. Let a_{j_1} denote the first a_j to belong to A (thus, j_1 is the least index j such that a_j belongs to A). Let a_{j_2} be the second a_j to belong to A. In general, let a_{j_n} be the nth a_j to belong to A for $n = 1, 2, \ldots$. Every member of A is some a_j and hence will eventually be counted as an a_{j_k} for some k. Therefore,

$$A = \{a_{j_1}, a_{j_2}, \ldots\}.$$

Now if for $n = 1, 2, \ldots$, we assign the element a_{j_n} to the natural number n, we obviously have a one-to-one correspondence between the natural numbers and A. Therefore, A is denumerable.

Examples 1, 2, 3, and 7 are special cases of the result of Example 8. Also in view of this result, Example 5 is a consequence of Example 6.

Examples 7 and 8 tell us that any denumerable set is cardinally equivalent to a proper subset† of itself. We shall now see that any infinite set is cardinally equivalent to a proper subset of itself. To prove this, we must know that any infinite subset M contains a denumerable subset S. Once we know this, we can argue as follows. Let M_1 denote the set that remains after the members of S have been removed from M. Then M is the union of M_1 and S, which have no common elements.‡ Figure 14-7A is a schematic illustration, in which M_1 and S are represented by areas.) Since S is denumerable, S contains a proper subset S_1 that is also denumerable (see Example 7).

A

B

C

FIGURE 14-7   Diagram of a set and certain of its subsets.

(In Figure 14-7B an area supposed to represent S_1 is marked off by a dashed line from the area representing S.) The union of S_1 and M_1 is a proper subset of M. We shall call this proper subset N. (N is represented by the cross-hatched area in Figure 14-7C.) Our aim is to prove that M and N are cardinally equivalent. Since S and S_1 are both denumerable, a one-to-one correspondence between them exists; if z is an arbitrary member of S, let

$$g(z)$$

denote the member of S_1 assigned to z under this correspondence. To each x in M, now assign a member of N, as follows:

    (a) if x belongs to M_1, the member of N we assign to x is x itself, this belonging to M_1 and thus to N;

    (b) if x belongs to S, the member of N we assign to x is $g(x)$, this belonging to S_1 and thus to N.

---

    †Recall that a "subset" of a set A is a set all of whose members belong to A. The subset is "proper" if it does not contain all members of A.
    ‡"Element" and "member" are used synonomously.

Figure 14-8 illustrates this assignment. Under this assignment, one and just one element of N is allotted each element of M. On the other hand, we shall verify that each element of N is assigned to one, and just one, member of M. Let y be an arbitrary member of N. Since M_1 and S_1 make up N, y is either in M_1 or in S_1. If y is in M_1, then according to (a) y is assigned to one and only one element of M_1, namely to y itself. If y is in S_1, then according to (b) y is assigned to the one and only element z of S such that $g(z) = y$. Since M_1 and S have no elements in common, y is assigned in either case to one and just one element of M. Hence, the correspondence between M and N defined by (a) and (b) is one-to-one, and M and N are cardinally equivalent, as contended.

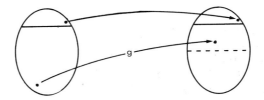

FIGURE 14-8 Diagrammatic representation of a certain correspondence between a set and a subset of itself.

We have yet to show that any infinite set M contains a denumerable subset. Since M is infinite, M contains, in particular, one element. Take such an element, calling it a_1, and consider the set M_1 of remaining elements. This set M_1 is again infinite and therefore certainly contains one element, which we shall call a_2. Removing a_2 from M_1 leaves a set M_2 that again is infinite, thus containing a new element, which we call a_3, and which we remove. We continue in this way. For any $n = 1, 2, 3, \ldots$, after we have removed n elements

$$a_1, a_2, a_3, \ldots, a_n$$

from M, infinitely many elements still remain, and we can remove one more, which we call

$$a_{n+1}.$$

Each member of the set

$$\{a_1, a_2, a_3, \ldots\}$$

thus has a successor, and the set therefore is infinite. By our previous remarks, it is denumerable. Hence, it is a denumerable subset of M, as was desired.

EXERCISES

5. No finite set is cardinally equivalent to a proper subset of itself, while, as we have proved, every infinite set has this property. In some treatments, infinite sets are *defined* to be sets that have proper subsets to which they are

cardinally equivalent. Why is this definition attractive logically? HINT: We defined infinite sets by means of the concept of number.

6. Consider a line segment of finite length including one or both end points. Use the preceding construction to prove that it is cardinally equivalent to a line segment not containing its end points. Then show its cardinal equivalence to an infinite line. HINT: For the latter point, see Exercise 6, Section 1.

3.

Degrees of infinitude†

Suppose two sets, A and B, to be given. If A is cardinally equivalent to a subset of B, but B is cardinally equivalent to no subset of A, then we shall consider B to be *more highly infinite* than A. We shall also say that B is infinite *to a higher degree* than A and, more briefly, that the *power* of B exceeds that of A.

EXERCISES

1. Why cannot B be more highly infinite than A and, at the same time, be cardinally equivalent to A?

2. Show that if the power of B exceeds that of A, then A is cardinally equivalent to a *proper* subset of B.

3. Can A be cardinally equivalent to a proper subset of B and B cardinally equivalent to a proper subset of A? HINT: See the examples of the previous subsection, for instance, Example 1.

4. Using the rules for negation (Section 7, Chapter 1), state the conditions under which B is *not* more highly infinite than A.

We shall now show that different degrees of infinitude exist. In fact, we shall show how every set leads to another set with higher power.

Theorem 1.   Given an arbitrary infinite set A, define S to be the collection of all subsets of A. Then S is more highly infinite than A.

PROOF: We must show two things: that (1) A is cardinally equivalent to a suitable subset of S, and that (2) S is cardinally equivalent to no subset of A. We now prove statement (1). For each member x of A, let $\{x\}$ denote the subset of A consisting of this single member x. Let S_1 be the subset of S that consists of all such singly membered subsets $\{x\}$ for x in A. Assigning to each x in A the cor-

---

† The tight reasoning in this section demands no prior knowledge other than that of how to think abstractly, and it provides very good exercise in doing that.

responding singly membered subset $\{x\}$ gives us a one-to-one correspondence between A and S_1, the existence of which proves A to be cardinally equivalent to a subset of S, as desired. Statement (1) is thus justified, and we turn to statement (2).

We must show that S is cardinally equivalent to no subset of A. Suppose that, to the contrary, S is cardinally equivalent to some subset E of A. For arbitrary x in E, let

$$f(x)$$

denote the member of S assigned to x under some particular one-to-one correspondence between E and S, such as exists under the supposition of cardinal equivalence. Then to every subset U of A (U is a member of S), one and only one member u of E exists such that $f(u) = U$. We shall call a member x of E "good"† if x is a member of $f(x)$; otherwise, we shall say that x is "bad." (An example of a good member of E is the member e such that $f(e) = E$. An example of a bad member is the member e_0 such that $f(e_0) = \varnothing$, where $\varnothing$ denotes the empty set, the set without members [see Chapter 12, Section 9]. These examples are not strictly necessary, since the argument to follow does not require us to know in advance whether good elements or bad elements actually occur.) Under these definitions, no member of E is both good and bad, while every member of E is either good or bad. We now define a particular subset Z (of A) as the set of all bad members of E. Let z, belonging to E, be such that

$$f(z) = Z.$$

This z is either good or bad, but not both. If z is good, it follows from the definition of good that z belongs to Z, while Z consists only of the bad members of E. This is a contradiction, and we deduce that z is bad. But then Z by its definition contains z as a member, under which circumstance z would be good, in contradiction to our assuming z to be bad. Thus, z is neither good nor bad, which is impossible. Therefore, z does not exist. Yet we can define z if a one-to-one correspondence exists between S and a subset of A. Hence, no such correspondence exists, and S is cardinally equivalent to no subset of A. The theorem is proved.

---

† I take this excellent term from I. P. Natanson, *Theory of Functions of a Real Variable*, Frederick Ungar Publishing Company, New York. Revised Edition, 1961, Volume I, p. 29.

EXERCISE

5. Prove our statement that no member of E is both good and bad, while every member of E is either good or bad.

The abstraction and elegance of this proof are typical of the theory of sets. Another such proof follows. In it, we use the customary notation

$$A \subset B, \text{ or } B \supset A,$$

to mean that A is a proper subset of B—i.e., that every member of A belongs to B, while at least one member of B does not belong to A—where A and B denote sets. By

$$A \subset C \subset B, \text{ or } B \supset C \supset A,$$

we mean that A is a proper subset of C and C a proper subset of B. Longer chains, such as

$$A_1 \subset A_2 \subset A_3 \subset A_4 \ldots$$

have analogous meanings. When X and Y are any sets, by the *difference*

$$X - Y$$

we mean the set of members of X that do *not* belong to Y.

Theorem 2. Suppose $A \supset A_1 \supset A_2$. If A is cardinally equivalent to A_2, then A is cardinally equivalent to A_1. In words: if A is cardinally equivalent to a proper subset of itself, then A is cardinally equivalent to any intermediate subset.

PROOF: The strategy in proving this theorem is somehow to break up both A and A_1 into infinitely many disjoint† subsets, say A into

$$G_1, G_2, G_3, \ldots$$

and A_1 into

$$H_1, H_2, H_3, \ldots,$$

where no two G's and no two H's have members in common, and where G_1 is cardinally equivalent to H_1, G_2 to H_2, and so forth. Once we obtain such a system of cardinal equivalences between paired subsets of A and A_1, it will be easy to see, as follows, that A and A_1 themselves are cardinally equivalent. First, cardinal equivalence of G_1 and H_1 means that a one-to-one correspondence between them exists. For any x in G_1, let $h_1(x)$ denote the member of H_1 assigned to x under this correspondence. More generally, for $k = 1, 2, 3, \ldots,$

---

†Two sets are *disjoint* if they have no members in common.

cardinal equivalence of G_k and H_k means that a one-to-one correspondence between these sets exists; let $h_k(x)$ denote the member of H_k thereby associated with an arbitrary member x of G_k. Now take any element x of A. Since the G_k are supposed to be disjoint and to have union A, x must fall in one, and one only, of these sets, say in G_r. We then assign $h_r(x)$, which is in H_r, to x. If we denote this assignment by the symbol $h(x)$, then for an arbitrary x in A,

$$h(x) = h_r(x) \quad \text{if } x \text{ is in } G_r.$$

This assignment defines a correspondence between A and A_1. The correspondence is one-to-one because each h_r is one-to-one between G_r and H_r, the G_r are disjoint and together fill A, and the H_r are disjoint and together fill A_1. The existence of this one-to-one correspondence implies that A and A_1 are cardinally equivalent.

To prove that A and A_1 are cardinally equivalent, it will thus suffice to find subsets of A that will play the roles of the G_i and subsets of A_1 that will play the roles of the H_i. We shall do so after some preliminaries.

By assumption, a one-to-one correspondence exists between A and A_2. For an arbitrary member x of A, let $f(x)$ denote the member of A_2 assigned to x under this correspondence. If B is any subset of A, let $f(B)$ denote the set of all members of A_2 thereby assigned to the members of B. Thus,

$$f(B) = \text{set of all elements } f(x) \text{ for which } x \text{ is in } B.$$

In this notation, we have by assumption

$$A_2 = f(A).$$

Let us now set

$$A_3 = f(A_1),$$
$$A_4 = f(A_2),$$
$$A_5 = f(A_3),$$

and so forth, defining successively for $n = 1, 2, 3, \ldots,$

$$A_{n+2} = f(A_n).$$

Note that A_3 is cardinally equivalent to A_1 and that by transitivity (Section 1) A_5, being cardinally equivalent to A_3, is also cardinally equivalent to A_1. In this way, we see that the sets

(1) $A_1, A_3, A_5, \ldots, A_{2n-1}, \ldots$ $(n = 1, 2, 3, \ldots)$

with odd indices are all cardinally equivalent. In a similar way, A and the sets with even indices,

(2) $A, A_2, A_4, A_6, \ldots, A_{2n}, \ldots$ $(n = 1, 2, 3, \ldots)$

are all cardinally equivalent.

Notice also that

(3) $A \supset A_1 \supset A_2 \supset A_3 \supset A_4 \supset \ldots.$

In fact, the inclusions

$$A \supset A_1 \supset A_2$$

imply

$$f(A) \supset f(A_1) \supset f(A_2),$$

or

$$A_2 \supset A_3 \supset A_4;$$

these inclusions imply

$$f(A_2) \supset f(A_3) \supset f(A_4),$$

or

$$A_4 \supset A_5 \supset A_6,$$

and so forth. Thus, the A_n are a decreasing sequence of subsets, as asserted.

A crude diagram may be helpful, in which A is represented as a vertical half-line stretching infinitely downwards. On this line, the difference $A - A_1$ is shown as a segment at the top end, the rest of the line representing A_1. Similarly, $A_1 - A_2$ is pictured as a segment of this line below and contiguous to the previous, and so forth, as in Figure 14-9. Thus, A_k is represented by the whole line below a

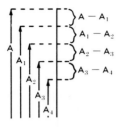

FIGURE 14-9   Diagrammatic representation of A.

certain point, which point we shall call "the top of A_k." The top of A_k is lower for higher k, consistently with relations (3). To indicate the cardinal equivalences between subsets of A, we use two parallel replicas of our vertical half-line, as in Figure 14-10. Then the cardinal equivalence between A and A_2, for instance, is indicated by drawing a line from the top of one of these replicas to the top of A_2 in the other replica. The cardinal equivalence between A_k and A_{k+2} for $k=1, 2, 3, \ldots$ is shown similarly by drawing a line between the top of A_k in the first replica to the top of A_{k+2} in the second.

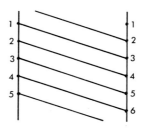

FIGURE 14-10 *Representation of cardinal equivalences.*

Figure 14-10 indicates that $A - A_1$ and $A_2 - A_3$ are cardinally equivalent, that $A_2 - A_3$ and $A_4 - A_5$ are cardinally equivalent, and so forth. (The figure is simply a diagram of the equivalences specified in (1) and (2).) In this way, we see that all the sets

(4) $\qquad A - A_1, A_2 - A_3, A_4 - A_5, A_6 - A_7, \ldots$

are cardinally equivalent. (Similarly, the sets

$$A_1 - A_2, A_3 - A_4, A_5 - A_6, A_7 - A_8, \ldots$$

are all cardinally equivalent, but we shall not use this fact.)

We are now almost ready to give decompositions of A and A_1 into nonoverlapping, pairwise cardinally equivalent subsets such as were described at the start of the proof. Notice first that A is the union of the sets

(5) $\qquad F, A - A_1, A_1 - A_2, A_2 - A_3, \ldots,$

where F consists of the members of A that belong to *all* the A_k for $k = 1, 2, 3, \ldots$. This means that every member of A either belongs to all the A_k—and thus to F—or else belongs to some A_n, but not to A_{n+1}. Similarly, A_1 is the union of the sets

(6) $\qquad F, A_1 - A_2, A_2 - A_3, \ldots.$

The sets listed as making up A and A_1 are mutually disjoint, i.e., have no members in common. Those displayed in (5), which unite into A, will be taken in order to be $G_1, G_2, \ldots$, respectively. The sets displayed in (6), uniting into A_1, will be H_1, H_2, and so forth, but not in the same order. Figure 14-11 tells us how to choose the H_i that is to be paired with G_i, and Table 14-5 records this choice in the first six

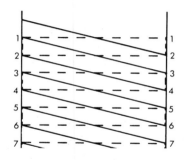

FIGURE 14-11 *The pairing of cardinally equivalent subsets of A and A_1.*

instances. The left-hand column of the table enumerates the G_i and the right-hand column the H_i $(i = 1, 2, 3, \ldots)$, in order. The first, third, fifth, and so forth, pairs in this table—i.e., G_1 and H_1, G_3 and H_3, G_5 and H_5, G_{2n-1} and H_{2n-1} for $n = 1, 2, \ldots$—are cardinally equivalent under the "identity" correspondence, under which x is assigned to x. The second, fourth, sixth, and so forth, pairs—i.e., G_2 and H_2, G_4 and H_4, G_6 and H_6, G_{2n} and H_{2n} for $n = 1, 2, 3, \ldots$—are cardinally equivalent according to (4). The theorem is thus proved.

Table 14-5 *Pairs of cardinally equivalent subsets of A and A_1*

Subset of A	Cardinally equivalent Subset of A_1
F	F
$A - A_1$	$A_2 - A_3$
$A_1 - A_2$	$A_1 - A_2$
$A_2 - A_3$	$A_4 - A_5$
$A_3 - A_4$	$A_3 - A_4$
$A_4 - A_5$	$A_6 - A_7$
$A_{2n-1} - A_{2n}$	$A_{2n-1} - A_{2n}$ for $n = 1, 2, 3, \ldots$
$A_{2n} - A_{2n+1}$	$A_{2n+2} - A_{2n+3}$ for $n = 1, 2, 3, \ldots$

Corollary. Two sets, each of which is cardinally equivalent to a subset of the other, are themselves cardinally equivalent.

PROOF: The cardinal equivalence is immediate if one of the subsets is improper. Therefore, we consider only the contrary case. Let A and B be any two sets, and suppose

$$A \supset A_1, B \supset B_1,$$

i.e., suppose A_1 and B_1 to be proper subsets of A and B, respectively. Furthermore, suppose that

A is cardinally equivalent to B_1, and
B is cardinally equivalent to A_1.

Under the cardinal equivalence of B to A_1, we see that B_1 is cardinally equivalent to a proper subset of A_1. Calling this subset A_2, we have

$$A \supset A_1 \supset A_2.$$

(See Figure 14-12.) Since A is cardinally equivalent to B_1 and B_1 to A_2, we see that A is cardinally equivalent to A_2. Thus, the hypotheses of Theorem 2 are satisfied, and Theorem 2 tells us that A and A_1 are cardinally equivalent. Since A_1 is cardinally equivalent to B, we have finally that A and B are cardinally equivalent, as asserted.

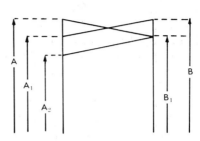

FIGURE 14-12 Diagram of cardinal equivalences between two sets and their subsets.

It follows from the last result and the definition of power that if one set A is cardinally equivalent to a subset of a second set B, then either A and B are cardinally equivalent, or else A is less highly infinite than B. Can A be not cardinally equivalent to B, not less highly infinite than B, and also not more highly infinite than B? In other words, is it possible for A to be cardinally equivalent to no subset of B and, at the same time, for B to be cardinally equivalent to no subset of A? The answer to this question is no, but the proof demands more preparation than we have time for. For a leisurely, understandable treatment of this and other more advanced topics in the theory of sets, we refer the reader to E. Kamke, *Theory of Sets*, Dover Publications, New York, 1950.

EXERCISES

6. Consider a line segment of finite length including one or both end points. Prove from the preceding theorem that it is cardinally equivalent to a line segment not containing its end points and thus is cardinally equivalent to an infinite line. (A more elementary proof was suggested in Exercise 6 of Section 2.)

7. Consider the following slightly varying squares:

$$S = \text{set of all points } (x, y) \text{ such that } \begin{cases} 0 < x \leq 1 \\ 0 < y \leq 1 \end{cases},$$

$$T = \text{set of all points } (x, y) \text{ such that } \begin{cases} 0 < x < 1 \\ 0 < y < 1 \end{cases},$$

$$U = \text{set of all points } (x, y) \text{ such that } \begin{cases} 0 \leq x \leq 1 \\ 0 \leq y \leq 1 \end{cases}.$$

Prove that they are all cardinally equivalent to the whole plane. HINT: By the previous theorem, one of these squares is strategic.

4.

The concept of limit

Since an imaginative, but somewhat muddled, suggestion of Antiphon of Athens (about 430 B.C.), so-called infinite processes have been proposed—and at times brilliantly executed—for the most diverse purposes in mathematics and its applications. Consistent general understanding of such processes developed only in the fullness of time, based on an abstract concept called "limit." This notion was invented by Augustin Cauchy at the beginning of the 19th Century after having eluded some of the greatest other mathematicians who ever lived, including Eudoxus (about 370 B.C.), Archimedes (287–212 B.C.), Newton, and Euler, whose work needed it and, as we can see with hindsight, pointed to it. From the time that this concept was clearly grasped, its influence can hardly be exaggerated.

An idea as subtle as that of limit must be explained gradually. We shall now do so, at first in simple and familiar contexts, later in connection with some of its uses. A roomful of volumes would not do full justice to these.

Our first move in the direction of the limit concept is to remark that the quantities†

$$10^{-1} = 1/10 = .1,$$
$$10^{-2} = 1/10^2 = .01,$$
$$10^{-3} = 1/10^3 = .001,$$
$$10^{-4} = 1/10^4 = .0001,$$
$$10^{-5} = 1/10^5 = .00001,$$

and so forth, all of which are representable as

$$10^{-k} = 1/10^k = \overbrace{.00 \ldots 01}^{k \text{ places}}$$

for $k = 1, 2, 3, \ldots$, come closer and closer to zero as k is made larger and larger. More precisely, if e is any positive number, no matter

---

†Recall the definition that if a and b are positive, then

$$a^{-b} = 1/a^b$$

thus, $a^{-b}a^b = 1$. Recall also that, by definition

$$a^0 = 1.$$

From these definitions it follows immediately that

$$a^c a^d = a^{c+d}$$

for any (positive, negative, zero) numbers c and d.

how small, then a corresponding *critical index* n exists such that the quantities

$$10^{-(n+1)}, \ 10^{-(n+2)}, \ 10^{-(n+3)}, \ \ldots$$

are less than e, i.e., such that

$$k > n \Rightarrow 10^{-k} < e.$$

(For instance, if $e = 1/1001$, then we can take $n = 3$; if $e = 1/4000$, again take $n = 3$; if $e = 1/40,000$, take $n = 4$.) To put the matter differently, for sufficiently large k all the quantities 10^{-k} are as small as you like. To describe this attribute of the sequence 10^{-k}, we say that 10^{-k} *approaches* zero, or *tends to* zero, or *converges to* zero, or *has limit* zero, as k *becomes infinite*.

A scale helps us to appreciate the rapidity with which 10^{-k} shrinks to zero as k increases. In Figure 14-13, 10 cm. is taken as the

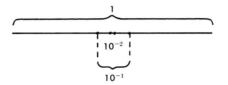

FIGURE 14-13 Decline in constant ratio.

unit. Of course, the quantity 1000^{-k} would dwindle even more dramatically. The classic picture of such geometrical decline, or decline in constant ratio, was given by Jonathan Swift, stirred by the discoveries in his day of life beyond the human eye:†

> So, naturalists observe, a flea
> Has smaller fleas that on him prey;
> And these have smaller still to bite 'em,
> And so proceed ad infinitum.

---

†Swift's works show a fascination with the microscope. See Marjorie Nicolson, *Science and Imagination*, Cornell University Press, 1956, Chapter V.

EXERCISES

1. Find an integer n such that if $k > n$, then:
   (a) $10^{-k} < 1/101,000$,
   (b) $17 \cdot 10^{-k} < 1/40$,
   (c) $2^{-k} < 1/1000$,
   (d) $15 \cdot 2^{-k} < 1/60$,
   (e) $k^{-2} < 1/100$,
   (f) $9k^{-2} < 1/40$,

(g) $17 \cdot 10^{-k} + 9k^{-2} < 1/20$,

(h) $5^{-k} + k^{-3} < 1/100$,

(i) $2^{-k} + 3 \cdot 5^{-k} + k^{-1} < 1/20$,

(j) $2^{-k} - 5^{-k} < 1/10$,

(k) $2^{-k}k^{-3} < 1/100$,

(l) $2^{-k}k^{-3} + k^{-1} < 1/50$.

2. Can the record time for running a mile diminish every year and yet never dip below 2 minutes? Explain.

Now consider the problem of representing the fraction 1/3 by a decimal. No decimal equals this fraction exactly, but a long string of threes preceded by a decimal point, for instance,

.33333333333333333333333333333333333333333333333333333,

is a very good approximation to 1/3. The longer the string of threes, the better the approximation, a thought that conceals the concept of limit as did a block of marble the statue Michelangelo carved out of it. Bringing out this concept requires us to consider explicitly the infinite sequence of decimals,

.3, .33, .333, .3333, .33333, .333333, .3333333, .33333333,

and so on. Since convenient symbols will be helpful, set

$$x_1 = .3$$
$$x_2 = .33$$
$$x_3 = .333$$
$$x_4 = .3333$$

and so forth, with x_k representing the decimal that consists of a string of k threes:

$$\overset{k \text{ places}}{\overbrace{x_k = .33 \ldots 3.}}$$

The deviations of the approximating decimals from 1/3 can be estimated from the facts that

$$3x_1 = .9 = 1 - .1 = 1 - 10^{-1},$$
$$3x_2 = .99 = 1 - .01 = 1 - 10^{-2},$$
$$3x_3 = .999 = 1 - .001 = 1 - 10^{-3},$$

and, in general,

$$3x_k = \overset{k \text{ places}}{\overbrace{.99 \ldots 9}} = 1 - \overset{k \text{ places}}{\overbrace{.00 \ldots 01}} = 1 - 10^{-k}$$

for $k = 1, 2, 3, \ldots$. Indeed, now dividing by 3, we have

$$x_k = 1/3 - (1/3)(10^{-k}).$$

Hence, the deviation of x_k from $1/3$ is

$$x_k - 1/3 = -(1/3)(10^{-k}).$$

We shall call the absolute value of this deviation the *error* committed when approximating $1/3$ by x_k. This error is

$$|x_k - 1/3| = (1/3)(10^{-k})$$

and thus, in particular, admits the following estimate:

$$|x_k - 1/3| < 10^{-k}.$$

In view of our earlier remarks about 10^{-k}, we see from this that if e is any positive number, no matter how small, then a corresponding *critical index* n exists such that

$$k > n \Rightarrow |x_k - 1/3| < e.$$

For sufficiently large k the error of approximation, $|x_k - 1/3|$, thus will be as small as we like. Extending our previous usage, we say that *the error $|x_k - 1/3|$ approaches zero, or tends to zero, or has limit zero, as k becomes infinite*. We also say that *the decimal x_k approaches $1/3$, or tends to $1/3$, or has limit $1/3$, as k becomes infinite*.

EXERCISES

3. Give a similar discussion of approximation by decimals of:
(a) 1/9,
(b) 1/99,
(c) 1/6.
Extend the new terminology appropriately in each case.

4. Extend the concepts of error, critical index, and limit to the approximation of 1 by a string of nines (preceded by a decimal point).

The problem of approximating $3/14$ by a decimal is similar to the previous problem but with more general features. No decimal is exactly equal to $3/14$, but decimals that approximate it as closely as we like can be obtained by carrying out a sufficient number of steps in the long division of 14 into 3. Here are the first few steps of the long division:

$$\begin{array}{r}
.2\,1\,4\,2\,8\,5 \\
14)\overline{3.0\,0\,0\,0\,0\,0} \\
2\,8 \\
\hline
2\,0 \\
1\,4 \\
\hline
6\,0 \\
5\,6 \\
\hline
4\,0 \\
2\,8 \\
\hline
1\,2\,0 \\
1\,1\,2 \\
\hline
8\,0 \\
7\,0 \\
\hline
1\,0
\end{array}$$

Wherever we break off the long division, we have a decimal that approximates 3/14 to some degree, and the later we break off, the better the approximation. We are thus led to consider the infinite sequence of decimals,

$$.2, .21, .214, .2142, .21428, .214285, \ldots ,$$

consisting, respectively, of the first place only, the first two places, the first three places, the first four places, and so forth in the decimal resulting from this long division. It is convenient to set

$$x_1 = .2,$$
$$x_2 = .21,$$
$$x_3 = .214,$$

and so forth with x_k representing the decimal that consists of the first k places resulting from the long division, $k = 1, 2, 3, \ldots$. The deviations from 3/14 of these decimals x_k are easily estimated from the nature of the long division process. Take $x_3 = .214$ as an example. How was x_3 determined? Narrowing this question, we ask: Having obtained the first two digits in x_3, how did we then determine the third? If you check through the actual steps in the long division, you will see that 4 was picked because .214 is less than (or at most equal to) 3/14, while .215 is greater than 3/14: in symbols, because $.214 \le 3/14$ and $.215 > 3/14$. These inequalities are conveniently combined into the statement,

$$.214 \le 3/14 < .215,$$

which we can read roughly as: "3/14 is between .214 and .215." This statement shows, in particular, that .214 and 3/14 differ by less than .001 and thus that

$$|x_3 - 3/14| < 10^{-3}.$$

It follows similarly that

$$| x_k - 3/14 | < 10^{-k}$$

for every $k = 1, 2, 3, \ldots$. Calling $| x_k - 3/14 |$ the *error* made when we approximate $3/14$ by x_k, we see that this error will be as small as we like if we make k sufficiently large. In more precise language, if e is any positive number (no matter how small), then a corresponding *critical index* n exists such that

$$k > n \Rightarrow | x_k - 3/14 | < e.$$

We say accordingly that x_k *approaches* $3/14$, or *tends to* $3/14$, or *has limit* $3/14$, as k becomes infinite.

A similar analysis can be made of the relation between any fraction and the decimal resulting from it by long division.

We are now ready to formulate the new concepts abstractly. Let

$$x_1, x_2, x_3, \ldots$$

be members of an infinite sequence of (positive, negative, or zero) numbers that approximate a given number a in a sense to be described. We represent these numbers more succinctly as

$$x_k, \ k = 1, 2, 3, \ldots.$$

The *error* in the approximation of a by x_k (for any k) is defined to be

$$| x_k - a |,$$

i.e., the absolute value of the deviation of x_k from a. When we prescribe a positive number e as the *allowed margin of error* in this approximation, we mean to require the actual error to be less than e and thus to confine k to such values that

$$| x_k - a | < e.$$

If n is such that

$$k > n \Rightarrow | x_k - a | < e,$$

we shall call n a *critical index* corresponding to e. If a critical index exists, then for all indices k greater than the critical index, the error in the approximation by x_k will be within the allowed margin of error e.

Limit is defined as follows.

Definition. If for any positive number e (no matter how small), a critical index n exists such that

$$k > n \Rightarrow |x_k - a| < e,$$

then we call a the *limit* of the x_k as k becomes infinite. We also say, synonymously, that x_k *converges to* a, *tends to* a, or *approaches* a, as k becomes infinite, and we write:

$$\lim_{k \to \infty} x_k = a,$$

the symbol ∞ being that for infinity.

The condition that $\lim_{k \to \infty} x_k = a$ means simply that a critical index exists corresponding to *any* positive number e prescribed as allowable margin of error. An equivalent condition is:

$$\lim_{k \to \infty} (x_k - a) = 0.$$

We continue with some further examples.

Example 1:   Consider the infinite sequence of numbers

$$0,\ 1/2,\ 2/3,\ 3/4,\ 4/5,\ 5/6,\ 6/7,\ 7/8,\ 8/9,\ 9/10, \ldots,$$

all of which are of the form

$$(k - 1)/k,\ k = 1, 2, 3, \ldots.$$

These numbers seemingly approach more and more nearly to 1. We can guess that 1 is their limit and shall show that this is so. Setting $x_k = (k-1)/k$, consider the deviation

$$x_k - 1 = (k - 1)/k - 1 = -1/k.$$

For the errors, defined to be the absolute values of the deviations, we have

$$|x_k - 1| = 1/k.$$

Taking a positive number e arbitrarily, are we certain to be able to find a critical index n so large that

$$k > n \Rightarrow |x_k - 1| < e?$$

Indeed we are, for by the previous equality we need merely take n so large that

$$1/n < e.$$

Since the condition $k > n$ is equivalent to

$$1/k < 1/n,$$

the transitive law gives us

$$k > n \Rightarrow 1/k < e.$$

Hence, for the n selected, it is indeed true that

$$k > n \Rightarrow |x_k - 1| = 1/k < e,$$

and we conclude that

$$\lim_{k \to \infty} x_k = 1.$$

Example 2:   If we define

$$x_k = k/(k^2 + 1)$$

for $k = 1, 2, 3, \ldots$, does x_k have a limit as k becomes infinite? We can guess the answer if we calculate x_k for several values of k, say

$$x_{10} = 10/101,$$
$$x_{100} = 100/(100^2 + 1) = 100/10{,}001,$$
$$x_{1000} = 1000/(1000^2 + 1) = 1000/1{,}000{,}001.$$

Notice that

x_{10} is approximately $10/100$, or $1/10$,
x_{100} is approximately $100/10{,}000$, or $1/100$,
x_{1000} is approximately $1000/1{,}000{,}000$, or $1/1000$.

If k is very large, we see that the 1 added to k^2 in the denominator makes very little difference and thus that

x_k is approximately k/k^2, or $1/k$.

Since $\lim_{k \to \infty} 1/k = 0$, we can guess that $\lim_{k \to \infty} x_k = 0$ as well. This conjecture can be justified by a clever (and venerable) argument. If we multiply the numerator and the denominator of a fraction by the same nonzero number, we do not change the value of the fraction. Hence,

$$x_k = k/(k^2 + 1) = \frac{(1/k^2)k}{(1/k^2)(k^2 + 1)} = \frac{1/k}{1 + 1/k^2}.$$

The last denominator is greater than 1. If we change this denominator to 1, we lessen it and thereby increase the value of the fraction as a whole, obtaining

$$x_k = \frac{1/k}{1 + 1/k^2} < \frac{1/k}{1} = 1/k.$$

If a positive number e is given arbitrarily, we have already noted that then a critical index n exists such that $k > n \Rightarrow 1/k < e$. Since $x_k > 0$ and $x_k < 1/k$, for the same value of n we also have

$$k > n \Rightarrow |x_k| < e.$$

Therefore,

$$\lim_{k \to \infty} x_k = 0$$

as we surmised.

Example 3: If we define

$$x_k = k/(k^2 - 10),$$

does x_k have a limit as k becomes infinite? Since, for instance,

$$x_{100} = 100/(100^2 - 10) = 100/9990,$$
$$x_{1000} = 1000/(1000^2 - 10) = 1000/999,990,$$

again we see that

$$x_{100} \text{ is approximately } 100/100^2, \text{ or } 1/100,$$
$$x_{1000} \text{ is approximately } 1000/1000^2, \text{ or } 1/1000.$$

Again we are led to surmise that for very large k

$$x_k \text{ is approximately } k/k^2, \text{ or } 1/k,$$

and thus tends to zero as k becomes infinite, and this proves to be the case. The previous trick is used again, but with a slight modification. First, multiply by $1/k^2$ the numerator and the denominator of the fraction in question to obtain:

$$x_k = k/(k^2 - 10) = \frac{(1/k^2)k}{(1/k^2)(k^2 - 10)} = \frac{1/k}{1 - 10/k^2}.$$

The last denominator resulting is *less than 1* but will be *greater than*, say, 1/2, for sufficiently large k. In fact,

$$1 - 10/k^2 > 1/2 \text{ if } k > 4.$$

Hence, if we change this denominator to 1/2, keeping $k > 4$, we decrease the denominator, thereby increasing the value of the fraction as a whole, to obtain

$$x_k = \frac{1/k}{1 - 10/k^2} < \frac{1/k}{1/2} = 2/k,$$

i.e.,

$$x_k < 2/k \text{ for } k > 4.$$

It is easy to show from this that $\lim_{k \to \infty} x_k = 0$. Taking any positive number e, we have to find a corresponding critical index n, for which

$$k > n \Rightarrow |x_k| < e.$$

Since $|x_k| = x_k < 2/k$ whenever $k > 4$, let us require of n that

(a) $n > 4$

and

(b) $2/n < e$.

The condition

$$k > n$$

implies that

$$1/k < 1/n$$

and therefore that

$$2/k < 2/n$$

From this, condition (b) gives us

$$2/k < e.$$

Since condition (a) implies $|x_k| < 2/k$, we thus have, finally, $|x_k| < e$ on condition that $k > n$, n satisfying conditions (a) and (b). For this n,

$$k > n \Rightarrow |x_k| < e,$$

and we conclude that

$$\lim_{k \to \infty} x_k = 0,$$

as surmised.

EXERCISES

5. Consider the sequence

$$x_k = (2k^2 + 1)/(9k^2), \quad k = 1, 2, 3, \ldots.$$

(a) What are x_1, x_2, x_3, in particular?

(b) What is the limit of the sequence as k becomes infinite? Justify your answer.

(c) Suppose we permit the margin of error .01 (i.e., we take $e = .01$). Which of the numbers 1, 2, 3, 4, 5 is a critical index corresponding to this prescribed margin of error?

(d) What is the least possible critical index for the margin of error $e = .0001$? Give your reasoning.

6. For each of the following sequences, find a critical index N for a margin of error in approximating the limit of the sequence of less than 1/10,000.

(a) $\{(k-1)/k\}$ (limit is 1).

(b) $\{k/(k^2-1)\}$ (limit is 0).

(c) $\{k/(k^2-10)\}$ (limit is 0).

(d) $\{k^2/(2k^2+7)\}$ (limit is 1/2).

(e) $\{(k+1)/(k+100)\}$ (limit is 1).

7. A sequence of numbers is said to diverge to infinity if to every positive integer M, no matter how large, there is a "critical index" N such that every term in the sequence with index greater than N exceeds M.

For each of the following sequences, all of which diverge to infinity, find a critical index for the stated value of M:

(a) $\{K^2\}$ $M = 1,000,000$,

(b) $\{(K^2+7)/(K+1)\}$ $M = 10,000$,

(c) $\{(K+3)^2\}$ $M = 100,000$,

(d) $\{K^3/K^2+9\}$ $M = 200,000$,

(e) $\{K^3/(K+9)^2\}$ $M = 200,000$,

(f) $\{\sqrt{K}/100,000\}$ $M = 100,000$.

8. The following are sequences:

(a) $\{1, -1, 1/2, -1/2, 1/3, -1/3, 1/4, -1/4, \ldots\}$

(b) $\{1, -1, 2, -2, 3, -3, 4, -4, \ldots\}$

(c) $\{1, 2, 3/2, 3/2, 5/3, 4/3, 7/4, 5/4, \ldots\}$,

where the nth term $= \begin{cases} 2n/(n+1) & \text{if } n \text{ is odd} \\ (n+2)/n & \text{if } n \text{ is even} \end{cases}$

(d) $\{1, -2, 3, -4, 5, -6, 7, -8, \ldots\}$

(e) $\{2, 1/2, 3, 1/3, 4, 1/4, \ldots\}$

(f) $\{3/2, 2/3, 4/3, 3/4, 5/4, 4/5, 6/5, 5/6, 7/6, 6/7, \ldots\}$, where the $2n$th term is $(n+1)/(n+2)$ and the $(2n-1)$-st term is $(n+2)/(n+1)$.

(g) $\{1/2, 1, 3/2, 2, 5/2, 3, \ldots\}$

(h) $\{0, 2, 1/2, 3/2, 2/3, 4/3, 3/4, 5/4, \ldots\}$

where the nth term $= \begin{cases} (n-1)/(n+1) & \text{if } n \text{ is odd} \\ (n+2)/n & \text{if } n \text{ is even} \end{cases}$

Answer the following questions for each of the sequences:

(i) Does the sequence converge? If so, what is the limit of the sequence?

(ii) If the sequence converges, find the critical index for a margin of error of 1/100.

(iii) A sequence is said to diverge to $+\infty$ if to every positive integer M there is a critical index N such that every term of the sequence beyond the Nth term is larger than M. Do any of the sequences diverge to ∞?

(iv) A sequence is said to diverge to $-\infty$ if to every negative integer $-M$ there is a critical index N such that every term of the sequence beyond the Nth term is less than $-M$. Do any of the sequences diverge to $-\infty$?

(v) Do any of the nonconvergent sequences have convergent subsequences? Which sequences? Which subsequences?

(vi) Do any of the sequences have subsequences that diverge to $+\infty$ or $-\infty$? Which sequences? Which subsequences?

(vii) Do any of the convergent sequences have nonconvergent subsequences? Which sequences? Which subsequences?

9. Following are descriptions of certain infinite sequences. In each case decide from the description whether

(a) the sequence converges,

(b) the sequence does not converge,

(c) there is not enough information to know for certain whether the sequence converges or not. Give examples wherever possible.

The numbers in each sequence are supposed to be positive.

(i) Infinitely many terms of the sequence have value greater than 1/2.

(ii) Each term of the sequence is greater than the corresponding term of a sequence that is known not to converge.

(iii) All the terms of the sequence are identical.

(iv) All but a finite number of the terms of the sequence have values less one.

(v) Each term of the sequence is exactly one thousand times as great as the corresponding term of a convergent sequence.

(vi) 384 terms of the sequence each have values greater than 100,000.

(vii) Each term is greater than the preceding.

(viii) If the sequence were started at the 1000th term instead of the 1st term, it would converge.

(ix) If the sequence were started at the 1000th term rather than at the 1st term, it would not converge.

Example 4:   Let r be a positive number less than 1:

$$0 < r < 1.$$

Having noticed before that

$$\lim_{k \to \infty} (1/2)^k = 0 \text{ and } \lim_{k \to \infty} (1/10)^k = 0,$$

we shall now prove the more general statement that

$$\lim_{k \to \infty} r^k = 0.$$

Since $r > 0$ and $r < 1$, we have

$$1/r > 1$$

and, therefore,

$$1/r = 1 + s,$$

where

$$s > 0.$$

Therefore,

$$(1/r)^k = (1 + s)^k.$$

We shall prove that

$$(1 + s)^k > ks.$$

Accepting this inequality for the present, from it we obtain

$$1/r^k = (1 + s)^k > ks$$

and, thus,

$$r^k < 1/ks .$$

If s had the particular value $1/2$, this inequality would read

$$r^k < 2/k$$

and from Example 3 we know how this implies that $\lim_{k \to \infty} r^k = 0$. We shall see that the same kind of reasoning works for any other value of s not zero. Taking any positive number e, we have to prove that a critical index n exists for which

$$k > n \Rightarrow r^k < e.$$

We choose n such that

$$1/ns < e$$

(which means that $1 < ens$ and thus that $1/es < n$). The condition

$$k > n$$

implies that

$$1/k < 1/n$$

and, since $s > 0$, that

$$1/ks < 1/ns .$$

Hence, since $1/ns < e$, the condition $k > n$ implies that

$$1/ks < e.$$

Since, however, $r^k < 1/ks$, we conclude that

$$k > n \Rightarrow r^k < e$$

and thus that

$$\lim_{k \to \infty} r^k = 0,$$

as asserted.

We have still to prove that for any positive integer k and any positive number s,

$$(1 + s)^k > ks.$$

We shall, in fact, show that

$$(1 + s)^k > 1 + ks \text{ for } k \geq 2,$$

which implies the inequality we need. We do so by mathematical induction, which takes two steps. The first step is to verify that the relation being justified holds for $k = 2$. Since $(1 + s)^2 = 1 + 2s + s^2$, this is immediate. In the second step, we assume the relation to be known for $k = n$, where n is any integer at least 2, and must then prove it for $k = n + 1$. Thus, we assume that

$$(1 + s)^n > 1 + ns.$$

It follows from this that

$$\begin{aligned}
(1 + s)^{n+1} &> (1 + s)(1 + ns) \\
&= 1 + ns + s + ns^2 \\
&= 1 + (n + 1)s + ns^2 \\
&> 1 + (n + 1)s
\end{aligned}$$

and thus that the relation being considered does hold for $k = n + 1$. This completes the mathematical induction.

We end this section with some simple, useful theoretical results.

Knowledge of the first would have shortened our labors in Examples 3 and 4. It says that if x_k tends to zero as k becomes infinite, then so does ax_k, where a is any constant.

Theorem 1.   If $\lim_{k \to \infty} x_k = 0$, then $\lim_{k \to \infty} ax_k = 0$, a being any number whatsoever.

PROOF: By assumption, if an arbitrary positive number e_1 is given, then a critical index n_1 can be found such that

$$(1) \qquad\qquad k > n_1 \Rightarrow |x_k| < e_1.$$

We wish to prove that if an arbitrary positive number e is prescribed as allowed margin of error in the approximation of 0 by ax_k, then a critical index n exists such that

$$(2) \qquad\qquad k > n \Rightarrow |ax_k| < e.$$

The problem is trivial if $a = 0$. Hence, assume $a \neq 0$, and take $e_1 = e/|a|$. We are promised an n_1 satisfying (1) corresponding to this (or any other) choice of e_1. The value of n_1 for this choice of e_1 will turn out to be an acceptable value of n. In fact, by (1) we have

$$k > n_1 \Rightarrow |x_k| < e_1 = e/|a|.$$

But the inequality $|x_k| < e/|a|$ is equivalent to $|ax_k| < e$. Hence,

$$k > n_1 \Rightarrow |ax_k| < e,$$

which means that (2) holds with $n = n_1$ and thus that $\lim_{k \to \infty} ax_k = 0$, as asserted.

We now generalize the last result to an arbitrary limit.

Theorem 2.   If $\lim_{k \to \infty} x_k = y$, then $\lim_{k \to \infty} ax_k = ay$ for any number a whatsoever.

PROOF: The assumption $\lim_{k \to \infty} x_k = y$ is equivalent to the condition $\lim_{k \to \infty} (x_k - y) = 0$. Hence, setting

$$z_k = x_k - y,$$

we have

$$\lim_{k \to \infty} z_k = 0.$$

It follows, in view of Theorem 1, that

$$\lim_{k \to \infty} az_k = 0,$$

i.e., that

$$\lim_{k \to \infty} (ax_k - ay) = 0$$

(since $az_k = ax_k - ay$), while the last relation is equivalent to

$$\lim_{k \to \infty} ax_k = ay.$$

Thus, the theorem is proved.

The next two results refer to addition. Before giving them, we mention the fact that any two numbers x and y will satisfy the relation:

$$|x + y| \leq |x| + |y|.$$

A few examples, for instance

$$
\begin{aligned}
x &= 3, \; y = 5, \\
x &= -3, \; y = -5, \\
x &= 3, \; y = -5, \\
x &= -3, \; y = 5,
\end{aligned}
$$

make this rather obvious, but we shall prove it formally. Since

$$
\begin{aligned}
x &= |x| \quad \text{if } x \geq 0 \\
&= -|x| \quad \text{if } x < 0,
\end{aligned}
$$

we have, in particular, that

$$x \leq |x| \quad \text{and} \quad x \geq -|x|.$$

Similarly,

$$y \leq |y| \quad \text{and} \quad y \geq -|y|.$$

Adding gives us

$$x + y \leq |x| + |y| \quad \text{and} \quad x + y \geq -|x| - |y| = -(|x| + |y|),$$

and these two inequalities tell us that

$$|x + y| \leq |x| + |y|,$$

as asserted.

Theorem 3.   If $\lim_{k \to \infty} x_k = 0$ and $\lim_{k \to \infty} y_k = 0$, then $\lim_{k \to \infty} (x_k + y_k) = 0$.

PROOF: By assumption, if arbitrary positive numbers e_1 and e_2 are given, then critical indexes n_1 and n_2 can be found such that

$$
\begin{aligned}
k > n_1 &\Rightarrow |x_k| < e_1, \\
k > n_2 &\Rightarrow |y_k| < e_2.
\end{aligned}
$$

If we take n_3 to be the larger of n_1 and n_2, we then have

$$k > n_3 \Rightarrow |x_k| < e_1 \quad \text{and} \quad |y_k| < e_2.$$

We wish to prove that for any positive number e taken arbitrarily, a critical index n exists such that

$$k > n \Rightarrow |x_k + y_k| < e.$$

For this purpose, take $e_1 = e_2 = e/2$ and find n_3 correspondingly. Since $|x_k + y_k| \leq |x_k| + |y_k|$, we have for $k > n_3$

$$|x_k + y_k| \leq e/2 + e/2 = e.$$

Thus, n_3 will serve as the desired critical index n, and the theorem is proved.

Theorem 4. If $\lim_{k \to \infty} x_k = u$ and $\lim_{k \to \infty} y_k = v$, then $\lim_{k \to \infty} (x_k + y_k) = u + v$. In other words, the limit of a sum is the sum of the limits.

PROOF: We have

$$x_k + y_k - (u + v) = (x_k - u) + (y_k - v),$$

while $x_k - u$ and $y_k - v$ by hypothesis tend to zero as k becomes infinite. Theorem 3 shows that $(x_k - u) + (y_k - v)$ and, therefore,

$$x_k + y_k - (u + v)$$

tend to zero as k becomes infinite. This means that the limit of $x_k + y_k$ is $u + v$ as $k \to \infty$, as asserted.

Corollary.   If $\lim_{k \to \infty} x_k = u$ and $\lim_{k \to \infty} y_k = v$, then for any numbers a and b,

$$\lim (ax_k + by_k) = au + bv.$$

Hence, in particular,

$$\lim (x_k - y_k) = u - v.$$

In words: the limit of a linear combination is the linear combination of the limits, and the limit of a difference is the difference of the limits.

PROOF: We have

$$\lim_{k \to \infty} (ax_k + by_k) = \lim_{k \to \infty} ax_k + \lim_{k \to \infty} by_k \qquad \text{(by Theorem 4)}$$

$$= au + bv \qquad \text{(by Theorem 2).}$$

Choosing $a = 1$ and $b = -1$ gives the result concerning differences.

An analogous result concerning the limit of reciprocals requires the fact that arbitrary numbers x and y satisfy the condition

$$|x - y| \geq |x| - |y|.$$

This says that the absolute value of a difference is not less than the difference of absolute values. An equivalent form of the inequality,

$$|x + y| \geq |x| - |y|,$$

results from the original by replacing y by $-y$. The inequality is a consequence of the previously proved relation

$$|u + v| \leq |u| + |v|,$$

holding for all pairs of numbers u and v. Indeed, set $x = u + v$, and express v in terms of x and u as $v = x - u$. We obtain

$$|x| \leq |u| + |x - u|,$$

or

$$|x - u| \geq |x| - |u|.$$

Since u and v were permitted any values, the same is true of u and x. Hence, the last inequality is what we wished.

We use the inequality just deduced to prove a simple fact about convergent sequences necessary in considering the reciprocal of a limit.

Lemma.   If $u \neq 0$ and $\lim_{k \to \infty} x_k = u$, then an index K exists such that

$$k \geq K \Rightarrow |x_k| > |u|/2.$$

PROOF: Since $\lim_{k \to \infty} x_k = u$, an index K exists such that

$$k \geq K \Rightarrow |x_k - u| < |u|/2.$$

(Here, the allowed margin of error is $|u|/2$.) Then for $k \geq K$, we have

$$|x_k| = |u + (x_k - u)| \geq |u| - |x_k - u|$$
$$> |u| - |u|/2 = |u|/2.$$

Now we can take up the result referred to concerning reciprocals.

Theorem 5.   If $x_k \neq 0$, for $k = 1, 2, \ldots$, $u \neq 0$, and $\lim_{k \to \infty} x_k = u$, then

$$\lim_{k \to \infty} x_k^{-1} = u^{-1}.$$

In words: if the limit of nonvanishing terms is not zero, then the reciprocal of the limit is the limit of the reciprocals.

PROOF: We have

$$1/x_k - 1/u = (u - x_k)/ux_k.$$

Since $\lim_{k \to \infty} x_k = u$, an index K exists such that

$$k \geq K \Rightarrow |x_k| > |u|/2.$$

Then for $k \geq K$

$$|1/x_k| < 2/|u|,$$

and by the identity with which we began,

$$|x_k^{-1} - u^{-1}| = |(u - x_k)u^{-1}x_k^{-1}| \leq 2|u - x_k||u|^{-2}.$$

Now choose an arbitrary positive number e and take N to exceed K and also to satisfy the condition

$$k > N \Rightarrow |u - x_k| < e|u|^2/2.$$

Then we have

$$|x_k^{-1} - u^{-1}| \leq 2|u - x_k||u|^{-2} < e,$$

and our contention is proved.

Our last theorem is to the effect that no sequence has more than one limit, or, in other words, that the limits of sequences are unique.

Theorem 6.   If $\lim_{k \to \infty} x_k = a$ and $\lim_{k \to \infty} x_k = b$, then $a = b$.

PROOF: Corresponding to any positive number e, critical indexes n_1 and n_2 are assumed to exist such that

$$k > n_1 \Rightarrow |x_k - a| < e,$$
$$k > n_2 \Rightarrow |x_k - b| < e.$$

Letting n denote the larger of the two critical indexes n_1 and n_2, we then have

$$k > n \Rightarrow |x_k - a| < e \quad \text{and} \quad |x_k - b| < e.$$

We shall apply this fact to the relation

$$b - a = x_k - a - (x_k - b),$$

or rather to its consequence,

$$|b - a| \leq |x_k - a| + |x_k - b|.$$

Indeed,

$$k > n \Rightarrow |x_k - a| + |x_k - b| < e + e = 2e$$

and therefore,

$$|b - a| < 2e.$$

This being true for every positive number e, we can only conclude that $|b - a| = 0$, i.e., that $a = b$, as asserted.

EXERCISES

10. Prove that if $\lim_{k \to \infty} x_k = u$ and $\lim_{k \to \infty} y_k = v$, then $\lim_{k \to \infty} (x_k - y_k) = u - v$.

11. If $\lim_{k \to \infty} x_k = a$, prove that $\lim_{k \to \infty} (x_k + b) = a + b$, where b is any number.

12. Suppose that $\lim_{k \to \infty} x_k = a$, $\lim_{k \to \infty} y_k = a$, and

$$x_k < b < y_k,$$

where a and b are fixed numbers independent of k. Prove that $a = b$.

13. Suppose that $a < b$ and $\lim_{k \to \infty} x_k = b$. Prove that

$$a < x_k$$

for all sufficiently large k. This means: prove that an index n exists such that

$$k > n \Rightarrow a < x_k.$$

Appendix to Section 4

Later (Section 10) we shall need a slight extension of the concept of limit we have been describing. The following considerations are completely parallel to those of pp. 615-616. Let $f(s)$ denote a function defined, say, for all values of the independent variable s. We suppose that $f(s)$ for *small* values of $|s|$ approximates a certain number g in a sense to be described. (For instance, $1 + s$ or $(1 + s)^2$ approximates 1 if $|s|$ is small.) If we prescribe an arbitrary positive number e as *allowed margin of error*, we mean to make the actual error less than e by keeping s sufficiently near 0. A value of d such that

$$|s| < d \Rightarrow |f(s) - g| < e$$

is called a *critical value of s corresponding to e*. If such d exists, then for all lesser values of $|s|$, the error of approximation $|f(s) - g|$ will be within the allowed margin of error. Accordingly, we state the following definition.

Definition. If for any positive number e (no matter how small), a critical value d exists such that

$$|s| < d \Rightarrow |f(s) - g| < e,$$

then we call g the *limit* of $f(s)$ as s approaches zero. We also say, synonymously, that $f(s)$ *converges to g, tends toward g,* or *approaches g,* as s approaches zero, and we write

$$\lim_{s \to 0} f(s) = g.$$

The condition that $\lim_{s \to 0} f(s) = g$ means simply that a critical value of s exists for *any* positive number e prescribed as allowed margin of error.

Theorems 1 to 6 have analogues here. We state, in particular, the following theorems.

Theorem 2'. If $\lim_{s \to 0} f(s) = u$, then $\lim_{s \to 0} af(s) = au$ for any number a whatsoever.

Theorem 4'. If $\lim_{s \to 0} f(s) = u$ and $\lim_{s \to 0} g(s) = v$, then $\lim_{s \to 0} (f(s) + g(s)) = u + v$.

Example 1: Prove that $\lim_{s \to 0} (1 - 2s) = 1$. Here, $f(s) = 1 - 2s$, and $f(s) - 1 = -2s$. Choose an arbitrary margin of error e, $e > 0$. We must find a corresponding critical value d such that

$$|s| < d \implies |f(s) - 1| = |-2s| = 2|s| < e.$$

The value $d = e/2$ will do, since $|s| < d$ implies that $2|s| < 2d = e$, as required.

Example 2: Prove that $\lim_{s \to 0} (3 + 4s + s^2) = 3$. The fastest way to do this is to apply Theorem 4', but we shall give a direct method. Here, $f(s) = 3 + 4s + s^2$. Choose an arbitrary margin of error e, $e > 0$. We must find a corresponding critical value d such that

$$|s| < d \implies |f(s) - 3| = |4s + s^2| = |s(4 + s)| = |s||4 + s| < e.$$

Since

$$|4 + s| \leq 4 + |s| < 4 + d \text{ if } |s| < d,$$

we can greatly simplify the algebra by taking $d < 1$. Indeed, with this choice,

$$|4 + s| < 4 + d < 5 \text{ if } |s| < d,$$

and it suffices now to require also that $d < e/5$. The condition $|s| < d$ then implies that

$$|s||4 + s| < d5 < e,$$

as required.

EXERCISES

1. Prove that $\lim_{s \to 0} (1 - s) = 1$ and apply this fact to Example 1, Section 4.

HINT: $(k - 1)/k = 1 - 1/k = 1 - s$ with $s = 1/k$.

2. Prove that $\lim_{s \to 0} (1 + s + s^3) = 1$.

3. Prove that $\lim_{s \to 0} (1 + s)^2 = 1$.

4. Find $\lim_{s \to 0} (1 + s)^3$.

5. Prove that $\lim_{s \to 0} 1/(1 - s) = 1$. HINT: Here, $f(s) = 1/(1 - s)$, and $f(s) - 1 = s/(1 - s)$. For any choice of e, require d to be, in particular, less than 1/2. The rules for inequalities on pp. 104-105 show that $1 - s > 0$ and that

$$1/(1 - s) < 2$$

(see Exercises 20 and 21, p. 107).

It follows that

$$| f(s) - 1 | = | s(1 - s)^{-1} | = | s |(1 - s)^{-1}$$
$$< 2 | s |.$$

5.

Infinite summation

a. AN EXAMPLE

We saw in the previous section that the decimals that are strings of threes after a decimal point – for instance, .33333333333333333 – tend to 1/3 as limit. In the same way, or from this result just by dividing by 3, we can verify that the analogous strings of ones tend to 1/9. In other words, if we set

$$s_1 = .1,$$
$$s_2 = .11,$$
$$s_3 = .111,$$
$$s_4 = .1111,$$

and, in general,

$$s_k = \overbrace{.11 \ldots 1}^{k \text{ places}} \text{ for } k = 1, 2, 3, \ldots,$$

then

$$\lim_{k \to \infty} s_k = 1/9.$$

For the error in the approximation of 1/9 by s_k, we have

(1) $$| s_k - 1/9 | < 10^{-k}.$$

By the meaning of decimals,

$$s_1 = 1/10$$
$$s_2 = 1/10 + 1/10^2$$
$$s_3 = 1/10 + 1/10^2 + 1/10^3$$

and, in general,

$$s_k = 1/10 + 1/10^2 + \ldots + 1/10^k \text{ for } k = 1, 2, 3, \ldots.$$

Thus, s_k is the sum of the first k members of the infinite geometric progression

$$1/10, 1/10^2, 1/10^3, 1/10^4, \ldots.$$

The estimate (1) tells us, for instance, that s_{10}, the sum of the first 10 members of this progression, deviates from the limit 1/9 by less than 10^{-10}. The sum of the first 1000 members of the progression deviates from 1/9 by less than 10^{-1000}, the sum of the first 1,000,000 members by less than $10^{-1,000,000}$. This is truly a microscopic error, yet the approximation to 1/9 becomes closer yet for sums of more than 1,000,000 terms. Why not agree therefore to call 1/9 the sum of *all* the terms of the progression? Perhaps Archimedes (about 225 B.C.) was the first to think of doing such a thing. Taking this point of view ourselves, let us regard

(2) $$s_k = 1/10 + 1/10^2 + 1/10^3 + \ldots + 1/10^k$$

as a *partial* summation, and the limit

$$\lim_{k \to \infty} s_k$$

as the *infinite* summation, of the quantities

$$1/10, 1/10^2, 1/10^3, \ldots.$$

The infinite summation is usually written, in analogy with (2), as

(3) $$1/10 + 1/10^2 + 1/10^3 + \ldots$$

and is then called an *infinite series;* each s_k is called a partial sum for this series. *The sum of the infinite series* by definition is the value of the limit of the partial sums and thus is 1/9.

Along with the infinite series (3), we can also introduce the infinite decimal

$$.111\ldots$$

with the same meaning and thus the value 1/9.

A particularly clear and beautiful statement of these ideas from a slightly different viewpoint has been given by Rozsa Peter: †

A well-known mathematician while still a child formulated for himself the meaning of the sum of an infinite series in the following way.

There was a type of chocolate which the manufacturers were trying to popularize by putting a coupon in the silver-paper wrapping, and anyone who could produce 10 such coupons would get another bar of chocolate in exchange. If we have such a bar of chocolate, what is it really worth?

Of course it is worth more than just one bar of chocolate, because there is a coupon in it, and for each coupon you can get 1/10 of a bar of chocolate (since for 10 you can obtain one bar of chocolate). But with this 1/10th of a bar will go one-tenth of a coupon, and if for one coupon we get 1/10th of a bar of chocolate, for 1/10th of a coupon we get one-tenth of this, i.e., 1/100th of a bar of chocolate. To this 1/100th of a bar of chocolate belongs 1/100th of a coupon, and for this we again get one-tenth as much chocolate, and one-tenth of 1/100 is 1/1000th of a bar of chocolate, and so on indefinitely. It is obvious that this will never stop, so that my one bar of chocolate together with its coupons is in fact worth

$$1 + 1/10 + 1/100 + 1/1000 + \ldots \text{ bars of chocolate.}$$

On the other hand, we can show that this is worth exactly 1 1/9 of a bar of chocolate.

The 1 in this is of course the value of the actual chocolate, so all that needs to be shown is that the coupon that goes with it is worth 1/9th of a bar of chocolate. It is enough to demonstrate that 9 coupons are worth one bar of chocolate, since then it is certain that one coupon is worth 1/9th of this. Suppose that I have 9 coupons, then I can go into the shop and say: 'Please can I have a bar of chocolate? I should like to eat it here and now and I will pay afterwards.' I eat the chocolate, take out the accompanying coupon, and now I have 10 coupons, with which in fact I can actually pay and the whole business is concluded, I have eaten the chocolate and I have no coupons left. So the exact value of 9 coupons is in fact one bar of chocolate, the value of one coupon is 1/9th of a bar of chocolate, one bar of chocolate with a coupon is worth 1 1/9 bars of chocolate. So the sum of the infinite series

$$1 + 1/10 + 1/100 + 1/1000 + 1/10{,}000 + \ldots$$

is exactly 1 1/9, quite tangibly, even edibly.

We can sum up the result roughly as follows: if something is equal to 1 as a first rough approximation, equal to $1 + 1/10$ as a slightly better approximation, equal to $1 + 1/10 + 1/100$ as a still better approximation but still not exact, and so on indefinitely, then it is equal to 1 1/9 exactly, not approximately.

b. THE GEOMETRIC SERIES

The infinite series just described is an example of what is known as the geometric series. Let r be any number with absolute value less than 1:

$$|r| < 1.$$

---

† *Playing with Infinity*, 1964, pp. 105-106. (c) by Rozsa Peter. Reprinted by permission of Simon & Schuster, Inc. I am indebted for this reference to Profs. Peter and Anneli Lax, who inform me that the child mathematician referred to was John von Neumann.

The following formula (which only requires that $r \neq 1$) was essentially known to the Greeks:

(4) $1 + r + r^2 + \ldots + r^k = (1 - r^{k+1})/(1 - r)$ for $k = 1, 2, 3, \ldots$.

We already obtained this formula by mathematical induction (Chapter 10, Section 4), but for variety's sake we shall prove it now by a different method. For any fixed value of k, set

$$u = 1 + r + r^2 + \ldots + r^k.$$

Since

$$u - r^k = 1 + r + r^2 + \ldots + r^{k-1},$$

we have

$$
\begin{aligned}
r(u - r^k) &= r(1 + r + r^2 + \ldots + r^{k-1}) \\
&= r + r^2 + \ldots r^k \\
&= u - 1.
\end{aligned}
$$

This gives us

$$ru - r^{k+1} = u - 1,$$

or

$$1 - r^{k+1} = u - ru = u(1 - r).$$

Since $r \neq 1$, we may divide by $1 - r$ obtaining

$$(1 - r^{k+1})/(1 - r) = u,$$

which is what the formula states.

The geometric series, which is an infinite summation, stems from the finite formula (4). For each $k = 1, 2, 3, \ldots$, define as *partial sum*

$$s_k = 1 + r + r^2 + \ldots + r^k.$$

We shall show that these partial sums converge as k becomes infinite and then shall call their limit the sum of the infinite series

$$1 + r + r^2 + r^3 + \ldots.$$

From (4),

$$s_k = (1 - r^{k+1})/(1 - r),$$

while, as we proved in the previous section,

$$\lim_{k \to \infty} r^k = 0.$$

If k is very large, r^{k+1} is very small, $1 - r^{k+1}$ is very close to 1, and we should expect

$$(1 - r^{k+1})/(1 - r)$$

to be very close to

$$1/(1 - r).$$

We can thus anticipate that

$$\lim_{k \to \infty} s_k = 1/(1-r)$$

and, in fact, shall prove that this is so. By Theorem 2, Section 4,

$$\lim_{k \to \infty} s_k = \lim_{k \to \infty} (1 - r^{k+1})/(1 - r) = \lim_{k \to \infty} (1/(1 - r))(1 - r^{k+1})$$
$$= (1/(1 - r)) \lim_{k \to \infty} (1 - r^{k+1}).$$

On the other hand, by Theorem 4, Section 4,

$$\lim (1 - r^{k+1}) = 1 - \lim r^{k+1}$$
$$= 1$$

(see Exercise 11, Section 4). Therefore,

$$\lim_{k \to \infty} s_k = 1/(1 - r) \; ,$$

as conjectured. The conventional name for $\lim s_k$ in this case is "the geometric series with ratio r," r being of course the ratio between successive terms of the series; the conventional notation is

$$1 + r + r^2 + r^3 + \ldots.$$

We have just proved that

$$1 + r + r^2 + r^3 + \ldots = 1/(1 - r) \text{ for } |r| < 1.$$

If a is an arbitrary number, we define the infinite series

$$a + ar + ar^2 + ar^3 + \ldots$$

to mean

$$\lim_{k \to \infty} (a + ar + ar^2 + ar^3 + \ldots + ar^k) = \lim_{k \to \infty} as_k.$$

It follows from Theorem 2, Section 4, that

$$a + ar + ar^2 + ar^3 + \ldots = a/(1 - r).$$

EXERCISES

1. A ball is dropped from a height of one foot. If the ball rebounds to half its height indefinitely often, what is the total distance that the ball travels?

2. The house that Jack built is in a valley, and the basement leaks. For every gallon pumped out of the basement, 2/5 gallons will seep back in again. Returning home after a heavy rain, Jack found 100 gallons of water on his basement floor. How many gallons did he have to pump out in all if no new water was added to the original amount?

3. Zeno of Elea (born about 490 B.C.) argued that motion is impossible, as follows. An object moving from one point to another must first cover half the distance between the two points, then half the remaining distance, and so forth, in this way having to traverse infinitely many small portions of the original distance. He deemed this to be impossible in a finite time. Analyze and criticize the argument assuming that the motion is at constant speed (see Exercise 12, p. 49).

4. Zeno also argued that Achilles, a fast runner, could not overtake a tortoise. Suppose they start at the same instant with the tortoise some distance ahead. By the time Achilles reaches the point from which the tortoise had started, the tortoise has advanced to a new position, and by the time Achilles arrives at the latter, the tortoise has advanced again. In fact, the tortoise will elude Achilles over and over again in this way, so that Achilles will never be able to catch up. Explain the paradox assuming each to move at constant speed, say Achilles at 10 miles per hour and the tortoise at 1 mile per hour.

5. Consider an infinite sequence of numbers

$$c_1, a_2, a_3, \ldots.$$

We say that the sum of these numbers is infinite if the "partial sums"

$$s_k = a_1 + a_2 + a_3 + \ldots + a_k$$

have the following property: for every positive integer M, no matter how large, a "critical index" N exists such that

$$k > N \Rightarrow s_k > M.$$

Taking $a_k = 2^k$, find a critical index for each of the following choices of M: (a) 100, (b) 200, (c) 300.

C. PERIODIC DECIMALS

We were led to define the infinite decimal

$$.1111111 \ldots,$$

consisting of an uninterrupted string of ones, as the infinite series

$$1/10 + 1/10^2 + 1/10^3 + \ldots.$$

The sum of the series — 1/9 — thus was the value ascribed to the decimal. The same idea enables us to define a large family of infinite decimals.

Example 1: We define the infinite decimal

(1) $$.01010101\ldots,$$

an infinite string of repetitions of the pattern 01, to be the geometric series

(2) $$1/100 + 1/100^2 + 1/100^3 + \ldots.$$

The sum of the series being

$$(1/100)(1 + 1/100 + 1/100^2 + \ldots) = (1/100)(1/(1 - 1/100)) = 1/99,$$

the value we ascribe to the infinite decimal (1) is 1/99. The reason for the definition is that the ordinary decimal consisting of, say, the first k digits of (1) is equal to a partial sum of the series (2) and thus tends to the sum of the series as k becomes infinite.

Example 2: The infinite decimal

$$.0303030303\ldots,$$

an infinite string of repetitions of the pattern 03, is defined to be the geometric series

$$3/100 + 3/100^2 + 3/100^3 + \ldots.$$

Thus, it has the value

$$(3/100)(1 + 1/100 + 1/100^2 + \ldots) = 3(1/99) = 1/33.$$

Example 3: The infinite decimal

$$.162162162162\ldots,$$

a string consisting of the pattern 162 repeated again and again is defined to be the geometric series

$$162/1000 + 162/1000^2 + 162/1000^3 + \ldots.$$

Thus, it has the value

$$(162/1000)(1 + 1/1000 + 1/1000^2 + 1/1000^3 + \ldots)$$
$$= (162/1000)\left(\frac{1}{1 - 1/1000}\right) = 162/999 = 6/37 \ .$$

Example 4:   The infinite decimal

$$.00162162162162 \ldots$$

with the eventually repeating pattern 162 is defined to be

$$(1/100) \, (.162162162 \ldots).$$

According to the previous example, its value is

$$(1/100)\,(6/37) = 3/1850 \, .$$

Example 5:   The infinite decimal

$$.25162162162162 \ldots$$

again with an eventually repeating pattern, 162, is defined to be

$$.25 + .00162162162 \ldots .$$

By the previous result, its value is

$$1/4 + 3/1850 = 1862/(4 \cdot 1850) = 931/3700.$$

Formally, an infinite decimal is simply an infinite sequence of digits that we imagine placed consecutively after a decimal point. If all but a finite number of the digits are zero, we say that the decimal is *terminating,* and we do not distinguish it from the ordinary decimals of arithmetic, which we are accustomed to regard as followed by as many zeros as we please. Thus, terminating decimals represent fractions in the usual way. An infinite decimal is called *periodic* if it contains a repeating pattern, a fixed finite succession of digits eventually appearing that immediately recommences each time it has run its course. All the infinite decimals in the preceding examples are periodic. Like them, any periodic decimal can be defined by means of an appropriate geometric series and thus is equal to some fraction.

EXERCISES

1. Find the repeating pattern in the decimal representation of each of the following fractions:

(a) 1/6,   (g) 2/11,
(b) 1/7,   (h) 1/17,
(c) 2/9,   (i) 1/13,
(d) 1/11,   (j) 4/15,
(e) 1/45,   (k) 3/7,
(f) 1/81,   (l) 5/13.

2. Find the fraction whose decimal expansion is
   (a) .714285714285 ...   (d) .212121 ...
   (b) .538461538461 ...   (e) .2195121951 ...
   (c) .7777 ...   (f) .51525152 ...

3. For each of the fractions whose decimal expansion is given in Exercise 2, find an approximating terminating decimal such that the error in approximating the fraction is less than 1/10,000.

We shall now show that the infinite decimal obtained from an arbitrary fraction by long division is necessarily periodic. Thus, a given infinite decimal represents a fraction if and only if the decimal is periodic. First, consider a special instance, that of the fraction 94/185, which, however, is typical. Here are the first few steps of the long division of 185 into 94, the lines of the calculation being numbered for reference from 0 to 11.

```
0                           .5 0 8 1 0 8 1
1               1 8 5 ) 9 4.0 0 0 0 0 0 0
2                          9 2 5
3                          (1 5)0 0
4                          1 4 8 0
5                            (2 0)0
6                            1 8 5
7                              (1 5)0 0
8                              1 4 8 0
9                                (2 0)0
10                               1 8 5
11                                 (1 5)
```

The encircled numbers are remainders, which must all be less than 185. The value of the remainder at each stage determines the entire subsequent course of the division. Since all remainders are less than 185, at least one remainder must occur a second time, the earliest to do so being 15 (lines 3 and 7). This remainder 15, before its recurrence, leads to the succession 081 in line 0. When the remainder appears for the second time, it results again in the succession 081 in line 0 and then again recurs, its third appearance being followed by another repetition of the same succession 081 (in line 0), which concludes with the fourth appearance of the remainder, and so forth. Thus, if the long division here is carried through a great many steps, a decimal of the form

$$.5081081081081081 \ldots$$

is obtained, in which the succession 081 is repeated again and again.

The general case is similar, as we can easily see, guided in all details by the previous example. Consider any fraction p/q with p and q positive integers and $p < q$, and perform the long division of q into p. The value of the remainder at each stage determines the entire subsequent course of the division. All remainders are necessarily less than q, and therefore at least one remainder must occur a second time. But the events that ensue after the first occurrence of this remainder will repeat themselves after the second. Hence, in particular, the remainder itself will eventually be repeated, and then the same events that followed upon its first appearance, and were repeated after its second, will be repeated again after its third. This repetition will lead to a fourth appearance of the remainder and, after that, to still another repetition of the same cycle of events, and so forth. In the decimal being calculated, the succession of digits that arises after the first appearance of the remainder in question and terminates with the second appearance of this remainder immediately recommences, to terminate again at the third appearance of the remainder, and then to begin again, and so forth. Thus, in any decimal obtained from a fraction by long division, a pattern will eventually occur that repeats and repeats without end. This decimal, in other words, is periodic, as contended.

EXERCISES

4. The periodic decimal .5081081081 . . . just obtained is defined by means of an infinite series. Calculate its value according to the definition and compare with the fraction 94/185. How does the theory of series explain the coincidence?

5. In Section 4, we studied the errors made in approximating the fraction 3/14 by the ordinary decimals that consist of the first k places obtained in dividing 14 into 3 ($k = 1, 2, 3, \ldots$). Make a similar analysis for the fraction 94/185. How does this analysis also show that the fraction and the infinite periodic decimal obtained from it must be equal?

d. THE THIN DISTRIBUTION OF RATIONALS

We are going to describe a remarkable phenomenon of geometry, quite outside the familiar tradition that stems from the Greeks. Take any straight line L upon which we impress a scale. Then every point of L can be named by its coordinate (see Section 2g, Chapter 2), which is a positive, zero, or negative number indicating the distance and direction of the point from the chosen origin. The property we wish to discuss has to do with collections of segments of L. The individual segments belonging to such a collection are supposed to be of finite length and may overlap or not. By the total length of the segments of a particular collection, we shall mean the sum of the individual lengths of the segments belonging to the collection. (This is interpreted as the sum of an infinite series in the case of an infinite collection. The total sum need not in general be finite, but will be finite in this discussion.)

Consider an arbitrary set S of points of L. A particular collection of segments of L will be said to *cover* S if every point of S is contained in at least one segment of the collection and is not an end point of this segment. For instance, the segment I from 0 to 1 of L is a point set that is covered by the segments of length 3/16 with centers at 0, 1/8, 1/4, 3/8, 1/2, 5/8, 3/4, 7/8, 1 (see Figure 14-14). Any collection of segments covering I must have a total length exceeding 1.

FIGURE 14-14   A collection of segments covering I.

Let F denote the set of points of I whose coordinates — distances from the origin — are *rational numbers*. We shall exhibit a collection of segments of L that cover F and yet have total length 1/2 or even an arbitrarily small total length. Let e be any positive number, no matter how small. Since the rational numbers are denumerable (Section 2), enumerate the points belonging to F as a sequence

$$P_1, P_2, P_3, \ldots.$$

A collection of covering segments is determined as follows. Let

I_1 be the segment of L of length $e/2$ and midpoint P_1,
I_2 the segment of L of length $e/4$ and midpoint P_2,
I_3 the segment of L of length $e/8$ and midpoint P_3,

and for $k = 1, 2, 3, \ldots$, let

I_k be the segment of L of length $e/2^{k+1}$ and midpoint P_k

(see Figure 14-15). The total length of these segments is given by the

FIGURE 14-15   A collection of intervals covering F.

infinite series

$$e/2 + e/4 + e/8 + \ldots$$

and thus by

$$(e/2)(1 + 1/2 + 1/4 + \ldots) = (e/2)2 = e,$$

the expression in parentheses representing the geometric series with ratio 1/2. At the same time, the aggregate of these segments certainly covers F, since each point of F is the midpoint of one of them.

This astonishing and nonintuitive result proclaims that the points with rational coordinates occur very thinly among all the points of I. We shall return to this matter later.

EXERCISE

1. State and prove a similar result for the whole line L in place of I.

e.   OTHER INFINITE SERIES

The importance of infinite series in general can hardly be over-stated. Convergence for any infinite series — just as for the geometric series — is defined in terms of its *partial sums*, which are the sums of the first k terms of the series, $k = 1, 2, 3, \ldots$. If the infinite *sequence* consisting of all the partial sums converges, then the infinite *series* itself is said to converge and to have as sum the limit of this sequence.

The following is another example of a convergent series that is easily discussed without any additional theory. The series is built up from the infinite sequence

$$\{1, 1/2, 1/3, 1/4, 1/5, 1/6, \ldots\}$$

whose kth term is $1/k$, $k = 1, 2, 3, 4, \ldots$. The members of this sequence tend to zero as k becomes infinite. Using them, we form what is called a "telescoping" series, in this case the series

(1) $(1 - 1/2) + (1/2 - 1/3) + (1/3 - 1/4) + (1/4 - 1/5) + \ldots,$

the kth term of which is $1/k - 1/(k + 1)$, $k = 1, 2, 3, \ldots$. The partial sums of this series are

$$s_1 = 1 - 1/2$$
$$s_2 = (1 - 1/2) + (1/2 - 1/3) = 1 - 1/3$$
$$s_3 = (1 - 1/2) + (1/2 - 1/3) + (1/3 - 1/4) = 1 - 1/4$$

and, in general, for $k = 1, 2, 3, \ldots$,

$$s_k = (1 - 1/2) + (1/2 - 1/3) + \ldots + (1/k - 1/(k + 1)) = 1 - 1/(k + 1).$$

Since $1/(k + 1)$ tends to zero as k becomes infinite, we easily see that

$$\lim_{k \to \infty} s_k = 1$$

(see Exercise 11, Section 4). Hence, we say that the infinite series (1) has sum 1. Since

$$1/k - 1/(k+1) = 1/(k(k+1)),$$

this infinite series can be written also as

(2) $$1/(1 \cdot 2) + 1/(2 \cdot 3) + 1/(3 \cdot 4) + 1/(4 \cdot 5) + \ldots$$

with the kth term $1/(k(k+1))$, $k = 1, 2, 3, \ldots$, and we conclude that the series (2) has sum 1. Note for reference that from the expressions for s_k, we have

(3) $$1/(1 \cdot 2) + 1/(2 \cdot 3) + 1/(3 \cdot 4) + 1/(4 \cdot 5) + \ldots$$
$$+ 1/(k(k+1)) = 1 - 1/(k+1)$$

EXERCISE

1. Form a telescoping series from the sequence

$$1, r, r^2, r^3, r^4, \ldots$$

(the kth term is r^{k-1}), and by means of it give another proof that the geometric series

$$1 + r + r^2 + r^3 + \ldots$$

converges to $1/(1-r)$ if $|r| < 1$.

f. A PROBLEM ON ILLUMINATION†

Physical problems often lead to or suggest infinite series. As an example, consider a long, straight street illuminated by a series of street lamps that are equally spaced and equally intense. Suppose nothing obstructs the light from any of these lamps to an observer at one end of the street. If the street is lengthened at the other end and additional lamps installed that are of the same strength and have the same spacing as before, then the observer's end of the street will become brighter and brighter. Will this brightness be limited, or will it rise beyond all bounds as the number of lamps continues to increase? In other language: as the street at the far end is lengthened infinitely, and the number of equally spaced, equally strong street lamps thus becomes infinite, does the illumination at the fixed end of the street become infinitely intense?

---

†This discussion arose out of a suggestion by Dr. Herbert Fox of the Applied Physics Laboratories, Johns Hopkins University.

This problem is related to the proposition in astronomy put forth by Digges and Bruno that stars — which we may take to be of approximately uniform intensity — are distributed more or less uniformly throughout infinite space. Can this proposition be true and starlight yet be finite? We shall return to this question later.

Any problem that is to receive mathematical treatment must be idealized. Therefore, in place of a street, we consider a half-line L starting at an arbitrary point P_0. In place of street lamps, we consider an infinite sequence of points $P_0, P_1, P_2, P_3, \ldots$ of L, P_k being situated k units from P_0. In place of an observer, we take a point Q one unit from P_0 on a line perpendicular to L. The half-line and these points are our geometrical idealizations (see Figure 14-16).

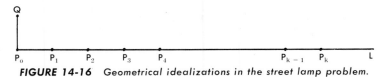

FIGURE 14-16   *Geometrical idealizations in the street lamp problem.*

The physical elements of the problem must also be idealized. Experiments show that light intensities — measured, say, by a photographic light meter — conform well to certain rules. We shall adopt among our physical premises two of these rules, idealized as follows:

(I) Suppose a point O to be the only source of light. Then the intensity of the light at any other point P is inversely proportional to the square of the distance OP. This means that a constant c exists such that the light intensity measured at P is equal to

$$c/(OP)^2.$$

The constant c is the same for two sources of equal strength (i.e., intensity). It is positive if the point O is emitting light and otherwise is zero.

The second law is concerned with situations in which light is received at a given point P from more than one source. By the *partial intensity* of light at P *owing to* a particular source, we shall mean the intensity of light that would be measured at P if this source were the only one. The second law states:

(II) If light is received at a given point P from n sources at once, then the intensity of the light measured at P can be calculated as the sum of the partial intensities owing to the n individual sources. In other words, the effects of the individual sources combine additively.

In our idealized version of the street lamp problem, law (I) tells us how to formulate mathematically the requirement that the points $P_0, P_1, P_2, \ldots$ be light sources of equal intensity. We simply require that the constant of proportionality c be the same for each such source. This is our final assumption. It implies that the partial intensity at Q owing to the source P_k is equal to

$$c/(QP_k)^2.$$

Let I_n denote the light intensity at Q owing to the first $n + 1$ sources $P_0, P_1, \ldots, P_n$. According to our last remark and law (II),

$$I_n = c/(QP_0)^2 + c/(QP_1)^2 + c/(QP_2)^2 + \ldots + c/(QP_n)^2$$
$$= c[1/(QP_0)^2 + 1/(QP_1)^2 + 1/(QP_2)^2 + \ldots + 1/(QP_n)^2].$$

This is the light intensity that would be observed at Q if the street were just n units long. The question we asked amounts to this: does a number B, independent of n, exist such that

$$I_n \le B \text{ for } n = 0, 1, 2, 3, \ldots ?$$

If so, the brightness at Q will not rise above a certain level no matter how many new lamps are installed along the street. If not, the brightness at Q will surpass any level when a sufficient number of lamps have been brought into use.

By Pythagoras's theorem,

$$(QP_k)^2 = 1 + k^2 \text{ for } k = 0, 1, 2, 3, \ldots.$$

Hence,

$$I_n = c[1/(1 + 0^2) + 1/(1 + 1^2) + 1/(1 + 2^2) + \ldots + 1/(1 + n^2)].$$

We shall prove from this that

$$I_n < 5c/2,$$

thus answering our question in the affirmative with $B = 5c/2$. Our method is based on formula (3), Subsection e, which suggests the following argument. First,

$$1/(1 + k^2) < 1/k^2 \text{ for } k > 0$$

since the denominator on the right is less than that on the left and the numerators are the same. Similarly

$$1/k^2 < 1/((k - 1)k) \text{ for } k > 1,$$

and by combining these two inequalities we have:

$$1/(1 + k^2) < 1/((k - 1)k) \text{ for } k > 1.$$

For instance,

$$1/(1 + 2^2) < 1/(1 \cdot 2), \ 1/(1 + 3^2) < 1/(2 \cdot 3), \ 1/(1 + 4^2) < 1/(3 \cdot 4).$$

Therefore,

(1) $1/(1 + 2^2) + 1/(1 + 3^2) + 1/(1 + 4^2) + \ldots + 1/(1 + n^2)$
$$< 1/(1 \cdot 2) + 1/(2 \cdot 3) + 1/(3 \cdot 4) + \ldots + 1/((n - 1)n).$$

Formula (3) in Subsection e tells us, however, that

$$1/(1 \cdot 2) + 1/(2 \cdot 3) + 1/(3 \cdot 4) + \ldots + 1/((n-1)n) = 1 - 1/n.$$

We know that $1 - 1/n < 1$. Hence, by (1),

$$1/(1+2^2) + 1/(1+3^2) + 1/(1+4^2) + \ldots$$
$$+ 1/(1+n^2) < 1 \text{ for } n = 2, 3, 4, 5, \ldots.$$

Because of this,

$$I_n = c[1 + 1/2 + 1/(1+2^2) + 1/(1+3^2) + \ldots + 1/(1+n^2)]$$
$$< c(1 + 1/2 + 1) = 5c/2 \text{ for } n = 0,1,2,3,\ldots.$$

This proves our contention that the brightness at Q will not rise above a certain level no matter how many new light sources are brought into service along L.

Can we draw this conclusion—that the total light intensity attainable at Q is restricted below a certain level—from the bare fact that the more distant the light source, the more minute is its contribution to total intensity at Q? This question is a special case of the following: if

$$a_1, a_2, a_3, \ldots$$

are any positive quantities such that

$$\lim_{k \to \infty} a_k = 0,$$

do the partial sums

$$s_n = a_1 + a_2 + a_3 + \ldots + a_n$$

necessarily satisfy a condition of the form

(2) $$s_n < B \text{ for } n = 1, 2, 3, \ldots,$$

in which B is a fixed number independent of n? Or, to the contrary, as n increases, may s_n also increase beyond all fixed levels? We shall see in Subsection g that the answer to the second question is yes, for while the a_k do become very small, there are very many of them, and their cumulative effects can be considerable.

Now we return to the question in astronomy to which we alluded before: if stars of approximately equal intensity are distributed uniformly throughout infinite space, will starlight be of infinite intensity? If we idealize stars as points and also assume the same physical laws as before, we have a three-dimensional analogue of the street lamp problem just discussed. But the mathematical result in three dimensions is the opposite of that in one: equally intense point sources of light uniformly spaced in three dimensions would illuminate infinitely. Since starlight is not infinitely bright, we can only conclude that one or more of our suppositions is seriously wrong. At least two turn out to be so.

The fact that stars are not points is far more significant in this problem than may have appeared at first. Any star blocks from the view of an observer the light of other, more distant stars behind it. If stars are distributed uniformly throughout infinite space, a finite number of them, in fact, will suffice to obstruct from the observer's view all of the infinitely many beyond. Hence, starlight will be of finite intensity even if infinitely many stars exist.

On the other hand, a finite number of equally intense stars together covering the whole sky would communicate their surface temperature to the earth. The earth being much cooler than the surface of a star, some supposition we have made must still be wrong. We have not taken account, in particular, of the fact that the universe is expanding, the remoter stars receding from us at enormous rates. This motion invalidates law (I), which presupposes a stationary light source. If we correct the law and recalculate total starlight intensity accordingly, continuing to assume stars to be equally intense and uniformly distributed, we do at last arrive at results consistent with our actual experience.† Thus, we need not yet — in this connection at least — part company with Digges and Bruno.

The previous discussion involves an interesting geometrical point. Idealize a star as a sphere of any radius. Then the figure composed of the straight line segments from a distant point O to the points of the star will fill a region C shaped something like an ice cream cone. Imagine a sphere S of unit radius about O. The region C intersects S in a round patch (see Figure 14-17), which we shall call the

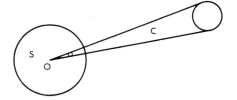

FIGURE 14-17   The projection of
a star upon a sphere.

projection of the star upon S. Suppose, in the spirit of the previous discussion, that there are infinitely many spherical stars and that their projections upon S completely cover S. This means that each point of S is inside at least one patch that is the projection of a star. From this it can be proved that a finite number of the projections will suffice

† See, for instance, D. W. Sciama, *The Unity of the Universe*, Doubleday and Co., Garden City, N.Y., 1961, Chap. 6, p. 71. For this reference and also some of the foregoing discussion, I am indebted to my colleague, Prof. J. B. Marion.

to cover S and, thus, that a finite number of the stars will cover the observer's sky. (This conclusion was crucial in the previous discussion.) This fact and its proof were never known to Euclid but are among the discoveries of the late 19th and early 20th Centuries that led to the development of the field known as "point set topology." We shall later explain the ideas involved in this "finite covering" phenomenon in the context of the following one-dimensional analogue:

Let L be any straight line and I any segment of L that is of finite length and contains its own end points. Suppose a collection of segments of L to be given that *covers I* in the sense that every point of I is contained in—and is not an end point of—at least one segment of the collection. Then a finite number of segments of the given collection also suffice to cover I.

If the partial sums for an infinite summation satisfy condition (2), they are said to be *bounded.* The partial sums of a convergent series are obviously bounded, and later (Section 4, Chapter 15) we shall see that a series of positive terms converges if its partial sums are bounded. The following exercises are based on the methods of this section.

EXERCISES

1. Prove that the partial sums of the infinite series

$$1 + 1/4 + 1/9 + 1/16 + \ldots + 1/n^2 + \ldots$$

are bounded.

2. Prove from the previous result that the partial sums of the infinite series

$$1 + 1/8 + 1/27 + 1/64 + \ldots + 1/n^3 + \ldots$$

are bounded.

3. From the fact that the partial sums of the infinite series

$$1 + 1/2 + 1/4 + 1/8 + \ldots + 1/2^n + \ldots$$

are bounded, prove that the same is true of the series

$$1 + 1/(2 \cdot 1) + 1/(3 \cdot 2 \cdot 1) + 1/(4 \cdot 3 \cdot 2 \cdot 1) + \ldots$$
$$+ 1/(n(n-1)(n-2) \ldots 1) + \ldots.$$

g.   A CASE OF NONCONVERGENCE

Consider the infinite series

$$1 + 1/2 + 1/3 + 1/4 + 1/5 + 1/6 + \ldots,$$

the kth term of which is $1/k$. The contribution of this term is very small if k is very large. Nevertheless, this series fails to converge. On the contrary, its partial sums increase — very slowly — ultimately beyond all bounds. To see this, we shall consider successively s_4, s_8, s_{16}, s_{32}, and so on, s_k denoting the sum of the first k terms of the series. First,

$$s_4 = 1 + 1/2 + 1/3 + 1/4$$
$$> 1 + 1/2 + 1/4 + 1/4 = 2$$

since replacing $1/3$ by $1/4$ diminishes the sum. Secondly,

$$s_8 = 1 + 1/2 + 1/3 + 1/4 + 1/5 + 1/6 + 1/7 + 1/8$$
$$= s_4 + 1/5 + 1/6 + 1/7 + 1/8$$
$$> s_4 + 1/8 + 1/8 + 1/8 + 1/8 = s_4 + 1/2 > 2\ 1/2.$$

Thirdly,

$$s_{16} = s_8 + 1/9 + 1/10 + 1/11 + 1/12 + 1/13 + 1/14 + 1/15 + 1/16$$
$$> s_8 + 1/16 + 1/16 + 1/16 + 1/16 + 1/16 + 1/16 + 1/16 + 1/16$$
$$= s_8 + 1/2$$
$$> 3$$

Similarly,

$$s_{32} > 3\ 1/2, \quad s_{64} > 4, \quad s_{128} > 4\ 1/2, \quad s_{256} > 5,$$

and so forth. By mathematical induction, it is easily proved that

(1) $$s_{2^k} > 1 + k/2,$$

s_{2^k} denoting of course the sum of the first 2^k members of the series. Condition (1) implies, in particular, that the series we are considering does not converge, answering a question raised in the previous subsection.

EXERCISES

1. Prove inequality (1) by mathematical induction.

2. Consider an infinite series, denoting the kth term of the series by a_k. We assume all the terms to be positive: $a_k > 0$ for $k = 1, 2, 3, \ldots$. Explain under the following various additional hypotheses whether the infinite series (a) must converge, (b) must fail to converge, or (c) may either converge or not according to the information supplied. Give examples where pertinent.

(i) For infinitely many values of k, $a_k > .0000001$.

(ii) $a_k > 1/k$ for $k = 1, 2, 3, \ldots$.

(iii) $a_k > 1/2^k$ for $k = 1, 2, 3, \ldots$.

(iv) $a_k < 1/(2k)$ for $k = 1, 2, 3, \ldots$.

(v) The a_k diverge to $+\infty$. (See Exercise 8(iii), Section 4.)

(vi) A positive number c exists such that $\lim\limits_{k \to \infty} a_k = c$.

(vii) $\lim\limits_{k \to \infty} a_k = 0$.

(viii) All but a finite number of the terms of the series have values less than one.

(ix) All the terms of the series have the same nonzero value.

(x) Each term a_k is exactly one hundred times as great as the corresponding terms of a convergent sequence.

(xi) Each term of the series has exactly one hundredth of the value of the corresponding term of a nonconvergent sequence.

(xii) Each term a_k is equal to one-half the previous term.

(xiii) 267 of the terms of the series each have values exceeding 1,000,000.

(xiv) The infinite series obtained by adding the reciprocals of the a_k does not converge.

(xv) The infinite series obtained by adding the reciprocals of the a_k converges.

(xvi) Each term of the series is less than the preceding term.

(xvii) Each term of the series is greater than the preceding term.

(xviii) If the series were started at the 100th term instead of the first term, it would converge.

(xix) If the series were started at the 100th term instead of the first term, it would not converge.

3. General Bullmoose is adding less to his fortune every year and thinks that if this continues, then his ambition of owning everything on earth is doomed if he lives forever. Is he necessarily right? Why or why not?

4. (a) Show that $1/11 + 1/12 + 1/13 + \ldots + 1/100 > .9$.

(b) Show that $1/101 + 1/102 + 1/103 + \ldots + 1/1000 > .9$.

(c) Show that for any positive integer p,

$$1/(10^p + 1) + 1/(10^p + 2) + 1/(10^p + 3) + \ldots + 1/(10^{p+1}) > .9.$$

(d) How do (a), (b), and (c) enable you to give another proof that the series

$$1 + 1/2 + 1/3 + 1/4 + \ldots$$

does not converge?

6.

The method of sectional approximation of areas

What we shall call the method of local, or sectional, approximation is one of the most powerful of all mathematical techniques. We describe it first in the context of a problem of area.

What do we — what can we — mean by the area of a region which has a curved boundary? For instance, in the Cartesian plane take the curve with the equation

$$y = x^2.$$

This is called a parabola. A portion of its graph is shown in Figures 14-18A and B. To be specific, what shall we mean and how shall we calculate the area of the shaded region in Figure 14-18A between the parabola and the line $y = 4$? We might instead ask these questions concerning the shaded region in Figure 14-18B between the parabola,

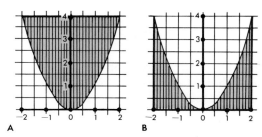

FIGURE 14-18 A, A re-
gion enclosed between a straight
line and a parabola. B, A region
enclosed by the x-axis, two vertical lines, and a parabola.

the x-axis, and the two lines $x = 2$ and $x = -2$. Indeed, the two questions are equivalent, since the regions involved unite into a square, their areas (once these areas are defined) therefore having to add up to the area of the square, which is 16. For purposes of ex-position, we prefer the second question and, in fact, shall simplify it somewhat to ask: how shall we define and calculate the area of the region R enclosed between the parabola

$$y = x^2$$

and the x-axis in the band

$$0 \leq x \leq 2?$$

This area is that shaded in Figure 14-19. In answering this question, we shall be guided by the following principle.

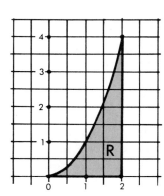

FIGURE 14-19 The area between a parabola
and the x-axis in a vertical band.

Guiding Principle. Let S and T be regions for which areas

$$A(S), A(T),$$

respectively, are defined. Suppose that R is an intermediate region sandwiched between S and T and, more precisely, that

$$S \subset R \subset T.$$

(This means that S is contained properly in R and R is contained properly in T.) Then the area of R, which we denote by $A(R)$, must satisfy the condition that

$$A(S) < A(R) < A(T).$$

As the simplest illustration of this principle, take T to be the rectangle of height 4 upon the segment of the x-axis from 0 to 2 as base. Since this rectangle contains R properly and has area 8, we have

$$A(R) < 8.$$

A systematic exploitation of the Guiding Principle will enable us to encage $A(R)$ within confines that are as narrow as we wish and then to define $A(R)$ exactly by a limiting procedure. We illustrate the encaging as follows. Mark off upon the x-axis the nine points with the abscissas

$$0, 1/4, 1/2, 3/4, 1, 5/4, 3/2, 7/4, 2,$$

and at each point erect the ordinate to our parabola, as in Figure 14-20. These nine ordinates (the one corresponding to $x = 0$ is de-

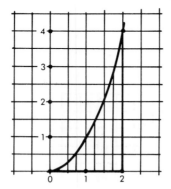

FIGURE 14-20 The region R cut up into strips.

generate, being of zero length and consisting of the origin alone) cut up R into 8 strips of uniform width 1/4. Consider any one of these strips, which we shall denote by R'. Let S' be the largest rectangular region contained in R' (see Figure 14-21A); the height of S' is equal

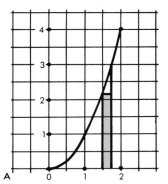
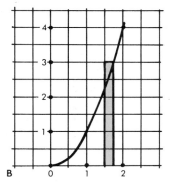

FIGURE 14-21 *Upper and lower rectangles approximating a given strip. A, the lower rectangle S'; B, the upper rectangle T'.*

to the smallest ordinate of R'. Let T' be the smallest rectangular region containing R' (see Figure 14-21B); the height of T' is equal to the greatest ordinate of R'. We shall call S' the *lower rectangle* approximating R' and T' the *upper rectangle* approximating R'. (Here, we use "rectangle" loosely for "rectangular region.") We have, in particular,

$$S' \subset R' \subset T'.$$

Each of the 8 strips into which R has been divided has a lower and an upper rectangle. (The lower rectangle to approximate the first strip on the left is degenerate, having height 0.) If we denote by S_8 the union of (i.e., the region covered by) the eight lower rectangles and by T_8 the union of the eight upper rectangles, then we have

$$S_8 \subset R \subset T_8$$

(see Figures 14-22A and B). According to our Guiding Principle, the

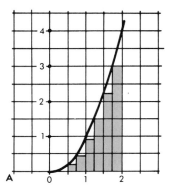
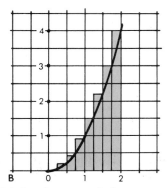

FIGURE 14-22 *A region approximated above and below by rectangled structures. A, union of lower rectangles; B, union of upper rectangles.*

area $A(R)$ — once we define it — must as a consequence satisfy the inequalities

(1) $$A(S_8) < A(R) < A(T_8).$$

Let us calculate $A(S_8)$ and $A(T_8)$, Table 14-6 displaying the details. Column I gives the intervals between the abscissas of consecutive points of subdivision of the x-axis. Column II gives for each interval the least ordinate of our parabola and Column III the greatest ordinate. (For instance, in the interval from 1/4 to 1/2, the parabola ordinate varies from $(1/4)^2$ to $(1/2)^2$, the ordinate being equal to the square of the abscissa. Hence, the least ordinate in this interval is $(1/4)^2 = 1/16$, and the greatest ordinate is $(1/2)^2 = 1/4$.) In each interval, the least ordinate is the height of the corresponding lower rectangle, the greatest ordinate the height of the corresponding upper rectangle. Multiplying the heights by the uniform width of 1/4 gives the areas of the rectangles, which appear in Columns IV and V.

Table 14-6   The areas of the upper and the lower rectangles for a particular subdivision of a region into strips

I	II	III	IV	V
Abscissa Interval	Least Ordinate on Interval	Greatest Ordinate on Interval	Area of Lower Rectangle	Area of Upper Rectangle
0 to 1/4	0	1/16	0	1/64
1/4 to 1/2	1/16	1/4	1/64	1/16
1/2 to 3/4	1/4	9/16	1/16	9/64
3/4 to 1	9/16	1	9/64	1/4
1 to 5/4	1	25/16	1/4	25/64
5/4 to 3/2	25/16	9/4	25/64	9/16
3/2 to 7/4	9/4	49/16	9/16	49/64
7/4 to 2	49/16	4	49/64	1

The sum of Column IV is $A(S_8)$. Thus,

$$A(S_8) = 1/64 + 1/16 + 9/64 + 1/4 + 25/64 + 9/16 + 49/64$$
$$= (1/64)(1 + 4 + 9 + 16 + 25 + 36 + 49)$$
$$= (1/64)(1^2 + 2^2 + 3^2 + 4^2 + 5^2 + 6^2 + 7^2).$$

The sum of Column V gives us $A(T_8)$, for which we obtain in a similar way:

$$A(T_8) = (1/64)(1^2 + 2^2 + 3^2 + 4^2 + 5^2 + 6^2 + 7^2 + 8^2).$$

It will be convenient to have a symbol for the sum of the first n positive integers squared. Let us therefore set

$$p_n = 1^2 + 2^2 + 3^2 + \ldots + n^2.$$

In this notation, we can write

$$A(S_8) = (1/64)\, p_7,\ A(T_8) = (1/64)\, p_8,$$

inequalities (1) thus reading:

$$(1/64)\, p_7 < A(R) < (1/64)\, p_8.$$

Computing p_7 and p_8, we have

$$2\ 3/16 < A(R) < 3\ 3/16,$$

encaging inequalities that delimit $A(R)$ to a stretch 1 unit long.

Narrower delimitations of $A(R)$ result if we use the same process we have just described but with more than nine points for our subdivisions. Let the segment of the x-axis between 0 and 2 be divided by $n+1$ points (including 0 and 2) into n equal intervals. Since the length of each interval must be $2/n$, the $n+1$ points of this subdivision must be

$$0, 2/n, 4/n, 6/n, 8/n, \ldots, 2(n-1)/n, 2.$$

At each of these points, erect an ordinate to the parabola, as was done in the case $n=8$. The $n+1$ ordinates (again, the ordinate corresponding to $x=0$ is degenerate) dissect R into n strips of width $2/n$, each strip *containing* a lower rectangle, and *being contained in* an upper rectangle, as defined previously. The union of the n lower rectangles is a region properly contained in R that we shall denote by S_n; the union of the n upper rectangles is a region properly containing R that we shall denote by T_n. We shall call S_n and R_n, respectively, *lower* and *upper rectangled structures* approximating R. Since

$$S_n \subset R \subset T_n \text{ for } n = 2, 3, 4, \ldots,$$

our Guiding Principle requires of $A(R)$ that

(2) $$A(S_n) < A(R) < A(T_n) \text{ for } n = 2, 3, 4, \ldots.$$

As n becomes larger and larger, the lower and the upper rectangled structures squeeze more and more tightly towards R and towards each other. At the same time, the *areas* of the lower and the upper rectangled structures come to differ less and less, the area of R (always assuming that this can be defined) abiding fixed between them. These geometrical perceptions suggest that the areas of the lower rectangled structures,

$$A(S_n),\ n = 1, 2, 3, \ldots,$$

and the areas of the upper rectangled structures,

$$A(T_n), \; n = 2, 3, 4, \ldots,$$

should both have limits as n becomes infinite and that these limits should be the same. We shall show that this is the case. Conditions (2) will then lead us to define $A(R)$ as this common limit.

To carry out what we have proposed, we must calculate $A(S_n)$ and $A(T_n)$. The essential data for the lower and upper rectangles are given in Table 14-7 which is completely analogous to Table 14-6. Recall that, in each interval, the least ordinate is the height of the lower rectangle and the greatest ordinate the height of the upper rectangle. Each rectangle having width $2/n$, its area (Columns IV and V) is found from its height (Columns II and III) by multiplying by $2/n$. The sum of Column IV gives the area of the lower rectangled structure S_n:

$$\begin{aligned}
A(S_n) &= (2/n)(2/n)^2 + (2/n)(4/n)^2 + \ldots + (2/n)(2(n-1)/n)^2 \\
&= (2/n^3)[2^2 + 4^2 + 6^2 + \ldots + 2^2(n-1)^2] \\
&= (2/n^3)2^2[1^2 + 2^2 + 3^2 + \ldots + (n-1)^2] \\
&= (2/n)^3 p_{n-1},
\end{aligned}$$

Table 14-7   The areas of upper and lower rectangles for strips of uniform width

I	II	III	IV	V
Abscissa Interval	Least Ordinate on Interval	Greatest Ordinate on Interval	Area of Lower Rectangle	Area of Upper Rectangle
0 to $\dfrac{2}{n}$	0	$\left(\dfrac{2}{n}\right)^2$	0	$\dfrac{2}{n}\left(\dfrac{2}{n}\right)^2$
$\dfrac{2}{n}$ to $\dfrac{4}{n}$	$\left(\dfrac{2}{n}\right)^2$	$\left(\dfrac{4}{n}\right)^2$	$\dfrac{2}{n}\left(\dfrac{2}{n}\right)^2$	$\dfrac{2}{n}\left(\dfrac{4}{n}\right)^2$
$\dfrac{4}{n}$ to $\dfrac{6}{n}$	$\left(\dfrac{4}{n}\right)^2$	$\left(\dfrac{6}{n}\right)^2$	$\dfrac{2}{n}\left(\dfrac{4}{n}\right)^2$	$\dfrac{2}{n}\left(\dfrac{6}{n}\right)^2$
.....	....	....	.....	.....
$\dfrac{2(n-1)}{n}$ to 2	$\left(\dfrac{2(n-1)}{n}\right)^2$	4	$\dfrac{2}{n}\left(\dfrac{2(n-1)}{n}\right)^2$	$\dfrac{8}{n}$

p_{n-1} representing the sum of the squares of the first $n-1$ positive integers, according to our previous definition. The sum of Column V gives us similarly the area of the upper rectangled structure T_n:

$$\begin{aligned}
A(T_n) &= (2/n)(2/n)^2 + (2/n)(4/n)^2 + \ldots + (2/n)(2(n-1)/n)^2 + (2/n)4 \\
&= (2/n^3)2^2[1^2 + 2^2 + 3^2 + \ldots + (n-1)^2 + n^2] \\
&= (2/n)^3 p_n.
\end{aligned}$$

Condition (2) thus gives us

$$(2/n)^3 p_{n-1} < A(R) < (2/n)^3 p_n \text{ for } n = 2, 3, 4, \ldots,$$

inequalities that will prove to encage $A(R)$ as tightly as we wish. In fact, we shall show that

$$(2/n)^3 p_n$$

and

$$(2/n)^3 p_{n-1}$$

have limits as n becomes infinite and that these limits are the same. Our method is based on this formula for the sums of squares:

$$p_n = (1/6) \, n(n+1)(2n+1).$$

(The formula is easily proved by mathematical induction [see Exercise 2(b), p. 389].) According to this formula,

(3)
$$\begin{aligned}
(2/n)^3 p_n &= 8n(n+1)(2n+1)/(6n^3) \\
&= 4(2n^3 + 3n^2 + n)/(3n^3) \\
&= 8/3 + 4/n + 4/(3n^2).
\end{aligned}$$

As n becomes infinite, the second and third terms on the right tend to zero, the sum of the three terms on the right thus tending to 8/3. Therefore,

$$\lim_{n \to \infty} (2/n)^3 p_n = 8/3.$$

A parallel calculation would show that

$$\lim_{n \to \infty} (2/n)^3 p_{n-1} = 8/3,$$

but we can argue from the fact that

(4)
$$\begin{aligned}
(2/n)^3 p_{n-1} &= (2/n)^3 p_n - (2/n)^3 (p_n - p_{n-1}) \\
&= (2/n)^3 p_n - (2/n)^3 n^2 \\
&= (2/n)^3 p_n - 8/n.
\end{aligned}$$

As n becomes infinite, the first term on the right tends to 8/3, the second term to zero, and the two terms together thus to 8/3. This, therefore, is the limit of the quantity on the left, as stated before.
    Formula (3) implies that

$$(2/n)^3 p_n > 8/3,$$

and formulas (3) and (4) show that

$$\begin{aligned}
(2/n)^3 p_{n-1} &= (2/n)^3 p_n - 8/n \\
&= 8/3 + 4/n + 4/(3n^2) - 8/n \\
&= 8/3 - 4/n + 4/(3n^2) \\
&= 8/3 - 4(3n-1)/(3n^2) \\
&< 8/3.
\end{aligned}$$

These two inequalities together state that

$$(2/n)^3 p_{n-1} < 8/3 < (2/n)^3 p_n.$$

The calculations just completed show that, as n becomes infinite, the quantities $A(S_n)$ and $A(T_n)$ have a common limit, 8/3, for which

$$A(S_n) < 8/3 < A(T_n) \text{ for } n = 2, 3, 4, \ldots.$$

This common limit 8/3 thus satisfies the requirements upon $A(R)$ that we accepted in (2). Furthermore, no other number satisfies these requirements. Indeed, suppose a to be any such number:

$$A(S_n) < a < A(T_n) \text{ for } n = 2, 3, 4, \ldots.$$

If $a < 8/3$, we have

$$A(S_n) < a < 8/3 < A(T_n) \text{ for } n = 2, 3, 4, \ldots,$$

(see Figure 14-23), and thus

(5) $$A(T_n) - A(S_n) > 8/3 - a.$$

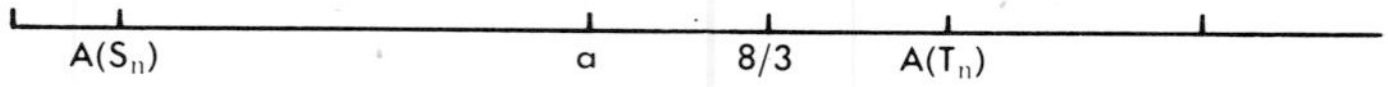

FIGURE 14-23

On the other hand,

$$\lim_{n \to \infty} (A(T_n) - A(S_n)) = \lim_{n \to \infty} A(T_n) - \lim_{n \to \infty} A(S_n)$$
$$= 8/3 - 8/3$$
$$= 0$$

(see Theorem 4 and Exercise 10 in Section 4). This means that to every positive number e, a critical index N exists such that

$$n > N \Rightarrow |A(T_n) - A(S_n)| < e.$$

But for $e < 8/3 - a$, this result contradicts (5), and we must admit that a is not less than 8/3. By an analogous argument, a is not greater than 8/3. Hence $a = 8/3$, which is to say that no number other than 8/3 satisfies the requirements imposed upon $A(R)$, as asserted. Therefore, we are forced to define:

$$A(R) = \lim_{n \to \infty} A(S_n)$$
$$= \lim_{n \to \infty} A(T_n)$$
$$= 8/3.$$

Other problems of area for regions with curved boundaries can also be attacked by the method we have just illustrated. In every ordinary case, the region will contain lower rectangled structures and will be contained in upper rectangled structures, whose areas have a common limit. This common limit is then defined to be the area of the region itself.

EXERCISES

1. Find the area between the parabola $y = x^2$ and the x-axis in the band $0 \leq x \leq 1$.

2. Ditto in the band $1 \leq x \leq 2$.

3. Find the area between the parabola $y = x^2$ and the y-axis in the horizontal band $0 \leq y \leq 1$.

4. Ditto in the band $1 \leq y \leq 2$.

5. Find the area between the parabola $y = x^2$ and the line $y = 4$ (see Figure 14-18).

6. The curve with the equation $y = 1 - x^2$ is also called a parabola. Find the area between the x-axis and this parabola.

7. Consider any of the rectangled structures in Figure 14-22, say S_n, in the band $0 \leq x \leq 2$. Let c be such that $0 < c < 2$, and denote by S_n' the part of S_n within the band $0 \leq x \leq c$ and by S_n'' the part of S_n within the band $c \leq x \leq 2$ (see Figure 14-24). It follows from the definitions in Chapter 7, Section 3, that

$$A(S_n') + A(S_n'') = A(S_n).$$

$0 < x < c$ $c < x < 2$

0   c   2

FIGURE 14-24   A vertical band subdivided.

How? If R' denotes the part of R in the band $0 \leq x \leq c$ and R'' the part of R in the band $c \leq x \leq 2$, is it similarly true that

$$A(R') + A(R'') = A(R)?$$

Exercises 1 and 2 answer this question affirmatively in the case $c = 1$. Can you see reasons for the same answer in general as a mathematical consequence of our definition of $A(R)$? HINT: See Theorem 4, Section 4.

8. Refer to Figure 14-18. The shaded regions in these figures, which unite to fill a square of area 16, have individual areas that are defined by arithmetical processes such as we have described before. Can you give general reasons, based on the nature of these processes, to expect the sum of the individual areas to be 16?

7.

Sectional approximation of volumes

In Section 3, Chapter 7, we arrived at definitions of the volumes of rectangular boxes but said little about more general solid figures. What, for instance, is the volume of a pyramid? Its boundary surfaces are planar, not curved, but the answer is still far from apparent. To work it out, we shall be guided by the following principle, suggested by that used so successfully for areas:

Principle for Defining Volumes. Let S and T be solid figures for which volumes

$$V(S), V(T),$$

respectively, are defined. Suppose that R is an intermediate solid figure in the sense that

$$S \subset R \subset T.$$

Then the volume of R, which we denote by $V(R)$, must satisfy the condition that

$$V(S) < V(R) < V(T).$$

We shall consider a right pyramid with a square base. Let B, C, D, E denote the vertices of the base, say in the order of a circuit in a particular direction (see Figure 14-25), and let O be the fifth vertex

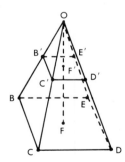

FIGURE 14-25   A right pyramid with a square base.

of the pyramid. We call O the *apex* of the pyramid. Let F be the center of the square $BCDE$: F is the intersection of the diagonals BD and CE. The line OF is called the *axis* of the pyramid. The stipulation that the pyramid $BCDEO$ be a *right* pyramid means that OF is perpendicular to the plane of the base $BCDE$. This property implies that

$$OB = OC = OD = OE,$$

since $FB = FC = FD = FE$ and the angles OFB, OFC, OFD, OFE are right angles.

Let M be any plane parallel to the base plane (the plane of $BCDE$), and let M intersect

$$OB \text{ in } B',$$
$$OC \text{ in } C',$$
$$OD \text{ in } D',$$
$$OE \text{ in } E',$$
$$OF \text{ in } F'$$

(see Figure 14-25). We shall have to know that $B'C'D'E'$ is a square with center F' and that

(1) $$A(B'C'D'E') = A(BCDE) \cdot (OF'/OF)^2,$$

$A(BCDE)$ representing the area of $BCDE$, and so on. In the first place, $B'C'$ and BC are parallel, being contained in respective planes that never meet and also both being in the plane of OBC. Hence, the laws of similar triangles show (see Figure 14-26) that

$$B'C'/BC = OB'/OB;$$

FIGURE 14-26 *Similar triangles in the pyramid.*

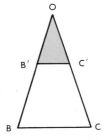

on the other hand, Figure 14-27 shows that

$$OB'/OB = OF'/OF$$

FIGURE 14-27 *Similar triangles in the pyramid.*

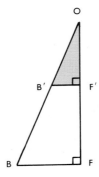

since angles $OF'B'$ and OFB are both right angles. Together with the previous relation, this proves

$$B'C'/BC = OF'/OF.$$

We thus have the first of the following statements:

(2)
$$\begin{aligned}
&B'C' \text{ is parallel to } BC,\\
&C'D' \text{ is parallel to } CD,\\
&D'E' \text{ is parallel to } DE,\\
&E'B' \text{ is parallel to } EB;
\end{aligned}$$

and we have the first of the following proportionalities:

(3)
$$\begin{aligned}
B'C'/BC &= OF'/OF,\\
C'D'/CD &= OF'/OF,\\
D'E'/DE &= OF'/OF,\\
E'B'/EB &= OF'/OF.
\end{aligned}$$

The other statements and the other proportionalities are proved in just the same way. Because of the parallelisms, $B'C'D'E'$ is a rectangle. Because of the proportionalities, it is a square and

$$\begin{aligned}
A(B'C'D'E') &= B'C' \cdot D'E'\\
&= BC \cdot OF'/OF \cdot DE \cdot OF'/OF\\
&= A(BCDE)\,(OF'/OF)^2,
\end{aligned}$$

since of course $A(BCDE) = BC \cdot DE$. Formula (1) is thus justified.

We must still prove the assertion that F' is the center of $B'C'D'E'$, i.e., belongs to both diagonals $B'D'$ and $C'E'$. Let us show, in particular, that F' is a point of $B'D'$; F' can be seen to be a point of $C'E'$ in exactly the same way. We shall appeal to the principle that a straight line is the shortest distance between two points, or, more precisely, that if R is a point not on a line segment PQ, then†

$$PR + RQ > PQ.$$

(see Figure 14-28.) This principle (or rather its contrapositive form)

---

†The principle follows from the Pythagorean law, as follows. Let R' be the point of the straight line PQ such that RR' is perpendicular to PQ. Then by Pythagoras's theorem,

$$PR > PR', \; RQ > R'Q.$$

If R' is a point of the segment PQ, then $PQ = PR' + R'Q$, and the last inequalities at once imply $PQ < PR + RQ$. If R' is not a point of the segment PQ, suppose P, Q, and R' occur in that order. Then $PR' > PQ$, while by Pythagoras's theorem $PR > PR'$. Therefore, $PR > PQ$, so that certainly $PR + RQ > PQ$. The result is similar if R', P, Q is the order of these points. Under all circumstances, therefore, the stated inequality holds.

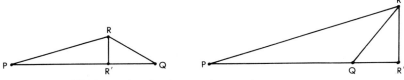

FIGURE 14-28   The shortest distance between two points.

tells us that F' belongs to $B'D'$ if

(4) $$B'F' + F'D' = B'D'.$$

Thus, it suffices for us to establish (4). To do so, we note that

$$B'F' \text{ is parallel to } BF, \text{ that}$$
$$D'F' \text{ is parallel to } DF,$$

and that, correspondingly,

$$B'F'/BF = OF'/OF, \ D'F'/DF = OF'/OF.$$

These facts are proved like (2) and (3). If we set

$$OF'/OF = c,$$

the last proportionalities become

$$B'F' = c\,BF, \ D'F' = c\,DF,$$

and by adding we obtain

$$B'F' + F'D' = c\,BF + c\,FD$$
$$= c\,(BF + FD)$$
$$= c\,BD,$$

since F is a point of the segment BD. On the other hand, relations (3) show, in particular, that,

$$B'C' = c\,BC, \ C'D' = c\,CD.$$

Since $B'C'D'E'$ and $BCDE$ are both squares, considerations of similar triangles in Figure 14-29 show that

$$B'D' = c\,BD.$$

FIGURE 14-29   The base of the pyramid and a section parallel to the base.

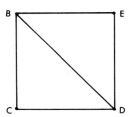

Consequently,

$$B'F' + F'D' = B'D',$$

and we conclude that F' is indeed a point of $B'D'$. Similarly, F' is a point of $C'E'$ and thus is the center of the square $B'C'D'E'$, as asserted.

Now choose Cartesian coordinates with origin O, with OF as the z-axis and with x- and y-axes parallel to BC and BE, respectively. Let the positive direction along the z-axis be that from O to F, and choose OF as the unit of length. (Thus, F has z-coordinate 1 and the Cartesian representation $(0,0,1)$.) We shall subdivide the segment of the z-axis between O and F by $n+1$ points (including O and F) into n equal intervals. The length of each interval is $1/n$, and the $n+1$ points of subdivision are those with the z-coordinates

$$0,\ 1/n,\ 2/n,\ 3/n,\ 4/n,\ \ldots,\ (n-1)/n,\ 1.$$

The full Cartesian representations of these points are, of course, $(0,0,0)$, $(0,0,1/n)$, $(0,0,2/n)$, and so forth. Figure 14-30 illustrates.

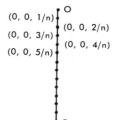

FIGURE 14-30   *Subdivision of the axis of a pyramid.*

Through each of these points of subdivision of the z-axis, we consider the plane parallel to the pyramid's base and thus parallel to the xy-plane. Denote by Z_k the plane parallel to the xy-plane through $(0,0,k/n)$. Then Z_0 intersects the pyramid in the single point O, Z_n in the base. For $0 < k \leq n$, Z_k cuts the pyramid in a square such as $B'C'D'E'$ in Figure 14-25 with $OF' = k/n$. By formula (1), the area of this square is

(5) $$(k/n)^2(BC)^2,$$

since $OF' = k/n$, $OF = 1$, and $A(BCDE) = BC \cdot BE = (BC)^2$.

The $n+1$ planes Z_0, Z_1, $\ldots$, Z_n divide the pyramid into n sections of uniform thickness $1/n$. According to (5), the lower face of the section between Z_{k-1} and Z_k ($k = 1, 2, \ldots, n$) has area

$$(k/n)^2(BC)^2;$$

the area of the upper face is

$$((k-1)/n)^2(BC)^2.$$

Let us denote by R_k the section of the pyramid between Z_{k-1} and Z_k, $k = 1, \ldots, n$. The box of height $1/n$ that has the same lower face as R_k contains R_k, as Figure 14-31 illustrates. The box of height $1/n$ that

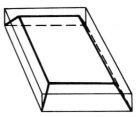

FIGURE 14-31 The box of height $1/n$ over the lower face of a section of thickness $1/n$ of the pyramid.

has the same upper face as R_k is contained in R_k. Hence, denoting these boxes by T_k and S_k, respectively, we have

$$S_k \subset R_k \subset T_k.$$

(Figure 14-31 illustrates the second inclusion.) By (5), the volume of the larger box is

$$V(T_k) = (1/n)(k/n)^2(BC)^2,$$

and the volume of the smaller box is

$$V(S_k) = (1/n)((k-1)/n)^2(BC)^2.$$

Let R denote the pyramid, S the union of all the S_k, and T the union of the T_k. Since

$$S \subset R \subset T,$$

our Principle for Defining Volumes requires that

$$V(S) < V(R) < V(T).$$

Since the S_k do not overlap and unite into S, we have

$$
\begin{aligned}
V(S) &= V(S_1) + V(S_2) + \ldots + V(S_n) \\
&= (1/n)(0/n)^2(BC)^2 + (1/n)(1/n)^2(BC)^2 + \ldots \\
&\quad + (1/n)((n-1)/n)^2(BC)^2 \\
&= (1/n^3)(BC)^2(1^2 + 2^2 + \ldots + (n-1)^2).
\end{aligned}
$$

Similarly,

$$
\begin{aligned}
V(T) &= V(T_1) + V(T_2) + \ldots + V(T_n) \\
&= (1/n^3)(BC)^2(1^2 + 2^2 + 3^2 + \ldots + n^2).
\end{aligned}
$$

Thus, in the notation of the previous subsection,

$$V(S) = (BC)^2 p_{n-1}/n^3, \quad V(T) = (BC)^2 p_n/n^3.$$

We showed in the previous subsection that

(6) $$\lim_{n \to \infty} p_n/n^3 = 1/3, \ \lim_{n \to \infty} p_{n-1}/n^3 = 1/3,$$

and also that

(7) $$p_{n-1}/n^3 < 1/3 < p_n/n^3.$$

It follows from (7) that

$$(BC)^2 p_{n-1}/n^3 < (BC)^2/3 < (BC)^2 p_n/n^3$$

and thus that

$$V(S) < (BC)^2/3 < V(T).$$

It follows from (6) that $V(S)$ and $V(T)$ both converge to $(BC)^2/3$ as n becomes infinite. Therefore, our Principle for Defining Volumes requires us to define

$$V(R) = (BC)^2/3.$$

EXERCISES

1. Work out the volume of a right square pyramid of altitude 2.
2. What is the volume of a right square pyramid of altitude h?
3. A *frustum* of a pyramid is defined to be the portion contained between two planes parallel to the base. Suppose these planes are at distances 1 and 2, respectively, from the apex of the pyramid. What is the volume of the frustum if the pyramid is a right pyramid with square base? What is the volume if the planes have distances 2 and 3, respectively, from the apex?
4. For a right pyramid of altitude 1 upon a triangular base, prove that the volume of the pyramid is 1/3 times the area of the base.
5. For a right pyramid of altitude 1 upon a rectangular base, prove that the volume of the pyramid is 1/3 times the area of the base.
6. For a right pyramid of altitude 1 upon a trapezoidal base, prove that the volume of the pyramid is 1/3 times the area of the base.

8.

The total force required to contain a static fluid

Consider a box-shaped† tank with a horizontal bottom containing water, for example, a fish tank or a swimming pool. Assuming the

---

† By a box we mean a rectangular parallelepiped. See "A remark on volumes," Section 3, Chapter 7.

water to be static (i.e., at rest), we ask for the force exerted by the water against the bottom and also against the sides of the tank. The force against the bottom will offer no difficulty, but that exerted upon the walls is more elusive and demands reasoning about limits.

We do not define the concept of force but state specific physical assumptions appropriate for these problems.

(I) Static fluid present on one side of a plane exerts upon the plane a certain force. This force is perpendicular to the plane. It is downward upon a horizontal plane (in particular, the bottom of the tank) and horizontally directed against a vertical plane (in particular, a wall).

We shall measure forces in pounds.

(II) Static fluid present on one side of a plane exerts upon any individual portion of the plane, perpendicularly to it, a certain share of the total force against the plane. If the plane is divided into nonoverlapping sections, then the sum of the forces upon the sections is equal to the total force of the fluid upon the plane. In this sense, fluid force upon a plane is *additive*.

(III) Of water at rest in a tank, the portion above an arbitrary depth h exerts the same force against the body of water below depth h as if this body below were not liquid, but solid. The portion above depth h thus weighs down upon the horizontal watery plane at depth h just as if this plane were a solid top of a solid body underneath. Unyielding because the fluid is static, this plane supports the liquid load above it like a table holding up so much ice. All our various assumptions concerning forces exerted upon planes apply to it.

The next assumption states the downward force upon a horizontal plane at depth h and, more generally, upon an arbitrary region R of this plane. Imagine the right prism with base R and height h; the top of the prism is at the surface of the water. We call the fluid contained in this imagined prism "the vertical column of fluid over R" and make the following assumption:

(IV) The fluid exerts a downward force upon the plane region R equal to the weight of the vertical column of fluid over R.

With this assumption, we can answer our first question as follows: the total downward force of the fluid upon the bottom of the tank is equal to the weight of the fluid in the tank.

If the area of R is a square feet, then the prism with base R and height h feet contains ah cubic feet of fluid. If 1 cubic foot of the fluid weighs w pounds — w is called the *density* of the fluid† — then ah

---

† The density of water at the temperature 4°C. is about 62.5 pounds per cubic foot.

cubic feet of fluid weigh *wah* pounds. Hence, this is the weight of the vertical column of fluid over R being considered. By assumption (IV), the downward force exerted by the fluid upon R therefore is *wah* pounds. We thus see, in particular, that the ratio

$$\frac{\text{the downward force upon } R}{\text{the area of } R} = \frac{wah \text{ pounds}}{a \text{ square feet}}$$

$$= wh \text{ pounds per square foot}$$

is independent of the area of R. This ratio is defined to be the *pressure* in the fluid at depth h. Denoting pressure (in pounds per square foot) by p, we thus have

(1) $$p = wh,$$

w being the density of the fluid expressed in pounds per cubic foot and h the depth in feet. The density being a constant, pressure p can be regarded simply as a function of depth h.

Our final physical assumption concerns the force of the fluid against nonhorizontal planes. It says essentially that the *force per unit area* against an arbitrary plane is different at different depths and at each depth is equal to the pressure. It says that the fluid exerts upon a portion or section of the plane not varying greatly in depth a force of nearly the same magnitude as if the section were horizontal. (The direction of the force, however, is always perpendicular to the plane.) Similar in spirit to the Principle for Defining Areas (Section 6), it is worded as follows:

(V) Consider a section of a nonhorizontal plane—for instance, a portion of one of the walls of the tank—upon which the fluid pressure p (determined at each point by the depth) is not less than p' nor greater than p'':

$$p' \leq p \leq p''.$$

If the section of plane considered has area a, then the force f of the fluid against it satisfies the conditions

(2) $$ap' < f < ap''.$$

(Recall that we measure f in pounds, a in square feet, and p, p', p'' in pounds per square foot.)

Since the least pressure p' is realized at the least depth h' and the greatest pressure p'' at the greatest depth h'' of the section of plane considered, from (1) we have $p' = wh'$ and $p'' = wh''$. Thus conditions (2) are equivalent to

(3) $$wah' < f < wah''.$$

Holding for every section of wall, no matter how narrow or small, they will lead us to the total force desired.

Suppose a wall of the tank is b feet wide and extends c feet below the surface of the water (see Figure 14-32). Let n be any positive

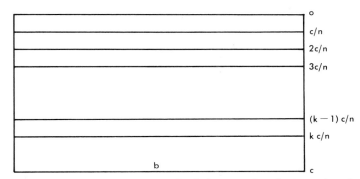

FIGURE 14-32   *A rectangular wall divided into uniform horizontal sections.*

integer, and divide the wall surface into n horizontal bands, each of height c/n feet and thus of area bc/n square feet. We shall apply (3) to estimate the force of the water upon each individual band. The first band at the top extends from depth 0 to depth c/n feet, i.e., $h' = 0$ and $h'' = c/n$ feet for this band; also, as we have just seen, its area $a = bc/n$ square feet. By (3), the force f_1 exerted by the fluid upon this band thus satisfies the conditions

$$w \cdot (bc/n) \cdot 0 < f_1 < w \cdot (bc/n) \cdot (c/n).$$

The second band from the top is situated at depths from c/n to $2c/n$ feet; hence, the force f_2 exerted by the fluid against it is such that

$$w \cdot (bc/n) \cdot c/n < f_2 < w \cdot (bc/n) \cdot 2c/n.$$

The third band is from $2c/n$ to $3c/n$ feet deep; therefore, the force f_3 of the fluid against this band is such that

$$w \cdot (bc/n) \cdot 2c/n < f_3 < w \cdot (bc/n) \cdot 3c/n.$$

The general case is not more difficult: for $k = 1, 2, \ldots, n$, the kth band from the top is situated at depths between $(k-1)c/n$ and kc/n feet, and its area is bc/n square feet. Hence, by assumption V, the force f_k (in pounds) exerted by the fluid against this band satisfies the inequalities

$$w \cdot (bc/n) \cdot (k-1)c/n < f_k < w \cdot (bc/n) \cdot kc/n,$$

i.e.,

$$(wbc^2/n^2)(k-1) < f_k < (wbc^2/n)k \text{ for } k=1, 2, \ldots, n.$$

This gives us the lower estimates

$$0 < f_1,$$
$$wbc^2/n^2 < f_2,$$
$$2\,wbc^2/n^2 < f_3,$$
$$3\,wbc^2/n^2 < f_4,$$
$$\ldots$$
$$(n-1)\,wbc^2/n^2 < f_n$$

and the upper estimates

$$f_1 < wbc^2/n^2,$$
$$f_2 < 2wbc^2/n^2,$$
$$f_3 < 3wbc^2/n^2,$$
$$\ldots$$
$$f_n < nwbc^2/n^2.$$

By assumption II, the total force against the wall exerted by the fluid is

$$F = f_1 + f_2 + f_3 + \ldots + f_n.$$

Adding the lower estimates gives

$$0 + wbc^2/n^2 + 2wbc^2/n^2 + 3wbc^2/n^2 + \ldots + (n-1)\,wbc^2/n^2$$
$$< f_1 + f_2 + f_3 + \ldots + f_n = F,$$

or

$$(wbc^2/n^2)(1 + 2 + 3 + \ldots + (n-1)) < F.$$

Since

$$1 + 2 + 3 + \ldots + (n-1) = (n-1)n/2 \qquad \text{(Chapter 10, Section 3),}$$

we thus have

$$(wbc^2/2)(n-1)/n < F.$$

By adding the upper estimates we have similarly

$$F = f_1 + f_2 + f_3 + \ldots + f_n$$
$$< wbc^2/n^2 + 2wbc^2/n^2 + 3wbc^2/n^2 + \ldots + nwbc^2/n^2$$
$$< (wbc^2/n^2)(1 + 2 + 3 + \ldots + n)$$
$$= (wbc^2/n^2)(n(n+1)/2)$$
$$= (wbc^2/2)(n+1)/n.$$

This and the previous result tell us, in sum,

(4) $$(wbc^2/2)(n-1)/n < F < (wbc^2/2)(n+1)/n.$$

Since $(n-1)/n = 1 - 1/n$ and $(n+1)/n = 1 + 1/n$, we see that both $(n-1)/n$ and $(n+1)/n$ tend toward 1 as n becomes infinite (Section 4). Therefore, the left and the right members of inequalities (4) both tend toward $wbc^2/2$ as n becomes infinite. Therefore,

(5) $F = wbc^2/2.$

This formula tells us the force of the fluid against a rectangular vertical wall b feet wide and c feet deep. It is worthwhile to interpret it physically and geometrically as follows. We define *average pressure on the wall* to be the quantity

F/A pounds per square foot,

where $A = $ area of wall $= bc$ square feet. According to our formula,

(5') $F/A = wbc^2/2bc = wc/2$ pounds per square foot.

Since the pressure at the deepest part of the wall is wc and the pressure at the top (water level) is 0 pounds per square foot, the average of the least and greatest pressures is

$(0 + wc)/2 = wc/2$ pounds per square foot.

Hence, in the form (5') our formula states:

(6) average pressure on the wall $=$ average of least and greatest pressures.

EXERCISES

1. What is the total force exerted by the water in a swimming pool upon the wall at the deeper end, which is 20 feet wide and extends 10 feet below the surface? What is the average pressure on the wall? What is the greatest pressure? What is the total force exerted by the water on the lower half of the submerged part of the wall? Does rule (6) apply to this lower half?

2. Consider a vertical wall shaped like a right triangle, with one arm horizontal at water level and the other extending vertically downwards beneath the surface. The submerged part of a side wall running the length of a swimming pool might be of this shape. Use the method of this section to calculate the total force exerted by the water on this wall. HINT: Use Figure 14-33 in place of Figure 14-32. If the wall is b feet wide, and c feet is its greatest depth, then its horizontal width x at depth d is determined by the proportionality $x/(c-d) = b/c$ (see Figure 14-34). Hence, $cx = b(c-d)$, and $x = b(1 - d/c)$. Therefore, in Figure 14-33, we have

$$BC = b(1 - k/n) \text{ feet,}$$
$$AD = b(1 - (k-1)/n) \text{ feet.}$$

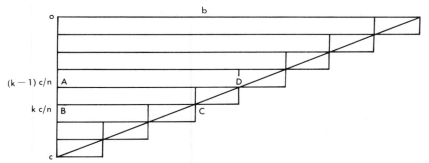

FIGURE 14-33   *Subdivision of a triangular wall.*

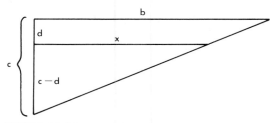

FIGURE 14-34   *Triangles in a similarity calculation.*

Since $AB = c/n$, we have

$$b(1 - k/n)(c/n) < ABCD < b(1 - (k - 1)/n)(c/n).$$

(ABCD is exactly $b(1 - (k - 1/2)/n)(c/n)$, but we do not have to be so precise.) The force f_k on the area ABCD can be estimated from this and assumption IV. Do this, sum over k ($k = 1, 2, \ldots, n$), and then let n become infinite, just as in the case of a rectangular wall treated in the text.

9.

Gravitational attraction

Queen Elizabeth's physician, William Gilbert, in 1601 expressed the most advanced views on gravitation of his time: earth substance is attracted to the earth, moon substance to the moon, and so forth, and this is why the earth and the heavenly bodies cohere instead of flying apart into pieces.[†] Kepler in 1609 suggested that *any* two bodies of earth matter *mutually* attract one another and that the moon, in particular, is composed of earth matter, its consequent pull upon the earth accounting for the ebb and flow of tides. In the same work, Kepler announced his discovery that planetary orbits around the sun

† Hall, ibid., p. 260-261.

are ellipses and guessed that they are caused by some "moving spirit" †
that resides in the sun. By 1619, he had completely formulated three
laws of planetary motion (including the one alluded to on the shapes
of orbits), which were to become "the observational axioms upon
which Newtonian celestial mechanics was to rest secure." ‡ The
three laws were overlooked for a generation, in effect concealed by
Kepler's obscure style. Meanwhile, Galileo founded the science of
mechanics, through which ultimately the description of planetary
motions would be reduced to the operation of simple, universal laws.
But Galileo left this science incomplete, in 1638. Before celestial
orbits could be treated, curved motion had to be mastered, Kepler's
laws absorbed, the true nature of gravitation grasped, and mathematics advanced prodigiously.

About 1666, Isaac Newton first surmised that the force of gravitation is universal. Tradition has it that an apple was involved, and we
now reproduce its story as told by William Stukeley. Hall cautions us
that Stukeley's memoir, written in 1752, dealt with recollections that
had been voiced by Newton in 1726 concerning thoughts and events
of sixty years before:

> After dinner, the weather being warm [the date was 15 April 1726], we went into
> the garden and drank tea, under the shade of some appletrees, only he and myself.
> Amidst other discourse, he told me, he was just in the same situation, as when
> formerly, the notion of gravitation came into his mind. It was occasion'd by the fall of an
> apple, as he sat in a contemplative mood. Why should that apple always descend
> perpendicularly to the ground, thought he to himself. Why should it not go sideways
> or upwards, but constantly to the earths centre? Assuredly the reason is, that the earth
> draws it. There must be a drawing power in matter: and the sum of the drawing power
> must be in the earths centre, not in any side of the earth. Therefore does this apple fall
> perpendicularly, or towards the centre. If matter thus draws matter, it must be in pro-
> portion of its quantity. Therefore, the apple draws the earth, as well as the earth draws
> the apple. That there is a power, like that we here call gravity, which extends itself
> thro the universe. §

The "quantity of matter" referred to is measured by the "mass"
of the matter. We can agree to adopt some substance, say water, as the
standard, declaring a certain quantity of water at a certain temperature to have *unit* mass. Then the mass of an arbitrary body can be
measured, at least in principle, by weighing it in a balance against
the standard substance. Thereby, mass is defined as a measure of the
quantity of matter irrespective of its nature, whether hydrogen or
wheat. Newton's idea was that any two bodies in the universe are
pulled, each to the other, with a force proportional to the mass of both
bodies. If the mass of either body is doubled, the positions of the
bodies not being changed, the attractive force of each upon the other
should double. More generally, if the bodies have masses m_1 and m_2,
respectively, Newton surmised the gravitational attraction of each
body upon the other to depend upon the product $m_1 m_2$ and, in fact,

---

† Ibid., p. 123.
‡ Ibid., p. 126.
§ William Stukeley: *Memoirs of Sir Isaac Newton's Life*, ed. by A. Hastings White
(London, 1936), pp. 19-20. Quoted from Hall, ibid., pp. 248-249.

to be of the form

$$Km_1m_2.$$

The factor K could be expected to be a function of the distance between the bodies, larger at the smaller distances and declining in magnitude as the bodies move farther apart.

Are Kepler's laws to be explained by such a force? If so, with what kind of K? In his first attack upon this problem, in 1666, Newton idealized material bodies as "mass points," points or particles endowed with mass. Also, he only considered circular orbits, which are permitted mathematically by Kepler's laws (circles are a kind of ellipse), but are only approximately followed by any actual celestial satellite. He knew from his great Dutch contemporary, Christian Huygens, exactly what force is required to hold a body in a circular path. With this information, he was able to make a calculation previously impossible indicating that a mass point held in a circular orbit by a force attracting it to another particle will obey Kepler's Third Law *only if* the attractive force is inversely proportional to the square of the distance between the two particles. Denote the distance between the particles by r. The previous condition means that the attractive force is proportional to $1/r^2$ and thus indicates that the factor K in the preceding paragraph should be proportional to $1/r^2$, i.e., that

$$K = k/r^2,$$

where k is a constant independent of the masses or the positions of the two points.

These considerations led Newton to consider the hypothesis that any two particles in the universe are pulled, each to the other, by a force of magnitude

$$km_1m_2/r^2,$$

where m_1 and m_2 are the respective masses of the particles, r is the distance between them, and k is an absolute constant independent of the particles or their positions. While this hypothesis deals explicitly only with particles, if true it ought to apply with some accuracy to bodies—for instance, the sun and its planets—that are tiny compared with the distances between and that thus can be considered almost to be mass points. The inverse square hypothesis, if true, therefore should imply that mass points have elliptical orbits. In the theory of motion, this is a purely mathematical question. It baffled Newton in 1666, and he apparently laid it aside for 13 years to be brought back to it in 1679 by Robert Hooke, who had recently also come to the notion of an inverse square law of gravitational attraction and then had propounded to Newton this same question. But Newton was now able to answer it affirmatively: under an inverse square law of gravitational attraction, mass points will indeed revolve in elliptical orbits. Five years later, he showed by calculation that such a law suffices to explain the *actual* orbits of the planets around the sun.

Many questions remained. Perhaps the most pressing was that of how the sizes and shapes of revolving bodies affect their motion. Newton confined himself to spherical shapes and asked what the inverse square law, which has to do explicitly only with *particles,* implies for the revolution of one *sphere* about another. This again is a purely mathematical problem, and it too defeated him in 1666. In 1685, he solved it "by showing that a sphere whose density at any point depends only on the distance from the centre attracts an external point as though its whole mass were concentrated at the centre."† This theorem reduced the problem of a revolving sphere to that of a revolving particle, whose orbits were known. Once possessing this theorem on spheres, Newton threw himself into the task of building up mathematically a cosmic system based only on the universal law of gravitation and the science of motion or mechanics, which he himself greatly advanced.‡ The outcome was his "incomparable"§ treatise, *Philosophiae naturalis principia mathematica,* first published in 1687. It founded modern theoretical physics. Depicting the cosmos as a giant mechanism obeying natural law, for many it was the final vindication of the Pythagorean faith in mathematical relation. It profoundly affected religion and philosophy. It influenced literature and esthetics.†† Pierre Simon Laplace a century later voiced the considered judgment of his age in according to Newton's Principia "a lasting pre-eminence over all other productions of the human mind.‡‡Alexander Pope was hardly thought to have exaggerated in these lines, intended to be Newton's epitaph:

> Nature and Nature's laws lay hid in night:
> God said, Let Newton be! and all was light.

Newton did not purport to explain gravitation, nor did he feel obliged to, grasping more clearly than other scientists of his day the crucial difference between fact and explanation. A natural law is an idealized description of observed facts. An explanation of a law is merely speculation, which never can be proved, but is eternally subject to disproof through the discovery of an unfavorable fact. In Newton's words: "For the best and safest method of philosophizing seems to be, first to enquire diligently into the properties of things,

---

†F. Cajori, *A History of Mathematics,* 2nd edition, Macmillan, 1961, p. 200.

‡Louis Trenchard More, *Isaac Newton.* Dover Publications, Inc., New York, 1962 (republication of book copyrighted in 1934.) pp. 302-3.

§Halley's expression in a letter to Newton, published in More, ibid., p. 305.

††See Morris Kline's eloquent account of Newtonian influence upon science, philosophy, religion, literature, and esthetics in Chapters 16 to 18 of *Mathematics in Western Culture.* Oxford University Press, 1953.

‡‡Quoted in Cajori, ibid., p. 201.

and of establishing those properties by experiments, and then to proceed more slowly to hypotheses for the explanation of them. For hypotheses should be subservient only in explaining the properties of things, but not assumed in determining them; unless so far as they may furnish experiments. For if the possibility of hypotheses is to be the test of the truth and reality of things, I see not how certainty can be obtained in any science; since numerous hypotheses may be devised .... Hence it has been here thought necessary to lay aside all hypotheses, as foreign to the purpose...."†

Newton's contemporaries seemed to Newton "absolutely unable to understand the fundamental difference between hypothesis and experimental law. As a result of this conviction, painfully borne in on him by altercation after altercation, he determined to discard the hypothetical method altogether.... The classic statement of this determination is given in the General Scholium at the end of the *Principia*: 'Hitherto I have not been able to discover the cause of those properties of gravity from phenomena, and I frame no hypotheses; for whatever is not deduced from the phenomena is to be called an hypothesis; and hypotheses, whether metaphysical or physical, whether of occult qualities or mechanical, have no place in experimental philosophy.... And to us it is enough that gravity does really exist, and act according to the laws which we have explained, and abundantly serves to account for all the motions of the celestial bodies, and of our sea.'"‡

The mathematics of gravitation is beyond our scope. Still we should like to give an idea of how to calculate the force of attraction to a material body under an inverse square law. We do so in a one-dimensional case, as follows. Imagine a thin, straight wire W idealized as a straight line segment AB endowed with mass. Assume that the mass m of an arbitrary subsegment of W is proportional to the length l of the subsegment, i.e., that

$$m = al,$$

where a is a constant; a is called the "linear density" of the wire W. Consider an arbitrary point O not on W, but on the same straight line, and attribute mass m_0 to O. (Thus, O is what we have called a "mass point.") Consider an arbitrary subsegment PQ of the wire W with $OP < OQ$ (Figure 14-35); the mass of the subsegment is $a \cdot PQ$. We assume the inverse square law of gravitational attraction in the following form: an arbitrary subsegment PQ of W attracts the mass point O with a force of magnitude f, where

$$km_0a \cdot PQ/(OQ)^2 < f < km_0a \cdot PQ/(OP)^2.$$

†Phil. Trans., No. 85, p. 5014. Quoted in L. T. More, ibid., p. 87.
‡More, ibid., pp. 105-106.

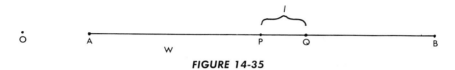

FIGURE 14-35

We also assume that if W is divided into nonoverlapping sublengths, then the force of attraction of O to W is the sum of the forces of attraction to the individual sublengths. We shall prove that the wire W then attracts the particle O with a force F given by

$$F = km_0m_1/(OA \cdot OB),$$

where m_1 is the mass of the wire, $m_1 = a \cdot AB$. If C is the point of W such that

$$OC = OA \cdot OB$$

$-OC$ is the geometric mean of the distances from O to the end points of W (see Chapter 11, Section 1)—we thus have:

$$F = km_0m_1/(OC)^2.$$

This shows that a wire W attracts an external particle O (in this instance, on the same straight line as the wire) as though the mass of W were concentrated at a single point C of W. The distance from O to C is the geometric mean of the distances from O to the end points of W.

Let c denote the least distance of O from W, say $c = OA$, as in Figure 14-36. Let l_1 denote the length of W; thus, $l_1 = AB$ and $m_1 = al_1$. Since in this notation $OA = c$ and $OB = c + l_1$, we must prove that

$$F = km_0m_1/(c(c + l_1)).$$

FIGURE 14-36   Mass point and subdivided wire.

To do so, divide W into n equal subintervals of length

$$h = l_1/n$$

(Figure 14-36). The distances of O from the points of subdivision are

$$c, c + h, c + 2h, \ldots, c + nh,$$

with $c + nh = c + l_1 = OB$. The distances of O from the end points of the jth interval of subdivision are

$$c + (j - 1)h, \; c + jh,$$

respectively, for $j = 1, 2, \ldots, n$. Denoting by f_j the force of attraction exerted upon O by this jth interval, we therefore have by assumption

$$km_0 ah/(c + jh)^2 < f_j < km_0 ah/(c + (j-1)h)^2,$$

ah being the mass of any segment of wire of length h.
The first inequality tells us that

(1)
$$\begin{aligned}
km_0 ah/(c + h)^2 &< f_1, \\
km_0 ah/(c + 2h)^2 &< f_2, \\
km_0 ah/(c + 3h)^2 &< f_3, \\
&\cdots \\
km_0 ah/(c + nh)^2 &< f_n
\end{aligned}$$

and the second inequality that

(2)
$$\begin{aligned}
f_1 &< km_0 ah/c^2, \\
f_2 &< km_0 ah/(c + h)^2, \\
f_3 &< km_0 ah/(c + 2h)^2, \\
&\cdots \\
f_n &< km_0 ah/(c - (n-1)h)^2.
\end{aligned}$$

Since the total force upon O is

$$F = f_1 + f_2 + f_3 + \ldots + f_n,$$

we have by adding inequalities (1)

$$km_0 ah/(c + h)^2 + km_0 ah/(c + 2h)^2 + \ldots + km_0 ah/(c + nh)^2 < F,$$

or

(3) $\quad km_0 a[h/(c + h)^2 + h/(c + 2h)^2 + \ldots + h/(c + nh)^2] < F.$

Adding inequalities (2) gives us similarly

$$F < km_0 ah/c^2 + km_0 ah/(c + h)^2 + \ldots + km_0 ah/(c + (n-1)h)^2$$

and thus

(4) $\quad F < km_0 a[h/c^2 + h/(c + h)^2 + \ldots + h/(c + (n-1)h)^2].$

To go further, we shall use a simple trick like that of Section 5f, based on the fact that

(5) $\quad h/[(c+(j-1)h)(c+jh)]=1/[c+(j-1)h]-1/[c+jh]$.

This identity enables us to estimate the summations that occur in (3) and (4). First, we have

$$\begin{aligned} h/(c+h)^2 &> h/[(c+h)(c+2h)]=1/(c+h)-1/(c+2h),\\ h/(c+2h)^2 &> h/[(c+2h)(c+3h)]=1/(c+2h)-1/(c+3h),\\ h/(c+3h)^2 &> h/[(c+3h)(c+4h)]=1/(c+3h)-1/(c+4h), \end{aligned}$$

and so forth. Adding gives us

$$\begin{aligned} h/(c+h)^2 + &h/(c+2h)^2 + h/(c+3h)^2 + \ldots + h/(c+nh)^2\\ &> [1/(c+h)-1/(c+2h)]+[1/(c+2h)-1/(c+3h)]\\ &\quad + [1/(c+3h)-1/(c+4h)]+\ldots\\ &\quad + [1/(c+nh)-1/(c+(n+1)h)]\\ &= 1/(c+h)-1/(c+(n+1)h), \end{aligned}$$

since the sum telescopes. Therefore, by (3),

(6) $\qquad km_0a[1/(c+h)-1/(c+(n+1)h)] < F$.

Now to estimate the summation in (4), assuming $h < c$, we apply (5) to obtain:

$$\begin{aligned} h/c^2 &< h/[c(c-h)]=1/(c-h)-1/c,\\ h/(c+h)^2 &< h/[c(c+h)]=1/c-1/(c+h),\\ h/(c+2h)^2 &< h/[(c+h)(c+2h)]=1/(c+h)-1/(c+2h), \end{aligned}$$

and so forth. Adding gives us

$$\begin{aligned} h/c^2 + &h/(c+h)^2 + h/(c+2h)^2 + \ldots + h/(c+(n-1)h)^2\\ &< [1/(c-h)-1/c]+[1/c-1/(c+h)]\\ &\quad + [1/(c+h)-1/(c+2h)]+\ldots\\ &\quad + [1/(c+(n-2)h)-1/(c+(n-1)h)]\\ &= 1/(c-h)-1/(c+(n-1)h), \end{aligned}$$

so that by (4),

(7) $\qquad F < km_0a[1/(c-h)-1/(c+(n-1)h)]$.

Since $nh = l_1$, we have $(n+1)h = nh + h = l_1 + l_1/n$ and similarly $(n-1)h = l_1 - l_1/n$. Making these substitutions in (6) and (7) gives us

(8) $\qquad km_0a[1/(c+l_1/n)-1/(c+l_1+l_1/n)] < F$

and

(9) $F < km_0 a [1/(c - l_1/n) - 1/(c + l_1 - l_1/n)]$.

As n becomes infinite, the quantity l_1/n approaches 0. Hence, the first member of (8) and the second member of (9) both approach

$$km_0 a [1/c - 1/(c + l_1)].$$

Since F is independent of n, but is encaged between two quantities that have the same limit as n becomes infinite, F must be equal to this limit, and we have

$$F = km_0 a [1/c - 1/(c + l_1)]$$
$$= km_0 a l_1 / [c(c + l_1)] = km_0 m_1 / [c(c + l_1)],$$

since $al_1 = m_1$. This is the formula we promised to derive.

EXERCISE

1. What do you think of Tolstoy's analogy between the forces that lead to historical change and gravitational force upon a body?† He regarded the summation of "an innumerable multitude of individual wills" as a far more potent cause of transformation of "the whole current of human life" than the influence of any particular man. For instance, he wrote: "The sum of men's individual wills produced both the French revolution and Napoleon; and only the sum of those wills endured them and then destroyed them."

---

†As my colleague, Prof. Bruce Kellogg, reminded me, Tolstoy pursues this line of thought at the beginning of Part II of *War and Peace*; the quotations are from pp. 766, 767 of the Modern Library Edition. The theme is further developed in the Epilogue to the book.

10.

Uniformly accelerated motion

a.   INTRODUCTION

The science of motion is called mechanics. Its principles govern projectiles, pistons, billiard balls, ocean waves, atmospheric currents, and colliding and rebounding molecules. Its concepts are involved in virtually every physical phenomenon. Mechanics today is as mathematical as geometry with principles perhaps as simple as the axioms of Euclid. But the laws of mechanics are far less intuitive, the reason no doubt for their late development in history. The first methods, the first concepts, and the first results in mechanics that can stand up to modern scrutiny originated with Galileo Galilei in work that spanned his career from 1581 to 1638. One of Galileo's most important discoveries is that a freely falling body is uniformly accelerated, which means that "its velocity receives equal increments in equal times."† His way to establish this fact was as important as the fact. Unable to measure the instantaneous speed of a falling body, he could not verify directly that the velocity of the body receives equal increments in equal times. Instead, he first deduced mathematically for a body *assumed* to be uniformly accelerated a formula giving the time in which the body covers a certain distance. Then he experimented with falling bodies to see if the formula held for them and found that it did. Agreement with the formula led him to conclude that the acceleration of a falling body must be uniform.‡

Freely falling bodies move too rapidly for the methods of measurement available to Galileo. Therefore in his experiments he made use of a straight, smooth, polished channel cut into a board. Inclining the board to the horizontal, he rolled down the sloping channel a "very round" bronze ball, timing its descent through the entire length of the channel or through half or two thirds or three fourths of its length, by means of a device like an hour glass from which water instead of sand trickled. In a hundred trials, he always found the times of descent to be in the ratios predicted from the formula for uniformly accelerated motion and concluded that the bronze ball, in rolling, always accelerated uniformly.§ This being so no matter how the channel on which the ball was to be rolled sloped down, the law of uniform acceleration was held also to govern *free* fall.††

Galileo's common-sense blend of reason and experiment, which this study of accelerated motion well illustrates, was an example of scientific method to the world. Galileo set another good example in his refusal, against the tendencies of his day, to become entangled in fanciful or metaphysical conjecture that cannot be decided. For instance, he wrote: "The present does not seem to be the proper time to investigate the cause of the acceleration of natural motion concerning which various opinions have been expressed by various philosophers, some explaining it by attraction to the center [of the earth], others by repulsion between the very small parts of the body, while still others attribute it to a certain stress in the surrounding medium which closes in behind the falling body and drives it from one of its positions to another. Now, all these fantasies, and others too, ought to be examined; but it is not really worth while. At present it is the purpose of our Author merely to investigate and to demonstrate some

---

†Galileo Galilei, *Two New Sciences*, translated by Henry Crew and Alfonso de Salvio, Dover Publications, New York, p. 169.

‡Ibid., p. 167.

§Ibid., pp. 178-179. We shall explain this reasoning in detail later.

††Other reasoning pointed to the same conclusion. See p. 185 ff, ibid.

of the properties of accelerated motion (whatever the cause of this acceleration may be) ...; and if we find the properties [of accelerated motion] ... are realized in freely falling ... bodies, we may conclude that the assumed definition includes such a motion of falling bodies ...."† Galileo seems to have valued idle speculation no more than Newton, whom we quoted out of chronological order (Section 9). Newton, born the year Galileo died (1642), brought mechanics to the climax the whole world by his day was striving for; his prestige must have been a potent factor in the spread of such views, totally opposed to the spirit of previous ages.

b.   UNIFORM MOTION. AVERAGE VELOCITY AND INSTANTANEOUS VELOCITY IN NONUNIFORM MOTION.

Here we shall discuss uniformly accelerated motion from a slightly more modern point of view. Idealizing the problem like Galileo, we confine our attention to a particle or point moving along a straight line L. Impressing a scale upon L, we first define uniform motion, already introduced briefly in an exercise (Exercise 12 in Section 1b, Chapter 2). In brief, a point moves "uniformly" along a straight line if the distance traveled by the point is proportional to the time of travel. More precisely, we state the following definition.

Definition 1.   A point moves *uniformly* along a straight line L if a constant (i.e., particular number) v exists with the following property: if t_1 and t_2 are different instants and x_1 and x_2 are the point's positions on the scale at these respective instants — the point thus travels the distance $x_2 - x_1$ in the time $t_2 - t_1$ — then

(1) $$x_2 - x_1 = v(t_2 - t_1).$$

The constant v is called the *velocity* of the point. If distance is measured in feet and time in seconds, then velocity, determined from (1) as

(1') $$v = (x_2 - x_1)/(t_2 - t_1),$$

is expressed in feet per second. Positive velocity refers to motion in the positive direction along L, negative velocity to motion in the negative direction (see Chapter 2, Section 2g). By *speed* we mean the absolute value of velocity.

Example 1:   Idealize an east-west road as a straight line L, and choose the positive sense as west to east. Consider an auto, idealized as a point, uniformly moving eastward on L and traveling 500 feet in 10 seconds. We shall be very formal in calculating its velocity in order to be certain of the sign. Suppose the time interval considered starts

---

†Ibid., pp. 166-167.

at time t_0 and ends at time t_1; then $t_1 - t_0 = 10$ seconds. Let x_0 and x_1 denote the respective positions of the car at times t_0 and t_1. Since the car is moving along L in the positive sense, $x_1 - x_0 = 500$ feet (see Figure 14-37A). Therefore,

$$v = (x_1 - x_0)/(t_1 - t_0) = 500 \text{ feet}/10 \text{ seconds} = 50 \text{ feet per second,}$$

and this, being positive, is also its speed.

FIGURE 14-37   Motion along a line (A) in the positive sense and (B) in the negative sense.

Example 2:   On the road L of Example 1, consider another auto traveling westward at a uniform rate of 500 feet in 10 seconds. As before, let t_0 and t_1 denote the first and last moments of the given interval of time, with $t_1 - t_0 = 10$ seconds. Let y_0 and y_1 denote the respective positions of the car at times t_0 and t_1; since this car is moving along L in the negative sense (see Figure 14-37B),

$$y_1 - y_0 = -500 \text{ feet.}$$

Hence, the velocity of this car is

$$(y_1 - y_0)/(t_1 - t_0) = -500 \text{ feet}/10 \text{ seconds} = -50 \text{ feet per second.}$$

Its speed is of course 50 feet per second.

The kind of motion we wish to treat here is nonuniform. For such motion, a concept of "instantaneous velocity" must be defined, translating into mathematical terms the intuitions we receive when we move at variable speeds. As a preliminary, we define "average velocity."

Definition 2.   Consider a point moving along a straight line L. Suppose that the point has position x_1 at time t_1 and position x_2 at time t_2, where $t_1 \neq t_2$. The ratio

$$v = (x_2 - x_1)/(t_2 - t_1)$$

is called the *average velocity* of the point during the interval *between times t_1 and t_2*.

If the motion happens to be uniform, then this average velocity is simply the velocity of the uniform motion.

In defining instantaneous motion at a specified instant t_0, it is convenient to use the notation $x(t)$ for the position on the scale of the moving point at time t. Thus, $x(t_0)$ denotes the position of the point at time t_0 and $x(t_0+h)$ the position at time t_0+h. Let $h \neq 0$, and consider the point's average velocity between the instants t_0 and $t_0 + h$. By definition, this average velocity is the ratio

$$[x(t_0 + h) - x(t_0)]/[(t_0 + h) - t_0],$$

i.e.,

(2) $$[x(t_0 + h) - x(t_0)]/h.$$

If the motion is very regular, as we conceive free fall to be, we should expect the average velocities for shorter and shorter intervals of time starting or ending at the moment t_0 to become more and more alike. In mathematical language, this means that the average velocity (2) should have a limit as $h \to 0$ (see the appendix to Section 4), and we define this limit, if it exists, to be the instantaneous velocity of the point at time t_0.

Definition 3.   Consider a point moving along a straight line L. Let $x(t)$ denote the point's position on the line at time t. If for a certain instant t_0 the limit

$$\lim_{h \to 0} [x(t_0 + h) - x(t_0)]/h$$

exists, we call it the *instantaneous velocity* of the point at time t_0. We shall denote it by $v(t_0)$. Analogously, for any time t we set

$$v(t) = \lim_{h \to 0} [x(t + h) - x(t)]/h$$

if the limit exists for that particular t. The term "velocity" without an adjective is used to mean "instantaneous velocity."

For motion in the positive direction, instantaneous velocity is non-negative; for motion in the negative direction, instantaneous velocity is nonpositive. This is because instantaneous velocity is a limit of average velocities, while the average velocity over an interval is positive for motion in the positive sense and negative for motion in the negative sense.

As an example, suppose

$$x(t) = t^2.$$

We shall prove that a particle moving under this law has an instantaneous velocity at every instant given by

$$v(t) = 2t.$$

We have to consider the average velocities

(3) $$[x(t + h) - x(t)]/h = [(t + h)^2 - t^2]/h$$

for $h \neq 0$, see whether they have a limit as $h \to 0$, and if so, find that limit. Since $(t+h)^2 = t^2 + 2th + h^2$, we have

$$[(t+h)^2 - t^2]/h = [(t^2 + 2th + h^2) - t^2]/h = (2th + h^2)/h$$
$$= h(2t+h)/h = 2t + h.$$

As h approaches zero, this quantity tends toward $2t$. Hence,

$$v(t) = 2t,$$

as contended.

The same kinds of calculations apply to the motion described by any expression of the form

$$x(t) = at^2 + bt + c,$$

where a, b, c are constants (i.e., particular numbers). We have

$$[x(t+h) - x(t)]/h = [a(t+h)^2 + b(t+h) + c - (at^2 + bt + c)]/h,$$

which after some algebraic re-arrangements and cancellations we see to be equal to

$$a(2t+h) + b.$$

This has the limit $2at + b$ as h approaches zero. Hence, in this case,

$$v(t) = 2at + b.$$

EXERCISES

1. Justify the last formula by carrying out the algebraic operations referred to.

2. Prove that if $x(t) = t^3$, then $v(t) = 3t^2$.

3. If $x(t) = t^2/2 - 3$, find the time at which instantaneous velocity is zero.

c. UNIFORM ACCELERATION

Now we shall attack the problem of uniformly accelerated motion. A point moving along a straight line "accelerates uniformly" if its instantaneous velocity changes during an arbitrary time interval, and the change is proportional to the duration of the interval. More precisely, we state the following definition.

Definition 4. Consider a point moving along a straight line L with instantaneous velocity $v(t)$ at each instant t. The point *accelerates uniformly* if a constant a exists such that for any two instants

t_1 and t_2,

(1) $$v(t_2) - v(t_1) = a(t_2 - t_1).$$

The constant a is called the *acceleration* of the point.

Acceleration and velocity are both rates of change per unit time, velocity the rate of change of position, and acceleration the rate of change of velocity.

If we measure distance in feet, time in seconds, and velocity, therefore, in feet per second, then we measure acceleration in feet per second per second. For convenience, we abbreviate feet by ft., seconds by sec., feet per second by ft./sec., and feet per second per second by ft./sec.² If an auto, accelerating uniformly from rest, acquires a velocity of 40 ft./sec.† in a ten second interval, the acceleration of the auto is

$$\frac{40 \text{ ft./sec.}}{10 \text{ sec.}} = 4 \text{ ft./sec.}^2$$

Acceleration is positive if the instantaneous velocity increases with time and is negative if the instantaneous velocity decreases as time increases.

Example 3:   As in Example 1, consider an auto, idealized as a point, moving in the positive direction along a straight line L. During a 10 second interval, its speed changes uniformly from 20 ft./sec. to 40 ft./sec. What is its acceleration during the interval? Again let t_0 and t_1 denote the first and last moments of the time interval considered, so that $t_1 - t_0 = 10$ seconds. Since the car is moving in the positive direction, its instantaneous velocity $v(t)$ is positive at each instant t, and we have

$$v(t_0) = 20 \text{ ft./sec.}, \quad v(t_1) = 40 \text{ ft./sec.}$$

Therefore,

$$a = [v(t_1) - v(t_0)]/(t_1 - t_0) = (40 - 20)/10 = 2 \text{ ft./sec.}^2$$

Example 4:   Change Example 3 just by assuming the auto to be moving in the negative direction. In this case,

$$v(t_0) = -20 \text{ ft./sec.}, \quad v(t_1) = -40 \text{ ft./sec.},$$

and

$$a = [-40 - (-20)]/10 = -2 \text{ ft./sec.}^2$$

---

†60 miles per hour = 88 ft./sec.

The acceleration is negative because the velocity is decreasing (from -20 to -40 ft./sec.)

The next three examples refer to free fall.

Example 5:   A body dropped from a height falls in a straight line L with a uniform acceleration of about 32 ft./sec.² If we choose the positive sense along L to be the downward direction, then the motion of fall is in the positive direction, and the instantaneous velocity of the body is positive. Since this velocity increases with time, the acceleration of the body is positive.

Example 6:   Change Example 5 just by choosing the positive sense along L to be the upward direction. In this case, the body falls in the negative direction. Its instantaneous velocity is negative and decreases algebraically as time increases. Hence, the acceleration of the body is negative, with the value -32 ft./sec.²

Example 7:   A ball is thrown upwards along a vertical straight line L, gravity communicating to the ball a uniform downward acceleration of 32 ft./sec.² Choose the downward as the positive direction along L. With this choice,

$$a = 32 \text{ ft./sec.}^2$$

Let t_0 denote the moment at which the ball is thrown and $v(t)$ the velocity of the ball at an arbitrary instant t not earlier than t_0 (i.e., $t_0 \le t$). Since the ball is thrown in the negative direction,

$$v(t_0) < 0.$$

Since $a > 0$, $v(t)$ increases as t increases, becoming less negative while the ball is slowing down, being zero instantaneously when the ball is at its greatest height, and finally becoming positive as soon as the ball begins to fall.

EXERCISE

1. Consider the situation in Example 7 with the upward direction chosen as the positive sense.

To obtain a complete mathematical description of uniformly accelerating motion, it is convenient to make the following assumption.

Law of Averages and Extremes.   The average velocity during an arbitrary time interval is between the least and the greatest velocities occurring in the interval.

Formulas for the position and velocity of a particle moving in a straight line with uniform acceleration will be derived from this assumption and will confirm it.

Consider an interval from time t_1 to time t_2, $t_1 < t_2$, and let v_{min} and v_{max} denote the least and greatest velocities, respectively, attained during that interval. The Law of Averages and Extremes says that

$$v_{min} \leq [x(t_2) - x(t_1)]/(t_2 - t_1) \leq v_{max},$$

$x(t)$ denoting the position of the particle on L. Since $t_2 - t_1 > 0$, these inequalities are equivalent to:

(2) $$v_{min}(t_2 - t_1) \leq x(t_2) - x(t_1) \leq v_{max}(t_2 - t_1).$$

Let us now consider a particle that, having started from a position of rest, moves along a straight line L with uniform acceleration a. To simplify notation, assume the motion to have commenced at the time $t = 0$, and take $x(0) = 0$. By $x(t)$ and $v(t)$ we denote the position on L and the velocity of the particle, respectively, at time t. Since the velocity is zero initially, we have $v(0) = 0$. In (1), replacing t_2 by t and t_1 by 0 gives us

$$v(t) = at \text{ for } t \geq 0.$$

Now take any time T, $T > 0$, and divide the interval from 0 to T into n equal subintervals of common length $T/n = h$. For each of these subintervals, we shall note the least and greatest instantaneous velocities v_{min} and v_{max} and thereby, applying the law we have assumed that the average is between the extremes, estimate above and below the distance traveled in this interval. Table 14-8 gives the details. Since $v(t) = at$, the least instantaneous velocity v_{min} in any interval is the earliest velocity, and the greatest instantaneous velocity v_{max} is the latest. For instance, in the interval from h to $2h$, $v_{min} = v(h) = ah$, and $v_{max} = v(2h) = 2ah$. All the entries in columns 2 and

Table 14-8 *A subdivided interval of uniformly accelerated motion*

Time interval	v_{min}	v_{max}	Distance traveled during interval	
			Lower estimate	Upper estimate
0 to h	0	ah	0	ah^2
h to 2h	ah	2ah	ah^2	$2ah^2$
2h to 3h	2ah	3ah	$2ah^2$	$3ah^2$
3h to 4h	3ah	4ah	$3ah^2$	$4ah^2$
. . . .				
$(j-1)h$ to jh	$(j-1)ah$	jah	$(j-1)ah^2$	jah^2
. . . .				
$(n-1)h$ to nh	$(n-1)ah$	nah	$(n-1)ah^2$	nah^2

3 of the table are filled in in this way. According to (2), the distance traveled during a time interval of length h is estimated below by $v_{min}h$ and above by $v_{max}h$. For instance, the distance moved from time h to time $2h$ is greater than or equal to

$$v_{min}h = ah \cdot h = ah^2$$

and less than or equal to

$$v_{max}h = 2ah \cdot h = 2ah^2.$$

The distances traveled in all the other intervals are estimated similarly and the results recorded in the last two columns of the table. Adding the lower estimates gives us a lower estimate of the distance $x(T) - x(0)$ traveled from time 0 to time T:

$$x(T) - x(0) \geq 0 + ah^2 + 2ah^2 + 3ah^2 + \ldots + (n-1)ah^2,$$

or

(3) $\qquad x(T) \geq ah^2(1 + 2 + 3 + \ldots + (n-1)) = ah^2(n-1)n/2,$

since $x(0) = 0$ and $1 + 2 + 3 + \ldots + (n-1) = (n-1)n/2$ (see Chapter 10, Section 3). Adding the upper estimates gives similarly

(4) $\qquad x(T) \leq ah^2 + 2ah^2 + 3ah^2 + \ldots + nah^2$
$\qquad\qquad = ah^2(1 + 2 + 3 + \ldots + n) = ah^2n(n+1)/2.$

Since $nh = T$, we have

$$h^2(n-1)n = (nh - h)nh = (T-h)T = T^2 - Th,$$
$$h^2n(n+1) = nh(nh + h) = T(T+h) = T^2 + Th.$$

Substituting these expressions in (3) and (4) gives

$$x(T) \geq (a/2)(T^2 - Th) = aT^2/2 - aTh/2$$

and

$$x(T) \leq (a/2)(T^2 + Th) = aT^2/2 + aTh/2,$$

and combining these,

$$aT^2/2 - aTh/2 \leq x(T) \leq aT^2/2 + aTh/2.$$

As h approaches zero, the upper and lower estimates for $x(T)$ both tend toward

$$aT^2/2.$$

Hence,

$$x(T) = aT^2/2.$$

This formula tells the distance traveled by a particle moving with uniform acceleration a during the first T seconds after starting from rest. Since T is arbitrary, the formula applies throughout the indicated motion, and for the sake of uniformity in notation, we may prefer to write it with t in place of T as

(5) $$x(t) = (1/2) at^2 \text{ for } t \geq 0.$$

We still have to test the formula. Does motion in a straight line governed by law (5) have uniform acceleration a? Are the initial conditions $x(0) = 0$ and $v(0) = 0$ satisfied? Is our provisional Law of Averages and Extremes confirmed? The condition $x(0) = 0$ is obvious from (5). To answer the other questions, we calculate $v(t)$ from (5) by the method of Subsection b, obtaining

$$v(t) = (1/2) a \cdot 2t = at.$$

This shows at once that $v(0) = 0$. Furthermore, for any positive times t_1 and t_2, this implies that

$$v(t_2) - v(t_1) = at_2 - at_1 = a(t_2 - t_1)$$

and thus that the motion does indeed have uniform acceleration a. Finally, let us check that under this law the average velocity of the particle during an arbitrary time interval is between the extreme velocities. If $t_1 < t_2$, the average velocity from time t_1 to time t_2 is, by definition,

$$
\begin{aligned}
[x(t_2) - x(t_1)]/(t_2 - t_1) &= [(1/2) at_2^2 - (1/2) at_1^2]/(t_2 - t_1) \\
&= (a/2)(t_2^2 - t_1^2)/(t_2 - t_1) \\
&= (a/2)(t_2 + t_1)(t_2 - t_1)/(t_2 - t_1) \\
&= (a/2)(t_2 + t_1).
\end{aligned}
$$

On the other hand,

$$v_{\min} = v(t_1) = at_1, \quad v_{\max} = v(t_2) = at_2,$$

$v_{\min}$ and $v_{\max}$ referring to the extreme values of v in the interval from t_1 to t_2. Therefore,

$$
\begin{aligned}
[x(t_2) - x(t_1)]/(t_2 - t_1) - v_{\min} &= (a/2)(t_2 + t_1) - at_1 \\
&= (a/2)(t_2 - t_1) \\
&> 0,
\end{aligned}
$$

so that average velocity does indeed exceed least instantaneous velocity during the interval. The analogous statement that average velocity falls short of the greatest instantaneous velocity v_{max} is obtained similarly.

EXERCISES

2. Consider a particle moving in a straight line L under a uniform acceleration of 8 ft./sec.^{2} Suppose that at time 0 the particle is at the origin of the scale on L and is moving with velocity 2 ft./sec. Divide the next 5 seconds into intervals of 1/2 sec. each and for these ten intervals make up a table analogous to Table 14-8. From the table, make upper and lower estimates of the distance traveled in 5 seconds.

3. Do the same thing for a problem identical with the previous except that the velocity of the particle at time 0 is −12 ft./sec.

4. Use the preceding procedure to discuss the motion of a point with uniform acceleration a, but starting with a prescribed velocity b. Assuming $x(0) = 0$, prove that the position of this particle at time t is given by the formula

$$x(t) = bt + at^2/2.$$

This formula applies, for instance, to a ball thrown vertically upwards or downwards with initial velocity b. If the ball is thrown upwards, a and b will have opposite signs (see Example 7).

5. Suppose a ball is thrown upwards along a vertical line L with an initial velocity of 20 ft./sec. The ball is subject to a uniform downward acceleration of 32 ft./sec.^{2}

    (a) Idealizing the ball as a particle and choosing as the origin on L the point at which the ball is initially launched, find the equation of motion of the ball.

    (b) Calculate the instantaneous velocity of the ball at an arbitrary time t after the launching.

    (c) How long will it take the ball to reach the highest point of its path?

    (d) How high above the origin is this highest point?

d. GALILEO'S EXPERIMENT

Let us now return to Galileo's experiment of rolling a bronze ball down a smooth, straight, sloping channel. Galileo ultimately proved that the motion of the ball is governed by formula (5) of the previous subsection, which says that a body starting from rest and moving along a straight line with constant acceleration a will travel the distance

(1) $$d = at^2/2$$

in the first t seconds of motion. (We measure distance in ft., velocity in ft./sec. and acceleration in ft./sec.²) He justified this formula without being able to measure a directly.

He accomplished this by timing the descent of the ball through *various* distances along the channel. If the ball, always starting from rest, will roll d_1 feet in t_1 seconds and also will roll d_2 feet in t_2 seconds, and if relation (1) applies to its motion, then we have

$$d_1 = at_1^2/2$$

and

$$d_2 = at_2^2/2.$$

Dividing gives us

(2) $$d_1/d_2 = \frac{at_1^2/2}{at_2^2/2} = \frac{t_1^2}{t_2^2} = (t_1/t_2)^2,$$

which says that the ratio of distances traveled is equal to the square of the ratio of the times of travel. Formula (2) holds for any uniformly accelerated motion and is independent of a. It is thus exactly what Galileo needed. Using a channel of fixed slope, he tested this formula for many different pairs of distances and always found it to fit. Repeating such experiments with channels of other slopes led to the same results. This is why he felt justified in asserting that a ball rolling down a smooth, straight channel accelerates uniformly.

EXERCISE

1. How can the acceleration owing to any particular slope be calculated from the results of one of Galileo's experiments as described? HINT: By (1),

$$d_1 = (a/2)t_1^2$$

and

$$d_2 = (a/2)t_2^2.$$

11.

Derivatives. Maxima and minima.

Consider any function $f(x)$ defined on part or all of the x-axis (i.e., for some or all numbers). The trend of the previous section suggests that we set up *difference quotients*

(1) $$[f(x+h) - f(x)]/h$$

for $h \neq 0$, f being supposed to be defined at both values x and $x + h$, and that we consider the limit

(2)
$$\lim_{h \to 0} [f(x + h) - f(x)]/h$$

if this limit exists. If we interpret x as time and $f(x)$ as the position of a particle along a straight line, then the difference quotient (1) represents the average velocity of the particle during the interval of time between x and $x + h$, and the limit (2), if it exists, is the instantaneous velocity of the particle. In general, the limit (2), if it exists, is called the *derivative* of f at the point x. We denote its value by $f'(x)$: thus,

$$f'(x) = \lim_{h \to 0} [f(x + h) - f(x)]/h$$

if the limit in question exists.

In this section, we give a geometrical interpretation of the derivative leading to further applications. Graphing the function $f(x)$ (Figure 14-38), consider the straight line passing through the two points

$$(x, f(x)) \text{ and } (x + h, f(x + h))$$

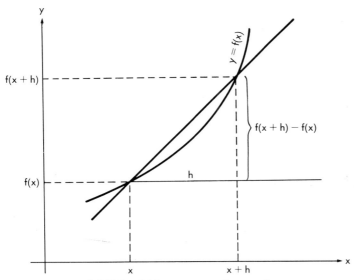

FIGURE 14-38   A secant of a graph.

of the graph. This line is called a *secant* of the graph. The difference quotient

(1)
$$[f(x + h) - f(x)]/h$$

is the slope of the secant, i.e., the tangent of the angle the line makes with the x-axis. For all (nonzero) values of h, the secant passes through the point $(x, f(x))$ in one direction or another. For no value of h need the secant coincide with the tangent to the graph at this point. But if the graph happens to be a smooth curve and have a tangent at the point $(x, f(x+h))$, the secant will tend more and more closely towards coincidence with the tangent as h approaches zero (see Figure 14-39). Thus, if the limit

(2) $$\lim_{h \to 0} [f(x+h) - f(x)]/h,$$

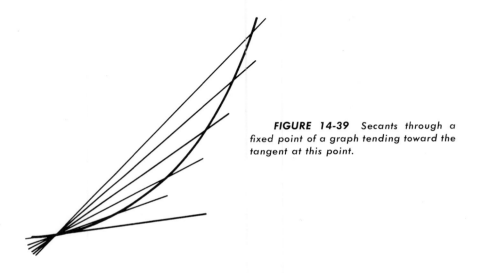

FIGURE 14-39 *Secants through a fixed point of a graph tending toward the tangent at this point.*

exists, it gives the slope of the tangent to the graph at the point $(x, f(x))$. For instance, a calculation in Section 10b shows that for the parabola

$$f(x) = x^2/2,$$

the slope at an arbitrary point $(x, f(x))$ is equal to $2x/2 = x$ (Figure 14-40).

In the limit process by which the derivative is defined, the increment h is permitted to take both positive and negative values as it approaches zero. The value of the limit (2) if h is restricted to positive values thus must be equal to the value of the limit if h is restricted to negative values. In Figure 14-41 a function is graphed for which, at the origin, these two limits are not the same and the function therefore does not have a derivative. Correspondingly, the graph of the function does not have a tangent at the origin.

Derivatives have an elementary and pretty application in the determination of local maxima and minima of functions.

Definition.   Let $f(x)$ be a function defined on a certain interval.

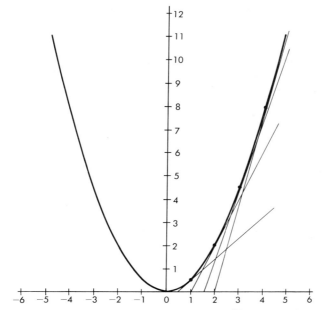

FIGURE 14-40   *Tangents to the parabola* $y = x^2/2$ *at several points.*

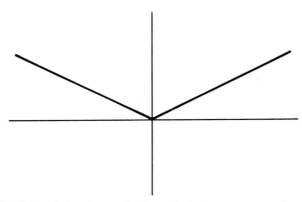

FIGURE 14-41   *A function not having a derivative at a particular point.*

If x_1 is a point of the interval for which

$$f(x_1) \geq f(x),$$

where x is an arbitrary point of the interval, we call $f(x_1)$ the *maximum* of f for the interval. If x_2 is a point of the interval for which

$$f(x_2) \leq f(x),$$

x again denoting an arbitrary point of the interval, we call $f(x_2)$ the *minimum* of f for the interval. An *extremum* is either a maximum or a minimum. If an extremum for an interval is realized at some point that is not an endpoint of the interval, then the extremum is said to be a *local* extremum.

Figure 14-42 shows some graphs of functions that have local ex-

FIGURE 14-42   Some graphs that have local extrema.

trema. As Figure 14-43 illustrates, a function need not have a local maximum, a local minimum, or a local extremum of either kind on any given interval.

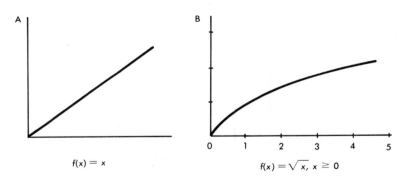

A

$f(x) = x$

B

$f(x) = \sqrt{x}, \ x \geq 0$

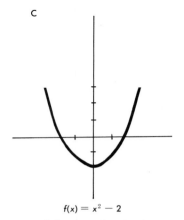

C

$f(x) = x^2 - 2$

FIGURE 14-43.   Functions without local extrema. A, no local extremum; B, no local extremum; C, a local minimum, but no local maximum.

If the graph of a function has a tangent at each point, the tangents just to the left of a local maximum have positive slopes, the tangents to the right have negative slopes, and the tangent at the local maximum is horizontal (Figure 14-44A). The tangents to the left of a local

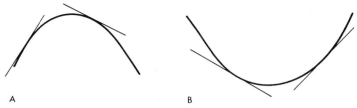

FIGURE 14-44 *Tangents in the neighborhood of local extrema: A, a local maximum; B, a local minimum.*

minimum have negative slopes, the tangents to the right have positive slopes, and the tangent at the minimum is horizontal with zero slope (Figure 14-44*B*). But the slopes of the tangents are given by the values of the derivative of the function. This suggests the following condition.

Criterion for Occurrence of Local Extrema. If a function f has a local extremum at a point x_0, and if f has a derivative f' at this point, then

$$f'(x_0) = 0.$$

This criterion goes back to Pierre de Fermat and is the very earliest use of the concept of derivative, no later than 1629.† Fermat did not justify it clearly enough to suit his contemporary, Descartes, nor are our diagrams sufficient grounds for this statement, which is of an arithmetical nature. The following is a modern proof of it.

PROOF OF CRITERION: Suppose that f has a local maximum at x_a. This means that an interval, say from x_1 to x_2 with $x_1 < x_2$, exists such that

$$x_1 < x_a < x_2$$

and

(3) $$f(x_a) \geq f(x) \quad \text{if} \quad x_1 < x < x_2$$

(see Figure 14-45). By definition, $f'(x_a)$ is the limit as h approaches

†Cajori, p. 164.

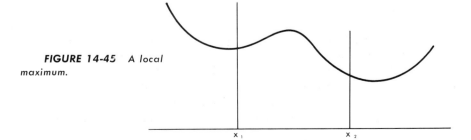

FIGURE 14-45 *A local maximum.*

zero of the difference quotients

(4) $$[f(x_a + h) - f(x_a)]/h.$$

Since we shall have h approach zero, we are justified in considering only those h for which $|h|$ is less than any positive number we find convenient. We accordingly require h to be so small that $x_a + h$ belongs to the interval in question, i.e., so small that $x_1 < x_a + h < x_2$. Then by (3)

$$f(x_a) \geq f(x_a + h),$$

which implies that the numerator of (4) is nonpositive. Since the denominator h may be either positive or negative, the difference quotient (4) assumes both positive and negative values for arbitrarily small values of $|h|$. By assumption, the difference quotient (4) has a limit as h approaches zero. This limit is not positive, because the difference quotient assumes negative values for arbitrarily small values of h; similarly, the limit is not negative. Therefore, the limit must be zero, as asserted.

The criterion is justified similarly in the case of a local minimum. Thus, it holds for any extremum, as claimed.

The criterion that the derivative vanish of course does not distinguish between maxima and minima, and moreover the derivative of a function may vanish at points that are neither. Any point at which

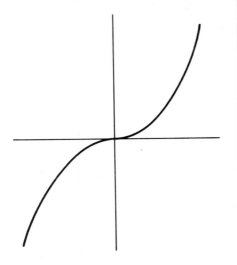

FIGURE 14-46   A stationary point not an extremum for the function $f(x) = x^3$.

the derivative of a function f vanishes is called a *stationary point* of the function. An example of a stationary point not an extremum is represented in Figure 14-46. If just to the left of a stationary point a function has a positive derivative and just to the right a negative derivative, it is apparent from Figure 14-44 that the stationary point is a maximum. If just to the left of a stationary point the function has a negative derivative and just to the right a positive derivative, then the stationary point must be a local minimum. These and other ways of characterizing how a function behaves near a stationary point can be justified mathematically, but by methods beyond our scope. In the problems we discuss, we shall consider it sufficient to be able to see intuitively, on geometrical or physical grounds, whether a particular stationary point we may have obtained gives a maximum, a minimum, or something else.

Example: The height (in feet) above the ground of a ball thrown upwards is given by the formula

$$H = 5 + 12t - 16t^2,$$

t being the time (in seconds) after the ball was thrown. What was the maximum height reached?

SOLUTION: We are assured physically that the ball rises to a maximum height and then descends. The maximum is a local maximum and thus corresponds to a stationary value of t. To find this stationary value, we calculate the derivative of the function

$$f(t) = 5 + 12t - 16t^2$$

representing the height. As follows from results of Section 10b,

$$f'(t) = 12 - 32t.$$

A stationary value t_0 is defined by the condition $f'(t_0) = 0$, which here takes the form

$$12 - 32t_0 = 0,$$

leading to the determination

$$t_0 = 12/32 = 3/8.$$

Since this is the only stationary point of the function, it must be that at which the maximum of the function is attained. Therefore, this maximum is $f(3/8) = 5 + 12(3/8) - 16(3/8)^2 = 29/4$ ft.

EXERCISES

1. Find two positive numbers whose sum is 20 and such that their product is as large as possible.

2. A square sheet of tin 20 inches on a side is to be used to make an open-top box by cutting a small square of tin from each corner and bending up the sides. How large a square should be cut from each corner in order that the box shall have as large a volume as possible?

3. One side of an open field is bounded by a river. How would you put a fence around the other three sides of a rectangular plot in order to enclose as great an area as possible with a given length of fence?

4. An open storage bin with square base and vertical sides is to be constructed from a given amount of material. Determine its dimensions if its volume is a maximum. (Neglect the thickness of the material and waste in construction.)

5. A box with square base and open top is to hold 32 cu. in. Find the dimensions which require the least amount of material. Neglect the thickness of the material and waste in construction.

6. A wire of length L is cut into two pieces, one being bent to form a square and the other to form an equilateral triangle. How should the wire be cut (a) if the sum of the two areas is a minimum, (b) if the sum of the areas is a maximum?

7. Show that the rectangle which has maximum area for a given perimeter is a square.

CHAPTER 15

REAL NUMBERS: THEIR REPRESENTATION, PROPERTIES, AND APPLICATIONS

We have been able to use limit methods very effectively in the problems so far considered, but in others we would be hampered or stopped by a critical inadequacy in arithmetic. Rational numbers, to which ordinary arithmetic is confined, do not suffice for the needs of mathematics. Apparently, the Pythagoreans were the first to find this out (see Section 1, Chapter 11). They knew the old Babylonian formula for right triangles giving the square of the hypotenuse as the sum of the squares of the sides and thus knew that the hypotenuse of an isosceles right triangle with unit sides has length $\sqrt{2}$ (Figure 15-1).

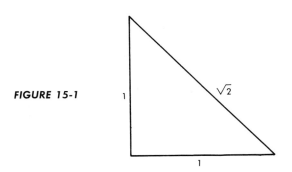

FIGURE 15-1

On the other hand, they appear to have conceived of the points on a line as lying side by side contiguously like peas in a pod, each individual point occupying a certain space and thus extending along the line a certain fundamental distance. Multiplying this fundamental distance by the number of points in a line segment should give the length of the segment. The ratio of the lengths of any two line segments should be just the ratio of the numbers of points in the respective segments, which is rational. Since $\sqrt{2}$ is the ratio of the hypotenuse to a side in an isosceles right triangle, $\sqrt{2}$ should be rational.

The Pythagoreans were badly jolted to discover perhaps about 450 B.C. that $\sqrt{2}$ is not rational. The following argument, which is essentially that given by Euclid, is believed to go back to them. Suppose positive integers p and q exist such that

$$(1) \qquad\qquad (p/q)^2 = 2,$$

and take p and q in lowest terms (i.e., assume p and q do not have a common factor). Then

$$(2) \qquad\qquad p^2 = 2q^2,$$

so that p^2 is even. Hence, p is even (see Proposition 1 in Section 9, Chapter 11), which means that an integer n exists such that $p = 2n$. Substituting $p^2 = 4n^2$ in (2) gives

$$4n^2 = 2q^2,$$

or

$$2n^2 = q^2,$$

which tells us that q^2 is even. Consequently, q is even, so that p and q are both even and thus have 2 as a common factor. This contradicts the assumption that p and q do not have a common factor. Since the contradiction stemmed from assuming (1), we see that (1) holds for no values of p and q, which means that $\sqrt{2}$ is not rational.

This discovery shows that whole numbers do not underlie everything, contrary to a basic tenet of Pythagorean religion. We can guess at the insecurity and the consternation this news must have caused among the devout. Numbers were in chaos, and geometry was threatened. Geometry could be redeemed if numerical lengths, angles, areas, and volumes could be avoided, but how? For instance, how can side ratios, which occur in the indispensable concept of similarity, be discussed without using any notion of length? The effort to do so must have been determined indeed, for after perhaps 50 or 75 years, it succeeded. Eudoxus (408–355 B.C.), a friend and protégé of Plato's, saw how to formulate the ratios of geometric entities in purely geometric terms† and how as a result to purge geometry of

---

†See Eves, p. 116 ff.

numbers, except for the positive integers themselves. The purge was carried out and is fully evident in Euclid.[†]

Eudoxus made it possible to do *geometry* without talking about numerical lengths, angles, areas, and so forth. While admiring his cleverness, we may well wonder whether it is good for *arithmetic* to have to shun such matters. If our stock of arithmetical notions is too poor to contain $\sqrt{2}$, or indeed all lengths of segments, ought we not to enlarge the stock? This question did not become urgent, nor was it even asked in this way, nor did means exist to answer it, until about the second half of the 19th Century, about 2300 years after Eudoxus's brilliant detour around it. Then several approaches were developed, the most enduring by Georg Cantor and Eduard Heine (1872) and by Richard Dedekind (1901).[‡] Our method is related to Dedekind's; we owe the idea of using infinite decimals to R. Courant's *Differential and Integral Calculus*, Introduction to Vol. 1.[§]

1.

Real numbers and points

a. REPRESENTATION OF REAL NUMBERS BY INFINITE DECIMALS

To see how real numbers might be based on infinite decimals, first consider any rational number r. Let n stand for the integral part of r, and suppose the fractional part to be represented by an infinite repeating decimal

$$.a_1 \, a_2 \, a_3 \, \ldots .$$

For instance, if $r = 17\ 3/14$, then $n = 17$, and we put

$$3/14 = .2142857142857 \cdots$$

(see Chapter 14, Section 4). Notice that

$$17.2 < 17\ 3/14 < 17.3$$
$$17.21 < 17\ 3/14 < 17.22$$
$$17.214 < 17\ 3/14 < 17.215$$
$$17.2142 < 17\ 3/14 < 17.2143$$
$$17.21428 < 17\ 3/14 < 17.21429,$$

[†] See Shanks's remarks, op. cit., pp. 123-130.
[‡] Clear amounts of these and other approaches of the period are given by J. H. Manheim in *The Genesis of Point Set Topology*, MacMillan, New York, 1964, pp. 76-96.
[§] Second edition, 1937. Interscience Publishers, New York.

and so forth. If for an arbitrary rational r we put

$$r_k = n + .a_1a_2 \cdots a_k$$

for $k = 1, 2, 3, \cdots$, we have likewise

$$r_1 \leq r \leq r_1 + 10^{-1},$$
$$r_2 \leq r \leq r_2 + 10^{-2},$$
$$r_3 \leq r \leq r_3 + 10^{-3},$$

and, in general,

(1) $$r_k \leq r \leq r_k + 10^{-k} \quad \text{for } k = 1, 2, 3, \ldots.$$

A similar pattern of inequalities appears if we obtain decimal approximations to $\sqrt{2}$. Even without an arithmetical concept of $\sqrt{2}$, we can still ask for a k-place decimal x_k for which x_k^2 is less than 2, but as near 2 as possible. Here are the first four findings under this criterion:

$1^2 = 1$ and $2^2 = 4$ $\Rightarrow x_1 = 1,$
$1.4^2 = 1.96$ and $1.5^2 = 2.15$ $\Rightarrow x_2 = 1.4,$
$1.41^2 = 1.9881$ and $1.42^2 = 2.0164$ $\Rightarrow x_3 = 1.41,$
$1.414^2 = 1.9993816$ and $1.415^2 = 2.0022025$ $\Rightarrow x_4 = 1.414.$

If we were permitted to regard $\sqrt{2}$ as a number, we should certainly have

$$1 < \sqrt{2} < 2,$$
$$1.4 < \sqrt{2} < 1.5,$$
$$1.41 < \sqrt{2} < 1.42,$$
$$1.414 < \sqrt{2} < 1.415$$

and, in general,

$$x_k < \sqrt{2} < x_k + 10^{-k} \quad \text{for } k = 1, 2, 3, \ldots.$$

Thus, x_k would approximate $\sqrt{2}$ with an error less than 10^{-k}, in complete analogy to (1).

These considerations suggest that we permit arbitrary "infinite decimals" without rejecting those that are not periodic. Accordingly, let

$$a_1, a_2, a_3, \ldots$$

be an infinite sequence of digits: each $a_k = 0, 1, 2, 3, 4, 5, 6, 7, 8,$ or 9. We shall say that the sequence determines an *infinite decimal*

$$.a_1a_2a_3 \ldots.$$

With each integer m and each infinite decimal $.a_1a_2a_3\ldots$ we associate an undefined mathematical object we shall call a real number and represent by the expression

$$(2) \qquad\qquad m + .a_1a_2a_3\ \ldots.$$

If $.a_1a_2a_3\ldots$ is periodic, then (2) represents a rational number r in the sense that

$$(3) \qquad m + .a_1a_2a_3\ldots a_k \le r \le m + .a_1a_2a_3\ldots a_k + 10^{-k}$$
$$\text{for } k = 1, 2, 3, \ldots,$$

as is indicated by (1). If $.a_1a_2a_3\ldots$ is not periodic, then (2) is not a rational number. A real number not a rational number is said to be *irrational*. We denote the set of all real numbers by R.

A simple example of a nonperiodic infinite decimal is

$$.101001000100001000001000001\ldots.$$

If the infinite decimal (1) is a terminating decimal, we shall call (2) a *terminating decimal representation* and, otherwise, a *nonterminating decimal representation*. A real number with a terminating decimal representation is an ordinary decimal and thus, in particular, is rational. Notice that even such a number has a nonterminating representation by means of an infinite decimal with an unbroken string of 9's: for instance,

$$.1 = .09999\ldots,$$
$$0 = -1 + .999\ \ldots.$$

Thus, every real number has a nonterminating decimal representation.

Proposition 1. Each rational number has but one nonterminating decimal representation. This means that if

$$m + .a_1a_2a_3\ldots \text{ and } n + .b_1b_2b_3\ldots$$

are nonterminating decimal representations for the same rational number r, then

$$m = n \text{ and } a_k = b_k \text{ for } k = 1, 2, 3, \ldots.$$

PROOF: We shall show in detail that $m = n$, the other equalities resulting one after the other similarly. If, say, $n < m$, then

$$n + 1 \le m,$$

since m and n are integers. Since the decimals are nonterminating,

$$r = m + .a_1a_2a_3\ldots > m,$$

while

$$r = n + .b_1b_2b_3 \ldots \leq n + 1.$$

The last two inequalities imply that $n + 1 > m$, contradicting a previous result, and we conclude that n cannot be less than m as assumed. Similarly, m is not less than n and, therefore, $m = n$, as claimed.

The last result suggests the following definition.

Definition 1. Two real numbers with nonterminating decimal representations

$$m + .a_1a_2a_3 \ldots . \text{ and } n + .b_1b_2b_3 \ldots$$

are *equal* if

$$m = n \text{ and } a_k = b_k \text{ for } k = 1, 2, 3, \ldots.$$

Proposition 1 implies, in particular, that 0 has only one non-terminating decimal representation, namely,

(4) $-1 + .999 \ldots.$

In view of this, we define positive and negative real numbers as follows.

Definition 2. An arbitrary real number x with a nonterminating decimal representation $m + .a_1a_2a_3 \ldots$ other than (4) will be called *positive* if $m \geq 0$ and *negative* if $m < 0$.

We now define the negatives of real numbers.

Definition 3. For an arbitrary real number x represented by means of a nonterminating decimal as

$$x = m + .a_1a_2a_3 \ldots,$$

we define the negative $-x$ as

$$-x = -m - 1 + .a_1'a_2'a_3' \ldots,$$

where

$$a_{k'} = 9 - a_k \text{ for } k = 1, 2, 3, \ldots.$$

(This representation of $-x$ is terminating if and only if $a_k = 9$ for all k greater than a particular value, say $k > i$.) We define as the *absolute value* of x

$$
\begin{aligned}
|x| &= x \text{ if } x \text{ is positive} \\
&= -x \text{ if } x \text{ is negative} \\
&= 0 \text{ if } x = 0.
\end{aligned}
$$

To illustrate Definition 3, $-.121212\ldots = -1 + .878787\ldots$, this equality stating that $-4/33 = -1 + 29/33$. More generally, we have the following proposition.

Proposition 2.   The negatives of all rational numbers conform to Definition 3.

PROOF: Let r be any rational number, represented by means of a nonterminating decimal as

$$r = m + .a_1 a_2 a_3 \ldots .$$

Let

$$r_k = m + .a_1 a_2 \ldots a_k, \quad r_k' = -m - 1 + .a_1' a_2' \ldots a_k',$$

where $a_k' = 9 - a_k$ for $k = 1, 2, 3, \ldots$. According to (3), $0 < r - r_k \leq 10^{-k}$, which implies that

$$\lim r_k = r;$$

this and the other limits to be considered are to be taken as $k \to \infty$. Since r is rational, its decimal representation is periodic. Hence, the infinite decimal $.a_1' a_2' a_3' \ldots$ is periodic, too, thus representing a rational number. The number

$$r' = -m - 1 + .a_1' a_2' a_3' \ldots$$

therefore is rational, and it satisfies the condition

$$\lim r_k' = r'.$$

We are to prove that $r' = -r$. By definition of r_k' and the formula for the sum of a geometric progression,

$$r_k + r_k' = -1 + .\overbrace{99 \ldots 9}^{k \text{ places}} = -10^{-k};$$

this implies that

$$\lim (r_k + r_k') = 0.$$

Since

$$r_k' = (r_k + r_k') - r_k,$$

we have by the previous limit relations

$$
\begin{aligned}
\lim r_k' &= \lim (r_k + r_k') - \lim r_k \quad \text{(Corollary to Theorem 4,} \\
&= \quad 0 \qquad\qquad - r \qquad \text{Section 4, Chapter 14)} \\
&= \quad -r.
\end{aligned}
$$

Therefore, $r' = -r$, the contention to be proved.

EXERCISE

1. In representing real numbers, we need not have used decimal fractions, for a numeral system with any other base (Chapter 3) would have done as well. What form should Definition 3 take in the binary system? (In the binary system $.a_1a_2a_3\ldots$ means $a_1 \cdot 2^{-1} + a_2 \cdot 2^{-2} + a_3 \cdot 2^{-3} + \ldots$.)

Since real numbers are conceived by means of an infinite process, we must expect to continue to use infinite processes in defining operations upon them. For this purpose, we associate with an arbitrary infinite decimal

$$.a_1 a_2 a_3 \ldots$$

the sequence of ordinary decimals

$$.a_1, .a_1a_2, .a_1a_2a_3, .a_1a_2a_3a_4, .a_1a_2a_3a_4a_5,$$

and so forth. We call these *truncations* of the infinite decimal: for any $k = 1, 2, 3, \ldots$, we define the *k-place truncation* of $.a_1a_2a_3 \ldots$ to be the ordinary decimal $.a_1 \ldots a_k$ consisting of the first k places in the infinite decimal given. Correspondingly, if a real number y is represented by means of a nonterminating decimal as

$$y = m + .a_1a_2a_3 \ldots,$$

we call the rational number

$$y_k = m + .a_1 \ldots a_k$$

the *k-place decimal truncation* of y. For instance, the one-place, two-place, and three-place decimal truncations of $17\,3/14$ are

$$17.2, 17.21, \text{ and } 17.214,$$

respectively (see beginning of section). The analogous decimal truncations of $-3 + 3/14$ are

$$-3 + .2 = -2.8,$$
$$-3 + .21 = -2.79,$$
$$-3 + .214 = -2.786.$$

EXERCISE

2. Let y and z be two real numbers and y_k and z_k their respective k-place decimal truncations. Prove that if

$$y_p < z_p$$

for some particular index p, then

$$y_k < z_k \text{ for } k > p.$$

HINT: If $y_p < z_p$, then

$$y_p + 10^{-p} \leq z_p.$$

Furthermore, for $k > p$, the $(p + 1)$-st to kth decimal places in y_k and z_k may be any digits, which may have the effect of increasing the original p-place decimal by any amount from 0 to $10^{-p} \times .99 \ldots \overbrace{9}^{k-p \text{ places}} = 10^{-p}(1 - 10^{-(k-p)})$ (see Section 4, Chapter 10). Hence, for $k > p$, we have

$$z_k \geq z_p, \quad y_k \leq y_p + 10^{-p}(1 - 10^{p-k}) < y_p + 10^{-p}.$$

Later we shall show how the decimal truncations y_k approximate y, satisfying conditions analogous to those in the rational case (inequalities (3)), how if y and z are two real numbers with the respective decimal truncations y_k and z_k ($k = 1, 2, 3, \ldots$), the sums $y_k + z_k$ can be used to define $y + z$ appropriately, and how by means of truncations all the arithmetical operations can be similarly defined and then satisfy the same formal laws that govern rational arithmetic. We shall use elementary, but necessarily rather abstract, arguments, which we give in Section 3. Machinery for these arguments and other significant applications, too, is developed in Section 2. At present, we return to the subject of length.

b. THE CORRESPONDENCE BETWEEN REAL NUMBERS AND THE POINTS ON A LINE

By means of real numbers, we can rescue the concept of length and therefore also that of scale. Consider a straight line L on which we select a unit of length, a positive direction, and an origin O. If P is an arbitrary point of L, we purported in Chapter 2 to define the coordinate of P in terms of the "distance" OP. At that time, we glossed over the difficulty that no rational number need exist to express this "distance." To right the matter, we shall now show how we can assign to P a real number x that is rational only if the distance OP is rational, in which case $|x| = OP$. We shall define the coordinate of P to be this real number x whether rational or not and shall define the distance OP to be $|x|$. Distances so defined will have the properties we expect of them on geometrical grounds.

If P is given arbitrarily, we determine its coordinate x as follows. In case OP is rational, we take $x = OP$. In case OP is not rational, we associate with P an integer n and an infinite decimal $.a_1 a_2 a_3 \ldots$ in the manner we now describe. First, divide L by the points with coordinates $0, 1, -1, 2, -2, 3, -3, \ldots$ into infinitely many segments of unit length. Since OP is not rational, P does not coincide with any point of subdivision and thus falls between two consecutive subdivision points, say between n and $n + 1$ (Figure 15-2). Divide the

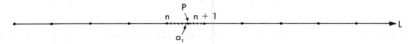

FIGURE 15-2   *A line devided into unit segments.*

interval between n and $n + 1$ into 10 equal subintervals, the nine points of subdivision being $n + .1, n + .2, \ldots, n + .9$. Again P does not coincide with any point of subdivision or an endpoint and thus falls inside one of these ten subintervals, say the interval between

$$n + .a_1 \text{ and } n - .a_1 + 10^{-1}.$$

Here, a_1 is a suitable digit, i.e., $0, 1, 2, 3, 4, 5, 6, 7, 8,$ or 9. This interval (of length 10^{-1}) we divide into 10 equal parts by new points of subdivision

$$n + .a_1 1, n + .a_1 2, n + .a_1 3, \ldots, n + .a_1 9,$$

and P must be inside one of these, say the interval from

$$n + .a_1 a_2 \text{ to } n + .a_1 a_2 + 10^{-2}$$

of length 10^{-2}. Again subdividing, we find P in an interval of length 10^{-3}, say that between

$$n + .a_1 a_2 a_3 \text{ and } n + .a_1 a_2 a_3 + 10^{-3}.$$

Continuing this process, from each additional subdivision we obtain another place in the decimal describing the position of P. After k subdivisions ($k = 1, 2, 3, \ldots$), we shall have k digits $a_1, a_2, \ldots, a_k$ such that the interval of length 10^{-k} between $n + .a_1 a_2 \ldots a_k$ and $n + .a_1 a_2 \ldots a_k + 10^{-k}$ contains P. These digits constitute an infinite sequence, the members of which in principle can be determined one by one, and we set

$$x = n + .a_1 a_2 a_3 \ldots.$$

We call x the coordinate of P, and reversing our original procedure, we define the distance OP in terms of this coordinate as

$$OP = |x|.$$

EXERCISE

1. If we were to bisect our intervals instead of dividing them into ten, we could use binary instead of decimal fractions with some gain in simplicity in the foregoing process. Explain fully!

Can we associate with any positive real number a line segment whose length is equal to this real number? This is to ask whether a point on a scale exists whose coordinate is an arbitrary real number. Points, like numbers, are idealizations: they have just the properties with which we endow them. Let us then postulate an affirmative answer to this question, laying down the premise that each real number is the coordinate of one and but one point on a scale. In this way, we arrive again at a one-to-one correspondence between numbers and points, such as we had conceived naively before facing the question of irrationality. In view of this correspondence, we shall not distinguish between points and their coordinates, but we shall treat them interchangeably.

Have we solved the problem that so baffled the Pythagoreans and their successors? By defining lengths to be real numbers, indeed we have begun to solve it, but there are many loose ends. How shall we decide which of two real numbers is the greater? Will greater segments turn out to have greater lengths? How do we add real numbers, and if a line is divided into parts, will the length of the line be the sum of the lengths of the parts? What about areas, in which products occur? Satisfactory answers to these and similar questions depend upon how we define arithmetical operations upon real numbers. But before going on to this, we reconsider a seeming paradox.

EXERCISES

2. Prove that $-(-x) = x$, where x is an arbitrary real number.

3. Prove that $|x|$ is positive, where x is an arbitrary real number.

4. On a given straight line L, a scale with specified origin O and specified unit length can be constructed in two ways, depending on the selection of the positive sense. Prove that if an arbitrary point P on L has the coordinate x on one of these scales, then its coordinate is $-x$ on the other scale.

HINT: Examine the process of determining the coordinate in the light of Figure 15-3.

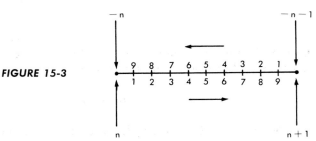

FIGURE 15-3

c. R IS NONDENUMERABLE

Recall that the set of rational points on a line can be covered by intervals of arbitrarily small total length (Chapter 14, Section 5d). As the proof shows, the same thing is true of any denumerable subset of a line. This suggests that the set of all points on a line may be nondenumerable, and in view of the correspondence we have just established between the set of points on a line and the set of real numbers R, it suggests that R may be nondenumerable. In fact, the following is true.

Proposition.   The set of nonterminating decimals

$$.a_1 a_2 a_3 \ldots$$

is nondenumerable.

PROOF: If the nonterminating decimals constitute a denumerable set, they can be arranged in a sequence, and suppose this to be the case. We have no clue to the order in which the nonterminating decimals appear in the sequence. (In fact, our intention is to prove that any such sequence is fictitious.) Hence, we must use notation general enough to cover all possibilities and write the members of the sequence, vertically arranged, as follows:

$$.a_1^{(1)} a_2^{(1)} a_3^{(1)} \ldots,$$
$$.a_1^{(2)} a_2^{(2)} a_3^{(2)} \ldots,$$
$$\cdots\cdots\cdots$$
$$.a_1^{(k)} a_2^{(k)} a_3^{(k)} \ldots,$$
$$\cdots\cdot$$

(An additional index has been attached to the symbols representing the digits in each decimal to indicate the decimal's place in the sequence.) We intend to show that, contrary to our supposition, a nonterminating decimal

$$(1) \qquad\qquad\qquad .b_1 b_2 b_3 \ldots$$

exists that is not in this sequence. This means that it is not equal to the first member of the sequence, or to the second member, or the third member, and so forth. If we take

$$b_1 \neq a_1^{(1)},$$

then by Definition 1, Subsection a., the new decimal (1) will certainly not be equal to the first member of the sequence. If we take

$$b_2 \neq a_2^{(2)},$$

the decimal (1) will similarly be unequal to the second member of the sequence. If for $k = 1, 2, 3, \ldots$, we take

$$b_k \neq a_k^{(k)},$$

decimal (1) will be different from the kth member of the sequence. Hence, decimal (1) will be different from every member of the sequence. Will it be nonterminating? To insure this, we add to the previous requirements the condition that

$$b_k \neq 0 \text{ for } k = 1, 2, 3, \ldots.$$

Decimal (1) will then indeed be a nonterminating decimal not included in the sequence supposedly containing all nonterminating decimals. We conclude that no such sequence exists and thus that the set of all nonterminating decimals is nondenumerable, as contended.

d. CARDINALITY AND DIMENSION

Decimal representations enable us to prove the following fact about cardinality.

Theorem.   The set of points in a plane is cardinally equivalent to the set of points on a line segment.

According to this theorem, dimension has no influence on cardinality. Most of us would have guessed otherwise, but who pretends to foresee all things mathematical? The most sober idealizations may produce the most surprising twists.

PROOF OF THEOREM: By the exercises on p. 609, an infinite straight line is cardinally equivalent to the segment

$$L = \text{all points } z \text{ such that } 0 < z \leq 1,$$

and a plane is cardinally equivalent to the square

$$S = \text{all points } (x, y) \text{ such that } \begin{cases} 0 < x \leq 1 \\ 0 < y \leq 1. \end{cases}$$

Hence, it suffices to prove that $L \sim S$. We shall do so by establishing a one-to-one correspondence between L and S as follows. Any point z of L can be represented by means of a nonterminating decimal fraction as

$$z = .a_1 a_2 a_3 \ldots,$$

We break up every such representation into sections, of which

$$.01 \mid 0003 \mid 5 \mid 07 \mid 001 \mid \ldots$$

is an example. Each section consists of one digit if this digit is nonzero, but otherwise is a string of digits that begins with zero and ends with the next digit not zero. Detach the odd sections and arrange them in the original order but without gaps to obtain a new infinite decimal. The new decimal is nonterminating and represents a real number we shall denote by x. In the preceding example $x = .015001....$ We define y similarly by detaching from the decimal representing z the even sections and arranging these in the original order without gaps. In our example, $y = .000307....$ Using the x and y described, we now define the correspondence

$$f(z) = (x, y)$$

assigning to an arbitrary point z of L the particular point (x, y) of S. Inversely, if an arbitrary point (x, y) of S is given, one and but one point z of L exists such that $f(z) = (x, y)$. Thus, f is a one-to-one correspondence between L and S, and $L \sim S$, as asserted.

EXERCISE

1. Prove that three-dimensional space is cardinally equivalent to a line segment.

2.

Ordering of real numbers. Least upper and greatest lower bounds.

Dedekind showed clearly that the concept of order is fundamental in the study of real numbers. Accordingly, we define $<$, the symbol for "less than," in the domain of real numbers R.

Definition 1. Consider two real numbers y and z with non-terminating representations

$$y = m + .b_1 b_2 b_3 \ldots, z = n + .c_1 c_2 c_3 \ldots.$$

We define the order relation

$$y < z$$

to mean that any one of the following conditions is satisfied:

$$m < n;$$
or
$$m = n, \ b_1 < c_1;$$

or $\qquad\qquad\qquad m = n,\, b_1 = c_1,\, b_2 < c_2;$

or $\qquad\qquad\qquad m = n,\, b_1 = c_1,\, b_2 = c_2,\, b_3 < c_3;$

or, in general, for some index p

$$m = n,\, b_1 = c_1,\, \ldots,\, b_p = c_p,\, b_{p+1} < c_{p+1}.$$

This definition is equivalent to the condition that an index p exist such that

$$y_p < z_p,$$

where, in general, y_k and z_k denote the k-place decimal truncations of y and z. If $y_p < z_p$ for a particular index p, then

$$y_k < z_k \text{ for } k > p.$$

(See the exercise on decimal truncations in Section 1a.)

EXERCISES

1. How would this definition work out if we permitted terminating decimals?
2. Prove that a real number x is positive (Definition 2, Section 1) if and only if $0 < x$.

Once $<$ is defined, the relations $\leq$, $>$, $\geq$ are defined by means of it in the usual way. All these relations reduce to the usual if y and z happen to be rational numbers.

From Definition 1 we have immediately the following theorem.

Theorem 1.   (a) For any two real numbers x and y, one of the following statements is true and the other two are false:

$$x = y,\, x < y,\, y < x.$$

(b) If x, y, z are three real numbers such that

$$x < y \text{ and } y < z,$$

then

$$x < z.$$

Properties (a) and (b) of Theorem 1 characterize R as *linearly ordered by the relation* $<$.

In terms of the new ordering relation, we can now state inequalities for real numbers analogous to those for rationals (inequalities (3) in Section 1).

Proposition 1. Let y be an arbitrary real number and y_k its k-place decimal truncation, $k = 1, 2, 3, \ldots$. Then

$$y_k < y \le y_k + 10^{-k} \text{ for } k = 1, 2, 3, \ldots.$$

Corollary. For all indices j and k,

$$y_j < y_k + 10^{-k}.$$

PROOF: Proposition 1 says that

$$y_j < y \text{ for } j = 1, 2, 3, \ldots$$

and also that

$$y \le y_k + 10^{-k} \text{ for } k = 1, 2, 3, \ldots.$$

The assertion made follows immediately.

Concerning negatives, we state the following proposition.

Proposition 2. If x and y are any real numbers such that

$$x < y,$$

then

$$-x > -y.$$

PROOF: The given numbers have nonterminating decimal representations

$$x = m + .a_1 a_2 a_3 \ldots, \, y = n + .b_1 b_2 b_3 \ldots.$$

In terms of these, we have

$$-x = -m - 1 + .a_1' a_2' a_3' \ldots, \, -y = -n - 1 + .b_1' b_2' b_3' \ldots,$$

where

$$a_i' = 9 - a_i, \, b_i' = 9 - b_i \text{ for } i = 1, 2, 3, \ldots.$$

Since $x < y$, certain cases arise. In the first case,

$$m < n,$$

which implies $-m > -n$ (Chapter 2, Section 5) and thus $-m - 1 > -n - 1$; therefore, $-x > -y$, since equality would require that all $b_i' = 9$, which is excluded. In the second case,

$$m = n, \, a_1 < b_1.$$

Thus, we have in this case,

$$-m - 1 = -n - 1, \, a_1' > b_1',$$

conditions that again imply $-x > -y$. The reasoning in subsequent cases is exactly like the foregoing, with the result that $-x > -y$ in all cases, as claimed.

Given distinct real numbers y and z, say with $y < z$, we shall have occasion to estimate the "gap" between them. If the numbers were rational, their difference $z - y$ would measure this gap, but as yet, we have no arithmetic for reals. We do not need to know the gap between y and z exactly, only how wide *at least* it is. In fact, a lower estimate of $s - r$, where r and s are any rational numbers such that

$$r < y \text{ and } z < s$$

(see Figure 15-4) will be good enough. Such an estimate is provided by the following proposition.

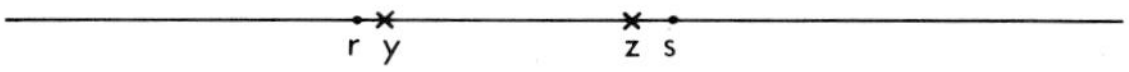

FIGURE 15-4 *The gap between two real numbers.*

Proposition 3. If y and z are any real numbers such that

$$y < z,$$

then a positive integer i exists with the following property: if r and s are arbitrary rational numbers such that

$$r < y < z < s,$$

then

$$s - r > 10^{-i}.$$

PROOF: Representing y and z by means of nonterminating decimals,

$$y = m + .a_1 a_2 a_3 \ldots, \; z = n + .b_1 b_2 b_3 \ldots,$$

let

$$y_k = m + .a_1 \ldots a_k, \; z_k = n + .b_1 \ldots b_k, \; k = 1, 2, \ldots,$$

be the k-place truncations. The condition $y < z$ means that either $m < n$, or

$$m = n, a_1 < b_1,$$

or for some index j greater than 1,

(1) $$m = n, a_1 = b_1, \ldots, a_{j-1} = b_{j-1}, a_j < b_j.$$

We shall explain the matter assuming (1), the reasoning being just

the same in the other cases. Condition (1) implies that
$.a_1 \ldots a_j + 10^{-j} \le .b_1 \ldots b_j$ and thus that

$$(2) \qquad\qquad y_j + 10^{-j} \le z_j.$$

Since the representations are nonterminating, an index i higher than j exists such that $b_i > 0$ and, therefore,
$.b_1 \ldots b_j + 10^{-i} \le .b_1 \ldots b_j \ldots b_i$; this implies

$$z_j + 10^{-i} \le z_i.$$

In view of (2), we have from the transitive law for rationals (Section 5, Chapter 2),

$$(3) \qquad\qquad y_j + 10^{-j} + 10^{-i} \le z_i.$$

The transitive law for real numbers (Theorem 1b) is employed next. Since $r < y$ and $y \le y_j + 10^{-j}$, we obtain

$$r < y_j + 10^{-j},$$

this and (3) together showing

$$(4) \qquad\qquad r + 10^{-i} < z_i.$$

Since $z < s$ and $z_i < z$, we have $z_i < s$, which with (4) gives

$$r + 10^{-i} < s.$$

All the numbers in the last inequality being rational, we can write it in the form

$$10^{-i} < s - r,$$

which is the relation asserted.

EXERCISES

3. Going through the steps of the preceding proof, state i and j for the following concrete choices of y and z:
(a) $y = 2/5$, $z = 3/7$;
(b) $y = 1/12$, $z = 1/11$.

4. For arbitrary real numbers y and z such that $y < z$, prove that a rational number r exists such that

$$y < r < z.$$

HINT: See inequality (3).

Further developments require some new definitions.

Definition 2.   If S is a set of real numbers and y is a real number such that

$$x \leq y \text{ for } x \text{ in } S,$$

then we say that y is an *upper bound for S*. If z is a given upper bound for S, and if any upper bound for S, say y, must satisfy the condition

$$z \leq y,$$

then we call z the *least upper bound for S*.

Examples: For the set

$$\{1, 2, 3, -1/2\},$$

the least upper bound is 3. More generally, the least upper bound for any finite set of real numbers is simply the largest number in the set. For the sequence

$$\{1/2, 2/3, 3/4, 4/5, 5/6, 6/7, \ldots\},$$

the kth term of which is $k/(k+1)$, 1 and 2 are both upper bounds, and 1 is the least upper bound. For the sequence

$$\{1, 2, 1/2, 2/3, 3/4, 4/5, 5/6, 6/7, \ldots\},$$

the least upper bound is 2. More generally, any set that contains an upper bound for itself, say y, has this y as least upper bound.

The following properties of least upper bounds also are immediate:

(A) The least upper bound of any set S is unique. This means that if y and z are both least upper bounds of S, then $y = z$.

PROOF: Both y and z are, in particular, upper bounds of S. Since y is a least upper bound, we have $y \leq z$; since z is a least upper bound, $z \leq y$. Theorem 1 shows that $y = z$.

(B) If x_k and y_k are two sequences of rational numbers having upper bounds M and N, respectively, then the sequence $x_k + y_k$ has the upper bound $M + N$.

PROOF: By assumption, $x_k \leq M$ and $y_k \leq N$. Adding gives $x_k + y_k \leq M + N$, which establishes the contention.

(C) If S is a set of real numbers and z its least upper bound, then for any real number u such that

$$u < z,$$

a member x of S exists such that

$$u < x \leq z.$$

PROOF: If no member of S exceeds u, then u is an upper bound for S. Since z is the least upper bound, we have $z \leq u$, a contradiction to the assumption made. Therefore, some member of S must exceed u, as contended.

Statement (C) tells us that if the least upper bound z of a set S does not itself belong to S, then members of S sift like powder into the gap between z and any lesser number.

Lower bound and greatest lower bound are defined analogously to upper bound and least upper bound: if S is a set of real numbers and u is a real number such that

$$u \leq x \text{ for all } x \text{ in } S,$$

then u is a *lower bound* for S. If v is a lower bound for S, and if an arbitrary lower bound for S, say u, must satisfy the condition

$$u \leq v,$$

then v is the *greatest lower bound* for S.

If y is the least upper bound of a sequence $\{x_1, x_2, x_3, \ldots\}$, we shall write

$$y = \text{l. u. b. } \{x_1, x_2, x_3, \ldots\}$$

or, more briefly,

$$y = \text{l. u. b. } \{x_k\}.$$

Similarly, if z is the greatest lower bound of this sequence, we write

$$z = \text{g. l. b. } \{x_k\}.$$

EXERCISES

5. What are the least upper and the greatest lower bounds for the following sequences:
(a) $\{1, -1, 1, -1, 1, -1, 1, -1, \ldots\}$,
(b) $\{1, 1/2, 1/3, 1/4, 1/5, 1/6, \ldots\}$,
(c) $\{1, -1/2, 1/3, -1/4, 1/5, -1/6, 1/7, \ldots\}$,
(d) $\{-1, 3/2, -1/3, 5/4, -1/5, 7/6, -1/7, 9/8, -1/9, \ldots\}$,
(e) $\{1, 3/2, 1/3, 5/4, 1/5, 7/6, 1/7, 9/8, 1/9, \ldots\}$,
(f) $\{1, 2/3, 1/3, 4/5, 1/5, 6/7, 1/7, 8/9, 1/9, \ldots\}$,
(g) $\{1, -2/3, 1/3, -4/5, 1/5, -6/7, 1/7, -8/9, 1/9, \ldots\}$,
(h) $\{2/3, 1/3, -4/5, -1/5, 6/7, 1/7, -8/9, -1/9, \ldots\}$.

6. Let $\{a_m\}$ be an increasing sequence and $\{b_n\}$ a decreasing sequence of real numbers such that

$$a_m < b_n \text{ for } m = 1, 2, 3, \ldots$$
$$\text{and } n = 1, 2, 3, \ldots.$$

Letting

$$u = \text{l. u. b. } \{a_m\}, \ v = \text{g. l. b. } \{b_n\},$$

show that

$$u \leq v.$$

7. Consider a real number u, an increasing sequence $\{x_k\}$, and a decreasing sequence $\{y_k\}$ such that

$$u = \text{l. u. b. } \{x_k\} = \text{g. l. b. } \{y_k\}.$$

Prove that if v is a real number such that

$$x_k < v < y_k \text{ for } k = 1, 2, 3, \ldots,$$

then $v = u$. HINT: If $v < u$, can v be an upper bound for $\{x_k\}$, and if $v > u$, can v be a lower bound for $\{y_k\}$?

In all their properties, lower and greatest lower bounds are mirror images of upper and least upper bounds. Proofs pertaining to the latter can be immediately turned around and applied to the former. In addition, a simple formal connection between upper bounds and lower bounds exists. If u is a lower bound for a set S, so that

$$u \leq x \text{ for all } x \text{ in } S,$$

we have

$$-u \geq -x \text{ for all } x \text{ in } S.$$

Therefore, $-u$ is an *upper* bound for the set T consisting of the negatives of all the numbers in S. If y is the greatest lower bound for S, we shall see similarly that $-y$ is the least upper bound for T. In the first place, $-y$ is an upper bound for T. If $-y$ is not the least upper bound for T, an upper bound $-v$ of T exists such that $-v < -y$ and thus that

$$-x \leq -v < -y \text{ for every } x \text{ in } S.$$

This follows from the definition of least upper bound, since every member of T is the negative of a member of S. By Proposition 2,

$$x \geq v > y \text{ for every } x \text{ in } S,$$

contrary to the assumption that y is the greatest lower bound in S. We conclude that $-y$ is the least upper bound for T, as asserted.

Definition 3. A sequence of real numbers $x_1, x_2, x_3, \ldots$, such that

$$x_1 < x_2 < x_3 < \ldots,$$

i.e., such that

$$x_k < x_{k+1} \text{ for } k = 1, 2, 3, \ldots$$

is said to be an increasing sequence. If

$$x_1 \leq x_2 \leq x_3 \leq \ldots,$$

i.e.,

$$x_k \leq x_{k+1} \text{ for } k = 1, 2, 3, \ldots,$$

we say that the sequence is *nondecreasing. Decreasing* and *nonincreasing* sequences are defined analogously.

Example 1:   If $.a_1a_2a_3 \ldots$ is an infinite decimal, the sequence of k-place truncations

$$A_k = .a_1 \ldots a_k, \quad k = 1, 2, 3, \ldots$$

is a nondecreasing sequence.

Example 2.   If $.a_1a_2a_3 \ldots$ is a nonterminating infinite decimal, and A_k denotes its k-place truncation, as before, then the sequence

$$\{A_k + 10^{-k}\}$$

is a nonincreasing sequence. Let us, for instance, prove that

$$A_2 + 10^{-2} \geq A_3 + 10^{-3}.$$

We have

$$\begin{aligned}
A_3 + 10^{-3} &= .a_1a_2a_3 + 10^{-3} \\
&= .a_1a_2 + .00a_3 + 10^{-3} \\
&= A_2 + (a_3 + 1)10^{-3} \\
&\leq A_2 + (9 + 1)10^{-3} = A_2 + 10^{-2},
\end{aligned}$$

since $a_3 \leq 9$. The reasoning to prove the general case,

$$A_k + 10^{-k} \geq A_{k+1} + 10^{-k-1} \text{ for } k = 1, 2, 3, \ldots,$$

is the same.

Our main tool will be the following proposition.

Proposition 4.   An increasing sequence of real numbers with an upper bound has a least upper bound. A decreasing sequence with a lower bound has a greatest lower bound.

PROOF: The two statements can be proved in the same way, and we concern ourselves just with the first. Let $\{x_1, x_2, x_3, \ldots\}$ be an increasing sequence:

$$x_1 < x_2 < x_3 < \ldots.$$

We assume the sequence to have an upper bound. Thus, a number N — say a positive integer — exists such that

$$x_k \leq N \text{ for } k = 1, 2, 3, \ldots.$$

Each of the real numbers x_k has a nonterminating decimal representation of the form

$$q + .d_1 d_2 d_3 \ldots.$$

Let us examine q for each member of the sequence in succession. Since $x_2 > x_1$, the value of q for x_2 is not less than that for x_1. Similarly, the value of q for x_3 is not less than that for x_2. More generally, for $k = 1, 2, 3, \ldots$, the value of q for x_{k+1} is not less than that for x_k. In other words, the respective values of q attached to $x_1, x_2, x_3, \ldots$, form a nondecreasing sequence. But the values of q are integers not exceeding N. Hence, a largest value among them exists. Let n denote this greatest value of q, which occurs, say, in the representation of

$$x_{k_0}.$$

For all subsequent members of the sequence (i.e., for all x_k for which $k > k_0$), $q = n$. This means that the members of the sequence after x_{k_0} all have representations of the form

$$n + .d_1 d_2 d_3 \ldots.$$

We now inspect the values of d_1 in the representations of

(1) $$x_{k_0}, x_{k_0+1}, x_{k_0+2}, x_{k_0+3}, \ldots.$$

These representations all start with the same integer n, and since the sequence is increasing, we can argue as in the previous paragraph that the value of d_1 attached to the respective numbers (1) form a nondecreasing sequence. But the values of d_1 are integers at most 9. Therefore, they have a largest value b_1. If this largest value, b_1, already occurs in the representation of x_{k_0}, we say that b_1 is *inert*. Otherwise, we call b_1 *lively*. If b_1 is inert, we set

$$k_1 = k_0.$$

If b_1 is lively and x_c is the first of the numbers (1) for which $d_1 = b_1$, we set

$$k_1 = c.$$

The numbers

(2) $$x_{k_1}, \ x_{k_1+1}, \ x_{k_1+2}, \ x_{k_1+3}, \ \ldots$$

all have representations of the form

$$n + .b_1 d_2 d_3 \ldots,$$

where n is the integer and b_1 the digit just determined. We now run through the values of d_2 in the representations for these numbers. A greatest value of d_2 exists, a digit we shall denote by b_2. If this greatest value already occurs in the representation of x_{k_1}, we say that b_2 is *inert*, and otherwise we call b_2 *lively*. If b_2 is inert, we set

$$k_2 = k_1.$$

If b_2 is lively and x_c is the first of the numbers (2) for which $d_2 = b_2$, we set

$$k_2 = c.$$

In that case, $k_1 < k_2$ and

$$x_1 < x_2 < \ldots < x_{k_2-1} < n + .b_1 b_2 < x_{k_2}.$$

Continuing in this way, we obtain, in addition to the integer n, an infinite sequence of digits

$$b_1, b_2, b_3, \ldots$$

and an infinite sequence of indices (positive integers)

$$k_1, k_2, k_3, \ldots$$

such that

$$k_1 \le k_2 \le k_3 \le \ldots.$$

For each $j = 1, 2, 3, \ldots$, the numbers

(3) $$x_{k_j}, \ x_{k_j+1}, \ x_{k_j+2}, \ x_{k_j+3}, \ \ldots$$

all have nonterminating representations of the form

$$n + .b_1 b_2 \ldots b_j d_{j+1} d_{j+2} d_{j+3} \ldots.$$

The digit b_{j+1} is determined as the largest value of d_{j+1} for all the numbers (3). If this largest value already appears in the representation of x_{k_j}, we say that b_{j+1} is *inert*, and otherwise we call b_{j+1} *lively*. If b_{j+1} is lively and x_c is the first of the numbers (3) for which $d_{j+1} = b_{j+1}$, then $k_{j+1} = c$. This implies, in particular, that

(4) $$k_{j+1} > k_j \text{ if } b_{j+1} \text{ is lively.}$$

If we replace $j+1$ by j (and j by $j-1$) in the foregoing discussion, we see that if b_j is lively, then

$$x_{k_j-1} < n + .b_1 b_2 \ldots b_j.$$

From the nature of the representation of x_{k_j},

$$n + .b_1 b_2 \ldots b_j < x_{k_j}.$$

These inequalities are the last two in the chain

(5) $$x_1 < x_2 < \ldots < x_{k_j-1} < n + .b_1 b_2 \ldots b_j < x_{k_j},$$

and hold if b_j is a lively digit. The first $k_j - 2$ inequalities in the chain result from the fact that the sequence $\{x_k\}$ was assumed to be increasing.

For the same reason, infinitely many b_j are lively. Hence, (4) holds for infinitely many values of j, which implies that

(6) $$\lim_{j \to \infty} k_j = \infty;$$

this means that the k_j will surpass any number stipulated, no matter how large, if j is sufficiently high.

Now define

$$z = n + .b_1 b_2 b_3 \ldots .$$

The infinite decimal is nonterminating, again because infinitely many of the b_j are lively. We shall see that z is the sought-for least upper bound of the sequence $\{x_k\}$. Since

$$n + .b_1 b_2 \ldots b_j < z \text{ for } j = 1, 2, 3, \ldots,$$

we have from (5) that

$$x_k < z \text{ for } k = 1, 2, \ldots, k_{j-1}$$

if b_j is a lively digit. Since the k_j take arbitrarily large values (condition (6)), we can conclude that

(7) $$x_k < z \text{ for } k = 1, 2, 3, \ldots,$$

which means that z is an upper bound for the sequence $\{x_k\}$. To show that z is the least upper bound, suppose y to be an upper bound such that

(8)
$$y < z.$$

Using the nonterminating representation of y,

$$y = m + .a_1 a_2 a_3 \ldots,$$

we shall show that none of the conditions for (8) is satisfied. First, if $m < n$, then $y < x_{k_0}$: in this event, y would not be an upper bound. Secondly, suppose

$$m = n, \; a_1 < b_1.$$

In this case, $y < x_{k_1}$, and again y could not be an upper bound. If thirdly,

$$m = n, \; a_1 = b_1, \; a_2 < b_2,$$

we would have $y < x_{k_2}$, another contradiction. Subsequent cases are shown to lead to contradictions in the same way. We conclude that (8) is impossible, and thus that z is the least upper bound of the sequence $\{x_k\}$, as asserted.

EXERCISE

8. Use Proposition 3 to give a reasonable definition of the total illumination at Q in the problem discussed in Section 5f, Chapter 14.

The following is an easy and immensely useful generalization of Proposition 3.

Theorem 2.   A nondecreasing sequence of real numbers with an upper bound has a least upper bound. A nonincreasing sequence with a lower bound has a greatest lower bound.

PROOF: It suffices to consider the first assertion. Suppose $y_1, y_2, y_3, \ldots$ to be a nondecreasing sequence. Thus,

$$y_1 \leq y_2 \leq y_3 \leq \ldots.$$

It may happen that for some index p, $y_p = y_{p+1} = y_{p+2} = \ldots$. In this case, y_p is an upper bound for the sequence; belonging to the sequence, y_p is the least upper bound. If no member of the sequence is an upper bound of the sequence, then no index p exists such that $y_p = y_{p+1} = y_{p+2} = \ldots$. Hence, in particular, if the value y_1 is repeated, an index $q > 1$ exists such that

$$y_1 = y_2 = \ldots = y_q \text{ with } y_q < y_{q+1}.$$

Then delete $y_2, \ldots, y_q$ from the sequence. Similarly, discard all other repetitions in the sequence. Take in their original order the terms that remain and relabel them consecutively

$$x_1, x_2, x_3, \ldots.$$

The new sequence includes no duplications and, therefore, is an increasing sequence. Every value occurring in the original sequence is represented in the new sequence; hence, the two sequences have the same least upper bound. In view of the previous proposition, our theorem is proved.

The previous theorem applies, for instance, to the decimal truncations y_k, $k = 1, 2, 3, \ldots$, of an arbitrary real number y. We already noted (Examples 1 and 2 of nondecreasing and nonincreasing sequences) that $\{y_k\}$ is a nondecreasing and $\{y_k + 10^{-k}\}$ a nonincreasing sequence. With the help of Proposition 3, we shall now prove the following proposition.

Proposition 5.   In the notation just introduced,

$$y = \text{l. u. b. } \{y_k\} = \text{g. l. b. } \{y_k + 10^{-k}\}.$$

PROOF: Since $\{y_k\}$ is a nondecreasing sequence with an upper bound (namely, y), Theorem 1 shows that l. u. b. $\{y_k\}$ exists. Denote it by z:

$$z = \text{l.u.b. } \{y_k\}.$$

Since the y_k are truncations of a nonterminating decimal, no y_k is equal to z; hence,

$$y_k < z \text{ for } k = 1, 2, 3, \ldots.$$

Since y is an upper bound for the sequence of truncations y_k, we have

$$z \leq y.$$

Hence, either $z = y$, a statement we wish to prove, or

$$z < y.$$

Since $y_k < z$ and $y \leq y_k + 10^{-k} < y_k + 2 \cdot 10^{-k}$, we have in the latter case

(9) $y_k < z < y < y_k + 2 \cdot 10^{-k}$ for $k = 1, 2, 3, \ldots.$

But Proposition 3 says that if $z < y$, and if r and s are rational numbers such that

$$r < z < y < s,$$

then $s - r > 10^{-q}$ with some fixed integer q independent of r and s. This contradicts (9). Hence, the supposition $z < y$ is untenable. We conclude that $y = z$, which means that

$$y = \text{l. u. b. } \{y_k\},$$

as asserted.

The nonincreasing sequence $\{y_k + 10^{-k}\}$ has a lower bound, for instance, y_1 (Corollary to Proposition 1). Hence, the previous theorem implies that the sequence has a greatest lower bound w. We can identify w with y by an argument similar to the one just given with respect to z and y. The proposition is proved.

We conclude this section with a further generalization of Proposition 4 and some applications. Unlike the foregoing, these will not be needed later on.

Theorem 3. Any set of real numbers with an upper bound has a least upper bound. Any set of real numbers with a lower bound has a greatest lower bound.

PROOF: Consider an arbitrary set S of real numbers with an upper bound y_1, which we shall assume to be rational. Let x_1 be any rational value not an upper bound for S, and consider the average

$$a_1 = (x_1 + y_1)/2,$$

the midpoint of the segment between x_1 and y_1 (see Figure 15-5).

FIGURE 15-5

If a_1 is not an upper bound for S, set

$$x_2 = a_1,$$
$$y_2 = y_1,$$

in which case

$$x_1 < x_2 < y_2 = y_1$$

and

$$y_2 - x_2 = y_1 - (x_1 + y_1)/2$$
$$= (y_1 - x_1)/2.$$

Figure 15-5A illustrates this case. If a_1 is an upper bound for S, set

$$x_2 = x_1,$$
$$y_2 = a_1,$$

in which case

$$x_1 = x_2 < y_2 < y_1$$

and

$$y_2 - x_2 = (x_1 + y_1)/2 - x_1$$
$$= (y_1 - x_1)/2.$$

This case is illustrated in Figure 15-5B. In either case, y_2 is an upper bound for S, and x_2 is not an upper bound. Both are rational and satisfy the conditions

$$x_1 \leq x_2 < y_2 \leq y_1$$

and

$$y_2 - x_2 = (y_1 - x_1)/2.$$

Now consider the average

$$a_2 = (x_2 + y_2)/2,$$

the midpoint of the segment between x_2 and y_2. If a_2 is not an upper bound for S, set

$$x_3 = a_2,$$
$$y_3 = y_2,$$

in which case

$$x_2 < x_3 < y_3 = y_2$$

and

$$y_3 - x_3 = y_2 - (x_2 + y_2)/2$$
$$= (y_2 - x_2)/2.$$

Figures 15-6AA and BA illustrate this case. If a_2 is an upper bound

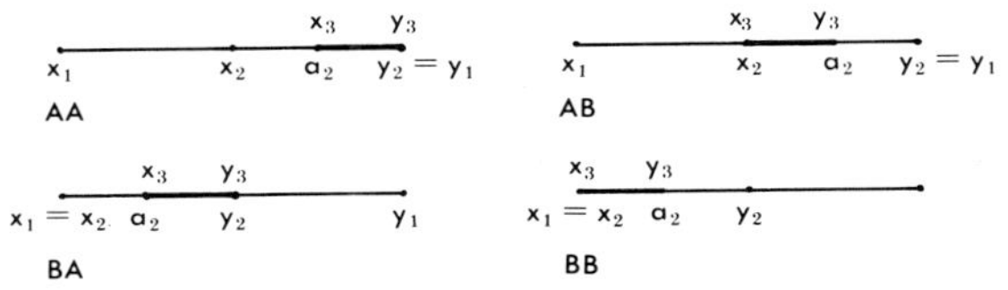

FIGURE 15-6 The second step in finding a least upper bound.

for S, set

$$x_3 = x_2,$$
$$y_3 = a_2,$$

in which case

$$x_2 = x_3 < y_3 < y_2$$

and

$$y_3 - x_3 = (x_2 + y_2)/2 - x_2$$
$$= (y_2 - x_2)/2.$$

This case is illustrated in Figures 15-6AB and BB. In either case, y_3 is a rational upper bound for S, x_3 is a rational number not an upper bound for S, and the following conditions are satisfied:

$$x_1 \leq x_2 \leq x_3 < y_3 \leq y_2 \leq y_1,$$
$$y_3 - x_3 = (y_2 - x_2)/2 = (y_1 - x_1)/4.$$

The reasoning we have twice illustrated enables us to treat the general case inductively, as follows. Suppose that for some positive integer n we have determined n rational numbers $y_1, y_2, \ldots, y_n$ that are upper bounds for S, and n rational numbers $x_1, x_2, \ldots, x_n$ that are not upper bounds for S. Suppose these numbers to satisfy the conditions

(10) $$x_1 \leq x_2 \leq \ldots \leq x_n < y_n \leq \ldots \leq y_2 \leq y_1$$

and

(11) $$y_n - x_n = (y_1 - x_1)/2^{n-1}.$$

We shall show how to find a rational upper bound for S, y_{n+1}, and a rational number x_{n+1} not an upper bound for S, such that equality (11) and the chain of the inequalities (10) will hold with $n+1$ in place of n. To do so, define the average

$$a_n = (x_n + y_n)/2,$$

which is the point midway between x_n and y_n. If a_n is not an upper bound for S, set

$$x_{n+1} = a_n,$$
$$y_{n+1} = y_n;$$

if a_n is an upper bound for S, set

$$x_{n+1} = x_n,$$
$$y_{n+1} = a_n.$$

In either case, y_{n+1} is an upper bound for S, and x_{n+1} is not an upper bound for S. Both are rational. Calculations in both cases that are the same as those given explicitly in the first two steps show that

$$x_n \leq x_{n+1} < y_{n+1} \leq y_n$$

and

$$y_{n-1} - x_{n+1} = (y_n - x_n)/2.$$

Referring to (10), we obtain

$$x_1 \leq x_2 \leq \ldots \leq x_n \leq x_{n+1} < y_{n+1} \leq y_n \leq \ldots \leq y_2 \leq y_1,$$

the desired chain of inequalities of the same form as (10), but with n replaced by $n+1$. Referring to (11) gives us

$$y_{n+1} - x_{n+1} = (y_n - x_n)/2 = (y_1 - x_1)/2^n,$$

which is of the form (11), but with $n+1$ in place of n. We have shown that if x_1 and y_1 are given, with $x_1 < y_1$, then we can define a sequence of rational numbers

$$y_1, y_2, y_3, \ldots$$

that are upper bounds for S, and a sequence of rational numbers

$$x_1, x_2, x_3, \ldots$$

that are not upper bounds for S, such that (10) and (11) are satisfied for every positive integer n. Figure 15-7 illustrates a possible situation with $n = 5$.

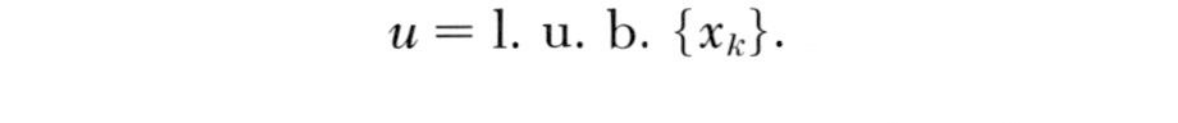

FIGURE 15-7 *Five steps in determining a least upper bound.*

Since $\{x_k\}$ is a nondecreasing sequence with an upper bound (for instance, y_1), Theorem 2 tells us that a real number u exists such that

$$u = \text{l. u. b. } \{x_k\}.$$

Since $\{y_k\}$ is a nonincreasing sequence with a lower bound (for instance, x_1), a real number v exists such that

$$v = \text{g. l. b. } \{y_k\}.$$

For each fixed positive integer n, we have (by (10))

$$x_k < y_n \text{ for } k = 1, 2, 3, \ldots.$$

Thus, y_n is an upper bound for the sequence $\{x_k\}$, and since u is the least upper bound for the sequence,

$$u \leq y_n.$$

732 REAL NUMBERS: THEIR REPRESENTATION, PROPERTIES, AND APPLICATIONS

This inequality holding for every positive integer n, we see that u is a lower bound for the sequence $\{y_k\}$. Therefore,

$$u \leq v,$$

for v is the greatest lower bound of $\{y_n\}$. We shall show that

$$u = v.$$

Otherwise,

$$u < v.$$

But $x_n \leq u$ and $v \leq y_n$ for $n = 1, 2, 3, \ldots$. Therefore, $x_n - 10^{-n} < u$, $v < y_n + 10^{-n}$, and if $u < v$, we have

(12) $$x_n - 10^{-n} < u < v < y_n + 10^{-n}.$$

Proposition 3 tells us that if r and s are rational numbers such that

$$r < u < v < s,$$

then $s - r > 10^{-q}$, where q is a positive integer independent of the choice of r and s. In view of (11), this contradicts (12), and we conclude that

(13) $$u = v,$$

as asserted.

From the fact that each y_n is an upper bound for S, we deduce that v also is an upper bound. Otherwise, a number x belonging to S would exist such that

$$v < x.$$

By the property for greatest lower bounds analogous to (C), an index k would exist such that

$$v \leq y_k < x,$$

but this contradicts the fact that y_k is an upper bound for S. Therefore, v is an upper bound for S, as asserted. We shall prove, finally, that v is the least upper bound of S. We must show simply that if w is any upper bound for S, then

$$v \leq w.$$

Suppose that, to the contrary,

$$w < v.$$

Then $w < u$ (since $u = v$), and by property (C) of least upper bounds, we can find an index m such that

$$w < x_m \leq u.$$

Since x_m is not an upper bound for S, this inequality shows that w is not an upper bound either, contrary to our supposition. We conclude that w is not less than v, i.e., that

$$w \geq v.$$

This was our contention and proves that v is the least upper bound for S, as asserted. The theorem is proved.

EXERCISE

9. Let S be an arbitrary set of real numbers with a positive least upper bound z less than 1. Show how the construction used in the previous proof gives directly an infinite binary fraction for z. (See Exercise 1, p. 708.)

We give just one application of this far-reaching result, a proof of the "finite covering" theorem, which arose in our discussion (Chapter 14, Section 5f) of starlight and the distribution of stars.

Finite Covering Theorem. Let L be any straight line and I any segment of L that is of finite length and contains its own end points. Suppose a collection of segments of L to be given that *covers I* in the sense that every point of I is contained in—and is not an end point of—at least one segment of the collection. Then a finite number of segments of the given collection also suffice to cover I.

PROOF: Let us choose a scale upon L with respect to which

$$I = \text{set of all points } x \text{ such that } 0 \leq x \leq 1.$$

For any positive number u, define the interval

$$I_u = \text{set of all points } x \text{ such that } 0 \leq x \leq u.$$

(Thus, I_1 coincides with I.)

The first step in our proof is to notice that a segment of the given collection exists that "covers" 0 in the sense that 0 belongs to the segment and is not an end point. This segment also covers an interval I_{x_1}, where x_1 is any positive number less than the right end point of the segment (see Figure 15-8).

0   x_1 1

FIGURE 15-8   *A segment covering 0.*

Let us say that a given positive number u is *good* if a finite number of segments of the given collection suffice to cover I_u. Defining U to be the set of all positive numbers u that are good, we have just seen that U is not empty (it contains x_1). Notice also that if u is in U, then every positive number less than u also is in U. Our aim is to prove that 1 belongs to U. If U has no upper bound, this is certainly so. If U has an upper bound, then by Theorem 3 U has a least upper bound, which we denote by v. If $1 < v$, then by a previous remark, 1 is in U, and we have finished. Consider the opposite possibility that

$$v \le 1.$$

A segment T of the given collection exists that covers v and thus covers all points between two values v' and v'' such that

$$v' < v < v''$$

(see Figure 15-9). Property (C) for the least upper bound v tells us that a good number w—a number belonging to U—exists such that

$$v' < w < v.$$

FIGURE 15-9 *A segment covering the least upper bound v and U.*

Then T covers w. Since w is good, a finite number of segments of the given collection cover I_w, and if we add T to these we have a finite number of segments that cover $I_{v''}$. This being so, v is not an upper bound for U, contrary to our supposition. We conclude that $v > 1$. Therefore, 1 is in U, and the proof is complete.

3.

Arithmetic for real numbers

The previous section prepared us technically to define the addition and multiplication of real numbers and to demonstrate their laws. When applied to rational numbers, the new definitions will reduce to the old. Under the new definitions, the commutative, associative, and distributive laws, and the rules for adding zero and multiplying by 1, will hold in the entire domain of real numbers. A negative will be an additive inverse, and every nonzero real number will have a reciprocal, or multiplicative inverse. Thus, the nine laws originally premised for rationals in the algebraic discussions of Section 2, Chapter 2, will hold in the larger domain of real numbers. The deductions we drew from these laws—for instance, the proposition that no number has more than one reciprocal, or the formula $(x/y)^{-1} = y/x$ $(x \neq 0, y \neq 0)$ —therefore will hold for arbitrary real numbers as well as for rationals; all formal algebraic rules will extend without change from rational numbers to real.

The same is true of the rules for inequalities. The order relation for reals we have been using in this chapter will be seen to satisfy the condition employed to define $<$ for rationals (Section 5, Chapter 2). This condition, which was the source of our rules for rationals, leads in the same way to the same rules for reals.

a. ADDITION

Let y and z be real numbers and y_k and z_k their respective k-place decimal truncations. We shall now define $y + z$ and investigate the properties of sums in R. From Example 1 after Definition 3, Section 2, $\{y_k\}$ and $\{z_k\}$ are nondecreasing sequences, and, hence, the sequence $\{y_k + z_k\}$ is nondecreasing. Since

$$y_k < y_1 + 10^{-1} \text{ and } z_k < z_1 + 10^{-1} \text{ for } k = 1, 2, 3, \dots$$

(Corollary to Proposition 1, Section 2), by adding we have also

$$y_k + z_k < y_1 + z_1 + 2 \cdot 10^{-1},$$

which tells us that the sequence $\{y_k + z_k\}$ has an upper bound. Therefore, it has a least upper bound (Theorem 2, Section 2), and we define $y + z$ to be this least upper bound:

(1) $$y + z = \text{l. u. b. } \{y_k + z_k\}.$$

This definition needs justification. Is it correct for rational y and z? Would analogous definitions in terms of other nondecreasing sequences that approximate y and z, respectively, always produce the same value of $y + z$? Answering these questions in reverse order, we next prove the following proposition.

Proposition 1. Let y and z be any real numbers, y_k and z_k their respective k-place decimal truncations $(k = 1, 2, 3, \dots)$, and $\{u_k\}$ and $\{v_k\}$ arbitrary nondecreasing sequences of rational numbers such that

$$y = \text{l. u. b. } \{u_k\} \text{ and } z = \text{l. u. b. } \{v_k\}.$$

Then the sequence $\{u_k + v_k\}$ has a least upper bound equal to $y + z$.

PROOF: Since

$$y \leq y_1 + 10^{-1} \text{ and } z \leq z_1 + 10^{-1}$$

and

$$u_k \leq y \text{ and } v_k \leq z \text{ for } k = 1, 2, 3, \ldots,$$

we have

$$u_k \leq y_1 + 10^{-1} \text{ and } v_k \leq z_1 + 10^{-1}.$$

Adding the last two inequalities shows that the sequence $\{u_k + v_k\}$ has an upper bound. Like the sequence $\{y_k + z_k\}$ previously discussed, it therefore has a least upper bound w:

$$w = \text{l. u. b. } \{u_k + v_k\}.$$

We wish to prove that $w = y + z$. By Proposition 1, Section 2,

$$y_k < y \text{ for } k = 1, 2, 3, \ldots,$$

and since $y = \text{l. u. b. } \{u_k\}$, statement (C) (concerning least upper bounds) in Section 2 assures us that for each k an index q exists for which

$$y_k < u_q \leq y.$$

With k fixed arbitrarily, an index r similarly exists such that

$$z_k < v_r \leq z.$$

Hence, $\{u_k\}$ and $\{v_k\}$ being nondecreasing sequences, if s is the larger of the two indices q and r, we have

$$y_k < u_s,$$
$$z_k < v_s,$$

and by adding,

$$y_k + z_k < u_s + v_s.$$

Since

$$u_s + v_s \leq w,$$

we thus obtain

$$y_k + z_k < w,$$

which shows w to be an upper bound for the sequence $\{y_k + z_k\}$. Since this sequence has least upper bound $y + z$, we have

$$y + z \leq w.$$

The opposite inequality

$$w \leq y + z$$

can be proved in just the same way, and the two together imply (Theorem 1, Section 2) that

$$w = y + z,$$

as desired.

EXERCISE

1. Let $x = y + z$, where y and z are arbitrary real numbers, and let x_k, y_k, z_k denote the k-place decimal truncations of x, y, z, respectively. Prove that

(2) $$x_k = y_k + z_k \text{ or } y_k + z_k + 10^{-k}.$$

The preceding proposition enables us to answer our first question affirmatively.

Proposition 2. If y and z are rational numbers, then

$$y + z = \text{l. u. b. } \{y_k + z_k\}$$

in the ordinary sense of addition.

PROOF: Since y is rational, the infinite sequence

$$\{y, y, y, \ldots\}$$

is a nondecreasing sequence of rational numbers of which y is the least upper bound. Similarly, z is the least upper bound of the infinite nondecreasing sequence

$$\{z, z, z, \ldots\}.$$

By Proposition 1, the least upper bound of the sequence

$$\{y + z, y + z, y + z, \ldots\},$$

which is $y + z$ in the original sense, is equal to

$$\text{l. u. b. } \{y_k + z_k\},$$

or $y + z$ in the new sense. Thus, the new and the old meanings of $+$ here coincide, as asserted.

Proposition 3. Let y be a real number and $\{y_k\}$ any nondecreasing sequence of rational numbers of which y is the least upper bound. Then for any rational number r, we have

$$y + r = \text{l. u. b. } \{y_k + r\}.$$

PROOF: Apply Proposition 1 using the nondecreasing sequence $\{r, r, r, \ldots\}$. We may do so, since r is rational.

We now give proofs of the various algebraic properties of addition in R.

(i) *The additive property of* 0: for any real number y,

$$y + 0 = y.$$

This is an immediate consequence of Proposition 3.

(ii) *Commutativity:* for any real numbers y and z,

$$y + z = z + y.$$

This follows at once from the definition of $y + z$, for no effect is produced when y and z are interchanged.

(iii) *Associativity:* for any real numbers x, y, z, we have

$$x + (y + z) = (x + y) + z.$$

PROOF: Let x_k, y_k, z_k be the k-place truncations of x, y, z, respectively. By definition, $\{x_k + y_k\}$ is a nondecreasing sequence of rational numbers with $x + y$ as least upper bound. In addition, $\{z_k\}$ is a nondecreasing sequence with z as least upper bound, and Proposition 1 tells us that

$$(x + y) + z = \text{l. u. b. } \{(x_k + y_k) + z_k\}.$$

Similarly,

$$x + (y + z) = \text{l. u. b. } \{x_k + (y_k + z_k)\}.$$

Since the associative law already holds for rationals, the right hand sides of the last two equalities are equal, and the assertion is evident.

(iv) *The negative of a real number is its additive inverse:* i.e., for any real number x, $x + (-x) = 0$.

PROOF: If x has the nonterminating decimal representation

$$x = n + .a_1 a_2 a_3 \ldots,$$

then

$$-x = -n - 1 + .a_1' a_2' a_3' \ldots,$$

where

$$a_i + a_i' = 9 \text{ for } i = 1, 2, 3, \ldots.$$

The k-place decimal truncation of x is

$$x_k = n + .a_1 \ldots a_k,$$

and

$$-x = \text{l. u. b. } \{x_k'\},$$

where

$$x_k' = -n - 1 + .a_1' \ldots a_k'.$$

(The x_k' are the decimal truncations of $-x$ unless they are eventually all zero. Recall that decimal truncations pertain to the nonterminating decimal representation of the number in question.) Since

$$x_k + x_k' = -1 + \overbrace{.9 \ldots 9}^{k \text{ places}} = -10^{-k},$$

we have

$$x + (-x) = \text{l. u. b. } \{x_k + x_k'\} = 0.$$

Thus, the assertion is proved.

As with rationals, we define the *difference* $y - z$ to be

$$y - z = y + (-z)$$

for arbitrary real numbers y and z.

(v) *Inequalities and positivity:* for arbitrary real numbers y and z, the difference $y - z$ is positive if and only if $y > z$.

PROOF: Letting $u = y - z$, we have from the previous laws

$$y = z + (y + (-z)) = z + u.$$

We consider separately the cases in which $u = 0$, $u > 0$, and $u < 0$. In the first case, $y = z$. In the second case, an index j exists such that $u_j > 0$ and, in view of (2),

$$y_j \geq z_j + u_j > z_j.$$

(Here, y_j, z_j, u_j denote the j-place decimal truncations of y, z, u, respectively.) By the remark after Definition 1, Section 2, the inequality $y_j > z_j$, which has just been demonstrated, proves that $y > z$. In the third case, we assume that $u < 0$ and thus have

$$z = y + v,$$

where $v = -u > 0$. The second case applies to this, showing that

$z > y$. In sum:

$$y = z \text{ if } y - z = 0,$$
$$y > z \text{ if } y - z > 0,$$
$$y < z \text{ if } y - z < 0.$$

Thus, the assertion is proved.

The statement just proved is a counterpart for real numbers of the definition of $<$ for rationals in Section 5, Chapter 2. Together with our other knowledge of positive and negative real numbers, it enables us to justify all the rules for inequalities, except those that involve multiplication, in the same manner as in Chapter 2. These rules include, in particular, (a), (b), (c), (e), and that of Exercise 8 in the section cited.

As a result, we can, for instance, write the inequalities in Proposition 1, Section 2, in the form

(3) $$0 < y - y_k \leq 10^{-k} \text{ for } k = 1, 2, 3, \ldots,$$

y_k denoting the k-place decimal truncation of an arbitrary real number y.

Similarly, in the case of arbitrary nondecreasing sequences we can express assertion (C) (concerning least upper bounds), Section 2, in the following form.

Proposition 4. Suppose a nondecreasing sequence $\{a_k\}$ of real numbers to have the least upper bound A and that

(4) $$a_k < A \text{ for } k = 1, 2, 3, \ldots.$$

Then given an arbitrary positive number e, a "critical index" N exists such that

$$0 < A - a_k < e \text{ for } k \geq N.$$

PROOF: Let $u < A$. Assertion (C) in Section 2 assures us that an index N exists such that

$$u < a_N \leq A.$$

Since the sequence is nondecreasing and satisfies (4),

$$u < a_N \leq a_k < A \text{ for } k \geq N.$$

Therefore,

$$u < a_k < A \text{ for } k \geq N,$$

which implies

$$0 < A - a_k < A - u \text{ for } k \geq N.$$

Since u is an arbitrary number less than A, we can choose $A - u = e$, and determining N appropriately to this choice proves the proposition.

b. MULTIPLICATION

If y is any real number, we define its product with zero to be:

$$0 \cdot y = y \cdot 0 = 0.$$

Presently we shall define the product of nonzero real numbers y and z. The principal case is that in which y and z are positive:

$$y > 0, \ z > 0.$$

Denote their k-place decimal truncations by y_k and z_k, respectively. These are non-negative rational numbers, and the sequences $\{y_k\}$ and $\{z_k\}$ are nondecreasing with upper bounds. (For instance, $y_k > y_1 + 10^{-1}$ by Proposition 1, Section 1a.) Therefore, the sequence of products $\{y_k z_k\}$ is nondecreasing and has an upper bound. Theorem 2, Section 2, assures us that this sequence has a least upper bound, which we define to be the product yz:

$$yz = \text{l. u. b. } \{y_k z_k\}.$$

We can free this definition of its seeming dependence upon decimal truncations.

Proposition 1. Let y and z be any real numbers and y_k and z_k their respective decimal truncations. If $\{u_k\}$ and $\{v_k\}$ are arbitrary nondecreasing sequences of rational numbers such that

$$y = \text{l. u. b. } \{u_k\}, \ z = \text{l. u. b. } \{v_k\},$$

then

$$\text{l. u. b. } \{u_k v_k\}$$

exists and is equal to yz.

The proof of this proposition is like that of Proposition 1, Subsection a.

With the products of positive real numbers defined, we can now define products of arbitrary nonzero real numbers y and z. Recall that if $y < 0$, then $-y > 0$ (Proposition 2, Section 2). Accordingly, we specify:

$$\text{if } y < 0 \text{ and } z > 0, \text{ then } yz = -((-y)z);$$
$$\text{if } y > 0 \text{ and } z < 0, \text{ then } yz = -(y(-z));$$
$$\text{if } y < 0 \text{ and } z < 0, \text{ then } yz = (-y)(-z).$$

Properties of products analogous to those of sums can be deduced from these definitions by reasoning like that of Subsection a. The results are listed without justification unless new points are involved.

Proposition 2.   If y and z are positive rational numbers, then

$$yz = \text{l. u. b.} \ \{y_k z_k\}$$

in the ordinary sense of multiplication for rationals.

Proposition 3.   If y is a positive real number and r a positive rational number, then

$$ry = \text{l. u. b.} \ \{ry_k\},$$

where $\{y_k\}$ is any nondecreasing sequence of positive rational numbers for which y is the least upper bound.

Multiplication of real numbers has the following algebraic properties.

(i) *The multiplicative property of 1:* for any real number y, $y1 = 1y = y$. (Proposition 3 applies to positive y, and the definitions preceding Proposition 2 must be used if y is negative.)

(ii) *Commutativity:* for any real numbers y and z, $yz = zy$.

(iii) *Associativity:* for any real numbers x, y, z, we have

$$x(yz) = (xy)z.$$

(iv) *The multiplicative inverse:* for any nonzero real number y, a real number x exists such that

$$xy = 1.$$

We call x the *multiplicative inverse,* or the *reciprocal,* of y, writing it as $1/y$, or y^{-1}.

PROOF: Consider first the case in which $y > 0$. In this case, an index N exists such that

$$y_k > 0 \text{ for } k \geq N,$$

y_k denoting the k-place decimal truncation of y. Since the sequence $\{y_k + 10^{-k}\}$ is nonincreasing (see Example 2 of nonincreasing and nondecreasing sequences, Section 2), and since inequalities satisfied by rational positive numbers are obeyed in reverse by their reciprocals (Property (f), Section 5, Chapter 2), the sequence

(1) $\{1/(y_N + 10^{-N}), 1/(y_{N+1} + 10^{-N-1}), 1/(y_{N+2} + 10^{-N-2}), \ldots\}$

is nondecreasing. Furthermore, this sequence has an upper bound, the inequalities $y_k + 10^{-k} > y_N$ (Proposition 1, Section 2) implying

$$1/(y_k + 10^{-k}) < 1/y_N \text{ for } k \geq N.$$

Therefore, the sequence has a least upper bound, which we define to be y^{-1}:

$$y^{-1} = \text{l. u. b. } \{1/(y_N + 10^{-N}), 1/(y_{N+1} + 10^{-N-1}), \ldots\}.$$

For the moment, let us replace the symbol y^{-1} by x. We have to show that $xy = 1$. Proposition 1 permits us to represent y as the least upper bound of the sequence $\{y_N, y_{N+1}, y_{N+2}, \ldots\}$ and thus gives us the formula

(2) $\qquad xy = \text{l. u. b. } \{y_N/(y_N + 10^{-N}), y_{N+1}/(y_{N+1} + 10^{-N-1}),$
$\qquad\qquad y_{N+2}/(y_{N+2} + 10^{-N-2}), \ldots\}.$

We must show that the least upper bound on the right hand side of (2) is equal to 1.

Since $y_k > 0$ for $k \geq N$, we have

$$y_k/(y_k + 10^{-k}) = 1/(1 + 10^{-k}y_k^{-1}) < 1,$$

the middle term arising from the left term by multiplying numerator and denominator by y_k^{-1}. Hence, the least upper bound we are seeking is at most 1:

$$xy \leq 1.$$

To show that this least upper bound is in fact equal to 1, notice that for $k \geq N$

$$y_k/(y_k + 10^{-k}) = 1/(1 + 10^{-k}y_k^{-1}) \geq 1/(1 + 10^{-k}y_N^{-1}),$$

since the denominator in the middle term increases if y_k is replaced by the lesser number y_N. Furthermore, $1/(1 + 10^{-k}y_N^{-1}) > 1 - 10^{-k}y_N^{-1}$, because for any non-negative (rational) number a, we have $1/(1 + a) > 1 - a$. (The last inequality is equivalent to $1 > (1 - a)(1 + a) = 1 - a^2$, which is obviously true.) Consequently,

$$y_k/(y_k + 10^{-k}) > 1 - 10^{-k}y_N^{-1}.$$

As k increases, the quantity $10^{-k}y_N^{-1}$ approaches zero, and therefore no number less than 1 is an upper bound for the sequence (1). Hence, the least upper bound of this sequence is not less than 1: $xy \geq 1$. In view of our previous finding that $xy \leq 1$, we conclude that $xy = 1$, as asserted.

In the case in which $y < 0$, we define

$$y^{-1} = -(-y)^{-1}.$$

Since $-y > 0$, we have in this case

$$yy^{-1} = (-y)(-y)^{-1} = 1.$$

(v) *The distributive law:* if x, y, z are any real numbers, then

$$x(y + z) = xy + xz.$$

PROOF: The principal case is that in which $x > 0$, $y > 0$, $z > 0$, which we now assume. Let x_k, y_k, z_k denote the k-place decimal truncations of x, y, z, respectively. By definition,

$$y + z = \text{l. u. b. } \{y_k + z_k\},$$
$$xy = \text{l. u. b. } \{x_k y_k\},$$
$$xz = \text{l. u. b. } \{x_k z_k\}.$$

Proposition 1 insures that

$$x(y + z) = \text{l. u. b. } \{x_k(y_k + z_k)\}.$$

We first note that $xy + xz$ is an upper bound for the sequence $\{x_k(y_k + z_k)\}$:

(3) $$x_k(y_k + z_k) \leq xy + xz \text{ for } k = 1, 2, 3, \ldots.$$

This follows from the distributive law for rationals and the definitions of xy and xz. In fact,

$$x_k(y_k + z_k) = x_k y_k + x_k z_k \leq xy + xz,$$

since $x_k y_k \leq xy$ and $x_k z_k \leq xz$. Secondly, we shall show that if e is an arbitrary positive number, then an index m exists such that

(4) $$xy + xz - x_m(y_m + z_m) < e.$$

Indeed, by the distributive law for rationals, the commutative and associative laws for reals, and the rules for negatives, we have

(5) $$xy + xz - x_k(y_k + z_k) = xy + xz - x_k y_k - x_k z_k$$
$$= (xy - x_k y_k) + (xz - x_k z_k).$$

Proposition 4 at the end of Subsection a shows that an index m exists such that

$$xy - x_m y_m < e/2 \text{ and } xz - x_k z_k < e/2,$$

and taking $k = m$ in (5) and adding gives us (4). Because of (4), no number u less than $xy + xz$ is an upper bound for the sequence

$\{x_k(y_k + z_k)\}$, since by choosing $e = xy + xz - u$ in (4), we find that $x_m(y_m + z_m) > xy + xz - e = u$. Therefore, $xy + xz$ is the least upper bound for the sequence, which by definition, however, is $x(y + z)$. Thus, $xy + xz = x(y + z)$, and the distributive law in the positive case is proved.

All possible signs of x, y, z must be considered. Seven cases can be distinguished, as follows:

(a) $x = 0$, or $y = 0$, or $z = 0$;
(b) $x > 0$, $y > 0$, $z > 0$;
(c) $x > 0$, $y > 0$, $z < 0$, $y + z \geq 0$;
(d) $x > 0$, $y > 0$, $z < 0$, $y + z < 0$;
(e) $x > 0$, $y < 0$, $z > 0$;
(f) $x > 0$, $y < 0$, $z < 0$;
(g) $x < 0$.

Case (a) is trivial, and we have just done case (b). Case (c) is trivial if $y + z = 0$, and otherwise we proceed as follows. Take arbitrary positive p, q, r, and write the consequent equality

$$p(q + r) = pq + pr$$

in the form

$$p(q + r) - pq = pr.$$

Now set $q + r = u$, $r = u - q$, the preceding equality becoming

$$pu - pq = p(u - q).$$

If we also set $v = -q$, we obtain

$$pu + pv = p(u + v),$$

a relation that holds for any real quantities p, u, v such that

$$p > 0, \; v < 0, \; u > 0, \; u + v > 0.$$

(These conditions express the original restrictions that p, q, r be positive, for $q = -v$ and $r = u - q = u + v$.)

Thus, the distributive law is justified in case (c).

In case (d), we have $-y + (-z) > 0$, and thus by the previous case, with $-z$ and $-y$ now instead of y and z, respectively,

$$x(y + z) = - x(-y + (-z)) = -[x(-y) + x(-z)]$$
$$= -[-xy + (-xz)] = xy + xz.$$

In case (e), interchange y and z to reduce to case (c) or (d). Case (f) is based on the rules for negatives and is reduced to case (b). Case (g) uses the rules for negatives and all the previous cases.

EXERCISES

1. Prove the distributive rule in case (f).
2. Prove the distributive rule in case (g).

4.

On the existence of limits

The effort to extend arithmetic to real numbers is rewarded by a prodigious increase in the scope of limit processes. The notion of limit defined in Section 4, Chapter 14, applies to real numbers as well as rational numbers. Repeating it almost word for word, we say that a real number a is *the limit of a sequence* of real numbers

$$x_k, \quad k = 1, 2, 3, \ldots,$$

i.e., that

$$\lim_{k \to \infty} x_k = a,$$

if the following condition is satisfied: for any positive number e, a critical index N exists for which

$$k > N \Rightarrow |x_k - a| < e.$$

This extension of the concept of limit to real numbers loses none of the general properties of limits previously discussed. It is still true, in particular, that:

(A) For any (real) number a, if $\lim_{k \to \infty} x_k = y$, then

$$\lim_{k \to \infty} a x_k = a y.$$

(B) If $\lim_{k \to \infty} x_k = u$ and $\lim_{k \to \infty} y_k = v$, then

$$\lim_{k \to \infty} (x_k + y_k) = u + v.$$

(C) If $\lim_{k \to \infty} x_k = a$ and $\lim_{k \to \infty} x_k = b$, then $a = b$.

(See Section 4, Chapter 14.) One of the great gains from making this extension is that rational sequences without rational limits—for instance, the sequence of decimal truncations of $\sqrt{2}$ mentioned in Section 1—may have limits in the wider real number domain. Even more significantly, in this wider domain general conditions can be given to tell us whether a sequence of numbers has a limit or not.

As we shall illustrate in the next section, these general conditions are of the utmost utility.

We shall restrict ourselves to a particular condition applying to nondecreasing and nonincreasing sequences.

Convergence Criterion. A nondecreasing sequence of real numbers with an upper bound has a limit; this limit is the least upper bound of the sequence. A nonincreasing sequence of real numbers with a lower bound has a limit, which is the greatest lower bound of the sequence.

PROOF: Theorem 2, Section 2, says that a nondecreasing sequence with an upper bound has a least upper bound, and Proposition 4, Section 3, shows that the least upper bound is also the limit of the sequence.

As our first application of this Convergence Criterion, consider the sequence of values

$$u_n = 1/(1 + 0^2) + 1/(1 + 1^2) + 1/(1 + 2^2) \\ + 1/(1 + 3^2) + \ldots + 1/(1 + n^2)$$

for $n = 1, 2, 3, \ldots$. In Section 5f, Chapter 14, we found the light intensity I_n at a certain point Q owing to $n + 1$ equally bright street lamps spaced uniformly along a straight road. It was given by a formula of the form

$$I_n = cu_n,$$

where c is a constant (i.e., a number independent of n). We established that the brightness at Q will not rise above a certain level, no matter how many new lamps are installed along the street, or in other words that the infinite sequence $\{I_n\}$ has an upper bound. Now we can complete this line of thought by defining the concept of light intensity owing to infinitely many lamps along the street. Since the sequence $\{I_n\}$ is increasing and has an upper bound, our Convergence Criterion assures us that it has a limit. This limit we can reasonably define to be the light intensity at Q that would result from infinitely many lamps along the street. (In an earlier exercise, we essentially suggested that the least upper bound be used in this definition in place of the limit, which we had not yet introduced.)

Given an infinite sequence $\{a_k\}$, let us define

$$s_1 = a_1, \ s_2 = a_1 + a_2, \ s_3 = a_1 + a_2 + a_3,$$

and, in general,

$$s_n = a_1 + \ldots + a_n \text{ for } n = 1, 2, 3, \ldots.$$

We call the s_k *partial sums* of the *infinite series*

(1) $$a_1 + a_2 + a_3 + \ldots.$$

If the limit

$$\lim_{n \to \infty} s_n$$

exists, we call it the sum of the infinite series (1) and say that the series is *convergent*.

As we have just seen, our Convergence Criterion and such algebraic manipulations as were used in Section 5f, Chapter 14, may enable us to prove an infinite series to converge. Another example, which is of great importance in mathematics, is given in the next section. The following exercises require the same sorts of arguments we have already used.

EXERCISES

Show that the following infinite series are convergent.

1. $1/(1 + 100^2) + 1/(1 + 101^2) + 1/(1 + 102^2) + 1/(1 + 103^2) + \ldots$
2. $1/(2 + 1^2) + 1/(2 + 2^2) + 1/(2 + 3^2) + 1/(2 + 4^2) + \ldots$
3. $1/(1 + 1 \cdot 2) + 1/(1 + 2 \cdot 3) + 1/(1 + 3 \cdot 4) + 1/(1 + 4 \cdot 5) + \ldots$
4. $r/1 + r^2/2^2 + r^3/3^2 + r^4/4^2 + r^5/5^2 + \ldots \quad (0 \leq r \leq 1)$.
5. $1 + r + r^2/2 + r^3/3 + r^4/4 + \ldots \quad (0 \leq r \leq 1)$.

5.

The circumference and area of circles

a. INTRODUCTION

A circle of radius R about center O is defined as the set of points in a plane that have distance R from O. What shall be meant by its circumference?† Circumference is a simple concept for polygons, which are made up of straight line segments, but for circles it cannot be defined satisfactorily without some notion of real numbers. In fact, both the circumference and the area‡ of circles raise new issues not apparent in the problems for areas and volumes we have considered hitherto.

Intuitively, periphery and area have always made as good sense for round tables as for square, and at least since Old Babylonian times,§ the principal metric law for circles has been recognized and

---

†"Circumference" and "periphery," the one word from Latin and the other from Greek, are synonyms for the line around. They may also refer to the distance around, which is the exact meaning of "perimeter."

‡By the area of a circle we mean that of the region it encloses.

§See Neugebauer, p. 51 and p. 52. Also see our general remarks in Chapter 4 on the mathematics of the Old Babylonians.

used in calculation. This law, originally established no doubt by measurement with strings, says that the numerical value of the ratio

$$\frac{\text{circumference of a circle}}{\text{diameter of the circle}}$$

is the same for all circles, large and small, no matter what their diameters.† Since the 18th Century, A.D., this ratio has been denoted by the Greek letter π (pronounced "pie"). For a circle with radius R and circumference c, the law thus reads

$$c/2R = \pi.$$

It gives the circumference in terms of the radius as

(1) $$c = 2\,\pi\,R.$$

A companion formula, also going back at least to the Old Babylonians, says that the region enclosed by the circle has area

(2) $$A = \pi\,R^2.$$

The constant π is known today to be irrational and, despite its intuitive meaning, to be hedged about with the subtleties inherent in the concept of limit. An Athenian sophist Antiphon, contemporary with Socrates (about 430 B.C.), tried to fit π into the framework of elementary geometry. To define the area of a circle, he sought to regard the latter as a sort of regular polygon having infinitely many sides and thereby became perhaps the first person in history to stumble into the brambles surrounding limit processes. He had noticed that "by inscribing in a circle a square or an equilateral triangle, and on its sides erecting isosceles triangles with their vertices in the circumference, and on the sides of these triangles erecting new triangles, etc., one could obtain a succession of regular polygons, of which each approaches nearer to the area of the circle than the previous one . . ."‡ He seemed to think that continually doubling the number of sides of an inscribed polygon would lead eventually to a polygon having infinitely many sides that coincided with the circle. Each polygon having an area, this ultimate polygon too would have an area. Thus, the circle would be proved to have an area.

Antiphon's proposal to consider an infinite sequence of inscribed polygons was brilliant but could not be carried out without an understanding of limits. Since limits were to remain an enigma for the next 2400 years, his purpose was foredoomed. In fact, no thinker of antiquity succeeded in defining either the circumference or the area

---

†The diameter of a circle is twice its radius.

‡Cajori, p. 23. See our explanation to follow and also Figure 15-15.

of circles. Amid the rectangles, triangles, octagons, and such of Euclidean geometry, circles stubbornly stood out as round pegs in square holes.

The method of inscribed polygons thus did not enable Antiphon or his successors to *define* the area and circumference of circles, but after suitable modifications and improvements this method did provide ways to *calculate* area and circumference mathematically to any accuracy desired. The calculation problem is essentially that of approximating π. Archimedes (about 240 B.C.) was the first to prevail over its formidable difficulties. He assumed that a straight line exists with length equal to a circle's circumference, sidestepping the deeper question of whether the circumference exists. By means of inscribed polygons he found that $\pi > 223/71$ and by a similar use of circumscribed polygons that $\pi < 22/7$. (Recall that the Greeks did not have decimal numbers.) In a very modern spirit, he thus located π within the narrow interval: $223/71 < \pi < 22/7$. About 150 A.D., Claudius Ptolemy of Alexandria developed the closer approximation $377/120$, which to five decimal places is

$$3.1416;$$

for many practical purposes, this value is excellent. Greater and greater accuracy was achieved by a succession of later writers,[†] all being surpassed in 1961 by Daniel Shanks and J. W. Wrench of the David Taylor Model Basin Calculating Laboratory, who by means of an electronic computer (the IBM 7090) worked out π correctly to 100,000 decimal places. Shanks and Wrench in fact made the calculation by two independent methods, checked each result against the other, and thus showed incidentally that an electronic computer can run eight hours without a mistake.

The remainder of this section is devoted to a careful treatment of area and circumference of circles essentially by Archimedes' method modernized.

The trigonometric formulas of Chapter 7, Section 5 (particularly Section 5d on the double-angle formulas), will enter. We shall also refer to the Convergence Criterion of the last section.

b . CRITERIA FOR DEFINING THE AREA AND THE PERIMETER
  OF A CIRCLE

Like Archimedes, we base our discussion of circles upon properties of regular inscribed and circumscribed polygons. Some definitions come first.

The *perimeter* of a closed polygon g is the sum of the lengths of its sides. The *area* of the polygon is the area of the region enclosed.

—————————

†Eves, pp. 91-97.

We denote the perimeter of g by $p(g)$ and the area of g by $A(g)$. We shall only consider "regular" polygons, a closed polygon being *regular* if its sides are equal and its angles (the angles between contiguous sides) are equal. A polygon is *inscribed in* a circle C if C encloses the polygon except for its vertices, which are on C. A polygon G is *circumscribed about* C if its sides are tangent to C.

Figure 15-10 shows inscribed and circumscribed regular polygons of 4 and 12 sides.

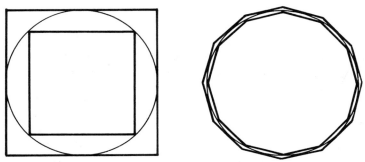

FIGURE 15-10   *Inscribed and circumscribed regular polygons.*

If a regular polygon g is inscribed in a circle of center O — or circumscribed about it — we also call O the *center of g*. If AB is a side of g (see Figure 15-11), we call $\angle AOB$ a *central angle* for g, and $\triangle AOB$ a *central triangle*.

FIGURE 15-11   *Center, central angle, and central triangle of regular polygon.*

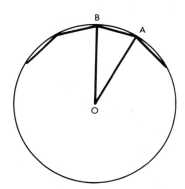

EXERCISE

1. Given a regular polygon g, prove that a circle C exists such that g is inscribed in C. Prove also that a circle C_1 exists such that g is circumscribed about C_1. HINT: We shall not discuss the case in which g is a triangle. Otherwise, let A, B, C, D denote consecutive vertices of g (see Figure 15-12).

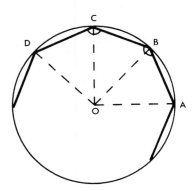

FIGURE 15-12   *The center of a regular polygon.*

Bisect the angles at B and C, and let the bisectors intersect at O. Then triangles DOC, COB, and BOA are all equal, and OD and OA bisect the angles at D and A, respectively.

Consider a circle C of radius R. The problem of defining the area $A(C)$ of the region enclosed by C is similar in principle to previous area problems discussed. If g is any closed polygon inscribed in C and G is any closed polygon circumscribed about C, it is reasonable to require $A(C)$ to be a number satisfying the condition

$$A(g) < A(C) < A(G).$$

But technically a more convenient—and just as reasonable—condition is obtained if we limit g and G to regular polygons with k sides, where k is required to be a power of 2: $k = 4, 8, 16, 32, \ldots$, i.e., $k = 2^n$ with $n = 2, 3, 4, \ldots$. If g_k and G_k denote k-sided inscribed and circumscribed regular polygons, respectively, the conditions upon $A(C)$ we propose to use thus read

(1) $A(g_{2^n}) < A(C) < A(G_{2^n})$ for $n = 2, 3, 4, \ldots$.

These are in accord with the Guiding Principle of Section 6, Chapter 14. While previously we could always carry out explicitly the limit processes the Guiding Principle suggests, here, however, we cannot. The limits of the left and right members of (1) as n becomes infinite cannot be found by an algebraic process. Furthermore, no algebraic formula describes them. To be assured that these limits exist (and represent the same number), we must use more abstract tools than algebraic calculation, and indeed we shall employ the Convergence Criterion of Section 5. For this purpose, we shall show that $\{A(g_{2^n})\}$ is an increasing sequence with an upper bound and $\{A(G_{2^n})\}$ a decreasing sequence (with lower bound zero) and that the difference $A(G_{2^n}) - A(g_{2^n})$ tends toward zero as n becomes infinite. The existence of a real number satisfying the conditions—inequalities (1)—imposed upon $A(C)$ will follow.

While studying inscribed and circumscribed polygons, as this program requires, we shall find that the rules for areas we mentioned have counterparts pertaining to perimeters. Accordingly, it is feasible in defining the perimeter $p(C)$ of the circle C to impose the conditions

(2) $$p(g_{2n}) < p(C) < p(G_{2n}) \text{ for } n = 2, 3, 4, \ldots,$$

which are intrinsically reasonable and completely analogous to (1).

C. PERIMETER AND AREA OF REGULAR INSCRIBED AND CIRCUMSCRIBED POLYGONS

The information we need about perimeter and area of polygons is summarized in Theorems 1, 2, 3. Leading up to them is a succession of more obvious facts formulated as propositions; we leave the proof of some of these to the reader.

Proposition 1. A square (a 4-sided regular polygon) can be circumscribed about any circle; a square can be inscribed in any circle. The circumscribed square, in particular, has perimeter $8R$ and area $4R^2$, where R denotes the radius of the circle. (See Figure 15-13.)

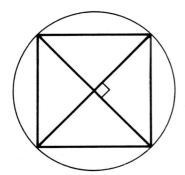 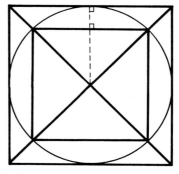

FIGURE 15-13 *Inscribed and circumscribed squares.*

Proposition 2. The central triangles of a regular k-sided polygon (inscribed in a circle, or circumscribed about it) are all equal. The central angles are equal to $360°/k$. (See Figure 15-14.) For each $k = 3, 4, 5, \ldots$, all k-sided regular polygons inscribed in a given circle are equal,† and all k-sided regular polygons circumscribed about the circle are equal.

---

†We call two polygons *equal* if their measurements are the same, i.e., if the sides of one polygon have a one-to-one correspondence with the sides of the other polygon under which (1) corresponding sides are equal, (2) a pair of sides of one polygon intersect if and only if the corresponding pair in the other polygon intersect, and (3) the angles between corresponding pairs of sides are the same.

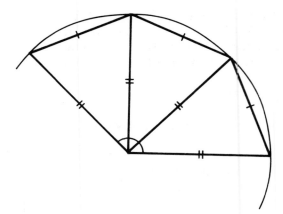

FIGURE 15-14   *Central angles of a regular polygon inscribed in a circle.*

Proposition 3.   If a k-sided regular polygon inscribed in a circle is given, we can construct a $2k$-sided regular polygon inscribed in the same circle. We can also construct a k-sided regular polygon circumscribed about the circle. (See Figures 15-15 and 15-16.)

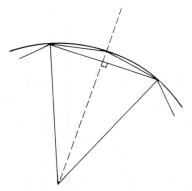

FIGURE   15-15   *Doubling   the number of sides of a regular polygon inscribed in a circle.*

FIGURE 15-16   *Circumscribing a regular polygon having the same number of sides as a given inscribed polygon.*

Proposition 4a.   The area of a regular polygon G circumscribed about a circle of radius R is

$$A(G) = Rp(G)/2.$$

PROOF: Supposing G to have k sides of individual length s, we have

$$p(G) = ks.$$

The area enclosed by G is k times the area of any central triangle, which is $Rs/2$ (see Figure 15-17): hence,

$$A(G) = kRs/2$$
$$= R(ks)/2$$
$$= Rp(G)/2.$$

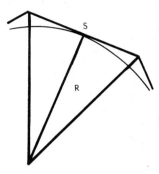

FIGURE 15-17 *A central triangle in a circum-scribed regular polygon.*

Proposition 4b. The area of a k-sided regular polygon g inscribed in a circle of radius R is

$$A(g) = (1/2)Rp(g) \cos (180°/k).$$

PROOF: Denote by h the distance from the center of the circle to a side of g. In Figure 15-18, we see that

$$h/R = \cos B,$$

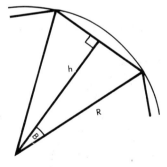

FIGURE 15-18 *A central triangle of an inscribed regular polygon.*

where B is half the central angle, so that $B = 180°/k$. Analogously to the formula for $A(G)$ in Proposition 4a, we have

$$A(g) = hp(g)/2,$$

and substituting $h = R \cos B$ gives the formula claimed.

Proposition 5a. For a k-sided regular polygon G circumscribed about a circle of radius R,

$$p(G) = 2kR \tan (180°/k), \quad A(G) = kR^2 \tan (180°/k).$$

PROOF: Setting $B = 180°/k$, we have $(s\ 2)/R = \tan B$, or

$$s = 2R \tan B.$$

(See Figure 15-19.) Hence $p(G) = ks = 2kR \tan B$, and $A(G) = Rp(G)/2 = R^2 k \tan B$, the asserted formulas.

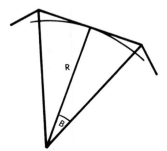

FIGURE 15-19 A central triangle of a circumscribed regular polygon relabeled.

Proposition 5b.   For a k-sided regular polygon g inscribed in a circle of radius R,

$$p(g) = 2kR \sin (180°/k),\ A(g) = (1/2)kR^2 \sin (360°/k).$$

PROOF: Again setting $B = 180°/k$, we have $(s/2)/R = \sin B$,

or

$$s = 2R \sin B.$$

(See Figure 15-20.) Hence, $p(g) = ks = 2kR \sin B$, one of the two

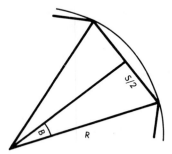

FIGURE 15-20 A central triangle of an inscribed regular polygon relabeled.

relationships claimed. Using this result in the formula for $A(g)$ in Proposition 4b gives

$$A(g) = (1/2)Rp(g) \cos B = kR^2 \sin B \cos B.$$

By a "double angle" formula (Chapter 7, Section 5d), we have

$$\sin 2B = 2 \sin B \cos B.$$

Hence,

$$A(g) = kR^2 \sin B \cos B = (1/2) kR^2 \sin 2B,$$

as stated.

Theorem 1.   Let g and g' be regular polygons inscribed in a given circle, g having k sides and g' having $2k$ sides. Then

$$p(g) < p(g') \text{ and } A(g) < A(g').$$

In words: If the number of sides of an inscribed regular polygon is doubled, both perimeter and area increase.

PROOF: As before, set $B = 180°/k$, and let R be the radius of the circle. By Proposition 5b,

$$p(g) = 2kR \sin B.$$

Since g' has twice as many sides as g and half the central angle, we have similarly

$$p(g') = 4kR \sin (B/2).$$

To compare these expressions, we again use a double angle formula of Chapter 7, Section 5d. It says, respecting B and $B/2$, that

$$\sin B = 2 \sin (B/2) \cos (B/2).$$

Since $\cos (B/2)$ is positive and less than 1, it follows that

$$\sin B < 2 \sin (B/2).$$

Hence,

$$p(g) = 2kR \sin B < 4kR \sin (B/2),$$

while the last expression equals $p(g')$. We thus have $p(g) < p(g')$, as asserted. The second inequality stated is proved in an exactly similar way from the area formula in Proposition 5b.

Theorem 2.   Let G and G' be regular polygons circumscribed about a given circle, G having k sides and G' having $2k$ sides. Then

$$p(G') < p(G) \text{ and } A(G') < A(G).$$

In words: If the number of sides of a circumscribed regular polygon is doubled, both perimeter and area decrease.

PROOF: Again set $B = 180°/k$, and let R denote the radius of the circle. By Proposition 5a,

$$p(G) = 2kR \tan B$$

and

$$p(G') = 4kR \tan (B/2),$$

G' having twice as many sides as G and half the central angle. To compare these expressions, both double angle formulas

$$\sin B = 2 \sin (B/2) \cos (B/2)$$
$$\cos B = \cos^2(B/2) - \sin^2(B/2)$$

are used (Chapter 7, Section 5d). They imply:

$$\tan B = \frac{\sin B}{\cos B} = \frac{2 \sin (B/2) \cos (B/2)}{\cos^2 (B/2) - \sin^2 (B/2)}$$

$$> \frac{2 \sin (B/2) \cos (B/2)}{\cos^2 (B/2)}$$

$$= \frac{2 \sin (B/2)}{\cos (B/2)} = 2 \tan (B/2).$$

This result immediately gives

$$p(G) = 2kR \tan B > 4kR \tan (B/2) = p(G'),$$

the inequality stated for the perimeter. The second inequality, for areas, follows similarly.

In the next theorem, two geometrical relations enter that we have not used so far. The first is expressed by the inequality

$$\cos x > \cos y \text{ if } 0° < x < y < 90°$$

and is obvious from Figure 15-21, depicting a circle of unit radius in which

$$\cos x = ON, \cos y = OM.$$

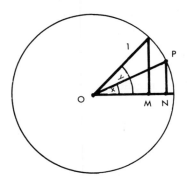

FIGURE 15-21   The cosines of acute angles.

Because of this inequality, we have

(1) $$\cos x > 1/2 \text{ if } 0° < x < 60°,$$

since $\cos 60° = 1/2$. The second relation is

(2) $$\lim_{x \to 0} \sin x = 0,$$

saying analytically that as the acute angle x tends towards 0, the segment NP representing $\sin x$ contracts more and more completely to a point. (This was mentioned in Chapter 2, Section 5a.)

Theorem 3. Let g and G be regular k-sided polygons, with g inscribed in a given circle and G circumscribed about the circle. Then

(3) $$p(g) < p(G), A(g) < A(G)$$
$$\text{for } k = 3, 4, 5, \ldots.$$

Furthermore, the differences

(4) $$p(G) - p(g) \text{ and } A(G) - A(g)$$

(which depend upon k) tend toward zero as k becomes infinite.

PROOF: By Propositions 5a and 5b we have

$$p(G) = 2kR \tan B, \; p(g) = 2kR \sin B,$$
$$A(G) = kR^2 \tan B, \; A(g) = (1/2)kR^2 \sin 2B,$$

where R denotes the radius of the circle and $B = 180°/k$. Hence, in particular,

$$p(G) - p(g) = 2kR \tan B - 2kR \sin B$$
$$= 2kR(\tan B - \sin B).$$

Since $\tan B = (\sin B)/(\cos B)$, we have

$$\tan B - \sin B = \sin B/\cos B - \sin B$$
$$= (\sin B) (1/\cos B - 1)$$
$$= (\sin B) (1 - \cos B)/\cos B.$$

Since $\sin B$ and $\cos B$ are positive and $\cos B < 1$ for any acute angle B, the last expression is positive, and we thus have

$$p(G) - p(g) > 0,$$

or $p(g) < p(G)$, as asserted. From inequality (1) we also have for $0° < B < 60°$,

$$\tan B - \sin B = (\sin B) (1 - \cos B)/\cos B < \sin B/(1/2),$$

which implies that

(5) $p(G) - p(g) = 2kR(\tan B - \sin B) < 4kR \sin B$
                    if $0° < B < 60°$.

Since $B = 180°/k$, B approaches zero as k becomes infinite, and relation (2) implies that $\sin B$ approaches 0. By inequality (5) the same must be true of $p(G) - p(g)$, which was one of our contentions.
    The assertions concerning area arise from considering

$$A(G) - A(g) = kR^2 \tan B - (1/2)kR^2 \sin 2B$$
$$= kR^2 [\tan B - (1/2) \sin 2B].$$

Making the substitutions $\tan B = (\sin B)/(\cos B)$ and $\sin 2B = 2 \sin B \cos B$, we have

$$\tan B - (1/2) \sin 2B = \sin B/\cos B - \sin B \cos B$$
$$= (\sin B) (1/\cos B - \cos B)$$
$$= (\sin B) (1 - \cos^2 B)/\cos B$$
$$= (\sin B)^3/\cos B,$$

since $1 - \cos^2 B = \sin^2 B$.[†] The last expression being positive and, for $0 < B < 60°$, less than $(\sin B)^3/(1/2) = 2(\sin B)^3$, we conclude that

$$A(G) - A(g) > 0$$

and

$$A(G) - A(g) < 2kR^2 (\sin B)^3 \text{ for } 0 < B < 60°.$$

Consequently $A(G) - A(g)$ approaches zero as k becomes infinite, our last contention.

d. A LIMIT PROCEDURE TO ARRIVE AT π

    Considering a circle C of radius R, let g_k denote a regular polygon of k sides inscribed in C and G_k a regular polygon of k sides circumscribed about C. Starting, say, with squares g_4 and G_4, we can construct infinite sequences

$$g_4, g_8, g_{16}, g_{32}, \ldots, G_4, G_8, G_{16}, G_{32}, \ldots$$

of inscribed and circumscribed regular polygons having 2^n sides for $n = 2, 3, 4, \ldots$. Theorem 1 tells us that the perimeters and areas of the inscribed polygons increase as the number of sides double:

$$p(g_4) < p(g_8) < p(g_{16}) < \ldots,$$
$$A(g_4) < A(g_8) < A(g_{16}) < \ldots.$$

---

†Conventionally, $\cos^2 x$ abbreviates $(\cos x)^2$, and so forth.

By Theorem 2, the perimeters and areas of the circumscribed polygons decrease as the number of sides double:

$$p(G_4) > p(G_8) > p(G_{16}) > \dots,$$
$$A(G_4) > A(G_8) > A(G_{16}) > \dots.$$

Thus, in particular,

$$p(G_{2^n}) < p(G_4) = 8R, A(G_{2^n}) < A(G_4) = 4R^2 \text{ for } n = 3, 4, 5, \dots.$$

(see Proposition 1 in Subsection c). Since by Theorem 3

$$p(g_{2^n}) < p(G_{2^n}), \quad A(g_{2^n}) < A(G_{2^n}),$$

we deduce that

$$p(g_{2^n}) < 8R, \quad A(g_{2^n}) < 4R^2.$$

Hence, the increasing sequences $\{p(g_{2^n})\}$ and $\{A(g_{2^n})\}$ have upper bounds. By the Convergence Criterion of Section 5, these sequences have limits.

We need apply this result only in the case in which $R = 1$, in which case we use the notation p_k and A_k in place of $p(g_k)$ and $A(g_k)$, respectively. From what we have just established, the sequences $\{p_{2^n}\}$ and $\{A_{2^n}\}$ have limits as n becomes infinite. By convention, the first limit is called 2π:

(1) $$2\pi = \lim_{n \to \infty} p_{2^n}.$$

By Proposition 5b of the previous subsection, $p_k = 2k \sin(180°/k)$, and for an inscribed polygon in a circle of arbitrary radius R,

$$p(g_k) = Rp_k.$$

Hence, from (1),

(2) $$\lim_{n \to \infty} p(g_{2^n}) = \lim_{n \to \infty} Rp_{2^n}$$

$$= R \lim_{n \to \infty} p_{2^n} = 2\pi R.$$

Since the limit $2\pi R$ also is the least upper bound of the sequence $\{p(g_k)\}$, we have

(3) $$p(g_{2^n}) < 2\pi R \text{ for } n = 2, 3, 4, \dots.$$

Proposition 5a of the preceding subsection shows that

$$p(G_k) = 2kR \tan(180°/k) = \frac{2kR \sin(180°/k)}{\cos(180°/k)} = Rp_k/\cos(180°/k);$$

hence,

$$p(G_{2^n}) = Rp_{2^n}/\cos B_n,$$

where $B_n = 180°/2^n$. As n becomes infinite, B_n approaches 0, and therefore (see Figure 15-21 or Chapter 2, Section 5a)

$$\lim_{n \to \infty} \cos B_n = 1.$$

Consequently,

$$\lim_{n \to \infty} p(G_{2^n}) = \lim Rp_{2^n}/\cos B_n = 2\pi R.$$

Since this limit is the greatest lower bound for the sequence $\{p(G_{2^n})\}$, we also have

(4) $2\pi R < p(G_{2^n})$ for $n = 2, 3, 4, \ldots$.

Conditions (3) and (4) show that the number $2\pi R$ satisfies all restrictions originally placed upon $p(C)$ (inequalities (2), Subsection b). No other number satisfies all these restrictions. Hence, we can define and must define the perimeter of the circle C as

$$p(C) = 2\pi R.$$

The discussion of areas is parallel to that of perimeters just concluded. The formulas in Propositions 5a and 5b of the previous subsection tell us that

$$\begin{aligned}
A(g_k) &= (1/2)R^2k \sin(360°/k) \\
&= (1/2)R^2k \, 2 \sin(180°/k) \cos(180°/k) \\
&= (1/2)R^2p_k \cos(180°/k)
\end{aligned}$$

and

$$\begin{aligned}
A(G_k) &= R^2k \tan(180°/k) \\
&= R^2k \sin(180°/k)/\cos(180°/k) \\
&= (1/2)R^2p_k/\cos(180°/k).
\end{aligned}$$

As n becomes infinite, the sequence $\{p_{2^n}\}$ has the limit 2π and the sequence $\{\cos(180°/2^n)\}$ the limit 1. Hence, both sequences $\{A(g_{2^n})\}$ and $\{A(G_{2^n})\}$ have the limit πR^2. This limit is the least upper bound of the first sequence and the greatest lower bound of the second and thus satisfies the requirements (inequalities (1), Subsection b) imposed upon the number $A(C)$ and, moreover, is the only number to do so. Therefore, we are forced to define:

$$A(C) = \pi R^2.$$

EXERCISES

1. Indicate in detail how we can define the length of a circular arc between two given points. (See Figure 15-22).

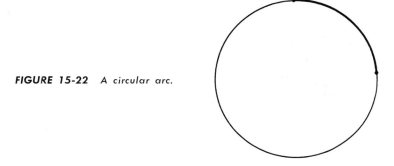

FIGURE 15-22   A circular arc.

2. The processes we used with polygons of 4 sides, 8 sides, 16 sides, and so forth can also be applied to polygons, for instance, of 3 sides, 6 sides, 12 sides, and so forth. (Archimedes himself employed the latter sequence of polygons, obtaining his upper and lower estimates of π from circumscribed and inscribed 96-sided regular polygons, respectively.) In what details must our procedures be modified if the second sequence of polygons is used instead of the first? Is it clear that the same value of π will be obtained?

6.

The volumes of cylinders, cones, and spheres

Boxes of unit cross section provide our standard of volume. (See the remark on volumes in Chapter 7, Section 3.) By definition, the volume of a 1 by 1 by c box is c. If a three-dimensional body can be cut up into parts that can be re-arranged to fill a box of unit cross section, then the volume of the body is defined to be that of the box. We showed, in particular, that an a by b by c box has volume abc. Another way to say this is that the volume of a right prism with *rectangular* base is equal to the area of the base multiplied by the height of the prism. It is also true that the volume of a right prism with *triangular* base is equal to the area of the base multiplied by the height of the prism. (The argument is similar to that for the box and involves dissecting the base triangle into pieces that can be re-arranged as a box.) If a body consists of a finite number of nonoverlapping parts each of which has an individual volume, then the volume of the body is the sum of the volumes of the parts. This is the basis of the following fact.

Proposition 1.   The volume of a right prism the base of which is the region enclosed by a regular polygon is equal to the area of the base multiplied by the height of the prism.

PROOF: A k-sided regular polygon g can be cut up into k equal triangles. Correspondingly, the prism over g (i.e., the prism with the region enclosed by g as base) is the union of k equal, nonoverlapping prisms, each of which has one of these triangles as its base. The volume of one of these constituent prisms is

$$hT,$$

where T is the area of one of the k triangles, and h is the height of the prism over it. Hence, the volume of the original prism is

$$k \cdot hT,$$

which is equal to $h \cdot kT$, the product of its height by the area of its base, as claimed.

We now introduce right circular cylinders. Let C denote a circle, and let D denote the region C encloses. At each point of C, construct the line perpendicular (in three-dimensional space) to the plane of C; the totality of these lines forms an infinitely long straight pipe or tube. This tube intersects any plane parallel to the plane of C in a circle C' having the same radius as C; let D' denote the portion of the plane enclosed by C'. Then the figure consisting of D and D' and the portion of the tube between we call a *right circular cylinder* (see Figure 15-24). D and D' are the *faces* of the cylinder, and either may be called its *base*. The perpendicular distance between the faces is the *height* of the cylinder. By the volume of the cylinder we mean the volume of the three-dimensional region enclosed.

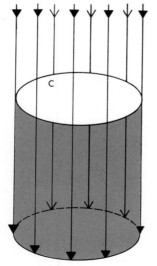

FIGURE 15-23   *Generation of a cylinder.*

FIGURE 15-24   *A right circular cylinder.*

The reader may use Proposition 1 and the Principle for Defining Volumes (Chapter 14, Section 7) to find the volume of a right circular cylinder. He will discover the following proposition.

Proposition 2. The volume of a right circular cylinder K is equal to the area of the base multiplied by the height h of the cylinder:

$$V(K) = \pi r^2 h,$$

r denoting the radius of the base and $V(K)$ the volume of K.

HINT: Consider prisms the bases of which are regular polygons inscribed in and circumscribed about the base of the cylinder.

Right circular cones are defined as follows. Consider a circle C of radius r and center A; let D denote the plane region enclosed by C. Let O be a point outside the plane of C such that OA is perpendicular to this plane and

$$OA = h.$$

(See Figure 15-25.) At each point of C, construct the half-line, or ray, issuing from O and passing through this point. The totality of

FIGURE 15-25 *A right circular cone.*

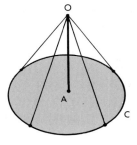

these rays form a surface, which we describe as *conical*. Then the figure consisting of D and the portion of the conical surface between O and D we call a *right circular cone*. D is called the *base* of the cone, the point O the *vertex* of the cone, the line OA the *axis* of the cone, and the distance OA the *height* of the cone. By the volume of the cone, we mean the volume of the three-dimensional region it encloses. The terms "vertex," "base," "axis," and "height" may be used with reference to this region with the same meanings as before.

We shall now show how Proposition 2 and our Principle for Defining Volumes (Chapter 14, Section 7) lead us to the well known formula for the volume of a cone.

Proposition 3. The volume of a right circular cone is one-third the product of its height by its base.

The proof depends upon the following geometrical observation.

Remark: Consider a plane parallel to the base of a right circular cone with vertex O. (See Figure 15-26.) Let B denote the point at

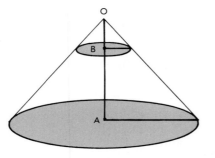

FIGURE 15-26 A cone cut by a plane parallel to its base.

which this plane cuts the axis of the cone, and suppose B to be distinct from the vertex O. Then considerations of similar triangles imply that the plane and the cone intersect in a circle with center B and radius equal to $(r/h) \cdot OB$, h being the height of the cone and r the radius of its base. The area enclosed by this circle is

$$\pi(r/h)^2 \, (OB)^2.$$

PROOF OF PROPOSITION 3. For simplicity, we shall assume $r = h$, leaving to the reader the slight changes in formulas required in the general case. The same kind of procedure we employed for pyramids will be used again (see Chapter 14, Section 7). As before, let O denote the vertex of the given cone and A the point in which the axis intersects the base. Impress a scale upon the axis reading zero at O and h at A. (Thus, $h = OA$.) Subdivide the straight line segment OA by $n + 1$ points (including O and A) into n equal intervals. The length of each interval is h/n, and the $n + 1$ points of subdivision are those with the scale coordinates

$$0, \; h/n, \; 2h/n, \; 3h/n, \; \ldots, \; (n-1)h/n, \; h.$$

Through each of these points of subdivision of the axis, we consider the plane parallel to the cone's base, denoting by Z_k the plane passing through the point with the coordinate hk/n. Z_0 intersects the cone just in its vertex O, and Z_n is the plane of the base. For $0 < k < n$, the Remark shows that Z_k cuts the cone in a circle of radius kh/n. The area of the circle is

(1) $$\pi h^2 k^2 / n^2.$$

The $n + 1$ planes $Z_0, Z_1, \ldots, Z_n$ divide the cone into n sections of uniform thickness h/n. For $k = 1, 2, \ldots, n$, the conical surface and the planes Z_k and Z_{k-1} enclose a solid region we denote by R_k. The region T_k enclosed by the right circular cylinder of height h/n with the same lower face as R_k contains R_k:

$$T_k \supset R_k.$$

(See Figures 15-27 and 15-28.)

FIGURE 15-27 *Sections of a cone and cylinder on the same base.*

FIGURE 15-28 Cone approximated outside by cylindrical sections.

The region S_k enclosed by the right circular cylinder of height h/n with the same upper face as R_k is contained in $R_k : S_k \subset R_k$. In view of this and the previous inclusion, we have

$$S_k \subset R_k \subset T_k.$$

According to (1), the lower face of R_k has the area $\pi h^2 k^2/n^2$ and the area of the upper face is $\pi h^2 (k-1)^2/n^2$. Since T_k has height h/n and the same lower face as R_k,

$$V(T_k) = (h/n)\,(\pi h^2 k^2/n^2) = \pi h^3 k^2/n^3.$$

Since S_k has height h/n and the same upper face as R_k,

$$V(S_k) = (h/n)\,[\pi\,h^2\,(k-1)^2/n^2] = \pi\,h^3\,(k-1)^2/n^3.$$

Let R denote the region enclosed by the cone, S the union of the S_k $(k = 1, 2, \ldots, n)$, and T the union of the T_k. We have

$$S \subset R \subset T.$$

Hence, our Principle for Defining Volumes (Chapter 14, Section 7) requires $V(R)$, the volume of R, to be such that

(2) $$V(S) < V(R) < V(T).$$

Since S is built of the S_k, $k = 1, 2, \ldots, n$, which do not overlap, we have

$$
\begin{aligned}
V(S) &= V(S_1) + V(S_2) + \ldots + V(S_n) \\
&= (\pi h^3/n^3)0^2 + (\pi h^3/n^3)1^2 + \ldots + (\pi h^3/n^3)\,(n-1)^2 \\
&= (\pi h^3/n^3)\,[0^2 + 1^2 + \ldots + (n-1)^2].
\end{aligned}
$$

Similarly,

$$V(T) = V(T_1) + V(T_2) + \ldots V(T_n)$$
$$= (\pi h^3/n^3)1^2 + (\pi h^3/n^3)2^2 + \ldots + (\pi h^3/n^3)n^2$$
$$= (\pi h^3/n^3)(1^2 + 2^2 + \ldots + n^2).$$

As before letting

$$p_k = 1^2 + 2^2 + \ldots + k^2,$$

we thus can write

$$V(S) = \pi h^3 p_{n-1}/n^3, \; V(T) = \pi h^3 p_n/n^3.$$

Substituting in (2) gives

$$\pi h^3(p_{n-1}/n^3) < V(R) < \pi h^3(p_n/n^3),$$

encaging inequalities that hold for every positive integer n. From these the argument at the end of Section 7, Chapter 14, shows that

$$V(R) = \pi h^3/3 = (1/3) \times \text{height} \times \text{area of base},$$

as contended.

Finally, we turn to spheres. By *the sphere with center O and radius r* we mean the set of points in three-dimensional space that have the distance r from O. Any straight line through O intersects the sphere in two points, say P and P', at the distance r from O; the segment PP' is called a *diameter* of the sphere, and the points P and P' are called *diametrically opposite* points of the sphere. (See Figure 15-29.) Any plane intersects the sphere in a circle, a single point, or

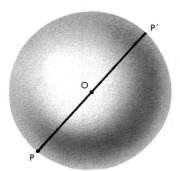

FIGURE 15-29 *A diameter of a sphere.*

the empty set. A plane through O intersects the sphere in a circle of radius r, called a *great circle*. (Figure 15-30). Such a plane divides the sphere into "hemispheres," one on either side of the plane. Diametrically opposite points not in the dividing plane belong to different hemispheres. (Postulate 5, Section 2, Chapter 9).

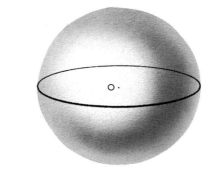

FIGURE 15-30   *A great circle.*

Proposition 4.   The volume of the region enclosed by a sphere of radius *r* is

$$(4/3)\,\pi r^3.$$

PROOF: Divide the sphere into hemispheres by any plane through the center *O*. Letting *R* denote the region enclosed by a hemisphere and the dividing plane, we shall show that

$$V(R) = (2/3)\pi r^3,$$

the formula for the sphere following from this.

Construct a line through *O* perpendicular to the dividing plane (Figure 15-31). This line intersects the hemisphere considered in a

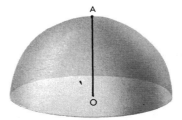

FIGURE 15-31   *Pole and axis of a hemisphere.*

single point *A*, which we call the *pole* of the hemisphere. We call the line segment *OA* the *axis* of the hemisphere and the portion of the dividing plane contained within the sphere the *base* of the hemisphere. Impress a scale upon the axis reading zero at *O* and *r* at *A*. (Thus, *r* = *OA*.) Subdivide the straight line segment *OA* by *n* + 1 points (including *O* and *A*) into *n* equal intervals (Figure 15-32).

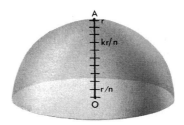

FIGURE   15-32   *Subdivision   of   axis   of hemisphere.*

The length of each interval is r/n, and the $n+1$ points of subdivision are those with the scale coordinates

$$O, r/n, 2r/n, 3r/n, \ldots, (n-1)r/n, r.$$

Through each of these points of subdivision of the axis, consider the plane parallel to the hemisphere's base, denoting by Z_k the plane passing through the point with the coordinate kr/n. Thus, Z_0 is the dividing plane (the plane of the base), and Z_n intersects the sphere in the single point A. For $0 \le k < n$, Z_k cuts the sphere in a circle having a radius we shall denote by s_k. Pythagoras's theorem (see Figure 15-33) shows that

$$s_k^2 + (kr/n)^2 = r^2$$

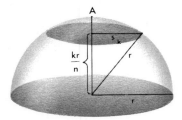

FIGURE 15-33 Intersection of a hemisphere with a plane parallel to its base.

and thus that

$$s_k^2 = r^2 - k^2 r^2/n^2 = r^2(1 - k^2/n^2).$$

The area enclosed by the circle is

$$\pi s_k^2 = \pi r^2(1 - k^2/n^2).$$

The $n+1$ planes $Z_0, Z_1, \ldots, Z_n$ divide R into n portions of uniform thickness r/n. Denote by R_k the portion between Z_k and Z_{k-1}. According to the last formula, the lower face of R_k has the area

$$\pi r^2[1 - (k-1)^2/n^2],$$

and the area of the upper face of R_k is

$$\pi r^2(1 - k^2/n^2).$$

The right circular cylinder of height r/n that has the same lower face as R_k encloses a region of space we denote by T_k; it includes R_k, i.e.,

$$T_k \supset R_k.$$

The right circular cylinder of height r/n that has the same upper face as R_k encloses a region of space we denote by S_k; it is included in R_k: $S_k \subset R_k$. In sum,

$$S_k \subset R_k \subset T_k.$$

Since T_k has height r/n and the same lower face as R_k,

$$V(T_k) = (r/n)\pi r^2[1 - (k-1)^2/n^2] = (\pi r^3/n)[1 - (k-1)^2/n^2].$$

Since S_k has height r/n and the same upper face as R_k,

$$V(S_k) = (r/n)\pi r^2(1 - k^2/n^2) = (\pi r^3/n)(1 - k^2/n^2).$$

Let S denote the union of the S_k and T the union of the T_k ($k = 1$, $2, \ldots, n$). Then

$$S \subset R \subset T,$$

and our Principle for Defining Volumes requires $V(R)$ to be such that

(3) $$V(S) < V(R) < V(T).$$

Since S is the union of the S_k, which do not overlap, we have

$$
\begin{aligned}
V(S) &= V(S_1) + V(S_2) + \ldots + V(S_n) \\
&= (\pi r^3/n)(1 - 1^2/n^2) + (\pi r^3/n)(1 - 2^2/n^2) + \ldots \\
&\quad + (\pi r^3/n)(1 - n^2/n^2) \\
&= (\pi r^3/n)[(1 - 1^2/n^2) + (1 - 2^2/n^2) + \ldots \\
&\quad + (1 - n^2/n^2)] \\
&= (\pi r^3/n)[1 + \underbrace{1 + \ldots + 1}_{n \text{ terms}} \\
&\quad - (1/n^2)(1^2 + 2^2 + \ldots + n^2)] \\
&= (\pi r^3/n)[n - p_n/n^2] \\
&= \pi r^3(1 - p_n/n^3),
\end{aligned}
$$

where again we have used the notation

$$p_k = 1^2 + 2^2 + \ldots + k^2.$$

Similarly, we have

$$
\begin{aligned}
V(T) &= V(T_1) + V(T_2) + \ldots V(T_n) \\
&= (\pi r^3/n)(1 - 0^2/n^2) + (\pi r^3/n)(1 - 1^2/n^2) + \ldots \\
&\quad + (\pi r^3/n)(1 - (n-1)^2/n^2) \\
&= (\pi r^3/n)(n - p_{n-1}/n^2) \\
&= \pi r^3(1 - p_{n-1}/n^3).
\end{aligned}
$$

Substituting for $V(S)$ and $V(T)$ in (3) gives us the encaging inequalities

$$\pi r^3[1 - p_n/n^3] < V(R) < \pi r^3[1 - p_{n-1}/n^3],$$

which hold for $n = 1, 2, 3, \ldots$. The argument used for both pyramids and cones at this point now implies that

$$V(R) = \pi r^3 (1 - 1/3) = (2/3)\pi r^3,$$

as asserted.

EXERCISES

1. Prove the following facts:
    (a) The volume of a right circular cone is one-third the volume of the right cylinder having the same base and height. (Democritus, about 460–370 B.C.)
    (b) The volume of a hemisphere is two-thirds the volume of the right circular cylinder having the same base and of height equal to its radius. (Archimedes, about 287–212 B.C.)

2. The water in a sphere of radius 6 inches is to be poured into a cylindrical container of circumference 2 inches. How high will the water be in the cylinder?

3. A cylinder with radius 5 inches and height 8 inches is filled with 6 inches of water. When a lead ball is placed in the cylinder, the water overflows. What at least is the radius of the lead ball?

4. Prove that Proposition 3 applies to an arbitrary right circular cone of height h having a base with radius r.

5. The base of an ice cream cone has radius 1 inch, and the cone is 5 inches long. It is packed solidly with ice cream and topped with a hemispherical scoop having the same base as the cone. What is the total volume of the ice cream?

INDEX

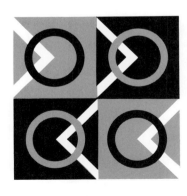

Index

Page numbers in *italics* refer to illustrations.

Points (*Continued*)
  distance between, 326-331
  fixed, of transformation, 259
  real, 703-714
  stationary, 698
  vanishing, 365
Pole, of hemisphere, 769
Polyclitus, 227
Polygon(s), 224, 402
  center of, 751
  central angle of, 751
  central triangle of, 751
  circumscribed, 751
    area of, 753-760
    perimeter of, 753-760
  closed, 402
    area of, 750
    perimeter of, 750
  convex, 403
  diagonal of, 403
  exterior angles of, 403-405
  inscribed, 751
    area of, 753-760
    perimeter of, 753-760
  mathematical induction for, 402-405
  number of vertices of, 403
  regular, 751
  triangulation of, 405
Polygonal spiral, 231, *232*
Polyhedron, 224
Polynomial(s), 156-166
  addition of, 159-160
  algebra of, 159-161
  coefficients of, 158
    uniqueness of, 164-166
  definition of, 156-159
  degrees of, 156
  equality of, 159
  graphs of, 274-276
  multiplication of, 160-164
  of zeroth degree, 157
Population, 570
Postulates, 468
  Euclid's, 467
Power, of set, 602
Premise, 9-11
Prime(s), 424-428
  definition of, 424
  factoring into, 426
    uniqueness of, 450-453
Prism, 224
  height of, 226
  right, 224, *224*
  volume of, 763
Probability(ies)
  additivity of, 565
  and statistics, 559-587
  calculation by counting, 566-574
  of event, 565
    simple and compound, 559-566
Proclos, 475
Programming, linear, 304-311
Progressions, arithmetic, 393-398
  geometric, 399-402
    ratio of, 399

Projection
  center of, 381
  central, 381
  in perspective, 362
  perpendicular, 317
Proof
  constructive, 436
  nonconstructive, 436
  theory of, 517-521
Proportions, human, 226
Proposition, 468
Pyramid
  apex of, 660
  axis of, 660
  frustum of, 666
  right, 660
Pythagoras, 415-420
Pythagorean theorem, 139, 204
  three-dimensional, 329
Pythagorean triples, 139-141, 453-457
  table of, 140

Quadratic formula, 147
Quadrilateral, 226
Quantifiers, existential, 518
  universal, 518
Quotient(s), 65
  difference, 692
  uniqueness of, 422

Random selection, 566
Ratio, cross, 378
  significance of, 380-383
  of geometric progression, 399
Rational number(s)
  definition of, 70
  negative, 70
    negative of, 70
    reciprocal of, 73
  non-negative, 68
  positive, 59-64
    general rules for, 64-66
  thin distribution of, 640-642
Rational number system, 69-75
Ray, 285
Real numbers, 701-772
  addition of, 735-741
  additive identity for, 738
  additive inverse of, 738
  arithmetic for, 734-746
  associativity of, 738, 742
  commutativity of, 738, 742
  correspondence to points on line, 709-711
  difference of, 739
  distributive law for, 744
  multiplication of, 741-746
  multiplicative identity of, 742
  multiplicative inverse of, 742
  nondenumerability of, 712-713
  ordering of, 714-734
  representation by infinite decimals, 703-709